Minnesota State Residential and Plumbing Code

ICC

INTERNATIONAL
CODE COUNCIL®

*Setting the Standard
for Building Safety*™

Made possible by the Association of Minnesota Building Officials

Minnesota State Residential and Plumbing Code

First Printing: June 2003

ISBN 1-58001-118-7

Copyright © 2003
by
International Code Council, Inc.
Based on

International Residential Code® for One- and Two-Family Dwellings
Copyright © 2000 by International Code Council, Inc.

PREFACE

Introduction

Internationally, code officials recognize the need for a modern, up-to-date residential code addressing the design and construction of one- and two-family dwellings and townhouses. The *International Residential Code®* is designed to meet these needs through model code regulations that safeguard the public health and safety in all communities, large and small.

This comprehensive, stand-alone residential code establishes minimum regulations for one- and two-family dwellings and townhouses using prescriptive provisions. It is founded on broad-based principles that make possible the use of new materials and new building designs. This edition is fully compatible with all the *International Codes™* ("I-Codes"™) published by the International Code Council® (ICC®), including the *International Building Code®*, *ICC Electrical Code™*, *International Energy Conservation Code®*, *International Existing Building Code®*, *International Fire Code®*, *International Fuel Gas Code®*, *International Mechanical Code®*, *ICC Performance Code™*, *International Plumbing Code®*, *International Private Sewage Disposal Code®*, *International Property Maintenance Code®*, *International Urban-Wildland Interface Code™* and *International Zoning Code®*.

The *International Residential Code* provisions provide many benefits, among which is the model code development process that offers an international forum for residential construction professionals to discuss prescriptive code requirements. This forum provides an excellent arena to debate proposed revisions. This model code also encourages international consistency in the application of provisions.

Development

This first edition of the *International Residential Code* is the culmination of an effort initiated in 1996 by a development committee appointed by the ICC and consisting of representatives of the three statutory members of the International Code Council: Building Officials and Code Administrators International, Inc. (BOCA), International Conference of Building Officials (ICBO) and Southern Building Code Congress International (SBCCI) and representatives from the National Association of Home Builders (NAHB). The intent was to draft a comprehensive, stand-alone residential code consistent with and inclusive of the scope of the existing model codes. Technical content of the 1998 *International One- and Two-Family Dwelling Code* and the latest model codes promulgated by BOCA, ICBO, SBCCI and ICC was utilized as the basis for the development, followed by public hearings in 1998 and 1999 to consider proposed changes.

This code is founded on principles intended to establish provisions consistent with the scope of a residential code that adequately protects public health, safety and welfare; provisions that do not unnecessarily increase construction costs; provisions that do not restrict the use of new materials, products or methods of construction; and provisions that do not give preferential treatment to particular types or classes of materials, products or methods of construction.

Adoption

The *International Residential Code* is available for adoption and use by jurisdictions internationally. Its use within a governmental jurisdiction is intended to be accomplished through adoption by reference in accordance with proceedings establishing the jurisdiction's laws. At the time of adoption, jurisdictions should insert the appropriate information in provisions requiring specific local information, such as the name of the adopting jurisdiction. These locations are shown in bracketed words in small capital letters in the code.

Maintenance

The *International Residential Code* is kept up to date through the review of proposed changes submitted by code enforcing officials, industry representatives, design professionals and other interested parties. Proposed changes are carefully considered through an open code development process in which all interested and affected parties may participate.

The contents of this work are subject to change both through the Code Development Cycles and the governmental body that enacts the code into law. For more information regarding the code development process, contact the Code and Standard Development Department of the International Code Council.

The maintenance process for the fuel gas provisions is based upon the process used to maintain the *International Fuel Gas Code*, in conjunction with the American Gas Association. The maintenance process for the electrical provisions is undertaken by the National Fire Protection Association.

While the development procedure of the *International Residential Code* assures the highest degree of care, ICC and the founding members of ICC — BOCA, ICBO, SBCCI — their members and those participating in the development of this code do not accept any liability resulting from compliance or noncompliance with the provisions because ICC and its founding members do not have the power or authority to police or enforce compliance with the contents of this code. Only the governmental body that enacts the code into law has such authority.

TABLE OF CONTENTS

Symbols and Notations in the Code

The symbols in the margins shall indicate the status of the code changes.

M
N   This symbol indicates that a Minnesota amendment has been added to the 2000 *Interna-*
M   *tional Residential Code for One- and Two-Family Dwellings.*
N

>   This symbol indicates deletion of IRC language by Minnesota.

Part I — Administrative

CHAPTER 1
ADMINISTRATION

This code shall be administered according to Minnesota Rules, Chapter 1300.

1300.0010
ADMINISTRATION

This chapter provides administrative provisions for all Minnesota State Building Code rule chapters identified in part 1300.0050. If specific administrative provisions are provided in a statute or rule chapter, the specific administrative provisions apply. Chapter 1315 shall be administered according to chapter 3800, and the Minnesota Electrical Act, Minnesota Statutes, sections 326.01, and 326.241 to 326.248. Provisions of this chapter that do not conflict with the Minnesota Electrical Act also apply.

1300.0020
TITLE

The chapters listed in part 1300.0050, including the standards they adopt by reference, are the Minnesota State Building Code and may be cited as or referred to as the "code."

1300.0030
PURPOSE AND APPLICATION

Subpart 1. **Purpose.** The purpose of the code is to provide minimum standards to safeguard life and limb, health, property, and public welfare by regulating and controlling the design, construction, quality of materials, use and occupancy, location, and maintenance of all structures and equipment specifically covered by the code in a jurisdiction that adopts and enforces the code. The purpose of the code is not to create, establish, or designate a particular class or group of persons who will or should be especially protected or benefited by the terms of the code.

Subp. 2. **Application.**

A. The code applies statewide except as provided in Minnesota Statutes, sections 16B.72 and 16B.73, and supersedes the building code of any municipality. The code does not apply to agricultural buildings except with respect to state inspections required or rulemaking authorized by Minnesota Statutes, sections 103F.141, subdivision 8, and 326.244.

B. The codes and standards referenced in a rule chapter are considered part of the requirements of the code to the prescribed extent of each reference. If differences occur between provisions of the code and referenced codes and standards, the provisions of the code apply.

1300.0040
SCOPE

The code applies to the construction, alteration, moving, demolition, repair, and use of any building, structure, or building service equipment in a municipality, except work located primarily in a public way, public utility towers and poles, mechanical equipment not specifically regulated in the code, and hydraulic flood control structures. Detached one- and two-family dwellings and multiple single-family dwellings (townhouses) not more than three stories high with separate means of egress and their accessory structures shall comply with chapter 1309 and other applicable rules. Other buildings and structures and appurtenances connected or attached to them shall comply with chapter 1305 and other applicable rules. If different provisions of the code specify different materials, methods of construction, or other requirements, the most restrictive provision governs. If there is a conflict between a general requirement and a specific requirement, the specific requirement applies. If reference is made in the code to an appendix, the provisions in the appendix do not apply unless specifically adopted by the code. Optional appendix chapters of the code identified in part 1300.0060 do not apply unless a municipality has specifically adopted them.

1300.0050
CHAPTERS OF MINNESOTA STATE
BUILDING CODE

The Minnesota State Building Code adopted under Minnesota Statutes, section 16B.61, subdivision 1, includes the following chapters:

A. 1300, Minnesota Building Code Administration;

B. 1301, Building Official Certification;

C. 1302, State Building Code Construction Approvals;

D. 1303, Special Provisions;

E. 1305, Adoption of the *International Building Code;*

F. 1306, Special Fire Protection Systems;

G. 1307, Elevators and Related Devices;

H. 1309, Adoption of the *International Residential Code;*

I. 1311, Minnesota Conservation Code for Existing Buildings;

J. 1315, Adoption of the *National Electrical Code;*

K. 1325, Solar Energy Systems;

L. 1330, Fallout Shelters;

M. 1335, Floodproofing Regulations;

N. 1341, Minnesota Accessibility Code;

O. 1346, Minnesota Mechanical Code;

P. 1350, Manufactured Homes;

Q. 1360, Prefabricated Structures;

R. 1361, Industrialized/Modular Buildings;

S. 1370, Storm Shelters (Manufactured Home Parks);

T. 4715, Minnesota Plumbing Code; and

U. 7670, 7672, 7674, 7676, and 7678, Minnesota Energy Code.

1300.0060
OPTIONAL ADMINISTRATION

The following chapters of the code are not mandatory but may be adopted without change by a municipality which has adopted the code:

A. Chapter 1306, Special Fire Protection Systems;

B. Grading, appendix chapter K, 2001 Supplements to *International Building Code;* and

C. Chapter 1335, Floodproofing Regulations, parts 1335.0600 to 1335.1200.

1300.0070
DEFINITIONS

Subpart. 1. **Scope; incorporation by reference.** The definitions in this part apply to parts 1300.0010 to 1300.0250. For terms that are not defined through the methods authorized by this chapter, the *Merriam-Webster Collegiate Dictionary,* available at www.m-w.com, shall be considered as providing ordinarily accepted meanings. The dictionary is incorporated by reference, is subject to frequent change, and is available through the Minitex interlibrary loan system.

Subp. 2. **Administrative authority.** "Administrative authority" means a municipality's governing body or its assigned administrative authority.

Subp. 3. **Adult day care center.** "Adult day care center" means a facility that provides adult day care to functionally impaired adults on a regular basis for periods of less than 24 hours a day in a setting other than a participant's home or the residence of the facility operator.

A. "Class E" means any building or portion of a building used for adult day care purposes, by more than five occupants, for those participants who are capable of taking appropriate action for self-preservation under emergency conditions as determined according to part 9555.9730, and must meet Group E occupancy requirements.

B. "Class I" means any building or portion of a building used for adult day care purposes, by more than five occupants, for those participants who are not capable of taking appropriate action for self-preservation under emergency conditions as determined according to part 9555.9730, and must meet Group I, Division 4 occupancy requirements.

Subp. 4. **Agricultural building.** "Agricultural building" means a building that meets the requirements of Minnesota Statutes, section 16B.60, subdivision 5.

Subp. 5. **Building official.** "Building official" means the municipal building code official certified under Minnesota Statutes, section 16B.65, subdivisions 2 and 3.

Subp. 6. **Building service equipment.** "Building service equipment" refers to the plumbing, mechanical, electrical, and elevator equipment, including piping, wiring, fixtures, and other accessories, that provides sanitation, lighting, heating, ventilation, cooling, refrigeration, firefighting, and transportation facilities essential to the occupancy of the building or structure for its designated use and occupancy.

Subp. 7. **City.** "City" means a home rule charter or statutory city.

Subp. 8. **Code.** "Code" means the Minnesota State Building Code adopted under Minnesota Statutes, section 16B.61, subdivision 1, and includes the chapters identified in part 1300.0020.

Subp. 9. **Commissioner.** "Commissioner" means the commissioner of administration.

Subp. 10. **Designate.** "Designate" means the formal designation by a municipality's administrative authority of a certified building official accepting responsibility for code administration.

Subp. 11. **Family day care home.** "Family day care home" means a residence or portion of a residence licensed by the Department of Human Services under chapter 9502 for no more than ten children at one time of which no more than six are under school age, and must meet Group R, Division 3 occupancy requirements.

Subp. 12. **Group day care home.** "Group day care home" means any residence or portion of a residence licensed by the Department of Human Services under chapter 9502 for no more than 14 children at any one time, and must meet Group R, Division 3 occupancy requirements.

Subp. 13. **Mandatory terms.** "Mandatory terms" include "must" and "shall," which have the same meaning.

Subp. 14. **Manufactured home.** "Manufactured home" has the meaning given in Minnesota Statutes, section 327.31, subdivision 3, and for the purpose of determining occupancy separations, is considered a Group R, Division 3 occupancy.

Subp. 15. **Master plan.** "Master plan" is a plan that has been reviewed for code compliance by the building official and stamped "Reviewed for Code Compliance."

Subp. 16. **Mayor and city council.** "Mayor" and "city council" mean governing body whenever they appear in the code.

Subp. 17. **Municipality.** "Municipality" means a city, county, or town; the University of Minnesota; or the state of Minnesota for public buildings and state licensed facilities.

Subp. 18. **Outpatient clinic.** "Outpatient clinic" means a building or part of a building used to provide, on an outpatient basis, surgical treatment requiring general anesthesia, kidney dialysis, or other treatment that would render patients incapable of unassisted self-preservation under emergency conditions. "Outpatient clinic" includes outpatient surgical centers, but does not include doctors' and dentists' offices or clinics for the practice of medicine or the delivery of primary care. Outpatient clinics must meet Group B occupancy requirements.

Subp. 19. **Performance-based design.** An engineering approach to design elements of a building based on agreed upon performance goals and objectives, engineering analysis, and quantitative assessment of alternatives against the design goals and objectives, using accepted engineering tools, methodologies, and performance criteria.

Subp. 20. **Recyclable materials.** "Recyclable materials" means materials that are separated from mixed municipal solid waste for the purpose of recycling, including paper, glass, plastic, metals, automobile oil, and batteries. Refuse-derived fuel or other material that is destroyed by incineration is not a recyclable material.

Subp. 21. **Recycling.** "Recycling" means the process of collecting and preparing recyclable materials and reusing the materials in their original form or using them in manufacturing processes that do not cause the destruction of recyclable materials in a manner that precludes further use.

Subp. 22. **Residential hospice facility.** "Residential hospice facility" means a facility located in a residential area that directly provides 24-hour residential and support services in a home-like setting for six to 12 persons who have been diagnosed as terminally ill with a probable life expectancy of under one year. A residential hospice facility must meet Group R-4 occupancy requirements.

Subp. 23. **Supervised living facility.** "Supervised living facility" means a facility in which there is provided supervision, lodging, meals, and according to the rules of the Minnesota Department of Human Services and the Minnesota Department of Health, counseling and developmental habilitative or rehabilitative services to persons who are mentally retarded, chemically dependent, adult mentally ill, or physically disabled.

A. "Class A-1 supervised living facility" means a supervised living facility for ambulatory and mobile persons who are capable of taking appropriate action for self-preservation under emergency conditions as determined by program licensure provisions for six or fewer persons, and must meet Group R, Division 3 occupancy requirements.

B. "Class A-2 supervised living facility" means a supervised living facility for ambulatory and mobile persons who are capable of taking appropriate action for self-preservation under emergency conditions as determined by program licensure provisions for seven to 16 persons, and must meet Group R, Division 4 occupancy requirements. Facilities with more than 16 persons must meet Group I-1 occupancy requirements.

C. "Class B-1 supervised living facility" means a supervised living facility for ambulatory, nonambulatory, mobile, or nonmobile persons who are not mentally or physically capable of taking appropriate action for self-preservation under emergency conditions as determined by program licensure provisions for six or fewer persons, and must meet Group R, Division 3 occupancy requirements.

D. "Class B-2 supervised living facility" means a supervised living facility for ambulatory, nonambulatory, mobile, or nonmobile persons who are not mentally or physically capable of taking appropriate action for self-preservation under emergency conditions as determined by program licensure provisions for seven to 16 persons, and must meet Group R, Division 4 occupancy requirements.

E. "Class B-3 supervised living facility" means a supervised living facility for ambulatory, nonambulatory, mobile, or nonmobile persons who are not mentally or physically capable of taking appropriate action for self-preservation under emergency conditions as determined by program licensure provisions for over 16 persons, and must meet Group I, Division 2 occupancy requirements.

Subp. 24. **State building official.** "State building official" means the person who, under the direction and supervision of the commissioner, administers the code.

Subp. 25. **State licensed facilities.** "State licensed facilities" means a building and its grounds that are licensed by the state as a hospital, nursing home, supervised living facility, free-standing outpatient surgical center, or correctional facility.

Subp. 26. **State-owned buildings.** "State-owned buildings" means buildings and structures financed in whole or in part by state funds that are under the exclusive jurisdiction and custodial control of one or more state department or agency.

1300.0080
CODE ADOPTION AND AMENDMENTS

Under Minnesota Statutes, section 16B.61, the code is adopted and periodically updated to include current editions of national model codes in general use and existing statewide specialty codes and their amendments. Under Minnesota Statutes, section 16B.64, subdivisions 5 and 6, amendments to the code may be proposed and initiated by any interested person. Proposed amendments must be submitted in writing on a form provided by the commissioner.

1300.0090
DEPARTMENT OF BUILDING SAFETY

Subpart 1. **Creation of enforcement agency.** There is hereby established in the municipality a code enforcement agency and the official in charge is the designated building official. The agency is referred to in the code as the "Department of Building Safety."

Subp. 2. **Appointment.** The building official shall be designated by the municipality according to Minnesota Statutes, section 16B.65.

1300.0110
DUTIES AND POWERS OF BUILDING OFFICIAL

Subpart 1. **General.** The building official shall enforce the code. The building official may render interpretations of the code and adopt policies and procedures in order to clarify its application. The interpretations, policies, and procedures shall be in conformance with the intent and purpose of the code. The policies and procedures shall not have the effect of waiving requirements specifically provided for in the code.

Subp. 2. **Deputies.** According to the prescribed procedures of the municipality and with the concurrence of the appointing authority, the building official may designate a deputy building official and related technical officers, inspectors, plan examiners, and other employees. The employees have the powers delegated by the building official.

Subp. 3. **Applications and permits.** The building official shall receive applications, review construction documents, and issue permits for the erection, alteration, demolition, moving, and repair of buildings and structures, including all other equipment and systems regulated by the code. The building official shall inspect the premises for which the permits have been issued and enforce compliance with the code.

Subp. 4. **Notices and orders.** The building official shall issue all necessary notices or orders to ensure compliance with the code.

Subp. 5. **Inspections.** The building official shall make all of the required inspections or accept reports of inspection by approved agencies or individuals. Reports of inspections shall be documented on the job site inspection card and kept on file at the jurisdiction including type of inspection, date of inspection, identification of the responsible individual making the inspection, and comments regarding approval or disapproval of the inspection. The building official may engage expert opinion necessary to report upon unusual technical issues that arise.

Subp. 6. **Identification.** The building official and deputies shall carry proper identification when inspecting structures or premises in the performance of duties under the code.

Subp. 7. **Right of entry.** If it is necessary to make an inspection to enforce the code or if the building official has reasonable cause to believe that there exists in a structure or upon a premises a condition contrary to or in violation of the code that makes the structure or premises unsafe, dangerous, or hazardous, the building official or designee may enter the structure or premises at reasonable times to inspect or to perform the duties imposed by the code, provided that if the structure or premises is occupied, credentials must be presented to the occupant and entry requested. If the structure or premises is unoccupied, the building official shall first make a reasonable effort to locate the owner or other person having charge or control of the structure or premises and request entry. If entry is refused, the building official shall have recourse to the remedies provided by law to secure entry.

Subp. 8. **Department records.** The building official shall keep official records of applications received, plans, specifications, surveys, plot plans, plan reviews, permits and certificates issued, reports of inspections, and notices and orders issued. The records shall be retained in the official records for the period required for the retention of public records under Minnesota Statutes, section 138.17. Department records shall be maintained by the municipality and readily available for review according to Minnesota Statutes, section 13.37.

Subp. 9. **Liability.** The building official, member of the Board of Appeals, or employee charged with the enforcement of the code, while acting for the jurisdiction in good faith and without malice in the discharge of the duties required by the code or other pertinent laws or ordinances, is not rendered personally liable and is relieved from personal liability for any damage accruing to persons or property as a result of any act or by reason of an act or omission in the discharge of official duties. Any suit instituted against an officer or employee because of an act performed by that officer or employee in the lawful discharge of duties and under the code shall be defended by the legal representative of the jurisdiction until the final termination of the proceedings. The building official or any subordinate is not liable for cost in any action, suit, or proceeding that is instituted in pursuance of the code.

Subp. 10. **Approved materials and equipment.** Materials, equipment, and devices approved by the building official shall be constructed and installed in the approved manner.

Subp. 11. **Used material and equipment.** The use of used materials that meet the requirements of the code for new materials is permitted. Used equipment and devices shall not be reused unless approved by the building official.

Subp. 12. **Modifications.** If there are practical difficulties involved in carrying out the provisions of the code, the building official may grant modifications for individual cases, upon application by the owner or owner's representative, provided the building official finds that special individual reason makes the strict letter of the code impractical, the modification is in compliance with the intent and purpose of the code, and the modification does not lessen health, life, and fire safety or structural requirements.

Subp. 13. **Alternative materials, design, and methods of construction and equipment.** The code is not intended to prevent the installation of any material or to prohibit any design or method of construction not specifically prescribed by the code, provided that any alternative has been approved. An alternative material, design, or method of construction shall be approved where the building official finds that the proposed design is satisfactory and complies with the intent of the code, and that the material, method, or work offered is, for the purpose intended, at least the equivalent of that prescribed in the code in quality, strength, effectiveness, fire resistance, durability, and safety. The details of any action granting approval of an alternate shall be recorded and entered in the files of the code enforcement agency.

Subp. 14. **Performance-based fire and life safety design.** The code official may approve performance-based fire and life safety designs if the code official finds that the proposed design has been conducted by an approved method. Approved performance-based designs are evidence of compliance with the intent of the code. Approvals under this subpart are subject to the approval of the building code official whenever the design involves matters regulated by the building code.

A. Design goals, objectives, and performance criteria shall be approved by the code official before submission of a performance-based design report, calculations, or analysis results. As a minimum, an approved performance-based design shall address the following objectives:

  (1) life safety of occupants;

  (2) firefighter safety;

  (3) property protection;

  (4) continuity of operations; and

  (5) safeguarding of the environment.

B. To determine the acceptability of a performance-based design, the code official may require the owner or agent to provide, without charge to the jurisdiction, a technical opinion and report. The code official may require the technical opinion and report to be prepared by, and bear the stamp of, a licensed design professional.

C. Performance-based designs shall be prepared by, and bear the stamp of, a licensed design professional competent in the area of work. The design professional shall provide written confirmation to the code official before a certificate of occupancy is issued that the performance-based design has been properly implemented, the operation or use of the building is within the limitations of the design, and adequate controls are in place to maintain compliance with the conditions of the design throughout the life of the building.

Subp. 15. **Tests.** If there is insufficient evidence of compliance with the code, or evidence that a material or method does not conform to the requirements of the code, or in order to substantiate claims for alternative materials or methods, the building official shall have the authority to require tests as evidence of compliance to be made at no expense to the municipality. Test methods shall be as specified in the code or by other recognized test standards. In the absence of recognized and accepted test methods, the building official shall approve the testing procedures. Tests shall be performed by an approved agency. Reports of the tests shall be retained by the building official.

1300.0120
PERMITS

Subpart 1. **Required.** An owner or authorized agent who intends to construct, enlarge, alter, repair, move, demolish, or change the occupancy of a building or structure; erect, install, enlarge, alter, repair, remove, convert, or replace any gas, mechanical, electrical, plumbing system, or other equipment, the installation of which is regulated by the code; or cause any such work to be done, shall first make application to the building official and obtain the required permit.

Subp. 2. **Annual permit.** In lieu of an individual permit for each alteration to an already approved building or electrical, gas, mechanical, or plumbing installation, the building official may issue an annual permit upon application for the permit to any person, firm, or corporation regularly employing one or more qualified trade persons in the building, structure, or on the premises owned or operated by the applicant for the permit.

Subp. 3. **Annual permit records.** The person to whom an annual permit is issued shall keep a detailed record of alterations made under the annual permit. The building official shall have access to the records at all times or the records shall be filed with the building official as designated.

Subp. 4. **Work exempt from permit.** Exemptions from permit requirements of the code do not authorize work to be done in any manner in violation of the code or any other laws or ordinances of this jurisdiction. Permits shall not be required for the following:

A. Building:

(1) one-story detached accessory structures, used as tool and storage sheds, playhouses, and similar uses, provided the floor area does not exceed 120 square feet (11.15 mm^2);

(2) fences not over six feet (1829 mm) high;

(3) oil derricks;

(4) retaining walls that are not over four feet (1219 mm) in height measured from the bottom of the footing to the top of the wall, unless supporting

a surcharge or impounding Class I, II, or III-A liquids;

(5) water tanks supported directly upon grade if the capacity does not exceed 5,000 gallons (18927 L) and the ratio of height to diameter or width does not exceed 2 to 1;

(6) sidewalks and driveways that are not part of an accessible route;

(7) decks and platforms not more than 30 inches (762 mm) above adjacent grade and not attached to a structure with frost footings and which is not part of an accessible route;

(8) painting, papering, tiling, carpeting, cabinets, countertops, and similar finish work;

(9) temporary motion picture, television, and theater stage sets and scenery;

(10) prefabricated swimming pools accessory to dwelling units constructed to the provisions of the International Residential Code or R-3 occupancies constructed to the provisions of the International Building Code, which are 24 inches (610 mm) or less in depth, do not exceed 5,000 gallons (19 000 L) and are installed entirely above ground;

(11) window awnings supported by an exterior wall of Group R-3, and Group U occupancies;

(12) movable cases, counters, and partitions not over five feet, nine inches (1753 mm) in height; and

(13) agricultural buildings as defined in Minnesota Statutes, section 16B.60, subdivision 5.

Unless otherwise exempted, plumbing, electrical, and mechanical permits are required for subitems (1) to (13).

B. Gas:

(1) portable heating, cooking, or clothes drying appliances; and

(2) replacement of any minor part that does not alter approval of equipment or make the equipment unsafe.

C. Mechanical:

(1) portable heating appliances;

(2) portable ventilation appliances and equipment;

(3) portable cooling units;

(4) steam, hot, or chilled water piping within any heating or cooling equipment regulated by this code;

(5) replacement of any part that does not alter approval of equipment or make the equipment unsafe;

(6) portable evaporative coolers; and

(7) self-contained refrigeration systems containing ten pounds (4.5 kg) or less of refrigerant or that are actuated by motors of one horsepower (0.75 kW) or less.

D. Plumbing: the clearing of stoppages, provided the work does not involve or require the replacement or rearrangement of valves, pipes, or fixtures.

E. Electrical: an electrical permit is not required if work is inspected by the State Board of Electricity or is exempt from inspection under Minnesota Statutes, section 326.244. Obtaining a permit from the Board of Electricity does not exempt the work from other Minnesota State Building Code requirements relating to electrical equipment, its location, or its performance.

Subp. 5. **Emergency repairs.** If equipment replacements and repairs must be performed in an emergency situation, the permit application shall be submitted to the building official within the next working business day.

Subp. 6. **Repairs.** Application or notice to the building official is not required for ordinary repairs to structures. The repairs shall not include the cutting away of any wall, partition, or portion of a wall or partition, the removal or cutting of any structural beam or load bearing support, or the removal or change of any required means of egress, or rearrangement of parts of a structure affecting the egress requirements; nor shall ordinary repairs include addition to, alteration of, replacement, or relocation of any standpipe, water supply, sewer, drainage, drain leader, gas, soil, waste, vent or similar piping, electric wiring, or mechanical or other work affecting public health or general safety.

Subp. 7. **Application for permit.** To obtain a permit, the applicant shall file an application in writing on a form furnished by the Department of Building Safety for that purpose. The application shall:

A. Identify and describe the work to be covered by the permit for which application is made;

B. Describe the land on which the proposed work is to be done by legal description, street address, or similar description that will readily identify and definitely locate the proposed building or work;

C. Indicate the use and occupancy for which the proposed work is intended;

D. Indicate the type of construction;

E. Be accompanied by construction documents and other information as required by the code;

F. State the valuation of the proposed work;

G. Be signed by the applicant, or the applicant's authorized agent; and

H. Give other data and information required by the building official.

Subp. 8. **Action on application.** The building official shall examine or cause to be examined applications for permits and amendments within a reasonable time after filing. If the application or the construction documents do not conform to the requirements of pertinent laws, the building official shall reject the application and notify the applicant, in writing, stating the reasons for the rejection. If the building official is satisfied that the proposed work conforms to the requirements of the code and applicable laws and ordinances, the building official shall issue a permit.

Subp. 9. **Time limitation of application.** An application for a permit for any proposed work shall be considered abandoned 180 days after the date of filing, unless the application has been pursued in good faith or a permit has been issued; except that the building official is authorized to grant one or more extensions of time for additional periods not exceeding 180 days each. The extension shall be requested in writing and justifiable cause demonstrated.

Subp. 10. **Validity of permit.** The issuance or granting of a permit or approval of plans, specifications, and computations, shall not be construed to be a permit for any violation of the code or of any other ordinance of the jurisdiction. Permits presuming to give authority to violate or cancel the provisions of the code or other ordinances of the jurisdiction are not valid. The issuance of a permit based on construction documents and other data shall not prevent the building official from requiring the correction of errors in the construction documents and other data. The building official may also prevent occupancy or use of a structure that violates the code or any other ordinance of this jurisdiction.

Subp. 11. **Expiration.** Every permit issued shall become invalid unless the work authorized by the permit is commenced within 180 days after its issuance, or if the work authorized by the permit is suspended or abandoned for a period of 180 days after the time the work is commenced. The building official may grant, in writing, one or more extensions of time, for periods not more than 180 days each. The extension shall be requested in writing and justifiable cause demonstrated.

Subp. 12. **Suspension or revocation.** The building official may suspend or revoke a permit issued under the code if the permit is issued in error; on the basis of incorrect, inaccurate, or incomplete information; or in violation of any ordinance or regulation or the code.

Subp. 13. **Placement of permit.** The building permit or a copy shall be kept on the site of the work until the completion of the project.

Subp. 14. **Responsibility.** Every person who performs work for the installation or repair of building, structure, electrical, gas, mechanical, or plumbing systems, for which the code is applicable, shall comply with the code.

1300.0130
CONSTRUCTION DOCUMENTS

Subpart 1. **Submittal documents.** Construction documents, special inspection and structural observation programs, and other data shall be submitted in one or more sets with each application for a permit.

Exception: The building official may waive the submission of construction documents and other data if the nature of the work applied for is such that reviewing of construction documents is not necessary to obtain compliance with the code.

The building official may require plans or other data be prepared according to the rules of the Board of Architecture, Engineering, Land Surveying, Landscape Architecture, Geoscience and Interior Design, chapter 1800, and Minnesota Statutes, sections 326.02 to 326.15, and other state laws relating to plan and specification preparation by occupational licenses. If special conditions exist, the building official may require additional construction documents to be prepared by a licensed design professional.

Subp. 2. **Information on construction documents.** Construction documents shall be dimensioned and drawn upon suitable material. Electronic media documents are permitted to be submitted when approved by the building official. Construction documents shall be of sufficient clarity to indicate the location, nature, and extent of the work proposed and show in detail that it will conform to the code and relevant laws, ordinances, rules, and regulations, as determined by the building official.

Subp. 3. **Manufacturer's installation instructions.** When required by the building official, manufacturer's installation instructions for construction equipment and components regulated by the code, shall be available on the job site at the time of inspection.

Subp. 4. **Site plan.** The construction documents submitted with the application for permit shall be accompanied by a site plan drawn to scale, showing the size and location of new construction and existing structures on the site, distances from lot lines, the established street grades, and the proposed finished grades, and it shall be drawn according to an accurate boundary line survey. In the case of demolition, the site plan shall show construction to be demolished and the location and size of existing structures and construction that are to remain on the site or plot. The building official may waive or modify the requirement for a site plan if the application for permit is for alteration or repair or when otherwise warranted.

Subp. 5. **Examination of documents.** The building official shall examine or cause to be examined the accompanying construction documents to ascertain whether the construction indicated and described complies with the requirements of the code and other pertinent laws and ordinances.

Subp. 6. **Approval of construction documents.** If the building official issues a permit, the construction documents shall be approved in writing or by stamp, as "Reviewed for Code Compliance." One set of the construction documents that were reviewed shall be retained by the building official. The other set shall be returned to the applicant, kept at the site of the work, and open to inspection by the building official or an authorized representative.

Subp. 7. **Previous approvals.** The code in effect at the time of application shall be applicable.

Subp. 8. **Phased approval.** The building official may issue a permit for the construction of foundations or any other part of a building or structure before the construction documents for the whole building or structure have been submitted, provided that adequate information and detailed statements have been filed complying with pertinent requirements of the code. The holder of the permit for the foundation or other parts of a building or structure shall proceed at the holder's own risk with the building operation and without assurance that a permit for the entire structure will be granted.

Subp. 9. **Design professional in responsible charge.**

A. The building official may require the owner to engage and designate on the building permit application a licensed design professional who shall act as the licensed design professional in responsible charge. If the circumstances require, the owner shall designate a substitute licensed design professional in responsible charge who shall perform the duties required of the original licensed design professional in responsible charge.

The building official shall be notified in writing by the owner if the licensed design professional in responsible charge is changed or is unable to continue to perform the duties.

The licensed design professional in responsible charge shall be responsible for reviewing and coordinating submittal documents prepared by others, including phased and deferred submittal items, for compatibility with the design of the building.

When structural observation is required by the code, the inspection program shall name the individual or firms who are to perform structural observation and describe the stages of construction at which structural observation is to occur.

B. For the purposes of this part, deferred submittals are defined as those portions of the design that are not submitted at the time of the application and that are to be submitted to the building official within a specified period.

Deferral of any submittal items shall have the prior approval of the building official. The licensed design professional in responsible charge shall list the deferred submittals on the construction documents for review by the building official.

Submittal documents for deferred submittal items shall be submitted to the licensed design professional in responsible charge who shall review them and forward them to the building official with a notation indicating that the deferred submittal documents have been reviewed and that they have been found to be in general conformance with the design of the building. The deferred submittal items shall not be installed until their design and submittal documents have been approved by the building official.

C. Work regulated by the code shall be installed according to the reviewed construction documents, and any changes made during construction that are not in compliance with the approved construction documents shall be resubmitted for approval as an amended set of construction documents.

1300.0140
VIOLATIONS

It is unlawful for any person, firm, or corporation to erect, construct, alter, extend, repair, move, remove, demolish, or occupy any building, structure, or equipment regulated by the code, or cause any of those actions, in conflict with or in violation of the code. The building official may serve a notice of violation or order on the person responsible for the erection, construction, alteration, extension, repair, moving, removal, demolition, or occupancy of a building or structure in violation of the code, or in violation of a permit or certificate issued under the code. The order shall direct the discontinuance of the illegal action or condition and the abatement of the violation.

1300.0150
VIOLATIONS, PENALTY

A violation of the code is a misdemeanor under Minnesota Statutes, section 16B.69.

1300.0160
FEES

Subpart 1. Schedule of permit fees. The applicant for a permit for a building; structure; or electrical, gas, mechanical, or plumbing system or alterations requiring a permit shall pay the fee by the municipality.

Subp. 2. Fees commensurate with service. Fees established by the municipality must be by ordinance and must be fair, reasonable, and proportionate to the actual cost of the service for which the fee is imposed.

Subp. 3. Building permit valuations. The applicant for a permit shall provide an estimated permit value at time of application. Permit valuations shall include total value of all construction work, including materials and labor, for which the permit is being issued, such as electrical, gas, mechanical, plumbing equipment, and permanent systems. Building permit valuation shall be set by the building official.

Exceptions: Building permit valuations for the following structures shall be based on the valuation of on-site work only:

A. Manufactured homes containing a Housing and Urban Development (HUD) certification label;

B. Prefabricated buildings with a Minnesota Building Codes and Standards Division prefabrication label; and

C. Industrialized/modular buildings with an Industrialized Building Commission (IBC) label.

Subp. 4. Building permit fees. Building permit fees shall be based on valuation.

Exceptions:

A. One- and two-family dwelling maintenance permits for roofing, siding, windows, doors, or other minor projects may be charged a fixed fee;

B. Permits for plumbing, mechanical, electrical, or other building service equipment systems may be based on valuation or charged a fixed fee; and

C. Replacement of a residential fixture or appliance cannot exceed the permit fee limitation established by Minnesota Statutes, section 16B.665.

Subp. 5. Plan review fees for similar plans. When submittal documents for similar plans are approved under subpart 6, plan review fees shall not exceed 25 percent of the normal building permit fee established and charged by the jurisdiction for the same structure.

Subp. 6. Plan review of similar plans.

A. Any number of similar buildings may be built from a master plan if:

(1) plan review fees have been paid for the master plan;

(2) a code change has not occurred that impacts the design of a master plan;

(3) the similar building has the same physical dimensions and structural design as the master plan;

Exception: The following modifications to the master plan are not considered to be significant modifications,

according to Minnesota statutes, section 16B.61, subdivison 1, and are permitted for "U" occupancies, and dwelling units built to the International Residential Code, and residential occupancies built to the International Building Code that are three stories and less in height:

(a) foundation types to include walkout, lookout, and full basement;

(b) foundation materials to include poured concrete, masonry units, and wood;

(c) garage dimensions;

(d) roof design changed by a revised truss plan approved by the building official;

(e) bays or cantilevered floor areas;

(f) decks and porches; and

(g) other modifications approved by the building official;

(4) occupancy groups other than those identified in the exceptions listed in part 1300.0160, subpart 6, item A, subitem (3), must be the same type of construction and occupancy classification and must have the same exit system;

Exception: Minor changes to the exit access; and

(5) the similar plan is based on a master plan for which the municipality has issued a permit within the last 12 months.

B. Plan review fees for similar building plans must be based on the costs commensurate with the direct and indirect cost of the service, but must not exceed 25 percent of the normal building permit fee established and charged by the municipality for the same structure.

C. The plan review fee charged for similar building plans applies to all buildings regulated by the code regardless of occupancy classification including industrialized/modular buildings constructed under a program specified in Minnesota Statutes, section 16B.75.

D. The applicant must submit a new plan set and other information as required by the building official for each building reviewed as a similar building.

Subp. 7. Payment of fees. A permit shall not be issued until the fees prescribed by the municipality have been paid.

Subp. 8. Work commencing before permit issuance. If work for which a permit is required by the code has been commenced without first obtaining a permit, a special investigation shall be made before a permit may be issued for the work. An investigation fee established by the municipality shall be collected and is in addition to the required permit fees, but it may not exceed the permit fee.

Subp. 9. Fee refunds. The municipality shall establish a permit and plan review fee refund policy.

Subp. 10. State surcharge fees. All municipal permits issued for work under the code are subject to a surcharge fee. The fees are established by Minnesota Statutes, section 16B.70. Reports and remittances by municipalities must be filed with the commissioner, directed to the attention of the state building official.

Surcharge fees imposed by the state are in addition to municipal permit fees. Surcharge report forms and information may be obtained by writing the commissioner, to the attention of the state building official.

1300.0170
STOP WORK ORDER

If the building official finds any work regulated by the code being performed in a manner contrary to the provisions of the code or in a dangerous or unsafe manner, the building official may issue a stop work order.

The stop work order shall be in writing and issued to the owner of the property involved, to the owner's agent, or to the person doing the work. Upon issuance of a stop work order, the cited work shall immediately cease. The stop work order shall state the reason for the order and the conditions under which the cited work will be permitted to resume.

1300.0180
UNSAFE BUILDINGS OR STRUCTURES

A building or structure regulated by the code is unsafe, for purposes of this part, if it is structurally unsafe, not provided with adequate egress, a fire hazard, or otherwise dangerous to human life.

Building service equipment that is regulated by the code is unsafe, for purposes of this part, if it is a fire, electrical, or health hazard; an unsanitary condition; or otherwise dangerous to human life. Use of a building, structure, or building service equipment constituting a hazard to safety, health, or public welfare by reason of inadequate maintenance, dilapidation, obsolescence, fire hazard, disaster, damage, or abandonment is, for the purposes of this part, an unsafe use. Parapet walls, cornices, spires, towers, tanks, statuary, and other appendages or structural members that are supported by, attached to, or a part of a building and that are in deteriorated condition or otherwise unable to sustain the design loads that are specified in the code are unsafe building appendages.

The building official may order any building or portion of a building to be vacated if continued use is dangerous to life, health, or safety of the occupants. The order shall be in writing and state the reasons for the action.

All unsafe buildings, structures, or appendages are public nuisances and must be abated by repair, rehabilitation, demolition, or removal according to Minnesota Statutes, sections 463.15 to 463.26.

1300.0190
TEMPORARY STRUCTURES AND USES

Subpart 1. **General.** The building official may issue a permit for temporary structures and temporary uses. The permit shall be limited as to time of service, but shall not be permitted for more than 180 days. The building official may grant extensions for demonstrated cause.

Subp. 2. **Conformance.** Temporary structures and uses shall conform to the structural strength, fire safety, means of egress, accessibility, light, ventilation, and sanitary requirements of the code as necessary to ensure the public health, safety, and general welfare.

Subp. 3. **Termination of approval.** The building official may terminate the permit for a temporary structure or use and order the temporary structure or use to be discontinued if the conditions required in this part have not been complied with.

1300.0210
INSPECTIONS

Subpart 1. **General.** Construction or work for which a permit is required is subject to inspection by the building official and the construction or work shall remain accessible and exposed for inspection purposes until approved. Approval as a result of an inspection is not approval of a violation of the code or of other ordinances of the jurisdiction. Inspections presuming to give authority to violate or cancel the provisions of the code or of other ordinances of the jurisdiction are not valid. It shall be the duty of the permit applicant to cause the work to remain accessible and exposed for inspection purposes. Neither the building official nor the jurisdiction is liable for expense entailed in the removal or replacement of any material required to allow inspection.

Subp. 2. **Preliminary inspection.** Before issuing a permit, the building official may examine, or cause to be examined, buildings, structures, and sites for which an application has been filed.

Subp. 3. **Inspection record card.** The building official shall identify which inspections are required for the work requiring a permit. Work requiring a permit shall not be commenced until the permit holder or an agent of the permit holder has posted or otherwise made available an inspection record card that allows the building official to conveniently make all required entries regarding inspection of the work. This card shall be maintained and made available by the permit holder until final approval has been granted by the building official.

Subp. 4. **Inspection requests.** The building official shall provide the applicant with policies, procedures, and a timeline for requesting inspections. The person doing the work authorized by a permit shall notify the building official that the work is ready for inspection. The person requesting an inspection required by the code shall provide access to and means for inspection of the work.

Subp. 5. **Approval required.** Work shall not be done beyond the point indicated in each successive inspection without first obtaining the approval of the building official. The building official, upon notification, shall make the requested inspections and shall either indicate the portion of the construction that is satisfactory as completed or notify the permit holder or an agent of the permit holder of any failures to comply with the code. Any portion that does not comply shall be corrected and the portion shall not be covered or concealed until authorized by the building official.

Subp. 6. **Required inspections.** The building official, upon notification, shall make the inspections in this part. In addition to the inspections identified in this subpart, see applicable rule chapters in part 1300.0050 for specific inspection and testing requirements.

A. Footing and foundation inspections shall be made after excavations for footings are complete and any required reinforcing steel is in place. For concrete foundations, any required forms shall be in place prior to inspection. Materials for the foundation shall be on the job, except that concrete need not be on the job if the concrete is ready mixed according to approved nationally recognized standards. The foundation inspection shall include excavations for thickened slabs intended for the support of bearing walls, partitions, structural supports, or equipment. If the foundation is to be constructed of approved treated wood, additional inspections may be required by the building official.

B. Concrete slab and under-floor inspections shall be made after in-slab or under-floor reinforcing steel and building service equipment, conduit, piping accessories, and other ancillary equipment items are in place, but before any concrete is placed or floor sheathing installed, including the subfloor.

C. Rough-in inspection of plumbing, mechanical, gas, and electrical systems shall be made before covering or concealment, before fixtures or appliances are set or installed, and before framing inspection.

D. Framing inspections shall be made after the roof, all framing, fire blocking, and bracing are in place and all pipes, chimneys, and vents are complete and the rough electrical, plumbing, gas, heating wires, pipes, and ducts are approved.

E. Energy efficiency inspections shall be made to determine compliance with Minnesota Energy Code requirements.

F. Lath and gypsum board inspections shall be made after lathing and gypsum board, interior and exterior, are in place, but before any plastering is applied or before gypsum board joints and fasteners are taped and finished.

Exception: Gypsum board that is not part of a fire-resistive assembly or a shear assembly.

G. Protection of joints and penetrations in fire-resistance-rated assemblies shall not be concealed from view until inspected and approved.

H. Installation of manufactured homes (mobile homes) shall be made after the installation of the support systems and all utility service connections are in place, but before any covering material or skirting is in place. Evaluation of an approved anchoring system is part of the installation inspection.

I. Fireplaces must be inspected for compliance with applicable requirements of the code and the manufacturer's installation instructions.

J. A final inspection shall be made for all work for which a permit is issued.

K. Special inspections shall be as required by the code.

L. In addition to the inspections in items A to J, the building official is authorized to make or require other inspections of any construction work to ascertain compliance with the code and other laws that are enforced by the Department of Building Safety.

Subp. 7. **Inspection agencies.** The building official is authorized to accept inspection reports by approved agencies.

1300.0220
CERTIFICATE OF OCCUPANCY

Subpart 1. **Use and occupancy.** No building or structure shall be used or occupied, and no change in the existing occupancy classification of a building, structure, or portion of a building or structure shall be made until the building official has issued a certificate of occupancy for the building or structure under this part. Issuance of a certificate of occupancy is not approval of a violation of the code or other ordinances of the municipality. Certificates presuming to give authority to violate or cancel the code or other ordinances of the municipality are not valid.

Exception: A municipality has the option of requiring certificates of occupancy for Group U occupancies and manufactured homes.

Subp. 2. **Existing structures.** The legal occupancy of any structure existing on the date of adoption of the code shall be permitted to continue without change except as specifically required in chapter 1311.

Subp. 3. **Change in use.** Changes in the character or use of an existing structure shall not be made except as specified in chapter 1311.

Subp. 4. **Moved buildings.** Buildings or structures moved into a jurisdiction shall comply with the provisions of the code for new buildings or structures.

Exception: A residential building relocated within or into a municipality need not comply with the Minnesota Energy Code or Minnesota Statutes, section 326.371.

Subp. 5. **Certificate issued.** After the building official inspects a building or structure and finds no violations of the code or other laws that are enforced by the Department of Building Safety, the building official shall issue a certificate of occupancy containing the following:

A. The building permit number;

B. The address of the structure;

C. The name and address of the owner;

D. A statement that the described portion of the structure has been inspected for compliance with the requirements of the code for the occupancy and division of occupancy and the use for which the proposed occupancy is classified;

E. The name of the building official;

F. The edition of the code under which the permit was issued;

G. The use and occupancy classification;

H. The type of construction;

I. If an automatic sprinkler system is provided; and

J. Any special stipulations and conditions of the building permit.

Subp. 6. **Temporary occupancy.** The building official is authorized to issue a temporary certificate of occupancy before the completion of the entire work covered by the permit, provided that the portion or portions shall be occupied safely. The building official shall set a time period during which the temporary certificate of occupancy is valid.

Subp. 7. **Revocation.** The building official may issue a written suspension or revocation of a certificate of occupancy issued under the code if the certificate is issued in error or on the basis of incorrect information supplied, or if the building or use of the building, structure, or portion of the building or structure is in violation of any ordinance or regulation or a provision of the code.

1300.0230
BOARD OF APPEALS

Subpart 1. **Local board of appeals.** In order to hear and decide appeals of orders, decisions, or determinations made by the building official relative to the application and interpretation of this code, there shall be and is hereby created a board of appeals. The building official shall be an ex officio member of said board but shall have no vote on any matter before the board. The board of appeals shall be designated by the governing body. Appeals hearings for one- and two-family buildings requested up to the time of permit issuance must occur within 15 working days of the application for appeal. Appeals hearings for one- and two-family buildings requested from the time of permit issuance through the issuance of the certificate of occupancy must occur within ten working days of the application for appeal.

Appeals hearings for other buildings or structures requested up to the time of permit issuance must occur within 30 working days of the application for appeal. Appeals hearings for other buildings or structures requested from the time of permit issuance through the issuance of the certificate of occupancy must occur within 20 working days of the application for appeal. The board shall adopt rules of procedures for conducting its business and shall render all decisions and findings in writing to the appellant with a duplicate copy to the building official and to the state building official within 15 days of the decision. For jurisdictions without a board of appeals, the appellant may appeal to an appeals board assembled by the state of Minnesota, Department of Administration's Building Codes and Standards Division.

Subp. 2. **Qualifications.** The board of appeals shall consist of members who are qualified by experience and training to pass on matters pertaining to building construction and are not employees of the affected jurisdiction.

Subp. 3. **Limitations on authority.** An application for appeal shall be based on a claim that the true intent of this code or the rules legally adopted thereunder have been incorrectly interpreted, the provisions of this code do not fully apply, or an equally good or better form of construction is proposed. The board shall have no authority to waive requirements of this code.

Subp. 4 **Final interpretive authority.** The state building official has final interpretive authority for all codes adopted as part of the code except for the plumbing code when enforced by the Commissioner of Health and the electrical code when enforced by the State Board of Electricity. A request for final interpretation must come from a local or state level building code board of appeals. The procedures for final interpretations by the state building official are as established in Minnesota Statutes, section 16B.63.

1300.0240
DISCLAIMER CLAUSE

The inclusion of specific requirements relative to the manner of installation of any building or portion of any building or building equipment in one or more parts of the code does not limit this procedure to any particular type of installer or provide a basis upon which determination of the right to perform a procedure shall be made. The authority for this determination is in the various licensing statutes or ordinances for each type of installer who performs the work.

1300.0250
SEVERABILITY

The invalidity of any provision of the Minnesota State Building Code does not affect any other provisions of the code that can be given effect without the invalid provision and, to this end, the provisions of the code are declared to be severable.

1303.1000
TITLE

This chapter shall be known as "Minnesota Provisions."

1303.1100
PURPOSE

This chapter contains requirements of the code that are mandated by Minnesota Statutes, are needed to address Minnesota's climatic conditions, or are otherwise determined necessary to provide a safe minimum level of construction in an area not appropriately regulated in the *International Building Code* or *International Residential Code*.

1303.1200
RESTROOM FACILITIES IN PUBLIC ACCOMMODATIONS

Subpart 1. **Ratio.** In a place of public accommodation subject to this part, the ratio of water closets for women to the total of water closets and urinals provided for men must be at least three to two, unless there are two or fewer fixtures for men.

Subp. 2. **Application.** This part applies only to the construction of buildings or structures of public accommodation or where the cost of alterations to an existing place of public accommodation exceeds 50 percent of the estimated replacement value of the existing facility.

Subp. 3. **Definition.** For purposes of this part, "place of public accommodation" means a publicly or privately owned sports or entertainment arena, stadium, theater, community or convention hall, special event center, amusement facility, or special event center in a public park, that is designed for occupancy by 200 or more people.

1303.1300
SPACE FOR COMMUTER VANS

Every parking ramp or other parking facility must include spaces for the parking of motor vehicles having a capacity of seven to 16 persons. The number of required spaces must be determined by two percent of the gross designed parking area with a minimum of two spaces. The minimum vertical clearance to and within required spaces is 98 inches.

1303.1400
AUTOMATIC GARAGE DOOR OPENING SYSTEMS

All automatic garage door opening systems that are installed, serviced, or repaired for garages serving residential buildings, must comply with the provisions of Minnesota Statutes, sections 325F.82 and 325F.83.

1303.1500
RECYCLING SPACE

Subpart 1. **Requirement.** Space must be provided for the collection, separation, and temporary storage of recyclable materials within or adjacent to all new or significantly remodeled buildings or structures that contain 1,000 square feet or more.

Exception: Residential structures with fewer than four dwelling units.

Subp. 2. **Location.** Space designated for recycling shall be located so it is at least as convenient as the location where other solid waste is collected. If feasible, recycling space should be adjacent to other solid waste collection space. Recycling space must be located and designed in accordance with the provisions of this code and ordinances of the jurisdiction.

Subp. 3. **Identification on plans.** Space designated for recycling must be identified on plans submitted for a building permit.

Subp. 4. **Minimum space.** Space designated for recycling must be sufficient to contain all the recyclable materials generated from the building. The minimum amount of recycling space required must be the number of square feet determined by multiplying the gross square feet of floor areas assigned to each use within a building as set forth in subpart 5, Table 1-A, times the corresponding factor.

Subp. 5. **TABLE 1-A MINIMUM RECYCLING SPACE REQUIREMENTS**

USE[1]	FACTOR
1. Aircraft hangers (no repair)	.001
2. Auction rooms	.0025
3[2]. Auditoriums, reviewing stands, stadiums, gymnasiums, public swimming pools, skating rinks	.001
4. Lodge rooms, conference rooms, lounges, stages, exhibit rooms	.0025
5. Dance floors, churches and chapels, lobby	.001
6. Dining rooms	.003
7[3]. Drinking establishments	.004
8[3]. Bowling alleys (excluding lanes)	.0025
9[3]. Children's homes and homes for the aged	.0025
10. Classrooms	.002
11. Courtrooms	.001
12. Dormitories	.0025
13. Exercise rooms	.001
14. Garages, parking	.001
15[3]. Hospitals and sanitariums, nursing homes	.0025
16[3]. Hotels	.002
17. Apartments	.0025
18. Kitchens - commercial	.003
19[3]. Libraries	.002

20. Locker rooms .001
21. Malls .0025
22. Manufacturing areas .0025
23. Mechanical equipment rooms .001
24[3]. Nurseries for children (day care) .002
25. Offices .0025
26. School shops and vocational rooms .0025
27. Storage and stock rooms .0025
28. Warehouses .001
29. All others .0025

Footnotes:

[1]The area of a use must include all areas serving or accessory to a use (corridors, accessory use areas, etc.).

[2]Exclude playing areas, courts, fields, and like areas.

[3]The factors for these uses are intended to include all incidental uses typical of these types of facilities. If the provisions of Table 1-A are excessive due to a specific use, space for recycling may be considered individually by the administrative authority.

1303.1600
FOOTING DEPTH FOR FROST PROTECTION

Subpart 1. **Minimum footing depth.** In the absence of a determination by an engineer competent in soil mechanics, the minimum allowable footing depth in feet due to freezing is five feet in Zone I and 3½ feet in Zone II. Zone I includes the counties of: Aitkin, Becker, Beltrami, Carlton, Cass, Clay, Clearwater, Cook, Crow Wing, Douglas, Grant, Hubbard, Itasca, Kanabec, Kittson, Koochiching, Lake, Lake of the Woods, Mahnomen, Marshall, Mille Lacs, Morrison, Norman, Otter Tail, Pennington, Pine, Polk, Red Lake, Roseau, St. Louis, Todd, Traverse, Wadena, and Wilkin. Zone II shall include the counties of: Anoka, Benton, Big Stone, Blue Earth, Brown, Carver, Chippewa, Chisago, Cottonwood, Dakota, Dodge, Faribault, Fillmore, Freeborn, Goodhue, Hennepin, Houston, Isanti, Jackson, Kandiyohi, Lac qui Parle, Le Sueur, Lincoln, Lyon, McLeod, Martin, Meeker, Mower, Murray, Nicollet, Nobles, Olmsted, Pipestone, Pope, Ramsey, Redwood, Renville, Rice, Rock, Scott, Sibley, Sherburne, Stearns, Steele, Stevens, Swift, Wabasha, Waseca, Washington, Watonwan, Winona, Wright, and Yellow Medicine. Less depths may be permitted when supporting evidence is presented by an engineer competent in soil mechanics.

Subp. 2. **Soil under slab on grade construction for buildings.** When soil, natural or fill, is sand or pit run sand and gravel, and of depth in accordance with minimum footing depth requirements for each zone, slab on grade construction which is structurally designed to support all applied loads is permitted. Sand must contain less than 70 percent material that will pass through a U.S. Standard No. 40 sieve and less than five percent material that will pass through a No. 200 sieve (five percent fines), or be approved by an engineer competent in soil mechanics. Footings for interior bearing walls or columns may be constructed to be integral with the slab on grade for any height building. Footings for exterior bearing walls or columns may be similarly constructed for any height building when supporting soil is as described in this subpart. Footing design must reflect eccentric loading conditions at slab edges, soil bearing ca-

pacity, and the requirements of *International Building Code,* Chapter 19. Slab on grade construction for detached buildings of Group U occupancies may be placed on any soil except peat or muck.

1303.1700
GROUND SNOW LOAD

The ground snow load, Pg, to be used in determining the design snow loads for buildings and other structures shall be 60 pounds per square foot in the following counties: Aitkin, Becker, Beltrami, Carlton, Cass, Clay, Clearwater, Cook, Crow Wing, Hubbard, Itasca, Kanabec, Kittson, Koochiching, Lake, Lake of the Woods, Mahnomen, Marshall, Mille Lacs, Morrison, Norman, Otter Tail, Pennington, Pine, Polk, Red Lake, Roseau, St. Louis, Todd, and Wadena. The ground snow load, Pg, to be used in determining the design snow loads for buildings and other structures shall be 50 pounds per square foot in all other counties.

1303.1800
RADIAL ICE ON TOWERS

The effect of one-half inch of radial ice must be included in the design of towers including all supporting guys. This effect must include the weight of the ice and the increased profile of each such tower component so coated.

1303.1900
CONVENTIONAL FOUNDATION CONSTRUCTION

Subpart 1. **Conventional foundation construction.** The provisions in this part may be used for the design and construction of conventional foundations serving Group R, Division 3, and Group U occupancies subject to the approval of the building official. Other methods may be used provided a satisfactory design is submitted showing compliance with the other provisions of this code.

TABLE 2-A—FOUNDATION WALL REINFORCEMENT REQUIREMENTS OF 12-INCH THICK HOLLOW UNIT MASONRY OR 8-INCH THICK CAST-IN-PLACE (CIP) CONCRETE.

HEIGHT OF UNBALANCED BACKFILL	SIZE OF VERTICAL REINFORCING BARS REQUIRED WHEN FOUNDATION WALL IS CONSTRUCTED IN SOIL GROUPS I OR II OF TABLE 2-B	
	Group I Soil	Group II Soil
5 feet	No. 4 bars	No. 4 bars
6 feet	No. 4 bars	No. 5 bars
7 feet	No. 4 bars	No. 5 bars
8 feet	No. 5 bars	No. 6 bars

[1]All reinforcing is to be installed vertically a maximum of six feet on center. Vertical reinforcing bars must be placed three inches clear maximum from the inside nonpressure face of masonry walls and 1½ inches clear maximum from the inside face of the CIP walls.

[2]Reinforcing may be omitted in wall sections ten feet or less in length that are bounded by wall corners or by wall offsets or returns at least two feet in depth.

[3]Reinforced cells of hollow unit masonry must be filled solid with grout having a specified compressive strength at 28 days of 2,000 psi. Reinforcing steel must be ASTM A615 grade 40 or grade 60.

[4] Hollow masonry units must be ASTM C-90 (average unit strength = 1,900 psi) and be installed in a running bond pattern with Type M or Type S mortar.

[5] Cast-in-place concrete must have a 28-day minimum strength of 3,000 psi.

[6] Anchor bolts must be installed to align with vertical reinforcing in addition to the locations and in the manner specified in *International Building Code,* Section 2308.6 or *International Residential Code,* Section R403.1.6.

[7] If foundation walls are parallel to floor framing, solid blocking or diagonal bracing must be installed at the anchor bolt locations in the first two joist or truss spaces.

[8] Floor framing must be nailed to the sill plate in accordance with *International Building Code,* Table 2304.9.1 or *International Residential Code,* Table R602.3(1). In addition, approved metal angle clips must be used to fasten floor joists, trusses, or blocking to the sill plate at the anchor bolt locations. The clips must not be less than 18 gauge and be fastened to the plate and ad-

joining joists, trusses, or blocking with at least three 1½ inch by 8d nails in each leg of the clip.

[9] Foundation walls must not exceed a height of 8½ feet, as measured from the basement floor. Height of unbalanced fill must also be measured from the basement floor.

[10] Prior to backfilling, foundation walls must be laterally supported by floor construction at both top and bottom or by adequate temporary bracing.

[11] A foundation drainage system must be installed, consisting of a foundation drain complying with *International Building Code,* Sections 1806.4.2 or 1806.4.3, *International Residential Code,* Section R405.1, or other approved design.

[12] Foundations must also comply with the applicable construction provisions of *International Building Code,* Chapters 19 and 21, or *International Residential Code,* Chapter 6.

Subp. 2. **Types of soils and their properties.**

TABLE 2-B—TYPES OF SOILS AND THEIR PROPERTIES

SOIL GROUP	UNIFIED SOIL CLASSIFICATION SYSTEM SYMBOL	SOIL DESCRIPTION	DRAINAGE CHARACTERISTICS	FROST HEAVE POTENTIAL	VOLUME CHANGE POTENTIAL EXPANSION
Group I	GW	Well-graded gravels, gravel sand mixtures, little or no fines.	Good	Low	Low
	GP	Poorly graded gravels or gravel sand mixtures, little or no fines.	Good	Low	Low
	SW	Well-graded sands, gravelly sands, little or no fines.	Good	Low	Low
	SP	Poorly graded sands or gravelly sands, little or no fines.	Good	Low	Low
	GM	Silty gravels, gravel-sand-silt mixtures.	Good	Medium	Low
	SM	Silty sand, sand silt mixtures.	Good	Medium	Low
Group II	GC	Clayey gravels, gravel-sand-clay mixtures.	Medium	Medium	Low
	SC	Clayey sands, sand-clay mixture.	Medium	Medium	Low
	ML	Inorganic silts and very fine sands, rock flour, silty or clayey fine sands or clayey silts with slight plasticity.	Medium	High	Low
	CL	Inorganic clays of low to medium plasticity, gravelly clays, sandy clays, silty clays, lean clays.	Medium	Medium	Medium to Low
Group III	CH	Inorganic clays of high plasticity, fat clays.	Poor	Medium	High
	MH	Inorganic silts, micaceous or diatomaceous fine sandy or silty soils, elastic silts.	Poor	High	High
Group IV	OL	Organic silts and organic silty clays of low plasticity.	Poor	Medium	Medium
	OH	Organic clays of medium to high plasticity, organic silts.	Unsatisfactory	Medium	High
	Pt	Peat and other highly organic soils.	Unsatisfactory	Medium	High

Table 2-B is reproduced by permission of the American Forest and Paper Association (formerly NFPA), Washington, D.C.

1303.2000
EXTERIOR WOOD DECKS, PATIOS, AND BALCONIES

The decking surface and upper portions of exterior wood decks, patios, and balconies may be constructed of any of the following materials:

A. The heartwood from species of wood having natural resistance to decay or termites, including redwood and cedars;

B. Grades of lumber which contain sapwood from species of wood having natural resistance to decay or termites, including redwood and cedars; or

C. Treated wood.

The species and grades of wood products used to construct the decking surface and upper portions of exterior decks, patios, and balconies must be made available to the building official on request before final construction approval.

MNMNMNMNMNMNMNMNMNMNMN

1303.2100
BLEACHER SAFETY

All new bleachers, manufactured, installed, sold, or distributed where the bleachers or bleacher open spaces will be over 55 inches above grade or the floor below, and all bleacher guardrails if any part of the guardrail will be over 30 inches above grade or the floor below must comply with the State Building Code in effect and the provisions of Minnesota Statutes, Section 16B.616.

MINNESOTA RULES, CHAPTER 1309

1309.0010
ADOPTION OF INTERNATIONAL RESIDENTIAL CODE (IRC) BY REFERENCE

Subpart 1. Generally. The 2000 edition of the *International Residential Code* (IRC) as promulgated by the International Code Council (ICC), Falls Church, Virginia, is incorporated by reference and made part of the Minnesota State Building Code except as qualified by the applicable provisions in Minnesota Rules, chapter 1300, and as amended in this chapter. The IRC is not subject to frequent change and a copy of the IRC, with amendments for use in Minnesota, is available in the office of the commissioner of administration.

Subp. 2. Mandatory chapters. The 2000 IRC Chapters 2 through 10, 43, and Appendix Chapter K, must be administered by any municipality that has adopted the code, except as qualified by the applicable provisions in Minnesota Rules, chapter 1300, and as amended by this chapter.

Subp. 3. Replacement chapters. The following 2000 IRC chapters are being deleted and replaced with the provisions listed below:

A. Chapter 1 of the 2000 IRC and any references to code administration in this code are deleted and replaced with Minnesota Rules, chapter 1300, Minnesota Administration Code.

B. Chapter 11 of the 2000 IRC and any references to energy in this code are deleted and replaced with Minnesota Statutes, section 16B.617.

C. Chapters 12 through 24 of the 2000 IRC and any references to mechanical matters in this code are deleted and replaced with Minnesota Rules, chapter 1346, Minnesota Mechanical Code.

D. Chapters 25 through 32 of the 2000 IRC and any references to plumbing in this code are deleted and replaced with Minnesota Rules, chapter 4715, Minnesota Plumbing Code.

E. Chapters 34 through 42 of the 2000 IRC and references to electrical matters in this code, other than Section R317 Smoke Alarms, are deleted and replaced with Minnesota Rules, chapter 1315, Minnesota Electrical Code.

Subp. 4. Seismic or earthquake provisions. Any seismic or earthquake provisions and any references to them are deleted and are not included in this code.

1309.0020
REFERENCES TO OTHER ICC CODES

Subpart 1. Generally. References to other codes and standards promulgated by the ICC in the 2000 IRC are modified as indicated in this part.

Subp. 2. Building code. References to the *International Building Code* in this code mean the Minnesota Building Code,

adopted pursuant to Minnesota Rules, chapter 1305, and Minnesota Statutes, section 16B.61, subdivision 1.

Subp. 3. Residential code. References to the IRC in this code mean the Minnesota Residential Code, adopted under Minnesota Rules, chapter 1309, and Minnesota Statutes, section 16B.61, subdivision 1.

Subp. 4. Electrical code. References to the ICC *Electrical Code* in this code mean the Minnesota Electrical Code, Minnesota Rules, chapter 1315, adopted under Minnesota Statutes, section 326.243.

Subp. 5. Fuel gas code. References to the *International Fuel Gas Code* in this code mean the Minnesota Mechanical Code, Minnesota Rules, chapter 1347, adopted under Minnesota Statutes, section 16B.61, subdivision 1.

Subp. 6. Mechanical code. References to the *International Mechanical Code* in this code mean the Minnesota Mechanical Code, Minnesota Rules, chapter 1346, adopted under Minnesota Statutes, section 16B.61, subdivision 1.

Subp. 7. Plumbing code. References to the *International Plumbing Code* in this code mean the Minnesota Plumbing Code, Minnesota Rules, chapter 4715, adopted under Minnesota Statutes, section 16B.61, subdivisions 1 and 2.

Subp. 8. Private sewage disposal code. References to the *International Private Sewage Disposal Code* in this code mean the Minnesota Pollution Control Agency's minimum standards and criteria for individual sewage treatment systems in Minnesota Rules, chapter 7080, adopted under Minnesota Statutes, chapters 103F, 103G, 115, and 116.

Subp. 9. Energy conservation code. References to the *International Energy Conservation Code* in this code mean the Minnesota Energy Code, adopted under Minnesota Statutes, section 16B.617.

Subp. 10. Property maintenance code. References to the *International Property Maintenance Code* in this code do not apply.

Subp. 11. Accessibility code. References to accessibility in this code mean the Minnesota Accessibility Code, Minnesota Rules, chapter 1341.

1309.0030
ADMINISTRATIVE PROCEDURE CRITERIA

Procedures relating to the administration and enforcement of this code under Minnesota Statutes, section 16B.57, are contained in Minnesota Rules, chapter 1300, Minnesota Administration Code. Minnesota Rules, chapter 1300, governs the application of this code.

MNMNMNMNMNM

1309.0040
VIOLATION

A violation of this code is a misdemeanor under Minnesota Statutes, section 16B.69.

Part II — Definitions

CHAPTER 2
DEFINITIONS

SECTION R201
GENERAL

R201.1 Scope. Unless otherwise expressly stated, the following words and terms shall, for the purposes of this code, have the meanings indicated in this chapter.

R201.2 Interchangeability. Words used in the present tense include the future; words in the masculine gender include the feminine and neuter; the singular number includes the plural and the plural, the singular.

R201.3 Terms defined in other codes. Where terms are not defined in this code such terms shall have meanings ascribed to them as in other code publications of the International Code Council.

R201.4 Terms not defined. Where terms are not defined through the methods authorized by this chapter, the *Merriam-Webster Collegiate Dictionary,* available at www.m-w.com, shall be considered as providing ordinarily accepted meanings. The dictionary is incorporated by reference, is subject to frequent change, and is available through the Minitex interlibrary loan system.

SECTION R202
DEFINITIONS

ACCESSIBLE. Signifies access that requires the removal of an access panel or similar removable obstruction.

ACCESSIBLE, READILY. Signifies access without the necessity for removing a panel or similar obstruction.

ACCESSORY STRUCTURE. In one- and two-family dwellings not more than three stories high with separate means of egress, a building, the use of which is incidental to that of the main building and which is located on the same lot.

ADDITION. An extension or increase in floor area or height of a building or structure.

AIR ADMITTANCE VALVE. A one-way valve designed to allow air into the plumbing drainage system when a negative pressure develops in the piping. This device shall close by gravity and seal the terminal under conditions of zero differential pressure (no flow conditions) and under positive internal pressure.

AIR BREAK, DRAINAGE SYSTEM. An arrangement in which a discharge pipe from a fixture, appliance or device drains indirectly into a receptor below the flood-level rim of the receptor.

AIR CIRCULATION, FORCED. A means of providing space conditioning utilizing movement of air through ducts or plenums by mechanical means.

AIR-CONDITIONING SYSTEM. A system that consists of heat exchangers, blowers, filters, supply, exhaust and return-air systems, and shall include any apparatus installed in connection therewith.

AIR GAP, DRAINAGE SYSTEM. The unobstructed vertical distance through free atmosphere between the outlet of a waste pipe and the flood-level rim of the fixture or receptor into which it is discharging.

AIR GAP, WATER-DISTRIBUTION SYSTEM. The unobstructed vertical distance through free atmosphere between the lowest opening from a water supply discharge to the flood-level rim of a plumbing fixture.

ALTERATION. Any construction or renovation to an existing structure other than repair or addition that requires a permit. Also, a change in a mechanical system that involves an extension, addition or change to the arrangement, type or purpose of the original installation that requires a permit.

ANCHORS. See "Supports."

ANTISIPHON. A term applied to valves or mechanical devices that eliminate siphonage.

APPLIANCE. A device or apparatus that is manufactured and designed to utilize energy and for which this code provides specific requirements.

APPROVED. Approved refers to approval by the building official as the result of investigation and tests conducted by him or her, or by reason of accepted principles or tests by nationally recognized organizations.

APPROVED AGENCY. An established and recognized agency regularly engaged in conducting tests or furnishing inspection services, when such agency has been approved by the building official.

ATTIC. The unfinished space between the ceiling joists of the top story and the roof rafters.

BACKFLOW, DRAINAGE. A reversal of flow in the drainage system.

BACKFLOW PREVENTER. A device or means to prevent backflow.

BACKFLOW PREVENTER, REDUCED-PRESSURE-ZONE TYPE. A backflow-prevention device consisting of two independently acting check valves, internally force loaded to a normally closed position and separated by an intermediate chamber (or zone) in which there is an automatic relief means of venting to atmosphere internally loaded to a normally open position between two tightly closing shutoff valves and with means for testing for tightness of the checks and opening of relief means.

BACKFLOW, WATER DISTRIBUTION. The flow of water or other liquids into the potable water-supply piping from any sources other than its intended source. Backsiphonage is one type of backflow.

BACKSIPHONAGE. The flowing back of used or contaminated water from piping into a potable water-supply pipe due to a negative pressure in such pipe.

BACKWATER VALVE. A device installed in a drain or pipe to prevent backflow of sewage.

BALCONY, EXTERIOR. An exterior floor projecting from and supported by a structure without additional independent supports.

BALL COCK. A valve that is used inside a gravity-type water closet flush tank to control the supply of water into the tank. It may also be called a flush-tank fill valve or water control.

BASEMENT. That portion of a building that is partly or completely below grade (see "Story above grade").

BASEMENT WALL. The opaque portion of a wall that encloses one side of a basement and has an average below grade wall area that is 50 percent or more of the total opaque and nonopaque area of that enclosing side.

BASIC WIND SPEED. Three-second gust speed at 33 feet (10 058 mm) above the ground in Exposure C (see Section R301.2.1) as given in Figure R301.2(4).

BATHROOM GROUP. A group of fixtures, including or excluding a bidet, consisting of a water closet, lavatory, and bathtub or shower. Such fixtures are located together on the same floor level.

BEND. A drainage fitting, designed to provide a change in direction of a drain pipe of less than the angle specified by the amount necessary to establish the desired slope of the line (see "Elbow" and "Sweep").

BOILER. A self-contained appliance from which hot water is circulated for heating purposes and then returned to the boiler, and which operates at water pressures not exceeding 160 pounds per square inch gage (psig) (1102 kPa gage) and at water temperatures not exceeding 250°F (121°C).

BOND BEAM. A horizontal grouted element within masonry in which reinforcement is embedded.

BRACED WALL LINE. A series of braced wall panels constructed in accordance with Section R602.10 for wood framing or Section R603.7 or R603.8.1.2 for cold-formed steel framing to resist racking from seismic and wind forces.

BRACED WALL PANEL. A section of a braced wall line constructed in accordance with Section R602.10 for wood framing or Section R603.7 or R603.8.1.2 for cold-formed steel framing, which extend the full height of the wall.

BRANCH. Any part of the piping system other than a riser, main or stack.

BRANCH, FIXTURE. See "Fixture branch, drainage."

BRANCH, HORIZONTAL. See "Horizontal branch, drainage."

BRANCH, INTERVAL. A distance along a soil or waste stack corresponding to a story height, but not less than 8 feet (2438 mm), within which the horizontal branches from one floor or story of a building are connected to the stack.

BRANCH, MAIN. A water-distribution pipe that extends horizontally off a main or riser to convey water to branches or fixture groups.

BRANCH, VENT. A vent connecting two or more individual vents with a vent stack or stack vent.

BTU/H. The listed maximum capacity of an appliance, absorption unit or burner expressed in British thermal units input per hour.

BUILDING. Building shall mean any one- and two-family dwelling or portion thereof, including townhouses, that is used, or designed or intended to be used for human habitation, for living, sleeping, cooking or eating purposes, or any combination thereof, and shall include accessory structures thereto.

BUILDING DRAIN. The lowest piping that collects the discharge from all other drainage piping inside the house and conveys it to the building sewer 30 inches (762 mm) outside the building wall.

BUILDING, EXISTING. Existing building is a building erected prior to the adoption of this code, or one for which a legal building permit has been issued.

BUILDING LINE. The line established by law, beyond which a building shall not extend, except as specifically provided by law.

BUILDING OFFICIAL. The officer or other designated authority charged with the administration and enforcement of this code.

BUILDING SEWER. That part of the drainage system that extends from the end of the building drain and conveys its discharge to a public sewer, private sewer, individual sewage-disposal system or other point of disposal.

BUILDING THERMAL ENVELOPE. The basement walls, exterior walls, floor, roof and any other building element that enclose conditioned spaces.

BUILT-UP ROOF COVERING. Two or more layers of felt cemented together and surfaced with a cap sheet, mineral aggregate, smooth coating or similar surfacing material.

CEILING HEIGHT. The clear vertical distance from the finished floor to the finished ceiling.

CHIMNEY. A primary vertical structure containing one or more flues, for the purpose of carrying gaseous products of combustion and air from a fuel-burning appliance to the outside atmosphere.

CHIMNEY CONNECTOR. A pipe that connects a fuel-burning appliance to a chimney.

CHIMNEY TYPES

Residential-type appliance. An approved chimney for removing the products of combustion from fuel-burning, residential-type appliances producing combustion gases not in excess of 1,000°F (538°C) under normal operating conditions, but capable of producing combustion gases of 1,400°F (760°C) during intermittent forces firing for periods up to 1 hour. All temperatures shall be measured at the appliance flue outlet. Residential-type appliance chimneys include masonry and factory-built types.

CIRCUIT VENT. A vent that connects to a horizontal drainage branch and vents two traps to a maximum of eight traps or trapped fixtures connected into a battery.

CLADDING. The exterior materials that cover the surface of the building envelope that is directly loaded by the wind.

CLEANOUT. An accessible opening in the drainage system used for the removal of possible obstruction.

CLOSET. A small room or chamber used for storage.

COMBINATION WASTE AND VENT SYSTEM. A specially designed system of waste piping embodying the horizontal wet venting of one or more sinks or floor drains by means of a common waste and vent pipe adequately sized to provide free movement of air above the flow line of the drain.

COMBUSTIBLE MATERIAL. Any material not defined as noncombustible.

COMBUSTION AIR. The air provided to fuel-burning equipment including air for fuel combustion, draft-hood dilution and ventilation of the equipment enclosure.

COMMON VENT. A single pipe venting two trap arms within the same branch interval, either back-to-back or one above the other.

CONDENSATE. The liquid that separates from a gas due to a reduction in temperature, e.g., water that condenses from flue gases and water that condenses from air circulating through the cooling coil in air conditioning equipment.

CONDENSING APPLIANCE. An appliance that condenses water generated by the burning of fuels.

CONDITIONED AIR. Air treated to control its temperature, relative humidity or quality.

CONDITIONED AREA. That area within a building provided with heating and/or cooling systems or appliances capable of maintaining, through design or heat loss/gain, 68°F (20°C) during the heating season and/or 80°F (27°C) during the cooling season, or has a fixed opening directly adjacent to a conditioned area.

CONDITIONED FLOOR AREA. The horizontal projection of the floors associated with the conditioned space.

CONDITIONED SPACE. For energy purposes, space within a building that is provided with heating and/or cooling equipment or systems capable of maintaining, through design or heat loss/gain, 50°F (10°C) during the heating season and 85°F (29°C) during the cooling season, or communicates directly with a conditioned space. For mechanical purposes, an area, room or space being heated or cooled by any equipment or appliance.

CONFINED SPACE. A room or space having a volume less than 50 cubic feet per 1,000 Btu/h (4.83 L/W) of the aggregate input rating of all fuel-burning appliances installed in that space.

CONSTRUCTION DOCUMENTS. Written, graphic and pictorial documents prepared or assembled for describing the design, location and physical characteristics of the elements of a project necessary for obtaining a building permit. Construction drawings shall be drawn to an appropriate scale.

CONTINUOUS WASTE. A drain from two or more similar adjacent fixtures connected to a single trap.

CONTROL, LIMIT. An automatic control responsive to changes in liquid flow or level, pressure, or temperature for limiting the operation of an appliance.

CONTROL, PRIMARY SAFETY. A safety control responsive directly to flame properties that senses the presence or absence of flame and, in event of ignition failure or unintentional flame extinguishment, automatically causes shutdown of mechanical equipment.

CONVECTOR. A system-incorporating heating element in an enclosure in which air enters an opening below the heating element, is heated and leaves the enclosure through an opening located above the heating element.

CORROSION RESISTANT. Any nonferrous metal or any metal having an unbroken surfacing of nonferrous metal, or steel with not less than 10-percent chromium or with not less than 0.20-percent copper.

COURT. A space, open and unobstructed to the sky, located at or above grade level on a lot and bounded on three or more sides by walls or a building.

CRAWL SPACE. Areas or rooms with less than 7 feet (2134 mm) ceiling height measured to the finished floor or grade below.

CROSS CONNECTION. Any connection between two otherwise separate piping systems whereby there may be a flow from one system to the other.

DALLE GLASS. A decorative composite glazing material made of individual pieces of glass that are embedded in a cast matrix of concrete or epoxy.

DAMPER, VOLUME. A device that will restrict, retard or direct the flow of air in any duct, or the products of combustion of heat-producing equipment, vent connector, vent or chimney.

DEAD END. A branch leading from a DWV system terminating at a developed length of 2 feet (610 mm) or more. Dead ends shall be prohibited except as an approved part of a rough-in for future connection.

DEAD LOADS. The weight of all materials of construction incorporated into the building, including but not limited to walls, floors, roofs, ceilings, stairways, built-in partitions, finishes, cladding, and other similarly incorporated architectural and structural items, and fixed service equipment.

DECK. An exterior floor system supported on at least two opposing sides by an adjoining structure and/or posts, piers, or other independent supports.

DECORATIVE GLASS. A carved, leaded or Dalle glass or glazing material whose purpose is decorative or artistic, not functional; whose coloring, texture or other design qualities or components cannot be removed without destroying the glazing material; and whose surface, or assembly into which it is incorporated, is divided into segments.

DESIGN PROFESSIONAL. See definition of "Registered design professional."

DEVELOPED LENGTH. The length of a pipeline measured along the center line of the pipe and fittings.

DIAMETER. Unless specifically stated, the term "diameter" is the nominal diameter as designated by the approved material standard.

DIAPHRAGM. A horizontal or nearly horizontal system acting to transmit lateral forces to the vertical resisting elements. When the term "diaphragm" is used, it includes horizontal bracing systems.

DILUTION AIR. Air that enters a draft hood or draft regulator and mixes with flue gases.

DIRECT-VENT APPLIANCE. A fuel-burning appliance with a sealed combustion system that draws all air for combustion from the outside atmosphere and discharges all flue gases to the outside atmosphere.

DRAFT. The pressure difference existing between the appliance or any component part and the atmosphere, that causes a continuous flow of air and products of combustion through the gas passages of the appliance to the atmosphere.

    Induced draft. The pressure difference created by the action of a fan, blower or ejector, that is located between the appliance and the chimney or vent termination.

    Natural draft. The pressure difference created by a vent or chimney because of its height, and the temperature difference between the flue gases and the atmosphere.

DRAFT HOOD. A device built into an appliance, or a part of the vent connector from an appliance, which is designed to provide for the ready escape of the flue gases from the appliance in the event of no draft, backdraft or stoppage beyond the draft hood; prevent a backdraft from entering the appliance; and neutralize the effect of stack action of the chimney or gas vent on the operation of the appliance.

DRAFT REGULATOR. A device that functions to maintain a desired draft in the appliance by automatically reducing the draft to the desired value.

DRAFT STOP. A material, device or construction installed to restrict the movement of air within open spaces of concealed areas of building components such as crawl spaces, floor-ceiling assemblies, roof-ceiling assemblies and attics.

DRAIN. Any pipe that carries soil and water-borne wastes in a building drainage system.

DRAINAGE FITTING. A pipe fitting designed to provide connections in the drainage system that have provisions for establishing the desired slope in the system. These fittings are made from a variety of both metals and plastics. The methods of coupling provide for required slope in the system (see "Durham fitting").

DUCT SYSTEM. A continuous passageway for the transmission of air which, in addition to ducts, includes duct fittings, dampers, plenums, fans and accessory air-handling equipment and appliances.

DURHAM FITTING. A special type of drainage fitting for use in the durham systems installations in which the joints are made with recessed and tapered threaded fittings, as opposed to bell and spigot lead/oakum or solvent/cemented or soldered joints. The tapping is at an angle (not 90 degrees) to provide for proper slope in otherwise rigid connections.

DURHAM SYSTEM. A term used to describe soil or waste systems where all piping is of threaded pipe, tube or other such rigid construction using recessed drainage fittings to correspond to the types of piping.

DWELLING. Any building that contains one or two dwelling units used, intended, or designed to be built, used, rented, leased, let or hired out to be occupied, or that are occupied for living purposes.

DWELLING UNIT. A single unit providing complete independent living facilities for one or more persons, including permanent provisions for living, sleeping, eating, cooking and sanitation.

DWV. Abbreviated term for drain, waste and vent piping as used in common plumbing practice.

EFFECTIVE OPENING. The minimum cross-sectional area at the point of water-supply discharge, measured or expressed in terms of diameter of a circle and if the opening is not circular, the diameter of a circle of equivalent cross-sectional area. (This is applicable to air gap.)

ELBOW. A pressure pipe fitting designed to provide an exact change in direction of a pipe run. An elbow provides a sharp turn in the flow path (see "Bend" and "Sweep").

EMERGENCY ESCAPE AND RESCUE OPENING. An operable window, door or similar device that provides for a means of escape and access for rescue in the event of an emergency.

EQUIPMENT. All piping, ducts, vents, control devices and other components of systems other than appliances that are permanently installed and integrated to provide control of environmental conditions for buildings. This definition shall also include other systems specifically regulated in this code.

EQUIVALENT LENGTH. For determining friction losses in a piping system, the effect of a particular fitting equal to the friction loss through a straight piping length of the same nominal diameter.

ESSENTIALLY NONTOXIC TRANSFER FLUIDS. Fluids having a Gosselin rating of 1, including propylene glycol; mineral oil; polydimenthyoil oxane; hydrochlorofluorocarbon, chlorofluorocarbon and hydrofluorocarbon refrigerants; and FDA-approved boiler water additives for steam boilers.

ESSENTIALLY TOXIC TRANSFER FLUIDS. Soil, water or gray water and fluids having a Gosselin rating of 2 or more including ethylene glycol, hydrocarbon oils, ammonia refrigerants and hydrazine.

EVAPORATIVE COOLER. A device used for reducing air temperature by the process of evaporating water into an airstream.

EXCESS AIR. Air that passes through the combustion chamber and the appliance flue in excess of that which is theoretically required for complete combustion.

EXHAUST HOOD, FULL OPENING. An exhaust hood with an opening at least equal to the diameter of the connecting vent.

EXISTING INSTALLATIONS. Any plumbing system regulated by this code that was legally installed prior to the effective date of this code, or for which a permit to install has been issued.

EXTERIOR INSULATION FINISH SYSTEMS (EIFS). Synthetic stucco cladding systems typically consisting of five layers: adhesive, insulation board, base coat into which fiberglass reinforcing mesh is embedded, and a finish coat in the desired color.

EXTERIOR WALL. An above-grade wall enclosing conditioned space. Includes between floor spandrels, peripheral edges of floors, roof and basement knee walls, dormer walls, gable end walls, walls enclosing a mansard roof, and basement walls with an average below grade wall area that is less than 50 percent of the total opaque and nonopaque area of that enclosing side.

FACTORY-BUILT CHIMNEY. A listed and labeled chimney composed of factory-made components assembled in the field in accordance with the manufacturer's instructions and the conditions of the listing.

FENESTRATION. Skylights, roof windows, vertical windows (whether fixed or moveable); opaque doors; glazed doors; glass block; and combination opaque/glazed doors.

FIREBLOCKING. Building materials installed to resist the free passage of flame to other areas of the building through concealed spaces.

FIREPLACE. An assembly consisting of a hearth and fire chamber of noncombustible material and provided with a chimney, for use with solid fuels.

Factory-built fireplace. A listed and labeled fireplace and chimney system composed of factory-made components, and assembled in the field in accordance with manufacturer's instructions and the conditions of the listing.

Masonry chimney. A field-constructed chimney composed of solid masonry units, bricks, stones or concrete.

Masonry fireplace. A field-constructed fireplace composed of solid masonry units, bricks, stones or concrete.

FIREPLACE STOVE. A free-standing, chimney-connected solid-fuel-burning heater designed to be operated with the fire chamber doors in either the open or closed position.

FIREPLACE THROAT. The opening between the top of the firebox and the smoke chamber.

FIRE SEPARATION DISTANCE. The distance measured from the building face to the closest interior lot line, to the centerline of a street, alley or public way, or to an imaginary line between two buildings on the property. The distance shall be measured at right angles from the lot line.

FIXTURE. See "Plumbing fixture."

FIXTURE BRANCH, DRAINAGE. A drain serving one or more fixtures that discharges into another portion of the drainage system.

FIXTURE BRANCH, WATER-SUPPLY. A water-supply pipe between the fixture supply and a main water-distribution pipe or fixture group main.

FIXTURE DRAIN. The drain from the trap of a fixture to the junction of that drain with any other drain pipe.

FIXTURE FITTING

Supply fitting. A fitting that controls the volume and/or directional flow of water and is either attached to or accessible from a fixture or is used with an open or atmospheric discharge.

Waste fitting. A combination of components that conveys the sanitary waste from the outlet of a fixture to the connection of the sanitary drainage system.

FIXTURE GROUP, MAIN. The main water-distribution pipe (or secondary branch) serving a plumbing fixture grouping such as a bath, kitchen or laundry area to which two or more individual fixture branch pipes are connected.

FIXTURE SUPPLY. The water-supply pipe connecting a fixture or fixture fitting to a fixture branch.

FIXTURE UNIT, DRAINAGE (d.f.u.). A measure of probable discharge into the drainage system by various types of plumbing fixtures, used to size DWV piping systems. The drainage fixture-unit value for a particular fixture depends on its volume rate of drainage discharge, on the time duration of a single drainage operation and on the average time between successive operations.

FIXTURE UNIT, WATER-SUPPLY (w.s.f.u.). A measure of the probable hydraulic demand on the water supply by various types of plumbing fixtures used to size water-piping systems. The water-supply fixture-unit value for a particular fixture depends on its volume rate of supply, on the time duration of a single supply operation and on the average time between successive operations.

FLAME SPREAD. The propagation of flame over a surface.

FLAME SPREAD INDEX. The numeric value assigned to a material tested in accordance with ASTM E 84.

FLOOD-LEVEL RIM. The edge of the receptor or fixture from which water overflows.

FLOOR DRAIN. A plumbing fixture for recess in the floor having a floor-level strainer intended for the purpose of the collection and disposal of waste water used in cleaning the floor and for the collection and disposal of accidental spillage to the floor.

FLOOR FURNACE. A self-contained furnace suspended from the floor of the space being heated, taking air for combustion from outside such space, and with means for lighting the appliance from such space.

FLOW PRESSURE. The static pressure reading in the water-supply pipe near the faucet or water outlet while the faucet or water outlet is open and flowing at capacity.

FLUE. See "Vent."

FLUE, APPLIANCE. The passages within an appliance through which combustion products pass from the combustion chamber to the flue collar.

FLUE COLLAR. The portion of a fuel-burning appliance designed for the attachment of a draft hood, vent connector or venting system.

FLUE GASES. Products of combustion plus excess air in appliance flues or heat exchangers.

FLUSH VALVE. A device located at the bottom of a flush tank that is operated to flush water closets.

FLUSHOMETER TANK. A device integrated within an air accumulator vessel that is designed to discharge a predetermined quantity of water to fixtures for flushing purposes.

FLUSHOMETER VALVE. A flushometer valve is a device that discharges a predetermined quantity of water to fixtures for flushing purposes and is actuated by direct water pressure.

FOAM PLASTIC INSULATION. A plastic that is intentionally expanded by the use of a foaming agent to produce a reduced-density plastic consisting open or closed cells distributed throughout the plastic and that has a density less than 20 pounds per cubic foot (320 kg/m^3).

FUEL-PIPING SYSTEM. All piping, tubing, valves and fittings used to connect fuel utilization equipment to the point of fuel delivery.

FULLWAY VALVE. A valve that in the full open position has an opening cross-sectional area equal to a minimum of 85 percent of the cross-sectional area of the connecting pipe.

FURNACE. A vented heating appliance designed or arranged to discharge heated air into a conditioned space or through a duct or ducts.

GLAZING AREA. The interior surface area of all glazed fenestration, including the area of sash, curbing or other framing elements, that enclose conditioned space. Includes the area of glazed fenestration assemblies in walls bounding conditioned basements.

GRADE. The finished ground level adjoining the building at all exterior walls.

GRADE FLOOR OPENING. A window or other opening located such that the sill height of the opening is not more than 44 inches (1118 mm) above or below the finished ground level adjacent to the opening.

GRADE, PIPING. See "Slope."

GRADE PLANE. A reference plane representing the average of the finished ground level adjoining the building at all exterior walls.

GROSS AREA OF EXTERIOR WALLS. The normal projection of all exterior walls, including the area of all windows and doors installed therein.

GROUND-SOURCE HEAT PUMP LOOP SYSTEM. Piping buried in horizontal or vertical excavations or placed in a body of water for the purpose of transporting heat transfer liquid to and from a heat pump. Included in this definition are closed loop systems in which the liquid is recirculated and open loop systems in which the liquid is drawn from a well or other source.

GUARD. A building component or a system of building components located near the open sides of elevated walking surfaces that minimizes the possibility of a fall from the walking surface to the lower level.

HABITABLE SPACE. A space in a building for living, sleeping, eating or cooking. Bathrooms, toilet rooms, closets, halls, storage or utility spaces and similar areas are not considered habitable spaces.

HANDRAIL. A horizontal or sloping rail intended for grasping by the hand for guidance or support.

HANGERS. See "Supports."

HAZARDOUS LOCATION. Any location considered to be a fire hazard for flammable vapors, dust, combustible fibers or other highly combustible substances.

HEATING DEGREE DAYS (HDD). The sum, on an annual basis, of the difference between 65°F (18°C) and the mean temperature for each day as determined from "NOAA Annual Degree Days to Selected Bases Derived from the 1960-1990 Normals" or other weather data sources acceptable to the code official.

HEAT PUMP. An appliance having heating or heating/cooling capability and that uses refrigerants to extract heat from air, liquid or other sources.

HEIGHT, BUILDING. The vertical distance from grade plane to the average height of the highest roof surface.

HEIGHT, STORY. The vertical distance from top to top of two successive tiers of beams or finished floor surfaces; and, for the topmost story, from the top of the floor finish to the top of the ceiling joists or, where there is not a ceiling, to the top of the roof rafters.

HIGH-TEMPERATURE (H.T.) CHIMNEY. A high temperature chimney complying with the requirements of UL 103. A Type H.T. chimney is identifiable by the markings "Type H.T." on each chimney pipe section.

HORIZONTAL BRANCH, DRAINAGE. A drain pipe extending laterally from a soil or waste stack or building drain, that receives the discharge from one or more fixture drains.

HORIZONTAL PIPE. Any pipe or fitting that makes an angle of less than 45 degrees (0.79 rad) with the horizontal.

HOT WATER. Water at a temperature greater than or equal to 110°F (43°C).

HURRICANE-PRONE REGIONS. Areas vulnerable to hurricanes, defined as the U.S. Atlantic Ocean and Gulf of Mexico coasts where the basic wind speed is greater than 110 miles per hour (177 km/h), and Hawaii, Puerto Rico, Guam, Virgin Islands, and America Samoa.

IGNITION SOURCE. A flame spark or hot surface capable of igniting flammable vapors or fumes. Such sources include appliance burners, burner ignitions and electrical switching devices.

INDIRECT WASTE PIPE. A waste pipe that discharges into the drainage system through an air gap into a trap, fixture or receptor.

INDIVIDUAL SEWAGE DISPOSAL SYSTEM. A system for disposal of sewage by means of a septic tank or mechanical treatment, designed for use apart from a public sewer to serve a single establishment or building.

INDIVIDUAL VENT. A pipe installed to vent a single-fixture drain that connects with the vent system above or terminates independently outside the building.

INDIVIDUAL WATER SUPPLY. A supply other than an approved public water supply that serves one or more families.

INSULATING CONCRETE FORM (ICF). A concrete forming system using stay-in-place forms of rigid foam plastic insulation, a hybrid of cement and foam insulation, a hybrid of cement and wood chips, or other insulating material for constructing cast-in-place concrete walls.

INSULATING SHEATHING. An insulating board having a minimum thermal resistance of R-2 of the core material.

JURISDICTION. The governmental unit that has adopted this code under due legislative authority.

KITCHEN. Kitchen shall mean an area used, or designated to be used, for the preparation of food.

LABEL. An identification applied on a product by the manufacturer which contains the name of the manufacturer, the function and performance characteristics of the product or material, and the name and identification of an approved agency and that indicates that the representative sample of the product or material has been tested and evaluated by an approved agency. (See also "Manufacturer's designation" and "Mark.")

LABELED. Devices, equipment or materials to which have been affixed a label, seal, symbol or other identifying mark of a testing laboratory, inspection agency or other organization concerned with product evaluation that maintains periodic inspection of the production of the above labeled items that attests to compliance with a specific standard.

LIGHT-FRAMED CONSTRUCTION. A type of construction whose vertical and horizontal structural elements are pri-

marily formed by a system of repetitive wood or light gage steel framing members.

LISTED AND LISTING. Terms referring to equipment that is shown in a list published by an approved testing agency qualified and equipped for experimental testing and maintaining an adequate periodic inspection of current productions and whose listing states that the equipment complies with nationally recognized standards when installed in accordance with the manufacturer's installation instructions.

LIVE LOADS. Those loads produced by the use and occupancy of the building or other structure and do not include construction or environmental loads such as wind load, snow load, rain load, earthquake load, flood load or dead load.

LIVING SPACE. Space within a dwelling unit utilized for living, sleeping, eating, cooking, bathing, washing and sanitation purposes.

LOT. A portion or parcel of land considered as a unit.

LOT LINE. A line dividing one lot from another, or from a street or any public place.

MACERATING TOILET SYSTEMS. A system comprised of a sump with macerating pump and with connections for a water closet and other plumbing fixtures, that is designed to accept, grind and pump wastes to an approved point of discharge.

MAIN. The principal pipe artery to which branches may be connected.

MAIN SEWER. See "Public sewer."

MANIFOLD WATER DISTRIBUTION SYSTEMS. A fabricated piping arrangement in which a large supply main is fitted with multiple branches in close proximity in which water is distributed separately to fixtures from each branch.

MANUFACTURED HOME. Manufactured home means a structure, transportable in one or more sections, which in the traveling mode is 8 body feet (2438 body mm) or more in width or 40 body feet (12 192 body mm) or more in length, or, when erected on site, is 320 square feet (30 m²) or more, and which is built on a permanent chassis and designed to be used as a dwelling with or without a permanent foundation when connected to the required utilities, and includes the plumbing, heating, air-conditioning and electrical systems contained therein; except that such term shall include any structure that meets all the requirements of this paragraph except the size requirements and with respect to which the manufacturer voluntarily files a certification required by the secretary (HUD) and complies with the standards established under this title. For mobile homes built prior to June 15, 1976, a label certifying compliance to the Standard for Mobile Homes, NFPA 501, in effect at the time of manufacture is required. For the purpose of these provisions, a mobile home shall be considered a manufactured home.

MANUFACTURER'S DESIGNATION. An identification applied on a product by the manufacturer indicating that a product or material complies with a specified standard or set of rules. (See also "Mark" and "Label.")

MANUFACTURER'S INSTALLATION INSTRUCTIONS. Printed instructions included with equipment as part of the conditions of listing and labeling.

MARK. An identification applied on a product by the manufacturer indicating the name of the manufacturer and the function of a product or material. (See also "Manufacturer's designation" and "Label.")

MASONRY CHIMNEY. A field-constructed chimney composed of solid masonry units, bricks, stones or concrete.

MASONRY, SOLID. Masonry consisting of solid masonry units laid contiguously with the joints between the units filled with mortar.

MASONRY UNIT. Brick, tile, stone, glass block or concrete block conforming to the requirements specified in Section 2103 of the *International Building Code.*

    Clay. A building unit larger in size than a brick, composed of burned clay, shale, fire clay or mixtures thereof.

    Concrete. A building unit or block larger in size than 12 inches by 4 inches by 4 inches (305 mm by 102 mm by 102 mm) made of cement and suitable aggregates.

    Glass. Nonload-bearing masonry composed of glass units bonded by mortar.

    Hollow. A masonry unit whose net cross-sectional area in any plane parallel to the loadbearing surface is less than 75 percent of its gross cross-sectional area measured in the same plane.

    Solid. A masonry unit whose net cross-sectional area in every plane parallel to the loadbearing surface is 75 percent or more of its cross-sectional area measured in the same plane.

MASS WALL. Masonry or concrete walls having a mass greater than or equal to 30 pounds per square foot (146 kg/m^2), solid wood walls having a mass greater than or equal to 20 pounds per square foot (98 kg/m^2), and any other walls having a heat capacity greater than or equal to 6 Btu/ft^2°F [266 J/(m^2·k)].

MEAN ROOF HEIGHT. The average of the roof eave height and the height to the highest point on the roof surface, except that eave height shall be used for roof angle of less than or equal to 10 degrees (0.18 rad).

MECHANICAL DRAFT SYSTEM. A venting system designed to remove flue or vent gases by mechanical means, that consists of an induced draft portion under nonpositive static pressure or a forced draft portion under positive static pressure.

    Forced-draft venting system. A portion of a venting system using a fan or other mechanical means to cause the removal of flue or vent gases under positive static pressure.

    Induced draft venting system. A portion of a venting system using a fan or other mechanical means to cause the removal of flue or vent gases under nonpositive static vent pressure.

    Power venting system. A portion of a venting system using a fan or other mechanical means to cause the removal of flue or vent gases under positive static vent pressure.

MECHANICAL EXHAUST SYSTEM. A system for removing air from a room or space by mechanical means.

MECHANICAL SYSTEM. A system specifically addressed and regulated in this code and composed of components, devices, appliances and equipment.

METAL ROOF PANEL. An interlocking metal sheet having a minimum installed weather exposure of at least 3 square feet (0.28 m^2) per sheet.

METAL ROOF SHINGLE. An interlocking metal sheet having an installed weather exposure less than 3 square feet (0.28 m^2) per sheet.

MEZZANINE, LOFT. An intermediate level or levels between the floor and ceiling of any story with an aggregate floor area of not more than one-third of the area of the room or space in which the level or levels are located.

MODIFIED BITUMEN ROOF COVERING. One or more layers of polymer modified asphalt sheets. The sheet materials shall be fully adhered or mechanically attached to the substrate or held in place with an approved ballast layer.

MULTIPLE STATION SMOKE ALARM. Two or more single station alarm devices that are capable of interconnection such that actuation of one causes all integral or separate audible alarms to operate.

NATURAL DRAFT SYSTEM. A venting system designed to remove flue or vent gases under nonpositive static vent pressure entirely by natural draft.

NONCOMBUSTIBLE MATERIAL. Materials that pass the test procedure for defining noncombustibility of elementary materials set forth in ASTM E 136.

NONCONDITIONED SPACE. A space that is not a conditioned space by insulated walls, floors or ceilings.

OCCUPIED SPACE. The total area of all buildings or structures on any lot or parcel of ground projected on a horizontal plane, excluding permitted projections as allowed by this code.

OFFSET. A combination of fittings that makes two changes in direction bringing one section of the pipe out of line but into a line parallel with the other section.

OWNER. Any person, agent, firm or corporation having a legal or equitable interest in the property.

PELLET FUEL-BURNING APPLIANCE. A closed combustion, vented appliance equipped with a fuel feed mechanism for burning processed pellets of solid fuel of a specified size and composition.

PELLET VENT. A vent listed and labeled for use with a listed pellet fuel-burning appliance.

PERMIT. An official document or certificate issued by the authority having jurisdiction that authorizes performance of a specified activity.

PERSON. An individual, heirs, executors, administrators or assigns, and also includes a firm, partnership or corporation, its or their successors or assigns, or the agent of any of the aforesaid.

PITCH. See "Slope."

PLATFORM CONSTRUCTION. A method of construction by which floor framing bears on load bearing walls that are not continuous through the story levels or floor framing.

PLENUM. A chamber that forms part of an air-circulation system other than the occupied space being conditioned.

PLUMBING. For the purpose of this code, plumbing refers to those installations, repairs, maintenance and alterations regulated by Minnesota Rules, Chapter 4715.

PLUMBING APPLIANCE. An energized household appliance with plumbing connections, such as a dishwasher, food-waste grinder, clothes washer or water heater.

PLUMBING APPURTENANCE. A device or assembly that is an adjunct to the basic plumbing system and demands no additional water supply nor adds any discharge load to the system. It is presumed that it performs some useful function in the operation, maintenance, servicing, economy or safety of the plumbing system. Examples include filters, relief valves and aerators.

PLUMBING FIXTURE. A receptor or device that requires both a water-supply connection and a discharge to the drainage system, such as water closets, lavatories, bathtubs and sinks. Plumbing appliances as a special class of fixture are further defined.

PLUMBING SYSTEM. Includes the water supply and distribution pipes, plumbing fixtures, supports and appurtenances; soil, waste and vent pipes; sanitary drains and building sewers to an approved point of disposal.

POSITIVE ROOF DRAINAGE. The drainage condition in which consideration has been made for all loading deflections of the roof deck, and additional slope has been provided to ensure drainage of the roof within 48 hours of precipitation.

POTABLE WATER. Water free from impurities present in amounts sufficient to cause disease or harmful physiological effects and conforming in bacteriological and chemical quality to the requirements of the public health authority having jurisdiction.

PRESSURE-RELIEF VALVE. A pressure-actuated valve held closed by a spring or other means and designed to automatically relieve pressure at the pressure at which it is set.

PUBLIC SEWER. A common sewer directly controlled by public authority.

PUBLIC WATER MAIN. A water-supply pipe for public use controlled by public authority.

PUBLIC WAY. Any street, alley or other parcel of land open to the outside air leading to a public street, which has been deeded, dedicated or otherwise permanently appropriated to the public for public use and that has a clear width and height of not less than 10 feet (3048 mm).

PURGE. To clear of air, gas or other foreign substances.

QUICK-CLOSING VALVE. A valve or faucet that closes automatically when released manually or controlled by mechanical means for fast-action closing.

_R_-VALUE, THERMAL RESISTANCE. The inverse of the time rate of heat flow through a building thermal envelope element from one of its bounding surfaces to the other for a unit temperature difference between the two surfaces, under steady state conditions, per unit area ($h \cdot ft^{2 \circ} F/Btu$).

RAMP. A walking surface that has a running slope steeper than 1 unit vertical in 20 units horizontal (5-percent slope).

RECEPTOR. A fixture or device that receives the discharge from indirect waste pipes.

REFRIGERANT. A substance used to produce refrigeration by its expansion or evaporation.

REFRIGERANT COMPRESSOR. A specific machine, with or without accessories, for compressing a given refrigerant vapor.

REFRIGERATING SYSTEM. A combination of interconnected parts forming a closed circuit in which refrigerant is circulated for the purpose of extracting, then rejecting, heat. A direct refrigerating system is one in which the evaporator or condenser of the refrigerating system is in direct contact with the air or other substances to be cooled or heated. An indirect refrigerating system is one in which a secondary coolant cooled or heated by the refrigerating system is circulated to the air or other substance to be cooled or heated.

REGISTERED DESIGN PROFESSIONAL. An individual who is registered or licensed to practice their respective design profession as defined by the statutory requirements of the professional registration laws of the state or jurisdiction in which the project is to be constructed.

RELIEF VALVE, VACUUM. A device to prevent excessive buildup of vacuum in a pressure vessel.

REPAIR. The reconstruction or renewal of any part of an existing building for the purpose of its maintenance.

REROOFING. The process of recovering or replacing an existing roof covering. See "Roof recover."

RESIDENTIAL BUILDING TYPE. The type of residential building for determining building thermal envelope criteria. Detached one- and two-family dwellings are Type A-1. Townhouses are Type A-2.

RETURN AIR. Air removed from an approved conditioned space or location and recirculated or exhausted.

RISER. A water pipe that extends vertically one full story or more to convey water to branches or to a group of fixtures.

ROOF ASSEMBLY. A system designed to provide weather protection and resistance to design loads. The system consists of a roof covering and roof deck or a single component serving as both the roof covering and the roof deck. A roof assembly includes the roof deck, vapor retarder, substrate or thermal barrier, insulation, vapor retarder, and roof covering.

ROOF COVERING. The covering applied to the roof deck for weather resistance, fire classification or appearance.

ROOF COVERING SYSTEM. See "Roof assembly."

ROOF DECK. The flat or sloped surface not including its supporting members or vertical supports.

ROOF RECOVER. The process of installing an additional roof covering over a prepared existing roof covering without removing the existing roof covering.

ROOF REPAIR. Reconstruction or renewal of any part of an existing roof for the purposes of its maintenance.

ROOFTOP STRUCTURE. An enclosed structure on or above the roof of any part of a building.

ROOM HEATER. A freestanding heating appliance installed in the space being heated and not connected to ducts.

ROUGH-IN. The installation of all parts of the plumbing system that must be completed prior to the installation of fixtures. This includes DWV, water supply and built-in fixture supports.

RUNNING BOND. The placement of masonry units such that head joints in successive courses are horizontally offset at least one-quarter the unit length.

SANITARY SEWER. A sewer that carries sewage and excludes storm, surface and groundwater.

SCUPPER. An opening in a wall or parapet that allows water to drain from a roof.

SEISMIC DESIGN CATEGORY. A classification assigned to a structure based on its Seismic Group and the severity of the design earthquake ground motion at the site.

SEPTIC TANK. A water-tight receptor that receives the discharge of a building sanitary drainage system and is constructed so as to separate solids from the liquid, digest organic matter through a period of detention, and allow the liquids to discharge into the soil outside of the tank through a system of open joint or perforated piping or a seepage pit.

SEWAGE. Any liquid waste containing animal matter, vegetable matter or other impurity in suspension or solution.

SEWAGE PUMP. A permanently installed mechanical device for removing sewage or liquid waste from a sump.

SHALL. The term, when used in the code, is construed as mandatory.

SHEAR WALL. A general term for walls that are designed and constructed to resist racking from seismic and wind by use of masonry, concrete, cold-formed steel or wood framing in accordance with Chapter 6 of this code and the associated limitations in Section R301.2 of this code.

SIDE VENT. A vent connecting to the drain pipe through a fitting at an angle less than 45 degrees (0.79 rad) to the horizontal.

SINGLE PLY MEMBRANE. A roofing membrane that is field applied using one layer of membrane material (either homogeneous or composite) rather than multiple layers.

SINGLE STATION SMOKE ALARM. An assembly incorporating the detector, control equipment and alarm sounding device in one unit that is operated from a power supply either in the unit or obtained at the point of installation.

SKYLIGHT AND SLOPED GLAZING. See Section R308.6.1.

SLIP JOINT. A mechanical-type joint used primarily on fixture traps. The joint tightness is obtained by compressing a friction-type washer such as rubber, nylon, neoprene, lead or special packing material against the pipe by the tightening of a (slip) nut.

SLOPE. The fall (pitch) of a line of pipe in reference to a horizontal plane. In drainage, the slope is expressed as the fall in units vertical per units horizontal (percent) for a length of pipe.

SMOKE-DEVELOPED RATING. A numerical index indicating the relative density of smoke produced by burning assigned to a material tested in accordance with ASTM E 84.

SOIL STACK OR PIPE. A pipe that conveys sewage containing fecal material.

SOLAR HEAT GAIN COEFFICIENT (SHGC). The solar heat gain through a fenestration or glazing assembly relative to the incident solar radiation ($Btu/h \cdot ft^2 \cdot {}^\circ F$).

SOLID MASONRY. Load-bearing or nonload-bearing construction using masonry units where the net cross-sectional area of each unit in any plane parallel to the bearing surface is not less than 75 percent of its gross cross-sectional area. Solid masonry units shall conform to ASTM C 55, C 62, C 73, C 145 or C 216.

STACK. Any main vertical DWV line, including offsets, that extends one or more stories as directly as possible to its vent terminal.

STACK BOND. The placement of masonry units in a bond pattern is such that head joints in successive courses are vertically aligned. For the purpose of this code, requirements for stack bond shall apply to all masonry laid in other than running bond.

STACK VENT. The extension of soil or waste stack above the highest horizontal drain connected.

STACK VENTING. A method of venting a fixture or fixtures through the soil or waste stack without individual fixture vents.

STANDARD TRUSS. Any construction that does not permit the roof/ceiling insulation to achieve the required *R*-value over the exterior walls.

STORM SEWER, DRAIN. A pipe used for conveying rainwater, surface water, condensate, cooling water or similar liquid wastes.

STORY. That portion of a building included between the upper surface of a floor and the upper surface of the floor or roof next above.

STORY ABOVE GRADE. Any story having its finished floor surface entirely above grade, except that a basement shall be considered as a story above grade where the finished surface of the floor above the basement is:

1. More than 6 feet (1829 mm) above grade plane.
2. More than 6 feet (1829 mm) above the finished ground level for more than 50 percent of the total building perimeter.
3. More than 12 feet (3658 mm) above the finished ground level at any point.

STRUCTURAL INSULATED PANELS (SIPS). Factory fabricated panels of solid core insulation with structural skins of oriented strand board (OSB) or plywood.

SUMP. A tank or pit that receives sewage or waste, located below the normal grade of the gravity system and that must be emptied by mechanical means.

SUMP PUMP. A pump installed to empty a sump. The pump is chosen to handle the type of material to be pumped—either clear water waste or soil-type sewage. The pump is selected for the specific head and volume of the load and is usually operated by level controllers.

SUPPLY AIR. Air delivered to a conditioned space through ducts or plenums from the heat exchanger of a heating, cooling or ventilating system.

SUPPORTS. Devices for supporting, hanging and securing pipes, fixtures and equipment.

SWEEP. A drainage fitting designed to provide a change in direction of a drain pipe of less than the angle specified by the amount necessary to establish the desired slope of the line. Sweeps provide a longer turning radius than bends and a less turbulent flow pattern (see "Bend" and "Elbow").

TEMPERATURE- AND PRESSURE-RELIEF (T AND P) VALVE. A combination relief valve designed to function as both a temperature-relief and pressure-relief valve.

TEMPERATURE-RELIEF VALVE. A temperature-actuated valve designed to discharge automatically at the temperature at which it is set.

THERMAL RESISTANCE, *R*-VALUE. The inverse of the time rate of heat flow through a body from one of its bounding surfaces to the other for a unit temperature difference between the two surfaces, under steady state conditions, per unit area $(h \cdot ft^2 \cdot °F/Btu)$.

THERMAL TRANSMITTANCE, *U*-FACTOR. The coefficient of heat transmission (air to air) through a building envelope component or assembly, equal to the time rate of heat flow per unit area and unit temperature difference between the warm side and cold side air films $(Btu/h \cdot ft^2 \cdot °F)$.

TOWNHOUSE. A single-family dwelling unit constructed in a group of three or more attached units in which each unit extends from foundation to roof and with open space on at least two sides.

TRAP. A fitting, either separate or built into a fixture, that provides a liquid seal to prevent the emission of sewer gases without materially affecting the flow of sewage or waste water through it.

TRAP ARM. That portion of a fixture drain between a trap weir and the vent fitting.

TRAP PRIMER. A device or system of piping to maintain a water seal in a trap, typically installed where infrequent use of the trap would result in evaporation of the trap seal, such as floor drains.

TRAP SEAL. The trap seal is the maximum vertical depth of liquid that a trap will retain, measured between the crown weir and the top of the dip of the trap.

TRIM. Picture molds, chair rails, baseboards, handrails, door and window frames, and similar decorative or protective materials used in fixed applications.

TRUSS DESIGN DRAWING. The graphic depiction of an individual truss, which describes the design and physical characteristics of the truss.

TYPE L VENT. A listed and labeled vent conforming to UL 641 for venting oil-burning appliances listed for use with Type L vents or with listed gas appliances.

***U*-FACTOR, THERMAL TRANSMITTANCE.** The coefficient of heat transmission (air to air) through a building envelope component or assembly, equal to the time rate of heat flow per unit area and unit temperature difference between the warm side and cold side air films $(Btu/h \cdot ft^2 \cdot °F)$.

UNCONFINED SPACE. A space having a volume not less than 50 cubic feet per 1,000 Btu/h $(4.8 \ m^3/kW)$ of the aggregate input rating of all appliances installed in that space. Rooms communicating directly with the space in which the appliances are installed, through openings not furnished with doors, are considered a part of the unconfined space.

UNDERLAYMENT. One or more layers of felt, sheathing paper, nonbituminous saturated felt, or other approved material over which a s roof covering, with a slope of 2 to 12 (17-percent slope) or greater, is applied.

UNUSUALLY TIGHT CONSTRUCTION. Construction in which:

1. Walls and ceilings comprising the building thermal envelope have a continuous water vapor retarder with a rating of 1 perm $[57.4 \ ng/(s \cdot m^2 \cdot Pa)]$ or less with openings therein gasketed or sealed.
2. Storm windows or weatherstripping is applied around the threshold and jambs of opaque doors and openable windows.
3. Caulking or sealants are applied to areas such as joints around window and door frames between sole plates and floors, between wall ceiling joints, between wall panels, at penetrations for plumbing, electrical and gas lines, and at other openings.

VACUUM BREAKERS. A device which prevents backsiphonage of water by admitting atmospheric pressure through ports to the discharge side of the device.

VAPOR RETARDER. A material having a permeance rating of 1.0 or less when tested in accordance with ASTM E 96.

VENT. A passageway for conveying flue gases from fuel-fired appliances, or their vent connectors, to the outside atmosphere.

VENT COLLAR. See "Flue collar."

VENT CONNECTOR. That portion of a venting system which connects the flue collar or draft hood of an appliance to a vent.

VENT DAMPER DEVICE, AUTOMATIC. A device intended for installation in the venting system, in the outlet of an individual, automatically operated fuel burning appliance and that is designed to open the venting system automatically when the appliance is in operation and to close off the venting system automatically when the appliance is in a standby or shutdown condition.

VENT GASES. Products of combustion from fuel-burning appliances, plus excess air and dilution air, in the venting system above the draft hood or draft regulator.

VENT STACK. A vertical vent pipe installed to provide circulation of air to and from the drainage system and which extends through one or more stories.

VENT SYSTEM. Piping installed to equalize pneumatic pressure in a drainage system to prevent trap seal loss or blowback due to siphonage or back pressure.

VENTILATION. The natural or mechanical process of supplying conditioned or unconditioned air to, or removing such air from, any space.

VENTING. Removal of combustion products to the outdoors.

VENTING SYSTEM. A continuous open passageway from the flue collar of an appliance to the outside atmosphere for the purpose of removing flue or vent gases. A venting system is usually composed of a vent or a chimney and vent connector, if used, assembled to form the open passageway.

VERTICAL PIPE. Any pipe or fitting that makes an angle of 45 degrees (0.79 rad) or more with the horizontal.

WALLS. Walls shall be defined as follows:

　Load-bearing wall is a wall supporting any vertical load in addition to its own weight.

　Nonbearing wall is a wall which does not support vertical loads other than its own weight.

WASTE. Liquid-borne waste that is free of fecal matter.

WASTE PIPE OR STACK. Piping that conveys only liquid sewage not containing fecal material.

WATER-DISTRIBUTION SYSTEM. Piping which conveys water from the service to the plumbing fixtures, appliances, appurtenances, equipment, devices or other systems served, including fittings and control valves.

WATER HEATER. Any heating appliance or equipment that heats potable water and supplies such water to the potable hot water distribution system.

WATER MAIN. A water-supply pipe for public use.

WATER OUTLET. A valved discharge opening, including a hose bibb, through which water is removed from the potable water system supplying water to a plumbing fixture or plumbing appliance that requires either an air gap or backflow prevention device for protection of the supply system.

WATER-SERVICE PIPE. The outside pipe from the water main or other source of potable water supply to the water-distribution system inside the building, terminating at the service valve.

WATER-SUPPLY SYSTEM. The water-service pipe, the water-distributing pipes and the necessary connecting pipes, fittings, control valves and all appurtenances in or adjacent to the building or premises.

WET VENT. A vent that also receives the discharge of wastes from other fixtures.

WIND BORNE DEBRIS REGION. Areas within hurricane-prone regions within one mile of the coastal mean high water line where the basic wind speed is 110 miles per hour (177 km/h) or greater; or where the basic wind speed is equal to or greater than 120 miles per hour (193 km/h); or Hawaii.

WOOD STRUCTURAL PANEL. A panel manufactured from veneers; or wood strands or wafers; bonded together with waterproof synthetic resins or other suitable bonding systems. Examples of wood structural panels are plywood, OSB or composite panels.

YARD. An open space, other than a court, unobstructed from the ground to the sky, except where specifically provided by this code, on the lot on which a building is situated.

Part III — Building Planning and Construction
CHAPTER 3
BUILDING PLANNING

SECTION R301
DESIGN CRITERIA

R301.1 Design. Buildings and structures, and all parts thereof, shall be constructed to safely support all loads, including dead loads, live loads, roof loads, flood loads, snow loads, wind loads and seismic loads as prescribed by this code. The construction of buildings and structures shall result in a system that provides a complete load path capable of transferring all loads from their point of origin through the load-resisting elements to the foundation. When a building of otherwise conventional construction contains structural elements that exceed the limits of Section R301, those elements shall be designed in accordance with accepted engineering practice.

R301.1.1 Construction systems. The requirements of this code are based on platform and balloon-frame construction for light-frame buildings. The requirements for concrete and masonry buildings are based on a balloon framing system. Other framing systems must have equivalent detailing to ensure force transfer, continuity and compatible deformations.

R301.1.2 Engineered design. When a building of otherwise conventional light-frame construction contains structural elements not conforming to this code, these elements shall be designed in accordance with accepted engineering practice. The extent of such design need only demonstrate compliance of nonconventional elements with other applicable provisions and shall be compatible with the performance of the conventional framed system.

R301.2 Climatic and geographic design criteria. Buildings shall be constructed in accordance with the provisions of this code as limited by the provisions of this section. Additional criteria shall be established by the local jurisdiction and set forth in Table R301.2(1).

R301.2.1 Wind limitations. Buildings and portions thereof shall be limited by wind speed, as defined in Table R301.2(1), and construction methods in accordance with this code. Basic wind speeds shall be determined from Figure R301.2(4). Where different construction methods and structural materials are used for various portions of a building, the applicable requirements of this section for each portion shall apply. Where loads for windows, skylights and exterior doors are not otherwise specified, the loads listed in Table R301.2(2) adjusted for height and exposure per Table R301.2(3) shall be used to determine design load performance requirements for windows and doors.

R301.2.1.1 Design criteria. Construction in regions where the basic wind speeds from Figure R301.2(4) equal or exceed 110 miles per hour (177.1 km/h) shall be designed in accordance with one of the following:

1. American Forest and Paper Association (AF&PA) Wood Frame Construction Manual for One- and Two-Family Dwellings (WFCM); or
2. Southern Building Code Congress International Standard for Hurricane Resistant Residential Construction (SSTD 10); or
3. Minimum Design Loads for Buildings and Other Structures (ASCE-7); or
4. Cold-formed steel construction shall be designed in accordance with the provisions of this code.

TABLE R301.2(1)
CLIMATIC AND GEOGRAPHIC DESIGN CRITERIA

ROOF SNOW LOAD[d]	WIND Speed[c] (mph)	SUBJECT TO DAMAGE FROM Weathering[a]	SUBJECT TO DAMAGE FROM Frost line depth[b]	FLOOD HAZARDS[h]
$p_f = 0.7 \times p_g$	90	Severe	See M.R. part 1303.1600	See M.R. Chapter 1335

For SI: 1 pound per square foot = 0.0479 kN/m², 1 mile per hour = 1.609 km/h.

a. Weathering may require a higher strength concrete or grade of masonry than necessary to satisfy the structural requirements of this code. The grade of masonry units shall be determined from ASTM C 34, C 55, C 62, C 73, C 90, C 129, C 145, C 216 or C 652.

b. The frost line depth may require deeper footings than indicated in Figure R403.1(1).

c. Wind exposure category shall be determined on a site-specific basis in accordance with Section R301.2.1.4.

d. The ground snow loads to be used in determining the design snow loads for buildings and other structures are given in Minnesota Rules, chapter 1303.

TABLE R301.2(2)
COMPONENT AND CLADDING LOADS FOR A BUILDING WITH A MEAN ROOF HEIGHT OF 30 FEET LOCATED IN EXPOSURE B

Section	Zone	Effective Wind Area (feet²)	85		90		100		105		110		120		125		130		140		145		150		170	
Roof > 0 to 10 degrees	1	10	10.0	-13.0	10.0	-14.6	10.0	-18.0	10.0	-19.8	10.0	-21.8	10.5	-25.9	11.4	-28.1	12.4	-30.4	14.3	-35.3	15.4	-37.8	16.5	-40.5	21.1	-52.0
	1	20	10.0	-12.7	10.0	-14.2	10.0	-17.5	10.0	-19.3	10.0	-21.2	10.0	-25.2	10.7	-27.4	11.6	-29.6	13.4	-34.4	14.4	-36.9	15.4	-39.4	19.8	-50.7
	1	50	10.0	-12.2	10.0	-13.7	10.0	-16.9	10.0	-18.7	10.0	-20.5	10.0	-24.4	10.0	-26.4	10.6	-28.6	12.3	-33.2	13.1	-35.6	14.1	-38.1	18.1	-48.9
	1	100	10.0	-11.9	10.0	-13.3	10.0	-18.5	10.0	-18.2	10.0	-19.9	10.0	-23.7	10.0	-25.7	10.0	-27.8	11.4	-32.3	12.2	-34.6	13.0	-37.0	16.7	-47.6
	2	10	10.0	-21.8	10.0	-24.4	10.0	-30.2	10.0	-33.3	10.0	-36.5	10.5	-43.5	11.4	-47.2	12.4	-51.0	14.3	-59.2	15.4	-63.5	16.5	-67.9	21.1	-87.2
	2	20	10.0	-19.5	10.0	-21.8	10.0	-27.0	10.0	-29.7	10.0	-32.6	10.0	-38.8	10.7	-42.1	11.6	-45.6	13.4	-52.9	14.4	-56.7	15.4	-60.7	19.8	-78.0
	2	50	10.0	-16.4	10.0	-18.4	10.0	-22.7	10.0	-25.1	10.0	-27.5	10.0	-32.7	10.0	-35.5	10.6	-38.4	12.3	-44.5	13.1	-47.0	14.1	-51.1	18.1	65.7
	2	100	10.0	-14.1	10.0	-15.8	10.0	-19.5	10.0	-21.5	10.0	-23.6	10.0	-28.1	10.0	-30.5	10.0	-33.0	11.4	-38.2	12.2	-41.0	13.0	-43.9	16.7	-56.4
	3	10	10.0	-32.8	10.0	-36.8	10.0	-45.4	10.0	-50.1	10.0	-55.0	10.5	-65.4	11.4	-71.0	12.4	-76.8	14.3	-89.0	15.4	-95.5	16.5	-102.2	21.1	-131.3
	3	20	10.0	-27.2	10.0	-30.5	10.0	-37.6	10.0	-41.5	10.0	-45.5	10.0	-54.2	10.7	-58.8	11.6	-63.6	13.4	-73.8	14.4	-79.1	15.4	-84.7	19.8	-108.7
	3	50	10.0	-19.7	10.0	-22.1	10.0	-27.3	10.0	-30.1	10.0	-33.1	10.0	-39.3	10.0	-42.7	10.6	-46.2	12.3	-53.5	13.1	-57.4	14.1	-61.5	18.1	-78.9
	3	100	10.0	-14.1	10.0	-15.8	10.0	-19.5	10.0	-21.5	10.0	-23.6	10.0	-28.1	10.0	-30.5	10.0	-33.0	11.4	-38.2	12.2	-41.0	13.0	-43.9	16.7	-56.4
Roof > 10 to 30 degrees	1	10	10.0	-11.9	10.0	-13.3	10.4	-16.5	11.4	-18.2	12.5	-19.9	14.9	-23.7	16.2	-25.7	17.5	-27.8	20.3	-32.3	21.8	-34.6	23.3	-37.0	30.0	-47.6
	1	20	10.0	-11.6	10.0	-13.0	10.0	-16.0	10.4	-17.6	11.4	-19.4	13.6	-23.0	14.8	-25.0	16.0	-27.0	18.5	-31.4	19.9	-33.7	21.3	-36.0	27.3	-46.3
	1	50	10.0	-11.1	10.0	-12.5	10.0	-15.4	10.0	-17.0	10.0	-18.6	11.9	-22.2	12.9	-24.1	13.9	-26.0	16.1	-30.2	17.3	-32.4	18.5	-34.6	23.8	-44.5
	1	100	10.0	-10.8	10.0	-12.1	10.0	-14.9	10.0	-16.5	10.0	-18.1	10.5	-21.5	11.4	-23.3	12.4	-25.2	14.3	-29.3	15.4	-31.4	16.5	-33.6	21.1	-43.2
	2	10	10.0	-25.1	10.0	-28.2	10.4	-34.8	11.4	-38.3	12.5	-42.1	14.9	-50.1	16.2	-54.3	17.5	-58.7	20.3	-68.1	21.8	-73.1	23.3	-78.2	30.0	-100.5
	2	20	10.0	-22.8	10.0	-25.6	10.0	-31.5	10.4	-34.8	11.4	-38.2	13.6	-45.4	14.8	-49.3	16.0	-53.3	18.5	-61.8	19.9	-66.3	21.3	-71.0	27.3	-91.2
	2	50	10.0	-19.7	10.0	-22.1	10.0	-27.0	10.0	-30.1	10.0	-33.0	11.9	-39.3	12.9	-42.7	13.9	-46.1	16.1	-53.5	17.3	-57.4	18.5	-61.4	23.8	-78.9
	2	100	10.0	-17.4	10.0	-19.5	10.0	-24.1	10.0	-26.6	10.0	-29.1	10.5	-34.7	11.4	-37.6	12.4	-40.7	14.3	-47.2	15.4	-50.6	16.5	-54.2	21.1	-69.6
	3	10	10.0	-25.1	10.0	-28.2	10.4	-34.8	11.4	-38.3	12.5	-42.1	14.9	-50.1	16.2	-54.3	17.5	-58.7	20.3	-68.1	21.8	-73.1	23.3	-78.2	30.0	-100.5
	3	20	10.0	-22.8	10.0	-25.6	10.0	-31.5	10.4	-34.8	11.4	-38.2	13.6	-45.4	14.8	-49.3	16.0	-53.3	18.5	-61.8	19.9	-66.3	21.3	-71.0	27.3	-91.2
	3	50	10.0	-19.7	10.0	-22.1	10.0	-27.3	10.0	-30.1	10.0	-33.0	11.9	-39.3	12.9	-42.7	13.9	-46.1	16.1	-53.5	17.3	-57.4	18.5	-61.4	23.8	-78.9
	3	100	10.0	-17.4	10.0	-19.5	10.0	-24.1	10.0	-26.6	10.0	-29.1	10.5	-34.7	11.4	-37.6	12.4	-40.7	14.3	-47.2	15.4	-50.6	16.5	-54.2	21.1	-69.6
Roof > 30 to 45 degrees	1	10	11.9	-13.0	13.3	-14.6	16.5	-18.0	18.2	-19.8	19.9	-21.8	23.7	-25.9	25.7	-28.1	27.8	-30.4	32.3	-35.3	34.6	-37.8	37.0	-40.5	47.6	-52.0
	1	20	11.6	-12.3	13.0	-13.8	16.0	-17.1	17.6	-18.8	19.4	-20.7	23.0	-24.6	25.0	-26.7	27.0	-28.9	31.4	-33.5	33.7	-35.9	36.0	-38.4	46.3	-49.3
	1	50	11.1	-11.5	12.5	-12.8	15.4	-15.9	17.0	-17.5	18.6	-19.2	22.2	-22.8	24.1	-24.8	26.0	-25.8	30.2	-31.1	32.4	-33.3	34.6	-35.7	44.5	-45.8
	1	100	10.8	-10.8	12.1	-12.1	14.9	-14.9	16.5	-16.5	18.1	-18.1	21.5	-21.5	23.3	-23.3	25.2	-25.2	29.3	-29.3	31.4	-31.4	33.6	-33.6	43.2	-43.2
	2	10	11.9	-15.2	13.3	-17.0	16.5	-21.0	18.2	-23.2	19.9	-25.5	23.7	-30.3	25.7	-32.9	27.8	-35.6	32.3	-41.2	34.6	-44.2	37.0	-47.3	47.6	-60.8
	2	20	11.6	-14.5	13.0	-16.3	16.0	-20.1	17.6	-22.2	19.4	-24.3	23.0	-29.0	25.0	-31.4	27.0	-34.0	31.4	-39.4	33.7	-42.3	36.0	-45.3	46.3	-58.1
	2	50	11.1	-13.7	12.5	-15.3	15.4	-18.9	17.0	-20.8	18.6	-22.9	22.2	-27.2	24.1	-29.5	26.0	-32.0	30.2	-37.1	32.4	-39.8	34.6	-42.5	44.5	-54.6
	2	100	10.8	-13.0	12.1	-14.6	14.9	-18.0	16.5	-19.8	18.1	-21.8	21.5	-25.9	23.3	-28.1	25.2	-30.4	29.3	-35.3	31.4	-37.8	33.6	-40.5	43.2	-52.0
	3	10	11.9	-15.2	13.3	-17.0	16.5	-21.0	18.2	-23.2	19.9	-25.5	23.7	-30.3	25.7	-32.9	27.8	-35.6	32.3	-41.2	34.6	-44.2	37.0	-47.3	47.6	-60.8
	3	20	11.6	-14.5	13.0	-16.3	16.0	-20.1	17.6	-22.2	19.4	-24.3	23.0	-29.0	25.0	-31.4	27.0	-34.0	31.4	-39.4	33.7	-42.3	36.0	-45.3	46.3	-58.1
	3	50	11.1	-13.7	12.5	-15.3	15.4	-18.9	17.0	-20.8	18.6	-22.9	22.2	-27.2	24.1	-29.5	26.0	-32.0	30.2	-37.1	32.4	-39.8	34.6	-42.5	44.5	-54.5
	3	100	10.8	-13.0	12.1	-14.6	14.9	-18.0	16.5	-19.8	18.1	-21.8	21.5	-25.9	23.3	-28.1	25.2	-30.4	29.3	-35.3	31.4	-37.8	33.6	-40.5	43.2	-52.0
Wall	4	10	13.0	-14.1	14.6	-15.8	18.0	-19.5	19.8	-21.5	21.8	-23.6	25.9	-28.1	28.1	-30.5	30.4	-33.0	35.3	-38.2	37.8	-41.0	40.5	-43.9	52.0	-56.4
	4	20	12.4	-13.5	13.9	-15.1	17.2	-18.7	18.9	-20.6	20.8	-22.6	24.7	-26.9	26.8	-29.2	29.0	-31.6	33.7	-36.7	36.1	-39.3	38.7	-42.1	49.6	-54.1
	4	50	11.6	-12.7	13.0	-14.3	16.1	-17.6	17.8	-19.4	19.5	-21.3	23.2	-25.4	25.2	-27.5	27.2	-29.8	31.6	-34.6	33.9	-37.1	36.2	-39.7	46.6	-51.0
	4	100	11.1	-12.2	12.4	-13.6	15.3	-16.8	16.9	-18.5	18.5	-20.4	22.0	-24.2	23.9	-26.3	25.9	-28.4	30.0	-33.0	32.2	-35.4	34.4	-37.8	44.2	-48.6
	5	10	13.0	-17.4	14.6	-19.5	18.0	-24.1	19.8	-26.6	21.8	-29.1	25.9	-34.7	28.1	-37.6	30.4	-40.7	35.3	-47.2	37.8	-50.6	40.5	-54.2	52.0	-69.6
	5	20	12.4	-16.2	13.9	-18.2	17.2	-22.5	18.9	-24.8	20.8	-27.2	24.7	-32.4	26.8	-35.1	29.0	-38.0	33.7	-44.0	36.1	-47.2	38.7	-50.5	49.6	-64.9
	5	50	11.6	-14.7	13.0	-16.5	16.1	-20.3	17.8	-22.4	19.5	-24.6	23.2	-29.3	25.2	-31.8	27.2	-34.3	31.6	-39.8	33.9	-42.7	36.2	-45.7	46.6	-58.7
	5	100	11.1	-13.5	12.4	-15.1	15.3	-18.7	16.9	-20.6	18.5	-22.6	22.0	-26.9	23.9	-29.2	25.9	-31.6	30.0	-36.7	32.2	-39.3	34.4	-42.1	44.2	-54.1

For SI: 1 foot = 304.8 mm, 1 square foot = 0.0929 m², 1 mile per hour = 1.609 km/h.

NOTES: For effective areas between those given above the load may be interpolated, otherwise use the load associated with the lower effective area.

Table values shall be adjusted for height and exposure by multiplying by the adjustment coefficient in Table R301.2(3).

See Figure R301.2(8) for location of zones.

Plus and minus signs signify pressures acting toward and away from the building surfaces.

TABLE R301.2(3)
HEIGHT AND EXPOSURE ADJUSTMENT COEFFICIENTS FOR TABLE R301.2(2)

MEAN ROOF HEIGHT	EXPOSURE		
	B	C	D
15	1.00	1.21	1.47
20	1.00	1.29	1.55
25	1.00	1.35	1.61
30	1.00	1.40	1.66
35	1.05	1.45	1.70
40	1.09	1.49	1.74
45	1.12	1.53	1.78
50	1.16	1.56	1.81
55	1.19	1.59	1.84
60	1.22	1.62	1.87

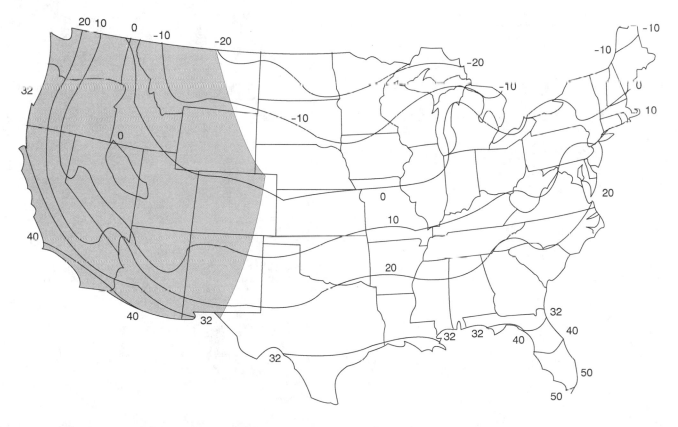

DESIGN TEMPERATURES IN THIS AREA MUST BE BASED ON ANALYSIS OF LOCAL CLIMATE AND TOPOGRAPHY

For SI: °C = [(°F)-32]/1.8.

FIGURE R301.2(1)
ISOLINES OF THE 97½ PERCENT WINTER (DECEMBER, JANUARY AND FEBRUARY) DESIGN TEMPERATURES (°F)

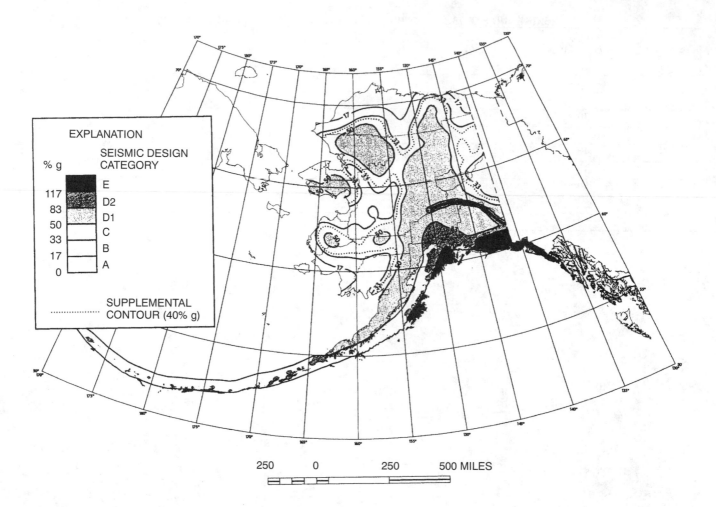

EXPLANATION

SEISMIC DESIGN CATEGORY

% g		
	■	E
117		D2
83		D1
50		C
33		B
17		A
0		

SUPPLEMENTAL CONTOUR (40% g)

250   0   250   500 MILES

Prepared by U.S. Geological Survey

Scale 1:17,000,000

REFERENCES

Digital data prepared with ARC/INFO 7.1.1
running under Solaris 2.5 on a UNIX workstation

Albers Equal-Area Conic Projection
Standard parallels 55°N and 65°N
Central Meridian 160°W

For SI: 1 mile = 1.61 km.

U.S. Geological Survey National Seismic-Hazard Mapping Project,
1998 Alaska Seismic-Hazard Maps: Documentation: U.S. Geological
Survey Open-File Report, in progress.

U.S. Geological Survey National Seismic-Hazard Mapping Project,
1998, Seismic-Hazard Maps of Alaska: U.S. Geological Survey Open-File
Report, 6 sheet, scale 1:5,000,000, in progress.

FIGURE R301.2(2)
INTERNATIONAL RESIDENTIAL CODE
SEISMIC DESIGN CATEGORIES—SITE CLASS D
(continued)

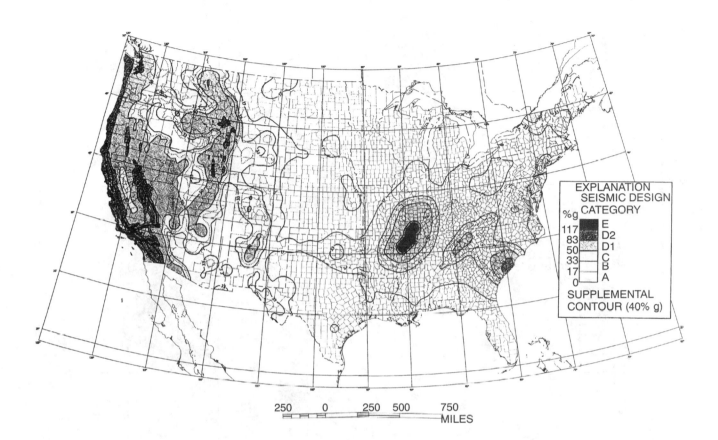

SCALE 1:15,000,000

REFERENCES

Digital data prepared with ARC/INFO 7.1.1
running under Solaris 2.5 on a UNIX workstation

Albers Equal-Area Conic Projection
Standard Parallels 29.5°N and 45.5°N
Central Meridian 95°W

Prepared by U.S. Geological Survey

For SI: 1 mile = 1.61 km.

Frankel, A. Mueller, C., Barnhard, T., Perkins, D., Leyendecker, E. V., Dickman, N., Hanson, S., and Hopper, M., 1996, National Seismic-Hazard Maps: Documentation June 1996: U.S. Geological Survey Open-File Report 96-532, 110 p.

Frankel, A., Muller, C., Barnhard, T., Perkins, D., Leyendecker, E. V., Dickman, N., Hanson, S., and Spectral Response Acceleration for 0.2 Second Period with 2% Probability of Exceedance in 50 Years: U. S. Geological Survey Open-File Report 97-131-F, scale 1:7,000,000.

Petersen, M., Bryant, W., Cramer, C., Cao, T., Reichle, M., Frankel, A., Lienkaemper, J., McCrory, P., and Schwartz, D., 1996, Probabilitic Seismic Hazard Assessment for the State of California: California Division of Mines and Geology Open-File Report 96-08, 66 p., and U.S. Geological Survey Open-File Report 96-706, 66 p.

**FIGURE R301.2(2)—continued
INTERNATIONAL RESIDENTIAL CODE
SEISMIC DESIGN CATEGORIES—SITE CLASS D**
(continued)

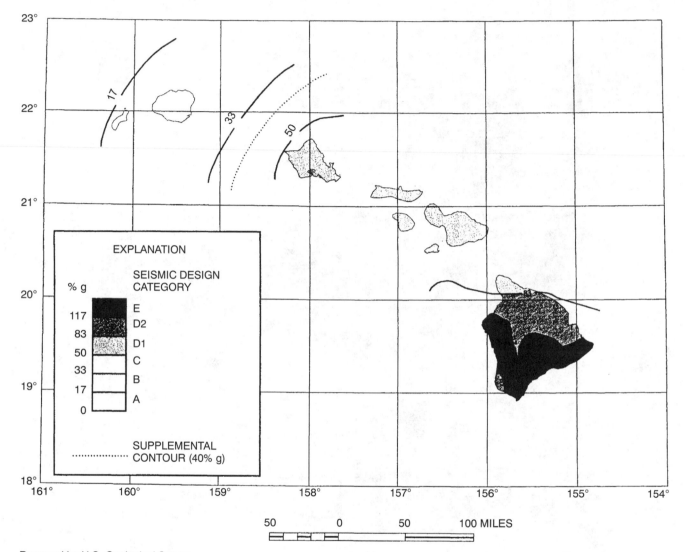

EXPLANATION

SEISMIC DESIGN CATEGORY

% g	
117	E
83	D2
50	D1
33	C
17	B
0	A

SUPPLEMENTAL
.... CONTOUR (40% g)

50   0   50   100 MILES

Prepared by U.S. Geological Survey

SCALE 1:3,500,000

Digital data prepared with ARC/INFO 7.1.1
running under Solaris 2.5 on a UNIX workstation

Albers Equal-Area Conic Projection
Standard parallels 8°N and 18°N
Central Meridian 157.5°W

For SI: 1 mile = 1.61 km.

REFERENCES

U.S. Geological Survey National Seismic-Hazard Mapping Project, 1998
Hawaii Seismic-Hazard Maps:
Documentation: U.S. Geological Survey Open-File Report, in progress.

U.S. Geological Survey National Seismic-Hazard Mapping Project, 1998,
Seismic-Hazard Maps of Hawaii: U.S. Geological Survey Open-File
Report, 6 sheet, scale 1:2,000,000, in progress.

**FIGURE R301.2(2)—continued
INTERNATIONAL RESIDENTIAL CODE
SEISMIC DESIGN CATEGORIES—SITE CLASS D**

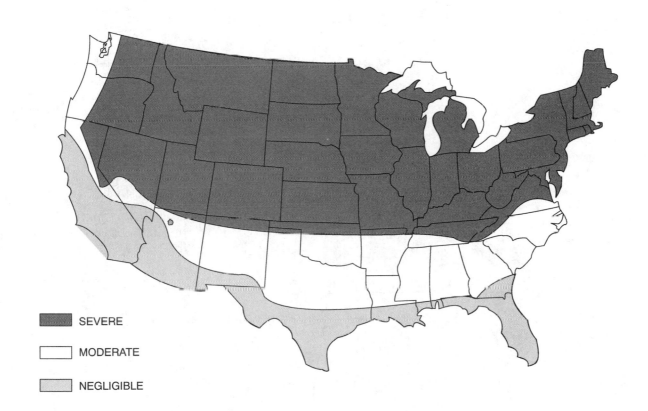

SEVERE

MODERATE

NEGLIGIBLE

a.   Alaska and Hawaii are classified as severe and negligible, respectively.
b.   Lines defining areas are approximate only. Local conditions may be more or less severe than indicated by region classification. A severe classifi-
     cation is where weather conditions result in significant snowfall combined with extended periods during which there is little or no natural thawing
     causing deicing salts to be used extensively.

FIGURE R301.2(3)
WEATHERING PROBABILITY MAP FOR CONCRETE

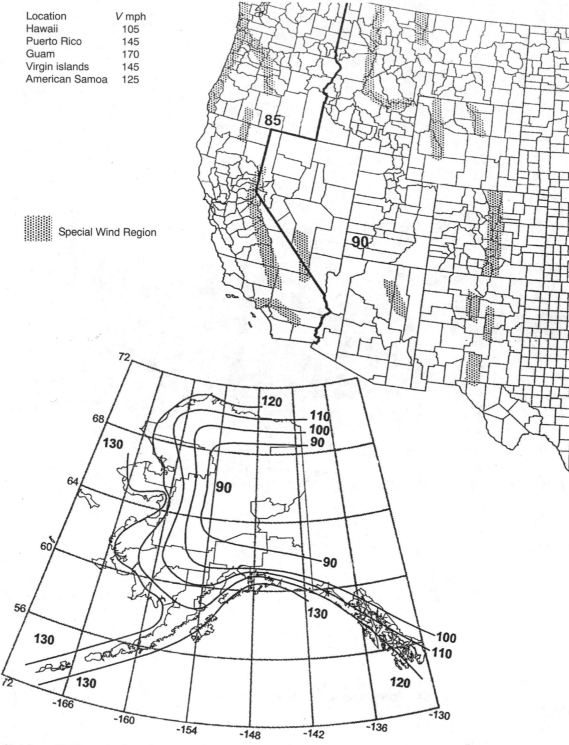

Location	V mph
Hawaii	105
Puerto Rico	145
Guam	170
Virgin islands	145
American Samoa	125

Special Wind Region

For SI: 1 foot = 304.8 mm, 1 mile per hour = 0.447 m/s.

a. Values are nominal design 3-second gust wind speeds in miles per hour at 33 feet above ground for Exposure C category.
b. Linear interpolation between wind contours is permitted.
c. Islands and coastal areas outside the last contour shall use the last wind speed contour of the coastal area.
d. Mountainous terrain, gorges, ocean promontories, and special wind regions shall be examined for unusual wind conditions.

FIGURE R301.2(4)
BASIC WIND SPEEDS FOR 50-YEAR MEAN RECURRENCE INTERVAL
(continued)

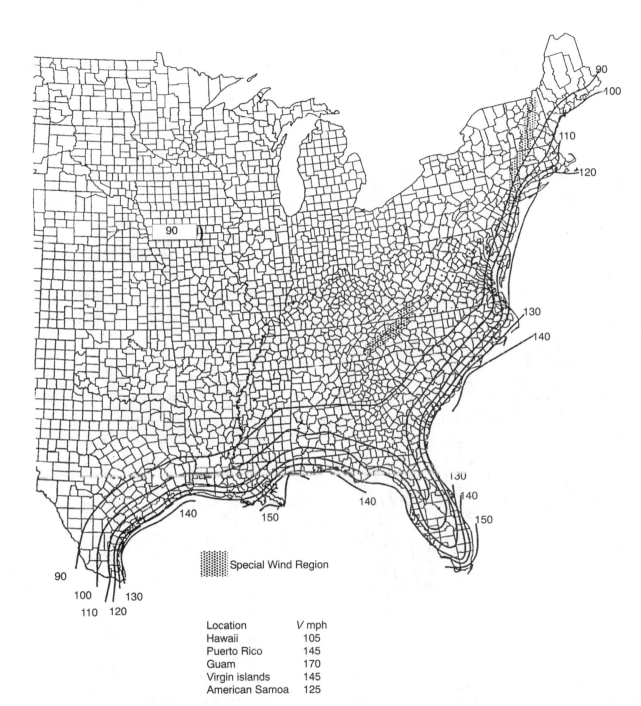

Special Wind Region

Location	V mph
Hawaii	105
Puerto Rico	145
Guam	170
Virgin islands	145
American Samoa	125

For SI: 1 foot = 304.8 mm, 1 mile per hour = 0.447 m/s.

a.   Values are nominal design 3-second gust wind speeds in miles per hour at 33 feet above ground for Exposure C category.
b.   Linear interpolation between wind contours is permitted.
c.   Islands and coastal areas outside the last contour shall use the last wind speed contour of the coastal area.
d.   Mountainous terrain, gorges, ocean promontories, and special wind regions shall be examined for unusual wind conditions.

FIGURE R301.2(4)—continued
BASIC WIND SPEEDS FOR 50-YEAR MEAN RECURRENCE INTERVAL
(continued)

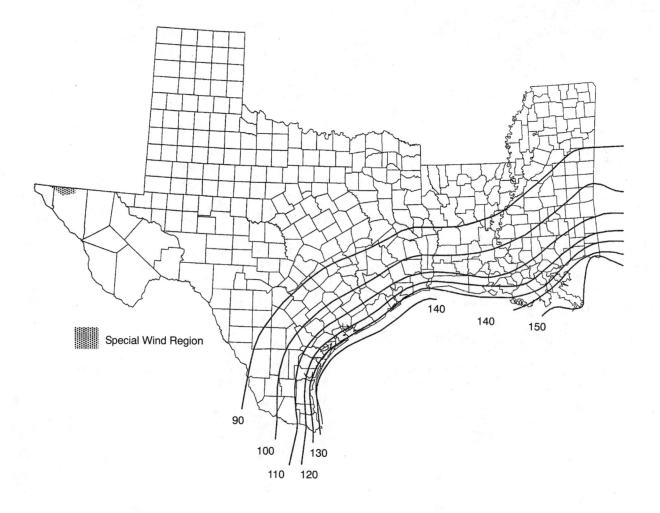

Special Wind Region

140
140
150

90
100   130
110   120

For SI: 1 foot = 304.8 mm, 1 mile per hour = 0.447 m/s.

a. Values are nominal design 3-second gust wind speeds in miles per hour at 33 feet above ground for Exposure C category.
b. Linear interpolation between wind contours is permitted.
c. Islands and coastal areas outside the last contour shall use the last wind speed contour of the coastal area.
d. Mountainous terrain, gorges, ocean promontories, and special wind regions shall be examined for unusual wind conditions.

FIGURE R301.2(4)—continued
BASIC WIND SPEEDS FOR 50-YEAR MEAN RECURRENCE INTERVAL
(continued)

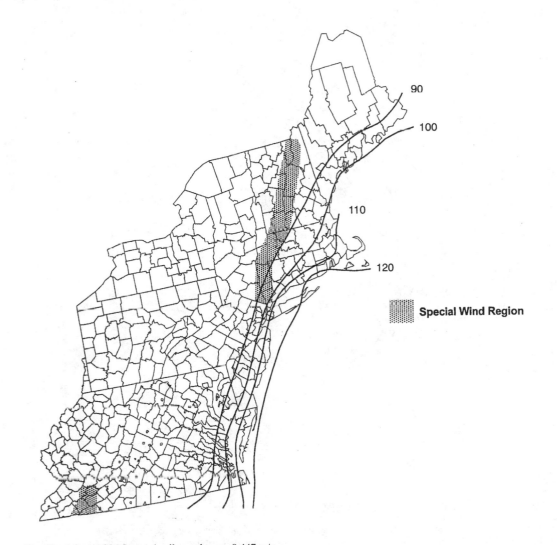

For SI: 1 foot = 304.8 mm, 1 mile per hour = 0.447 m/s.

a. Values are nominal design 3-second gust wind speeds in miles per hour at 33 feet above ground for Exposure C category.
b. Linear interpolation between wind contours is permitted.
c. Islands and coastal areas outside the last contour shall use the last wind speed contour of the coastal area.
d. Mountainous terrain, gorges, ocean promontories, and special wind regions shall be examined for unusual wind conditions.

FIGURE R301.2(4)—continued
BASIC WIND SPEEDS FOR 50-YEAR MEAN RECURRENCE INTERVAL
(continued)

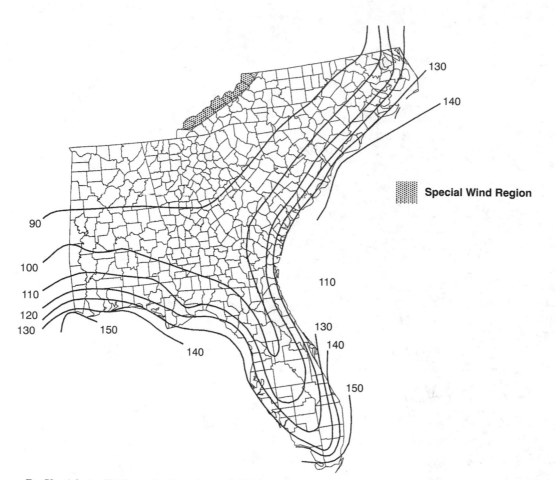

For SI: 1 foot = 304.8 mm, 1 mile per hour = 0.447 m/s.

a. Values are nominal design 3-second gust wind speeds in miles per hour at 33 feet above ground for Exposure C category.
b. Linear interpolation between wind contours is permitted.
c. Islands and coastal areas outside the last contour shall use the last wind speed contour of the coastal area.
d. Mountainous terrain, gorges, ocean promontories, and special wind regions shall be examined for unusual wind conditions.

FIGURE R301.2(4)—continued
BASIC WIND SPEEDS FOR 50-YEAR MEAN RECURRENCE INTERVAL

FIGURE R301.2(5)

Not adopted by the State of Minnesota

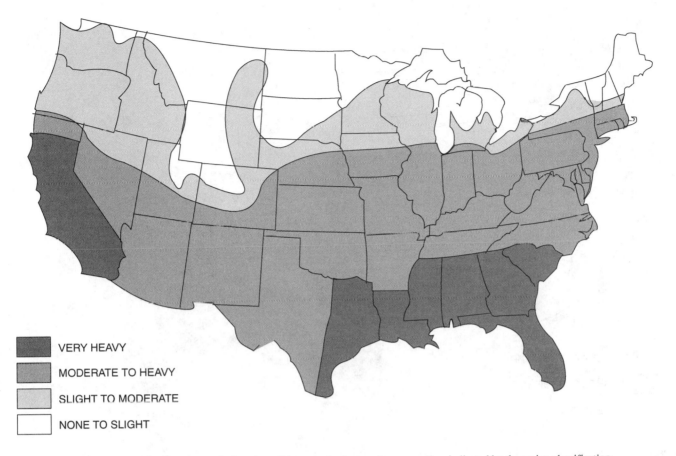

VERY HEAVY

MODERATE TO HEAVY

SLIGHT TO MODERATE

NONE TO SLIGHT

Note: Lines defining areas are approximate only. Local conditions may be more or less severe than indicated by the region classification.

FIGURE R301.2(6)
TERMITE INFESTATION PROBABILITY MAP

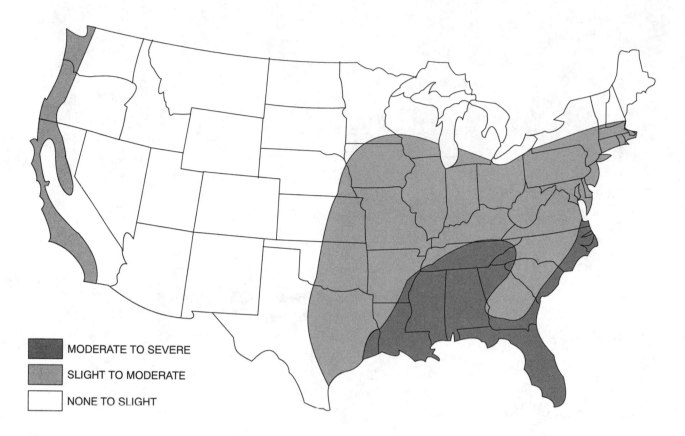

MODERATE TO SEVERE

SLIGHT TO MODERATE

NONE TO SLIGHT

Notes: Lines defining areas are approximate only. Local conditions may be more or less severe than indicated by the region classification.

**FIGURE R301.2(7)
DECAY PROBABILITY MAP**

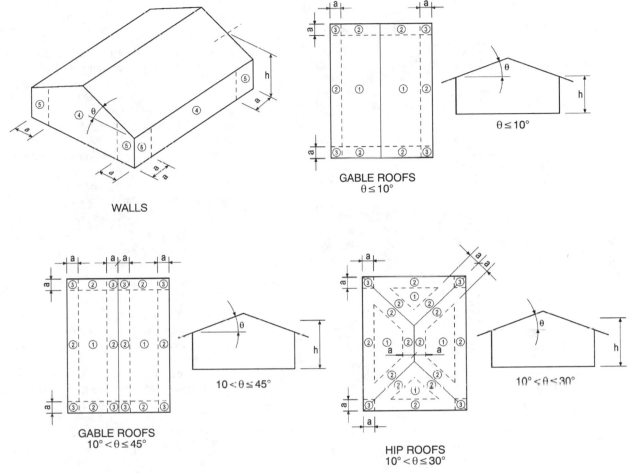

WALLS

GABLE ROOFS
$\theta \leq 10°$

$\theta \leq 10°$

GABLE ROOFS
$10° < \theta \leq 45°$

$10 < \theta \leq 45°$

HIP ROOFS
$10° < \theta \leq 30°$

$10° < \theta \leq 30°$

For SI: 1 foot = 304.8 mm, 1 degree = 0.009 rad.

Note: a = 4 feet in all cases

**FIGURE R301.2(8)
COMPONENT AND CLADDING PRESSURE ZONES**

R301.2.1.2 Internal pressure. Windows in buildings located in wind borne debris regions shall have glazed openings protected from windborne debris or the building shall be designed as a partially enclosed building in accordance with the *International Building Code.* Glazed opening protection for windborne debris shall meet the requirements of the Large Missile Test of ASTM E 1996 and of ASTM E 1886 referenced therein.

Exception: Wood structural panels with a minimum thickness of $^7/_{16}$ inch (11.1 mm) and a maximum span of 8 feet (2438 mm) shall be permitted for opening protection in one- and two-story buildings. Panels shall be precut to cover the glazed openings with attachment hardware provided. Attachments shall be provided in accordance with Table R301.2.1.2 or shall be designed to resist the components and cladding loads determined in accordance with the provisions of the *International Building Code.*

R301.2.1.3 Wind speed conversion. When referenced documents are based on fastest mile wind speeds, the three second gust wind velocities of Figure R301.2(4) shall be converted to fastest mile wind velocities using Table R301.2.1.3.

TABLE R301.2.1.2
WINDBORNE DEBRIS PROTECTION FASTENING SCHEDULE FOR WOOD STRUCTURAL PANELS[a,b,c,d]

FASTENER TYPE	FASTENER SPACING		
	Panel span ≤ 4 foot	4 foot < panel span ≤ 6 foot	6 foot < panel span ≤ 8 foot
$2^1/_2''$ #6 Wood screws	16″	12″	9″
$2^1/_2''$ #8 Wood screws	16″	16″	12″

For SI: 1 inch = 25.4 mm, 1 foot = 304.8 mm, 1 pound = 0.454 kg, 1 mile per hour = 1.609 km/h.

a. This table is based on 110 mph wind speeds and a 33-foot mean roof height.
b. Fasteners shall be installed at opposing ends of the wood structural panel.
c. Nails shall be 10d common or 12d box nails.
d. Where screws are attached to masonry or masonry/stucco, they shall be attached utilizing vibration-resistant anchors having a minimum ultimate withdrawal capacity of 490 pounds.

R301.2.1.4 Exposure category. For each wind direction considered, an exposure category that adequately reflects the characteristics of ground surface irregularities shall be determined for the site at which the building or structure is to be constructed. For a site located in the transition zone between categories, the category resulting in the largest wind forces shall apply. Account shall be taken of variations in ground surface roughness that arise from natural topography and vegetation as well as from constructed features. For any given wind direction, the exposure in which a specific building or other structure is sited shall be assessed as being one of the following categories:

1. Exposure A. Large city centers with at least 50 percent of the buildings having a height in excess of 70 feet (21 336 mm). Use of this exposure category shall be limited to those areas for which terrain representative of Exposure A prevails in the upwind direction for a distance of at least 0.5 mile (0.8 km) or 10 times the height of the building or other structure, whichever is greater. Possible channeling effects or increased velocity pressures due to the building or structure being located in the wake of adjacent buildings shall be taken into account.

2. Exposure B. Urban and suburban areas, wooded areas, or other terrain with numerous closely spaced obstructions having the size of single-family dwellings or larger. Exposure B shall be assumed unless the site meets the definition of another type exposure.

3. Exposure C. Open terrain with scattered obstructions, including surface undulations or other irregularities, having heights generally less than 30 feet (9144 mm) extending more than 1,500 feet (457 m) from the building site in any quadrant. This exposure shall also apply to any building located within Exposure B type terrain where the building is directly adjacent to open areas of Exposure C type terrain in any quadrant for a distance of more than 600 feet (183 m). This category includes flat open country, grasslands and shorelines in hurricane prone regions.

4. Exposure D. Flat, unobstructed areas exposed to wind flowing over open water (excluding shorelines in hurricane prone regions) for a distance of at least 1 mile (1.61 km). Shorelines in Exposure D include inland waterways, the Great Lakes and coastal areas of California, Oregon, Washington and Alaska. This exposure shall apply only to those buildings and other structures exposed to the wind coming from over the water. Exposure D extends inland from the shoreline a distance of 1,500 feet (457 m) or 10 times the height of the building or structure, whichever is greater.

TABLE R301.2.1.3
EQUIVALENT BASIC WIND SPEEDS[a]

3-second gust	85	90	100	105	110	120	125	130	140	145	150	160	170
Fastest mile	70	75	80	85	90	100	105	110	120	125	130	140	150

For SI: 1 mile per hour = 1.609 km/h.

a. Linear interpolation is permitted.

R301.2.2 Seismic provisions. The seismic provisions of this code shall apply to buildings constructed in Seismic Design Categories C, D_1, and D_2, as determined in accordance with this section.

> **Exception:** Detached one- and two-family dwellings located in Seismic Design Category C are exempt from the seismic requirements of this code.

The weight limitations of Section R301.2.2.4 shall apply to buildings in all Seismic Design Categories regulated by this code. Buildings in Seismic Design Category C shall be constructed in accordance with the additional requirements of Sections R301.2.2.3 and R301.2.2.4. Buildings in Seismic Design Categories D_1 and D_2 shall be constructed in accordance with the additional requirements of Sections R301.2.2.5 through R301.2.2.9. Buildings in Seismic Design Category E shall be designed in accordance with the *International Building Code*.

R301.2.2.1 Determination of seismic design category. Buildings shall be assigned a Seismic Design Category in accordance with Figure 301.2(2).

R301.2.2.1.1 Alternate determination of seismic design category. The Seismic Design Categories and corresponding Short Period Design Spectral Response Accelerations, S_{DS} shown in Figure R301.2(2) are based on soil Site Class D, as defined in Section 1615.1 of the *International Building Code*. If soil conditions are other than Site Class D, the Short Period Design Spectral Response Acceleration, S_{DS}, for a site can be determined according to Section 1615.1 of the *International Building Code*. The value of S_{DS} determined according to Section 1615.1 of the *International Building Code* is permitted to be used to set the Seismic Design Category according to Table R301.2.2.1.1, and to interpolate between values in Tables R602.10.1, R603.7, and other seismic design requirements of this code.

TABLE R301.2.2.1.1
SEISMIC DESIGN CATEGORY DETERMINATION

CALCULATED S_{DS}	SEISMIC DESIGN CATEGORY
$S_{DS} \leq 0.17g$	A
$0.17g < S_{DS} \leq 0.33g$	B
$0.33g < S_{DS} \leq 0.50g$	C
$0.50g < S_{DS} \leq 0.83g$	D_1
$0.83g < S_{DS} \leq 1.17g$	D_2
$1.17g < S_{DS}$	E

R301.2.2.1.2 Alternative determination of Seismic Design Category E. Buildings located in Seismic Design Category E in accordance with Figure R301.2(2) are permitted to be reclassified as being in Seismic Design Category D_2 provided one of the following is done:

1. A more detailed evaluation of the Seismic Design Category is made in accordance with the provisions and maps of the *International Building Code*. Buildings located in Seismic Design Category E per Table R301.2.2.1.1, but located in Seismic Design Category D per the *International Building Code*, may be designed using the Seismic Design Category D_2 requirements of this code.

2. Buildings located in Seismic Design Category E that conform to the following additional restrictions are permitted to be constructed in accordance with the provisions for Seismic Design Category D_2 of this code:

   2.1. All exterior shear wall lines or braced wall panels are in one plane vertically from the foundation to the uppermost story.

   2.2. Floors shall not cantilever past the exterior walls.

   2.3. The building is within all of the requirements of Section R301.2.2.6 for being considered as regular.

R301.2.2.2 Determination of seismic design category. It is permitted to determine the Seismic Design Category of a building in accordance with Figure R301.2(2), based on a default Site Class D soil. If soil conditions are other than Site Class D, as defined in the *International Building Code*, the Short Period Design Spectral Response Acceleration, S_{DS}, for a site shall be determined according to the *International Building Code*. The value of S_{DS} determined according to this section is permitted to be used to set the Seismic Design Category according to the legend of Figure R301.2(2) and to interpolate between values in Tables R602.10.3 and R603.7, and other seismic design requirements of this code.

R301.2.2.3 Anchored stone and masonry veneer in Seismic Design Category C. Anchored stone and masonry veneer in Seismic Design Category C shall be limited to the first story above grade and shall not exceed 5 inches (127 mm) in thickness.

> **Exception:** In Seismic Design Category C, anchored stone and masonry veneer not exceeding 5 inches (127 mm) in thickness shall be permitted to the height allowed in Section R703.7. In other than the topmost story, the length of wall bracing shall be 1.5 times the length otherwise required in Table R602.10.1.

R301.2.2.4 Weights of materials. Average dead loads shall not exceed 15 psf (0.72 kN/m^2) for roofs/ceiling assemblies or 10 psf (0.48 kN/m^2) for floor assemblies, except as further limited by Section R301.2.2. Dead loads for walls above grade shall not exceed:

1. Fifteen psf (0.72 kN/m^2) for exterior light-frame wood walls.
2. Fourteen psf (0.67 kN/m^2) for exterior light-frame cold-formed steel walls.
3. Ten psf (0.48 kN/m^2) for interior light-frame wood walls.
4. Five psf (0.24 kN/m^2) for interior light-frame cold-formed steel walls.
5. Eighty psf (3.83 kN/m^2) for 8-inch-thick (203 mm) masonry walls.
6. Eighty-five psf (4.07 kN/m^2) for 6-inch-thick (152 mm) concrete walls.

> **Exception:** Roof/ceiling dead loads not exceeding 25 psf (1.19 kN/m^2) shall be permitted in Seismic

Design Category D$_2$ provided the wall bracing amounts in Chapter 6 are increased in accordance with Table R301.2.2.4.

TABLE R301.2.2.4
WALL BRACING ADJUSTMENT FACTORS BY ROOF COVERING DEAD LOAD[a]

WALL SUPPORTING	ROOF/CEILING DEAD LOAD 15 psf or less	ROOF/CEILING DEAD LOAD 25 psf
Roof only	1.0	1.2
Roof plus one story	1.0	1.1

For SI: 1 pound per square foot = 0.0479 kN/m^2.

a. Linear interpolation shall be permitted.

R301.2.2.5 Masonry construction in Seismic Design Category C. Masonry construction in Seismic Design Category C shall comply with the requirements of Section R606.11.2.

R301.2.2.6 Height limitations in Seismic Design Categories D$_1$ and D$_2$. Wood frame buildings shall be limited to three stories above grade or the limits given in Table R602.10.3. Cold-formed steel frame buildings shall be limited to two stories above grade in accordance with Sections R505.1.1, R603.1.1 and R804.1.1. Masonry construction in Seismic Design Category D$_1$ shall be limited in accordance with Section R606.11.3. Masonry construction in Seismic Design Category D$_2$ shall be limited in accordance with Section R606.11.4. Mezzanines as defined in Section R202 shall not be considered as stories.

R301.2.2.7 Irregular buildings. Conventional light-frame construction shall not be used in irregular portions of structures in Seismic Design Categories C, D$_1$ and D$_2$. Only such irregular portions of structures shall be designed in accordance with accepted engineering practice to the extent such irregular features affect the performance of the conventional framing system. A portion of a building shall be considered to be irregular when one or more of the following conditions occur:

1. Exterior shear wall lines or braced wall panels are not in one plane vertically from the foundation to the uppermost story in which they are required.

   Exception: For wood light-frame construction, floors with cantilevers or setbacks not exceeding four times the nominal depth of the wood floor joists are permitted to support braced wall panels that are out of plane with braced wall panels below provided that:

   1.1. Floor joists are nominal 2 inches by 10 inches (51 mm by 254 mm) or larger and spaced not more than 16 inches (406 mm) on center.

   1.2. The ratio of the back span to the cantilever is at least 2 to 1.

   1.3. Floor joists at ends of braced wall panels are doubled.

   1.4. For wood frame construction, a continuous rim joist is connected to ends of all cantilever joists. When spliced, the rim joists shall be spliced us-

ing a galvanized metal tie not less than 0.058 inch (1.47 mm) (16 gage) and 1$^1/_2$ inches (38 mm) wide fastened with six 16d nails on each side of the splice or a block of the same size as the rim joist of sufficient length to fit securely between the joist space at which the splice occurs fastened with eight 16d nails on each side of the splice; and

   1.5. Gravity loads carried at the end of cantilevered joists are limited to uniform wall and roof load and the reactions from headers having span of 8 feet (2438 mm) or less.

2. A section of floor or roof is not laterally supported by shear walls or braced wall lines on all edges.

   Exception: Portions of floors that do not support shear walls or braced wall panels above, or roofs, shall be permitted to extend no more than 6 feet (1829 mm) beyond a shear wall or braced wall line.

3. The end of a braced wall panel occurs over an opening in the wall below and ends at a horizontal distance greater than 1 foot (305 mm) from the edge of the opening. This provision is applicable to shear walls and braced wall panels offset in plane and to braced wall panels offset out of plane as permitted by the exception to Item 1 above.

   Exception: For light-frame construction, a braced wall panel shall be permitted to extend more than 1 foot (305 mm) over an opening in the wall below provided that the opening includes a header in accordance with Chapter 6 of this code. The entire length of the braced wall panel shall not occur over an opening in the wall below.

4. An opening in a floor or roof exceeds the lesser of 12 feet (3657 mm) or 50 percent of the least floor or roof dimension.

5. Portions of a floor level are vertically offset.

   Exceptions:

   1. Framing supported directly by continuous foundations at the perimeter of the building.

   2. For wood light-frame construction, floors shall be permitted to be vertically offset when the floor framing is lapped or tied together as required by Section R502.6.1.

6. Shear walls and braced wall lines do not occur in two perpendicular directions.

7. Shear walls or braced wall lines are constructed of dissimilar bracing systems on any one story level above grade.

R301.2.2.8 Concrete construction in Seismic Design Categories D$_1$ and D$_2$. Buildings with above-grade concrete walls in Seismic Design Categories D$_1$ and D$_2$ shall be designed in accordance with accepted engineering practice.

R301.2.2.9 Irregular buildings in Seismic Design Categories D$_1$ and D$_2$. In Seismic Design Categories C, D$_1$ and D$_2$, irregular buildings shall have an engineered lateral-force-resisting system designed in accordance with accepted engineering practice. A building shall be considered to be irregular when one or more of the following conditions occur:

1. Exterior shear wall lines or braced wall panels are not in one plane vertically from the foundation to the uppermost story in which they are required.

Exception: For light-frame construction, floors with cantilevers or setbacks not exceeding four times the nominal depth of the wood floor joists or 24 inches (610 mm) for cold-formed steel joists are permitted to support braced wall panels that are out of plane with braced wall panels below provided that:

   1. Floor joists are nominal 2 inches by 10 inches (51 mm by 254 mm) or larger and spaced not more than 16 inches (406 mm) on center;

   2. The ratio of the back span to the cantilever is at least 2 to 1;

   3. Floor joists at ends of braced wall panels are doubled;

   4. For wood-frame construction, a continuous rim joist is connected to ends of all cantilever joists. When spliced, the rim joists shall be spliced using a galvanized metal tie not less than 0.058 inch (1.47 mm) (16 gage) and 1.5 inches (38 mm) wide fastened with six 16d nails on each side; and

   5. Gravity loads carried at the end of cantilevered joists are limited to uniform wall and roof load and the reactions from headers having span of 8 feet (2438 mm) or less.

2. A section of floor or roof is not laterally supported by shear walls or braced wall lines on all edges.

Exception: Portions of floors which do not support shear walls or braced wall panels above, or roofs, shall be permitted to extend no more than 6 feet (1829 mm) beyond a shear wall or braced wall line.

3. The end of a braced wall panel occurs over an opening in the wall below and ends at a horizontal distance greater than 1 foot (305 mm) from the edge of the opening. This provision is applicable to shear walls and braced wall panels offset in plane and to braced wall panels offset out of plane as permitted by the exception to Item 1 above.

Exception: For light-frame construction, a braced wall panel shall be permitted to extend more than 1 foot (305 mm) over an opening in the wall below provided that the opening includes a header in accordance with Chapter 6 of this code. The entire length of the braced wall panel shall not occur over an opening in the wall below.

4. An opening in a floor or roof exceeds the lesser of 12 feet (3657 mm) or 50 percent of the least floor or roof dimension.

5. Portions of a floor level are vertically offset.

   Exceptions:

   1. Framing supported directly by continuous foundations at the perimeter of the building.

2. For light-frame construction, floors shall be permitted to be vertically offset when the floor framing is lapped or tied together as required by Section R502.6.1 for wood framing and Section R505.3.1 for cold-formed steel framing.

6. Shear walls and braced wall lines do not occur in two perpendicular directions.

7. Shear walls or braced wall lines are constructed of dissimilar bracing systems on any one-story level above grade.

R301.2.3 Snow loads. Wood frame construction, cold-formed steel frame construction and masonry and concrete construction in regions with ground snow loads 70 psf (3.35 kN/m^2) or less shall be in accordance with Chapters 5, 6 and 8. Buildings in regions with ground snow loads greater than 70 psf (3.35 kN/m^2) shall be designed in accordance with accepted engineering practice.

R301.2.4 Floodplain construction. Buildings and structures constructed in flood hazard areas (including A or V Zones) as established in Table R301.2(1) shall be designed and constructed in accordance with Section R327.

Exception: Buildings in floodways that are designated on the Flood Insurance Rate Maps (FIRM) or the Flood Boundary and Floodway Maps (FBFM) that are provided by the National Flood Insurance Program shall not be approved under this section; the provisions of the *International Building Code* shall apply.

R301.3 Dead load. The actual weights of materials and construction shall be used for determining dead load with consideration for the dead load of fixed service equipment.

R301.4 Live load. The minimum uniformly distributed live load shall be as provided in Table R301.4.

TABLE R301.4
MINIMUM UNIFORMLY DISTRIBUTED LIVE LOADS
(in pounds per square foot)

USE	LIVE LOAD
Exterior balconies	60
Decks[f]	40
Fire escapes	40
Passenger vehicle garages[a]	50[a]
Attics without storage[b,e]	10
Attics with storage[b,e]	20
Rooms other than sleeping rooms	40
Sleeping rooms	30
Stairs	40[c]
Guardrails and handrails[d]	200

For SI: 1 pound per square foot = 0.0479 kN/m^2, 1 square inch = 645 mm^2, 1 pound = 4.45 N.

a. Elevated garage floors shall be capable of supporting a 2,000-pound load applied over a 20-square-inch area.

b. No storage with roof slope not over 3 units in 12 units.

c. Individual stair treads shall be designed for the uniformly distributed live load or a 300-pound concentrated load acting over an area of 4 square inches, whichever produces the greater stresses.

d. A single concentrated load applied in any direction at any point along the top.

(continued)

e. Attics constructed with wood trusses shall be designed in accordance with Section R802.10.1.

f. See Section R502.2.1 for decks attached to exterior walls.

R301.5 Roof load. Roof shall be designed for the live load indicated in Table R301.5 or the snow load indicated in Table R301.2(1), whichever is greater.

TABLE R301.5
MINIMUM ROOF LIVE LOADS IN POUNDS-FORCE PER SQUARE FOOT OF HORIZONTAL PROJECTION

ROOF SLOPE	TRIBUTARY LOADED AREA IN SQUARE FEET FOR ANY STRUCTURAL MEMBER		
	0 to 200	201 to 600	Over 600
Flat or rise less than 4 inches per foot (1:3)	20	16	12
Rise 4 inches per foot (1:3) to less than 12 inches per foot (1:1)	16	14	12
Rise 12 inches per foot (1:1) and greater	12	12	12

For SI: 1 square foot = 0.0929 m², 1 pound per square foot = 0.0479 kN/m², 1 inch per foot = 0.0833 mm/m.

R301.6 Deflection. The allowable deflection of any structural member under the live load listed in Sections R301.4 and R301.5 shall not exceed the values in Table R301.6.

TABLE R301.6
ALLOWABLE DEFLECTION OF STRUCTURAL MEMBERS

STRUCTURAL MEMBER	ALLOWABLE DEFLECTION
Rafters having slopes greater than 3/12 with no finished ceiling attached to rafters	L/180
Interior walls and partitions	H/180
Floors and plastered ceilings	L/360
All other structural members	L/240
Exterior walls with plaster or stucco finish	H/360
Exterior walls—wind loads[a] with brittle finishes	L/240
Exterior walls—wind loads[a] with flexible finishes	L/120

Note: L = span length, H = span height.

a. The wind load shall be permitted to be taken as 0.7 times the Component and Cladding loads for the purpose of the determining deflection limits herein.

R301.7 Nominal sizes. For the purposes of this code, where dimensions of lumber are specified, they shall be deemed to be nominal dimensions unless specifically designated as actual dimensions.

SECTION R302
LOCATION ON LOT

R302.1 Exterior walls. Exterior walls with a fire separation distance less than 3 feet (914 mm) shall have not less than a one-hour fire-resistive rating with exposure from both sides. Projections shall not extend beyond the distance determined by the following two methods, whichever results in the lesser projections:

1. A point one-third the distance to the property line from an assumed vertical plane located where protected openings are required.

2. More than 12 inches (305 mm) into areas where openings are prohibited.

Projections extending into the fire separation distance shall have not less than one-hour fire-resistive construction on the underside. The above provisions shall not apply to walls which are perpendicular to the line used to determine the fire separation distance.

Exception: Tool and storage sheds, playhouses and similar structures exempted from permits by Minnesota Rules, Chapter 1300 are not required to provide wall protection based on location on the lot. Projections beyond the exterior wall shall not extend over the lot line.

R302.2 Openings. Openings shall not be permitted in the exterior wall of a dwelling or accessory building with a fire separation distance less than 3 feet (914 mm). This distance shall be measured perpendicular to the line used to determine the fire separation distance.

Exceptions:

1. Openings shall be permitted in walls that are perpendicular to the line used to determine the fire separation distance.

2. Foundation vents installed in compliance with this code are permitted.

R302.3 Penetrations. Penetrations located in the exterior wall of a dwelling with a fire separation distance less than 3 feet (914 mm) shall be protected in accordance with Section R321.3.

Exception: Penetrations shall be permitted in walls that are perpendicular to the line used to determine the fire separation distance.

SECTION R303
LIGHT, VENTILATION AND HEATING

R303.1 Habitable rooms. All habitable rooms shall be provided with aggregate glazing area of not less than 8 percent of the floor area of such rooms. Natural ventilation shall be through windows, doors, louvers or other approved openings to the outdoor air. Such openings shall be provided with ready access or shall otherwise be readily controllable by the building occupants. The minimum openable area to the outdoors shall be 4 percent of the floor area being ventilated.

Exceptions:

1. The glazed areas need not be openable where the opening is not required by Section R310 and an approved

mechanical ventilation system is provided capable of producing 0.35 air change per hour in the room or a whole-house mechanical ventilation system is installed capable of supplying outdoor ventilation air of 15 cubic feet per minute (cfm) (7.08 L/s) per occupant computed on the basis of two occupants for the first bedroom and one occupant for each additional bedroom.

2. The glazed areas need not be provided in rooms where Exception 1 above is satisfied and artificial light is provided capable of producing an average illumination of 6 footcandles (6.46 lux) over the area of the room at a height of 30 inches (762 mm) above the floor level.

R303.2 Adjoining rooms. For the purpose of determining light and ventilation requirements, any room shall be considered as a portion of an adjoining room when at least one-half of the area of the common wall is open and unobstructed and provides an opening of not less than one-tenth of the floor area of the interior room but not less than 25 square feet (2.32 m^2).

R303.3 Bathrooms. Bathrooms, water closet compartments and other similar rooms shall be provided with aggregate glazing area in windows of not less than 3 square feet (0.279 m^2), one-half of which must be openable.

Exception: The glazed areas shall not be required where artificial light and a mechanical ventilation system are provided. The minimum ventilation rates shall be 50 cfm (23.6 L/s) for intermittent ventilation or 20 cfm (9.4 L/s) for continuous ventilation. Ventilation air from the space shall be exhausted directly to the outside.

R303.4 Stairway illumination. All interior and exterior stairways shall be provided with a means to illuminate the stairs, including the landings and treads. Interior stairways shall be provided with an artificial light source located in the immediate vicinity of each landing of the stairway. Exterior stairways shall be provided with an artificial light source located in the immediate vicinity of the top landing of the stairway. Exterior stairways providing access to a basement from the outside grade level shall be provided with an artificial light source located in the immediate vicinity of the bottom landing of the stairway.

Exception: An artificial light source is not required at the top and bottom landing, provided an artificial light source is located directly over each stairway section.

R303.4.1 Light activation. The control for activation of the required interior stairway lighting shall be accessible at the top and bottom of each stair without traversing any step of the stair. The illumination of exterior stairs shall be controlled from inside the dwelling unit.

Exception: Lights that are continuously illuminated or automatically activated.

R303.5 Required glazed openings. Required glazed openings shall open directly onto a street or public alley, or a yard or court located on the same lot as the building.

R303.5.1 Roofed porches. Required glazed openings may face into a roofed porch where the porch abuts a street, yard or court and the longer side of the porch is at least 65 percent

open and unobstructed and the ceiling height is not less than 7 feet (2134 mm).

R303.6 Required heating. When the winter design temperature in Table R301.2(1) is below 60ºF (16ºC), every dwelling unit shall be provided with heating facilities capable of maintaining a minimum room temperature of 68ºF (20ºC) at a point 3 feet (914 mm) above the floor and 2 feet (610 mm) from exterior walls in all habitable rooms at the design temperature.

SECTION R304
MINIMUM ROOM AREAS

R304.1 Minimum area. Every dwelling unit shall have at least one habitable room that shall have not less than 120 square feet (11.2 m^2) of gross floor area.

R304.2 Other rooms. Other habitable rooms shall have a floor area of not less than 70 square feet (6.5 m^2).

Exception: Every kitchen shall have not less than 50 square feet (4.64 m^2) of gross floor area.

R304.3 Minimum dimensions. Habitable rooms shall not be less than 7 feet (2134 mm) in any horizontal dimension.

Exception: Kitchens.

R304.4 Height effect on room area. Portions of a room with a sloping ceiling measuring less than 5 feet (1524 mm) or a furred ceiling measuring less than 7 feet (2134 mm) from the finished floor to the finished ceiling shall not be considered as contributing to the minimum required habitable area for that room.

SECTION R305
CEILING HEIGHT

R305.1 Minimum height. Habitable rooms, hallways, corridors, bathrooms, toilet rooms, and basements shall have a ceiling height of not less than 7 feet (2134 mm). The required height shall be measured from the finished floor to the lowest projection from the ceiling. Areas or rooms with ceiling heights less than 7 feet (2134 mm) are considered crawl spaces.

Exceptions:
1. Beams and girders spaced not less than 4 feet (1219 mm) on center may project not more than 6 inches (152 mm) below the required ceiling height.
2. Not more than 50 percent of the required floor area of a room or space is permitted to have a sloped ceiling less than 7 feet (2134 mm) in height with no portion of the required floor area less than 5 feet (1524 mm) in height.

SECTION R306
SANITATION

R306.1 Toilet facilities. Every dwelling unit shall be provided with a water closet, lavatory, and a bathtub or shower.

R306.2 Kitchen. Each dwelling unit shall be provided with a kitchen area and every kitchen area shall be provided with a sink.

R306.3 Sewage disposal. All plumbing fixtures shall be connected to a sanitary sewer or to an approved private sewage disposal system.

R306.4 Water supply to fixtures. All plumbing fixtures shall be connected to an approved water supply. Kitchen sinks, lavatories, bathtubs, showers, bidets, laundry tubs and washing machine outlets shall be provided with hot and cold water.

SECTION R307
TOILET, BATH AND SHOWER SPACES

R307.1 Space required. Fixtures shall be spaced as per Figure R307.2.

R307.2 Bathtub and shower spaces. Bathtub and shower floors and walls above bathtubs with installed shower heads and in shower compartments shall be finished with a nonabsorbent surface. Such wall surfaces shall extend to a height of not less than 6 feet (1829 mm) above the floor.

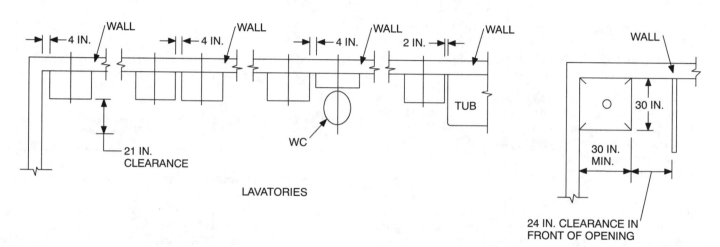

LAVATORIES

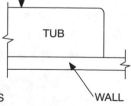

SHOWER

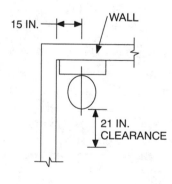

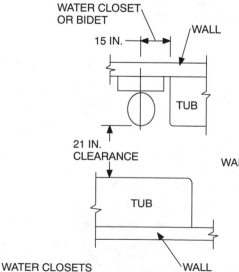

WATER CLOSETS

For SI: 1 inch = 25.4 mm.

FIGURE R307.2
MINIMUM FIXTURE CLEARANCES

SECTION R308
GLAZING

R308.1 Identification. Except as indicated in Section R308.1.1, each pane of glazing installed in hazardous locations as defined in Section R308.4 shall be provided with a manufacturer's or installer's label, designating the type and thickness of glass and the safety glazing standard with which it complies, which is visible in the final installation. The label shall be acid etched, sandblasted, ceramic-fired, embossed mark, or shall be of a type which once applied cannot be removed without being destroyed.

Exceptions:

1. For other than tempered glass, labels may be omitted provided the building official approves the use of a certificate, affidavit or other evidence confirming compliance with this code.

2. Tempered spandrel glass may be identified by the manufacturer with a removable paper label.

R308.1.1 Identification of multipane assemblies. Multipane assemblies having individual panes not exceeding 1 square foot (0.09 m^2) in exposed area shall have at least one pane in the assembly identified in accordance with Section R308.1. All other panes in the assembly shall be labeled "16 CFR 1201."

R308.2 Louvered windows or jalousies. Regular, float, wired or patterned glass in jalousies and louvered windows shall be no thinner than nominal $3/16$ inch (4.76 mm) and no longer than 48 inches (1219 mm). Exposed glass edges shall be smooth.

R308.2.1 Wired glass prohibited. Wired glass with wire exposed on longitudinal edges shall not be used in jalousies or louvered windows.

R308.3 Human impact loads. Individual glazed areas including glass mirrors in hazardous locations such as those indicated as defined in Section R308.4 shall pass the test requirements of CPSC 16 CFR, Part 1201. Glazing shall comply with the CPSC 16 CFR, Part 1201 criteria for Category I or II as indicated in Table R308.3.

Exceptions:

1. Polished wired glass for use in fire doors and other fire resistant locations shall comply with ANSI Z97.1.

2. Louvered windows and jalousies shall comply with Section R308.2.

TABLE R308.3
MINIMUM CATEGORY CLASSIFICATION OF GLAZING

EXPOSED SURFACE AREA OF ONE SIDE OF ONE LITE	GLAZING IN STORM OR COMBINATION DOORS (Category Class)	GLAZING IN DOORS (Category Class)	GLAZED PANELS REGULATED BY ITEM 7 OF SECTION R308.4 (Category Class)	GLAZED PANELS REGULATED BY ITEM 6 OF SECTION R308.4 (Category Class)	GLAZING IN DOORS AND ENCLOSURES REGULATED BY ITEM 5 OF SECTION R308.4 (Category Class)	SLIDING GLASS DOORS PATIO TYPE (Category Class)
9 sq. ft. or less	I	I	NR[a]	I	II	II
More than 9 sq. ft	II	II	II	II	II	II

For SI: 1 square foot = 0.0929 m^2

[a]NR means "No Requirement."

R308.4 Hazardous locations. The following shall be considered specific hazardous locations for the purposes of glazing:

1. Glazing in side-hinged doors except jalousies.

2. Glazing in fixed and sliding panels of sliding door assemblies and panels in sliding and bifold closet door assemblies.

3. Glazing in storm doors.

4. Glazing in all unframed swinging doors.

5. Glazing in doors and enclosures for hot tubs, whirlpools, saunas, steam rooms, bathtubs and showers. Glazing in any part of a building wall enclosing these compartments where the bottom exposed edge of the glazing is less than 60 inches (1524 mm) measured vertically above any standing or walking surface.

6. Glazing, in an individual fixed or operable panel adjacent to a door where the nearest vertical edge is within a 24-inch (610 mm) arc of the door in a closed position and whose bottom edge is less than 60 inches (1524 mm) above the floor or walking surface.

7. Glazing in an individual fixed or operable panel, other than those locations described in Items 5 and 6 above, that meets all of the following conditions:

7.1. Exposed area of an individual pane greater than 9 square feet (0.836 m^2).

7.2. Bottom edge less than 18 inches (457 mm) above the floor.

7.3. Top edge greater than 36 inches (914 mm) above the floor.

7.4. One or more walking surfaces within 36 inches (914 mm) horizontally of the glazing.

8. All glazing in railings regardless of an area or height above a walking surface. Included are structural baluster panels and nonstructural in-fill panels.

9. Glazing in walls and fences enclosing indoor and outdoor swimming pools, hot tubs and spas where the bottom edge of the pool or spa side is less than 60 inches (1524 mm) above a walking surface and within 60 inches (1524 mm) horizontally of the water's edge. This shall apply to single glazing and all panes in multiple glazing.

10. Glazing in walls enclosing stairway landings or within 60 inches (1524 mm) of the top and bottom of stairways where the bottom edge of the glass is less than 60 inches (1524 mm) above the walking surface.

Exception: The following products, materials and uses are exempt from the above hazardous locations:

1. Openings in doors through which a 3-inch (76 mm) sphere is unable to pass.

2. Decorative glass in Item 1, 6 or 7.

3. Glazing in Section R308.4, Item 6, when there is an intervening wall or other permanent barrier between the door and the glazing.

4. Glazing in all unframed swinging doors.

5. Glazing in Section R308.4, Item 6, where access through the door is to a closet or storage area 3 feet (914 mm) or less in depth.

6. Glazing in Section R308.4, Item 7, when a protective bar is installed on the accessible side(s) of the glazing 36 inches ± 2 inches (914 mm ± 51 mm) above the floor. The bar shall be capable of withstanding a horizontal load of 50 pounds per linear foot (74.5 kg/m) without contacting the glass and be a minimum of 1.5 inches (38 mm) in height.

7. Outboard panes in insulating glass units and other multiple glazed panels in Section R308.4, Item 7, when the bottom edge of the glass is 25 feet (7620 mm) or more above grade, a roof, walking surface, or other horizontal [within 45 degrees (0.79 rad) of horizontal] surface adjacent to the glass exterior.

8. Louvered windows and jalousies complying with the requirements of Section R308.2.

9. Mirrors and other glass panels mounted or hung on a surface that provides a continuous backing support.

R308.5 Site built windows. Site built windows shall comply with Section 2404 of the *International Building Code*.

R308.6 Skylights and sloped glazing. Skylights and sloped glazing shall comply with the following sections.

R308.6.1 Definition. Sloped glazing means any installation of glass or other transparent or translucent glazing material installed at a slope of more than 15 degrees (0.26 rad) from vertical. Glazing materials in skylights, solariums, sun spaces, roofs and sloped walls are included in this definition.

R308.6.2 Permitted materials. The following types of glazing may be used:

1. Laminated glass with a minimum 0.015-inch (0.38 mm) polyvinyl butyral interlayer for glass panes 16 square feet (1.5 m^2) or less in area located such that the highest point of the glass is not more than 12 feet (3658 mm) above a walking surface or other accessible area; for higher or larger sizes, the minimum interlayer thickness shall be 0.030 inch (0.76 mm).

2. Fully tempered glass.

3. Heat-strengthened glass.

4. Wired glass.

5. Approved rigid plastics.

R308.6.3 Screens, general. For fully tempered or heat-strengthened glass, a retaining screen meeting the requirements of Section R308.6.7 shall be installed below the glass, except for fully tempered glass that meets either condition listed in Section R308.6.5.

R308.6.4 Screens with multiple glazing. When the inboard pane is fully tempered, heat-strengthened, or wired glass, a retaining screen meeting the requirements of Section R308.6.7 shall be installed below the glass, except for either condition listed in Section R308.6.5. All other panes in the multiple glazing may be of any type listed in Section R308.6.2.

R308.6.5 Screens not required. Screens shall not be required when fully tempered glass is used as single glazing or the inboard pane in multiple glazing and either of the following conditions are met:

1. Glass area 16 square feet (1.49 m^2) or less. Highest point of glass not more than 12 feet (3658 mm) above a walking surface or other accessible area, nominal glass thickness not more than $^3/_{16}$ inch (4.76 mm), and (for multiple glazing only) the other pane or panes fully tempered, laminated or wired glass.

2. Glass area greater than 16 square feet (1.49 m^2). Glass sloped 30 degrees (0.52 rad) or less from vertical, and highest point of glass not more than 10 feet (3048 mm) above a walking surface or other accessible area.

R308.6.6 Glass in greenhouses. Any glazing material is permitted to be installed without screening in the sloped areas of greenhouses, provided the greenhouse height at the ridge does not exceed 20 feet (6096 mm) above grade.

R308.6.7 Screen characteristics. The screen and its fastenings shall be capable of supporting twice the weight of the glazing, be firmly and substantially fastened to the framing members, and have a mesh opening of no more than 1 inch by 1 inch (25.4 mm by 25.4 mm).

R308.6.8 Curbs for skylights. All unit skylights installed in a roof with a pitch flatter than three units vertical in 12 units horizontal (25-percent slope) shall be mounted on a curb extending at least 4 inches (102 mm) above the plane of the roof unless otherwise specified in the manufacturer's installation instructions.

SECTION R309
GARAGES AND CARPORTS

R309.1 Opening protection. Openings from a private garage directly into a room used for sleeping purposes shall not be permitted. Other openings between the garage and residence shall be equipped with solid wood doors not less than 1$^3/_8$ inch (35 mm) in thickness, solid or honeycomb core steel doors not less than 1$^3/_8$ inches (35 mm) thick, or 20-minute fire-rated doors.

R309.1.1 Duct penetration. Ducts in the garage and ducts penetrating the walls or ceilings separating the dwelling from the garage shall be constructed of a minimum No. 26 gage (0.48 mm) sheet steel or other approved material and shall have no openings into the garage.

R309.2 Separation required. The garage shall be separated from the residence and its attic area by not less than $^1/_2$-inch

(12.7 mm) gypsum board applied to the garage side. Where the separation is a floor-ceiling assembly, the structure supporting the separation shall also be protected by not less than $^{1}/_{2}$-inch (12.7 mm) gypsum board or equivalent.

R309.3 Floor surface. Garage floor surfaces shall be of approved noncombustible material.

The area of floor used for parking of automobiles or other vehicles shall be sloped to facilitate the movement of liquids to a drain or toward the main vehicle entry doorway.

R309.4 Carports. Carports shall be open on at least two sides. Carport floor surfaces shall be of approved noncombustible material. Carports not open on at least two sides shall be considered a garage and shall comply with the provisions of this section for garages.

Exception: Asphalt surfaces shall be permitted at ground level in carports.

The area of floor used for parking of automobiles or other vehicles shall be sloped to facilitate the movement of liquids to a drain or toward the main vehicle entry doorway.

R309.5 Flood hazard areas. For buildings located in flood hazard areas as established by Table 301.2(1), garage floors shall be:

1. Elevated to or above the design flood elevation as determined in Section R327; or

2. Located below the design flood elevation provided they are at or above grade on all sides, are used solely for parking, building access, or storage, meet the requirements of Section R327, and are otherwise constructed in accordance with this code.

SECTION R310
EMERGENCY ESCAPE AND RESCUE OPENINGS

R310.1 Emergency escape and rescue required. Basements with habitable space and every sleeping room shall have at least one openable emergency escape and rescue window or exterior door opening for emergency escape and rescue. Where openings are provided as a means of escape and rescue they shall have a sill height of not more than 44 inches (1118 mm) above the floor. Where a door opening having a threshold below the adjacent ground elevation serves as an emergency escape and rescue opening and is provided with a bulkhead enclosure, the bulkhead enclosure shall comply with Section R310.3. The net clear opening dimensions required by this section shall be obtained by the normal operation of the window or door opening from the inside. Escape and rescue window openings with a finished sill height below the adjacent ground elevation shall be provided with a window well in accordance with Section R310.2. A minimum ceiling height of 48 inches (1210 mm) shall be maintained above the exterior grade from the exterior wall to a public way.

R310.1.1 Minimum opening area. All emergency escape and rescue openings shall have a minimum net clear opening of 5.7 square feet (0.530 m²).

Exception: Grade floor openings shall have a minimum net clear opening of 5 square feet (0.465 m²).

R310.1.2 Minimum opening height. The minimum net clear opening height shall be 24 inches (610 mm).

R310.1.3 Minimum opening width. The minimum net clear opening width shall be 20 inches (508 mm).

R310.1.4 Operational constraints. Emergency escape and rescue openings shall be operational from the inside of the room without the use of keys or tools.

R310.1.5 Replacement windows. Replacement windows installed in buildings meeting the scope of the *International Residential Code* shall be exempt from the requirements of Sections R310.1.1, R310.1.2, and R310.1.3 if the replacement window meets the following conditions:

1. The existing height and width net clear opening shall not be reduced by more than 2 inches (51 mm) in either dimension;

2. The rooms or areas are not used for any Minnesota state licensed purpose;

3. The window is not required pursuant to the Minnesota Fire Code;

4. The sleeping room is not undergoing an addition, remodeling, or a change in occupancy; and

5. The window is not required to be replaced pursuant to a locally adopted housing, property maintenance, or rental licensing code.

R310.2 Window wells. Window wells required for emergency escape and rescue shall have horizontal dimensions that allow the door or window of the emergency escape and rescue opening to be fully opened. The horizontal dimensions of the window well shall provide a minimum net clear area of 9 square feet (0.84 m²) with a minimum horizontal projection and width of 36 inches (914 mm).

Exception: The ladder or steps required by Section R310.2.1 shall be permitted to encroach a maximum of 6 inches (152 mm) into the required dimensions of the window well.

R310.2.1 Ladder and steps. Window wells with a vertical depth greater than 44 inches (1118 mm) below the adjacent ground level shall be equipped with a permanently affixed ladder or steps usable with the window in the fully open position. Ladders or steps required by this section shall not be required to comply with Sections R314 and R315. Ladders or rungs shall have an inside width of at least 12 inches (305 mm), shall project at least 3 inches (76 mm) from the wall and shall be spaced not more than 18 inches (457 mm) on center vertically for the full height of the window well.

R310.3 Bulkhead enclosures. Bulkhead enclosures shall provide direct access to the basement. The bulkhead enclosure with the door panels in the fully open position shall provide the minimum net clear opening required by Section R310.1.1. Bulkhead enclosures shall also comply with Section R314.9.

R310.4 Bars, grills, covers and screens. Bars, grills, covers, screens or similar devices are permitted to be placed over emergency escape and rescue openings, bulkhead enclosures, or window wells that serve such openings, provided the minimum net clear opening size complies with Sections R310.1.1 to R310.1.3, and such devices shall be releasable or removable from the inside without the use of a key, tool or force greater than that which is required for normal operation of the escape and rescue opening.

SECTION R311
EXITS

R311.1 Exit door required. Not less than one exit door conforming to this chapter shall be provided from each dwelling unit. The required exit door shall provide for direct access from the habitable portions of the dwelling to the exterior without requiring travel through a garage.

R311.2 Type of lock or latch. All egress doors shall be readily openable from the side from which egress is to be made without the use of a key or special knowledge or effort.

R311.3 Type and size. The required exit door shall be a side-hinged door not less than 3 feet (914 mm) in width and 6 feet, 8 inches (2032 mm) in height. Other exterior hinged or sliding doors shall not be required to comply with these minimum dimensions.

R311.4 Hallways. The minimum width of a hallway shall be not less than 3 feet (914 mm).

R311.5 Exit facilities. Exterior exit balconies, stairs and similar exit facilities shall be positively anchored to the primary structure to resist both vertical and lateral forces. Such attachment shall not be accomplished by use of toenails or nails subject to withdrawal.

SECTION R312
LANDINGS

R312.1 General. Landings for stairways shall comply with this section.

R312.1.1 Landings for stairways. There shall be a floor or landing at the top and bottom of each stairway.

Exception: At the top of an interior flight of stairs, provided a door does not swing over the stairs.

R312.1.2 Landings at doors. There shall be a floor or landing on each side of each exterior door.

The floor or landing at a door shall be not more than 1.5 inches (38 mm) lower than the top of the threshold.

Exception: The landing at an exterior doorway shall not be more than 8 inches (197 mm) below the top of the threshold, provided that the door, other than an exterior storm or screen door, does not swing over the landing.

R312.2 Size. The width of each landing shall not be less than the stairway or door served. Every landing shall have a minimum dimension of 36 inches (914 mm) measured in the direction of travel.

SECTION R313
RAMPS

R313.1 Maximum slope. Ramps shall have a maximum slope of one unit vertical in eight units horizontal (12.5-percent slope).

R313.2 Handrails required. Handrails shall be provided on at least one side of all ramps exceeding a slope of one unit vertical in 12 units horizontal (8.33-percent slope).

R313.3 Landing required. A minimum 3-foot-by-3-foot (914 mm by 914 mm) landing shall be provided:

1. At the top and bottom of ramps.
2. Where doors open onto ramps.
3. Where ramps change direction.

SECTION R314
STAIRWAYS

R314.1 Width. Stairways shall not be less than 36 inches (914 mm) in clear width at all points above the permitted handrail height and below the required headroom height. Handrails shall not project more than 4.5 inches (114 mm) on either side of the stairway and the minimum clear width of the stairway at and below the handrail height, including treads and landings, shall not be less than 31.5 inches (787 mm) where a handrail is installed on one side and 27 inches (698 mm) where handrails are provided on both sides.

Exception: The width of spiral stairways shall be in accordance with Section R314.5.

R314.2 Treads and risers. The maximum riser height shall be 8 inches (203 mm) and the minimum tread depth shall be 9 inches (228 mm). The riser height shall be measured vertically between leading edges of the adjacent treads. The tread depth shall be measured horizontally between the vertical planes of the foremost projection of adjacent treads and at a right angle to the tread's leading edge. The walking surface of treads and landings of a stairway shall be sloped no steeper than one unit vertical in 48 units horizontal (2-percent slope). The greatest riser height within any flight of stairs shall not exceed the smallest by more than $3/8$ inch (9.5 mm). The greatest tread depth within any flight of stairs shall not exceed the smallest by more than $3/8$ inch (9.5 mm).

R314.2.1 Profile. Open risers are permitted, provided that the opening between treads does not permit the passage of a 4-inch-diameter (102 mm) sphere.

R314.3 Headroom. The minimum headroom in all parts of the stairway shall be not less than 6 feet, 8 inches (2032 mm) measured vertically from the sloped plane adjoining the tread nosing or from the floor surface of the landing or platform.

R314.4 Winders. Winders are permitted, provided that the width of the tread at a point not more than 12 inches (305 mm) from the side where the treads are narrower is not less than 9 inches (228 mm) and the minimum width of any tread is not less than 6 inches (152 mm). The continuous handrail required by Section R315.1 shall be located on the side where the tread is narrower.

R314.5 Spiral stairs. Spiral stairways are permitted, provided the minimum width shall be 26 inches (660 mm) with each tread having a $7^1/_2$-inch (190 mm) minimum tread width at 12 inches (305 mm) from the narrow edge. All treads shall be identical, and the rise shall be no more than $9^1/_2$ inches (241 mm). A minimum headroom of 6 feet, 6 inches (1982 mm) shall be provided.

R314.6 Circular stairways. Circular stairways shall have a tread depth at a point not more than 12 inches (305 mm) from the side where the treads are narrower of not less than 10 inches (254 mm) and the minimum depth of any tread shall not be less than 6 inches (152 mm). Tread depth at any walking line, measured a consistent distance from a side of the stairway, shall be uniform as specified in Section R314.2.

R314.7 Illumination. All stairs shall be provided with illumination in accordance with Section R303.4.

R314.8 Under stair protection. Enclosed accessible space under stairs shall have walls, under stair surface and any soffits protected on the enclosed side with $^1/_2$-inch (12.7 mm) gypsum board.

R314.9 Bulkhead enclosure stairways. Stairways serving bulkhead enclosures not part of the required building egress and providing access from the outside grade level to the basement shall be exempt from the requirements of Sections R312, R314 and R315 when the maximum height from the basement finished floor level to grade adjacent to the stairway is covered by a bulkhead enclosure with hinged doors or other approved means.

SECTION R315
HANDRAILS

R315.1 Handrails. Handrails having minimum and maximum heights of 34 inches and 38 inches (864 mm and 965 mm), respectively, measured vertically from the nosing of the treads, shall be provided on at least one side of stairways. All required handrails shall be continuous the full length of the stairs with four or more risers from a point directly above the top riser of a flight to a point directly above the lowest riser of the flight. Ends shall be returned or shall terminate in newel posts or safety terminals. Handrails adjacent to a wall shall have a space of not less than 1.5 inches (38 mm) between the wall and the handrail.

Exceptions:

1. Handrails shall be permitted to be interrupted by a newel post at a turn.

2. The use of a volute, turnout or starting easing shall be allowed over the lowest tread.

R315.2 Handrail grip size. The handgrip portion of handrails shall have a circular cross section of $1^1/_4$ inches (32 mm) minimum to $2^5/_8$ inches (67 mm) maximum. Other handrail shapes that provide an equivalent grasping surface are permissible. Edges shall have a minimum radius of $^1/_8$ inch (3.2 mm).

SECTION R316
GUARDS

R316.1 Guards required. Porches, balconies or raised floor surfaces located more than 30 inches (762 mm) above the floor or grade below shall have guards not less than 36 inches (914 mm) in height. Open sides of stairs with a total rise of more than 30 inches (762 mm) above the floor or grade below shall have guards not less than 34 inches (864 mm) in height measured vertically from the nosing of the treads.

R316.2 Guard opening limitations. Required guards on open sides of stairways, raised floor areas, balconies and porches shall have intermediate rails or ornamental closures that do not allow passage of a sphere 4 inches (102 mm) in diameter.

Exception: The triangular openings formed by the riser, tread and bottom rail of a guard at the open side of a stairway are permitted to be of such a size that a sphere 6 inches (152 mm) cannot pass through.

SECTION R317
SMOKE ALARMS

R317.1 Single- and multiple-station smoke alarms. Single- and multiple-station smoke alarms shall be installed in the following locations:

1. In each sleeping room.

2. Outside of each separate sleeping area in the immediate vicinity of the bedrooms.

3. On each additional story of the dwelling, including basements and cellars but not including crawl spaces and uninhabitable attics. In dwellings or dwelling units with split levels and without an intervening door between the adjacent levels, a smoke alarm installed on the upper level shall suffice for the adjacent lower level provided that the lower level is less than one full story below the upper level.

When more than one smoke alarm is required to be installed within an individual dwelling unit the alarm devices shall be interconnected in such a manner that the actuation of one alarm will activate all of the alarms in the individual unit. The alarm shall be clearly audible in all bedrooms over background noise levels with all intervening doors closed.

All smoke alarms shall be listed and installed in accordance with the provisions of this code and the household fire warning equipment provisions of NFPA 72.

R317.1.1 Alterations, repairs and additions. When interior alterations, repairs or additions requiring a permit occur, or when one or more sleeping rooms are added or created in existing dwellings, the individual dwelling unit shall be provided with smoke alarms located as required for new dwellings; the smoke alarms shall be interconnected and hard wired.

Exceptions:

1. Smoke alarms in existing areas shall not be required to be interconnected and hard wired where the alterations or repairs do not result in the removal of interior wall or ceiling finishes exposing the structure, unless there is an attic, crawl space, or basement

available which could provide access for hard wiring and interconnection without the removal of interior finishes.

2. Work on the exterior which does not require entry into the interior for inspection.

R317.2 Power source. In new construction, the required smoke alarms shall receive their primary power from the building wiring when such wiring is served from a commercial source, and when primary power is interrupted, shall receive power from a battery. Wiring shall be permanent and without a disconnecting switch other than those required for overcurrent protection. Smoke alarms shall be permitted to be battery operated when installed in buildings without commercial power or in buildings that undergo alterations, repairs or additions regulated by Section R317.1.1.

SECTION R318
FOAM PLASTIC

R318.1 General. The provisions of this section shall govern the requirements and uses of foam plastic insulation.

R318.1.1 Surface burning characteristics. Except where otherwise noted in Section R318.2, all foam plastic or foam plastic cores in manufactured assemblies used in building construction shall have a flame-spread rating of not more than 75 and shall have a smoke-developed rating of not more than 450 when tested in the maximum thickness intended for use in accordance with ASTM E 84.

R318.1.2 Thermal barrier. Foam plastic, except where otherwise noted, shall be separated from the interior of a building by minimum $^1/_2$-inch (12.7 mm) gypsum board or an approved finish material equivalent to a thermal barrier to limit the average temperature rise of the unexposed surface to no more than 250°F (121°C) after 15 minutes of fire exposure to the ASTM E 119 standard time temperature curve. The gypsum board shall be installed using a mechanical fastening system in accordance with Section R702.3.5. Reliance on adhesives to ensure that the gypsum board will remain in place when exposed to fire shall be prohibited.

R318.2 Specific requirements. The following requirements shall apply to all uses of foam plastic unless specifically approved in accordance with Section R318.3 or by other sections of the code.

R318.2.1 Masonry or concrete construction. Foam plastics may be used without the thermal barrier described in Section R318.1 when the foam plastic is protected by a minimum 1-inch (25.4 mm) thickness of masonry or concrete.

R318.2.2 Roofing. Foam plastic may be used in a roof-covering assembly without the thermal barrier when the foam is separated from the interior of the building by wood structural panel sheathing in accordance with Section R803, not less than $^{15}/_{32}$ inch (11.9 mm) in thickness bonded with exterior glue and identified as Exposure 1, with edge sup-

ported by blocking or tongue-and-groove joints. The smoke-developed rating shall not be limited.

R318.2.3 Attics and crawlspaces. Within attics and crawlspaces where entry is made only for service of utilities, foam plastics shall be protected against ignition by $1^1/_2$-inch-thick (38 mm) mineral fiber insulation, $^1/_4$-inch-thick (6.4 mm) wood structural panels, $^3/_8$-inch (9.5 mm) particleboard, $^1/_4$-inch (6.4 mm) hardboard, $^3/_8$-inch (9.5 mm) gypsum board, or corrosion-resistant steel having a base metal thickness of 0.016 inch (0.406 mm).

R318.2.4 Foam-filled doors. Foam-filled doors are exempt from the requirements of Section R318.1.

R318.2.5 Siding backer board. Foam plastic board of not more than $^1/_2$-inch (12.7 mm) thickness may be used as siding backer board when separated from interior spaces by not less than 2 inches (51 mm) of mineral fiber insulation or $^1/_2$-inch (12.7 mm) gypsum wallboard or installed over existing exterior wall finish in conjunction with re-siding, providing the plastic board does not have a potential heat of more than 2,000 Btu per square foot (22 720 kJ/m^2) when tested in accordance with NFPA 259.

R318.2.6 Interior trim. Foam plastic trim defined as picture molds, chair rails, baseboards, handrails, ceiling beams, door trim and window trim may be installed, provided:

1. The minimum density is 20 pounds per cubic foot (3.14 kg/m^3).
2. The maximum thickness of the trim is 0.5 inch (12.7 mm) and the maximum width is 4 inches (102 mm).
3. The trim constitutes no more than 10 percent of the area of any wall or ceiling.
4. The flame-spread rating does not exceed 75 when tested per ASTM E 84. The smoke-developed rating is not limited.

R318.2.7 Sill plate and headers. Foam plastic shall be permitted to be spray-applied to a sill plate and header (rim joist) without thermal barrier if all of the following conditions exist:

1. The maximum thickness of the foam plastic shall not exceed $3^1/_4$ inches (82.6 mm).
2. The density of the foam plastic shall be between 0.5 and 2.0 pcf (24 to 32 kg/m).
3. The foam plastic shall have a flame spread index of 25 or less and an accompanying smoke developed index of 450 or less when tested in accordance with ASTM E 84.

R318.3 Specific approval. Plastic foam not meeting the requirements of Sections R318.1 and R318.2 may be specifically approved on the basis of one of the following approved tests: ASTM E 84, FM 4880, UL 1040, ASTM E 152, or UL 1715, or fire tests related to actual end-use configurations. The specific approval may be based on the end use, quantity, location and similar considerations where such tests would not be applicable or practical.

R318.4 Interior finish. Foam plastics that are used as interior finish shall also meet the flame-spread requirements for interior finish.

R318.5 Termite damage. The use of foam plastics in areas of "very heavy" termite infestation probability shall be in accordance with Section R324.4.

SECTION R319
FLAME SPREAD AND SMOKE DENSITY

R319.1 Wall and ceiling. Wall and ceiling finishes shall have a flame-spread classification of not greater than 200.

> **Exception:** Flame-spread requirements for finishes shall not apply to trim defined as picture molds, chair rails, baseboards and handrails; to doors and windows or their frames; or to materials that are less than $1/28$ inch (0.907 mm) in thickness cemented to the surface of walls or ceilings if these materials have a flame-spread characteristic no greater than paper of this thickness cemented to a noncombustible backing.

R319.2 Smoke-developed index. Wall and ceiling finishes shall have a smoke-developed index of not greater than 450.

R319.3 Testing. Tests shall be made in accordance with ASTM E 84.

SECTION R320
INSULATION

R320.1 Insulation. Insulation materials, including facings, such as vapor barriers or breather papers installed within floor-ceiling assemblies, roof-ceiling assemblies, wall assemblies, crawl spaces and attics shall have a flame-spread index not to exceed 25 with an accompanying smoke-developed index not to exceed 450 when tested in accordance with ASTM E 84.

> **Exceptions:**
> 1. When such materials are installed in concealed spaces, the flame-spread and smoke-developed limitations do not apply to the facings, provided that the facing is installed in substantial contact with the unexposed surface of the ceiling, floor or wall finish.
> 2. Cellulose loose-fill insulation, which is not spray applied, complying with the requirements of Section R320.3, shall only be required to meet the smoke-developed index of not more than 450.

R320.2 Loose-fill insulation. Loose-fill insulation materials that cannot be mounted in the ASTM E 84 apparatus without a screen or artificial supports shall have a flame-spread rating not to exceed 25 with an accompanying smoke-developed factor not to exceed 450 when tested in accordance with CAN/ULC-S102.2.

> **Exception:** Cellulose loose-fill insulation shall not be required to comply with this test method provided that such insulation complies with the requirements of Section R320.3.

R320.3 Cellulose loose-fill insulation. Cellulose loose-fill insulation shall comply with CPSC 16 CFR, Parts 1209 and 1404. Each package of such insulating material shall be clearly labeled in accordance with CPSC 16 CFR, Parts 1209 and 1404.

R320.4 Exposed attic insulation. All exposed insulation materials installed on attic floors shall have a critical radiant flux not less than 0.12 watt per square centimeter.

R320.5 Testing. Tests for critical radiant flux shall be made in accordance with ASTM E 970.

SECTION R321
DWELLING UNIT SEPARATION

R321.1 Two-family dwellings. Dwelling units in two-family dwellings shall be separated from each other by wall and/or floor assemblies of not less than 1-hour fire-resistive rating when tested in accordance with ASTM E 119. Fire-resistance-rated floor-ceiling and wall assemblies shall extend to and be tight against the exterior wall, and wall assemblies shall extend to the underside of the roof sheathing.

> **Exception:** A fire resistance rating of $1/2$ hour shall be permitted in buildings equipped throughout with an automatic sprinkler system installed in accordance with NFPA 13.
>
> **R321.1.1 Supporting construction.** When floor assemblies are required to be fire-resistance-rated by Section R321.1, the supporting construction of such assemblies shall have an equal or greater fire-resistive rating.

R321.2 Townhouses. Each townhouse shall be considered a separate building and shall be separated by fire-resistance-rated wall assemblies meeting the requirements of Section R302 for exterior walls.

> **Exception:** A common 2-hour fire-resistance-rated wall is permitted for townhouses if such walls do not contain plumbing or mechanical equipment, ducts or vents in the cavity of the common wall. Electrical installations shall be installed in accordance with Minnesota Rules, Chapter 1315, Minnesota Electrical Code. Penetrations of electrical outlet boxes shall be in accordance with Section R321.3.

R321.2.1 Continuity. The common wall for townhouses shall be continuous from the foundation to the underside of the roof sheathing, deck or slab and shall extend the full length of the common wall.

R321.2.2 Parapets. Parapets constructed in accordance with Section R321.2.3 shall be provided for townhouses as an extension of common exterior or walls in accordance with the following:

1. Where roof surfaces adjacent to the wall or walls are at the same elevation, the parapet shall extend not less than 30 inches (762 mm) above the roof surfaces.
2. Where roof surfaces adjacent to the wall or walls are at different elevations and the higher roof is not more than 30 inches (762 mm) above the lower roof, the parapet shall extend not less than 30 inches (762 mm) above the lower roof surface.

> **Exception:** A parapet is not required in the two cases above when the roof is covered with a minimum class C roof covering, and the roof decking or sheathing is of

noncombustible materials or approved fire-retardant-treated wood for a distance of 4 feet (1219 mm) on each side of the wall or walls, or one layer of $^5/_8$-inch (15.9 mm) Type X gypsum board is installed directly beneath the roof decking or sheathing for a distance of 4 feet (1219 mm) on each side of the wall or walls.

3. A parapet is not required where roof surfaces adjacent to the wall or walls are at different elevations and the higher roof is more than 30 inches (762 mm) above the lower roof. The common wall construction from the lower roof to the underside of the higher roof deck shall not have less than a 1-hour fire-resistive rating. The wall shall be rated for exposure from both sides.

R321.2.3 Parapet construction. Parapets shall have the same fire-resistance rating as that required for the supporting wall or walls. On any side adjacent to a roof surface, the parapet shall have noncombustible faces for the uppermost 18 inches (457 mm), to include counterflashing and coping materials. Where the roof slopes toward a parapet at slopes greater than two units vertical in 12 units horizontal (16.7-percent slope), the parapet shall extend to the same height as any portion of the roof within a distance of 3 feet (914 mm), but in no case shall the height be less than 30 inches (762 mm).

R321.2.4 Structural independence. Each individual town-house shall be structurally independent.

Exceptions:

1. Foundations supporting exterior walls or common walls.

2. Structural roof and wall sheathing from each unit may fasten to the common wall framing.

3. Nonstructural wall coverings.

4. Flashing at termination of roof covering over common wall.

5. Townhouses separated by a common 2-hour fire-resistance-rated wall as provided in Section R321.2.

R321.3 Rated penetrations. Penetrations of wall or floor/ceiling assemblies required to be fire-resistance-rated in accordance with Section R321.1 or R321.2 shall be protected in accordance with this section.

R321.3.1 Through penetrations. Through penetrations of fire-resistance-rated wall or floor assemblies shall comply with Section R321.3.1.1 or R321.3.1.2.

Exception: Where the penetrating items are steel, ferrous or copper pipes or steel conduits, the annular space shall be permitted to be protected as follows:

1. In concrete or masonry wall or floor assemblies where the penetrating item is a maximum 6 inches (152 mm) nominal diameter and the opening is a maximum 144 square inches (92 900 mm^2), concrete, grout or mortar shall be permitted where installed to the full thickness of the wall or floor assembly or the thickness required to maintain the fire-resistance rating.

2. The material used to fill the annular space shall prevent the passage of flame and hot gases sufficient to ignite cotton waste where subjected to ASTM E 119 time temperature fire conditions under a minimum positive pressure differential of 0.01 inch of water (3 Pa) at the location of the penetration for the time period equivalent to the fire-resistance rating of the construction penetrated.

R321.3.1.1 Fire-resistance-rated assembly. Penetrations shall be installed as tested in the approved fire-resistance-rated assembly.

R321.3.1.2 Penetration firestop system. Penetrations shall be protected by an approved penetration firestop system installed as tested in accordance with ASTM E 814, with a minimum positive pressure differential of 0.01 inch of water (3 Pa) and shall have an F rating of not less than the required fire-resistance rating of the wall or floor/ceiling assembly penetrated.

R321.3.2 Membrane penetrations. Membrane penetrations shall comply with Section R321.3.1. Where walls are required to have a minimum 1-hour fire-resistance rating, recessed light fixtures shall be so installed such that the required fire resistance will not be reduced.

Exceptions:

1. Steel electrical boxes that do not exceed 16 square inches (0.0103 m^2) in area provided the total area of such openings does not exceed 100 square inches (0.0645 m^2) for any 100 square feet (9.29 m^2) of wall area. Outlet boxes on opposite sides of the wall shall be separated as follows:

    1.1. By a horizontal distance of not less than 24 inches, or

    1.2. By a horizontal distance of not less than the depth of the wall cavity when the wall cavity is filled with cellulose loose-fill or mineral fiber insulation, or

    1.3. By molded fire blocking in accordance with Section R602.8, or

    1.4. By other listed materials and methods.

2. Two-hour fire-resistance-rated nonmetallic electrical outlet boxes shall be installed in accordance with their listings.

3. The annular space created by the penetration of a fire sprinkler provided it is covered by a metal escutcheon plate.

SECTION R322
MOISTURE VAPOR RETARDERS

R322.1 Moisture control. In all framed walls, floors and roof/ceilings comprising elements of the building thermal envelope, a vapor retarder shall be installed on the warm-in-winter side of the insulation.

Exceptions: In construction where moisture or freezing will not damage the materials.

SECTION R323
PROTECTION AGAINST DECAY

R323.1 Location required. In areas subject to decay damage as established by Figure R301.2(7), the following locations shall require the use of an approved species and grade of lumber, pressure preservatively treated in accordance with AWPA C1, C2, C3, C4, C9, C15, C18, C22, C23, C24, C28, P1, P2 and P3, or decay-resistant heartwood of redwood, black locust, or cedars.

1. Wood joists or the bottom of a wood structural floor when closer than 18 inches (457 mm) or wood girders when closer than 12 inches (305 mm) to exposed ground in crawl spaces or unexcavated area located within the periphery of the building foundation.

2. All sills or plates that rest on concrete or masonry exterior walls and are less than 8 inches (203 mm) from exposed ground.

3. Sills and sleepers on a concrete or masonry slab that is in direct contact with the ground unless separated from such slab by an impervious moisture barrier.

4. The ends of wood girders entering exterior masonry or concrete walls having clearances of less than 0.5 inch (12.7 mm) on tops, sides and ends.

5. Wood siding, sheathing and wall framing on the exterior of a building having a clearance of less than 6 inches (152 mm) from the ground.

6. Wood structural members supporting moisture-permeable floors or roofs that are exposed to the weather, such as concrete or masonry slabs, unless separated from such floors or roofs by an impervious moisture barrier.

7. Wood furring strips or other wood framing members attached directly to the interior of exterior masonry walls or concrete walls below grade except where an approved vapor retarder is applied between the wall and the furring strips or framing members.

R323.1.1 Ground contact. All wood in contact with the ground and that supports permanent structures intended for human occupancy shall be approved pressure preservatively treated wood suitable for ground contact use, except untreated wood may be used where entirely below groundwater level or continuously submerged in fresh water.

R323.1.2 Geographical areas. In geographical areas where experience has demonstrated a specific need, approved naturally durable or pressure preservatively treated wood shall be used for those portions of wood members that form the structural supports of buildings, balconies, porches or similar permanent building appurtenances when such members are exposed to the weather without adequate protection from a roof, eave, overhang or other covering that would prevent moisture or water accumulation on the surface or at joints between members. Depending on local experience, such members may include:

1. Horizontal members such as girders, joists and decking.
2. Vertical members such as posts, poles and columns.
3. Both horizontal and vertical members.

R323.1.3 Posts, poles and columns. Posts, poles and columns supporting permanent structures that are embedded in concrete in direct contact with the ground or embedded in concrete exposed to the weather shall be approved pressure preservatively treated wood suitable for ground contact use.

R323.1.4 Wood columns. Wood columns shall be approved wood of natural decay resistance or approved pressure preservatively treated wood.

Exception: Posts or columns supported by piers or metal pedestals projecting 1 inch (25.4 mm) above the floor or finish grade and are separated therefrom by an approved impervious moisture barrier.

R323.2 Quality mark. Lumber and plywood required to be pressure preservatively treated in accordance with Section R323.1 shall bear the quality mark of an approved inspection agency that maintains continuing supervision, testing and inspection over the quality of the product and that has been approved by an accreditation body that complies with the requirements of the American Lumber Standard Committee treated wood program.

R323.2.1 Required information. The required quality mark on each piece of pressure preservatively treated lumber or plywood shall contain the following information:

1. Identification of the treating plant.
2. Type of preservative.
3. The minimum preservative retention.
4. End use for which the product was treated.
5. Standard to which the product was treated.
6. Identity of the approved inspection agency.
7. The designation "Dry," if applicable.

Exception: Quality marks on lumber less than 1 inch (25.4 mm) nominal thickness, or lumber less than nominal 1 inch by 5 inches (25.4 mm by 127 mm) or 2 inches by 4 inches (51 mm by 102 mm) or lumber 36 inches (914 mm) or less in length shall be applied by stamping the faces of exterior pieces or by end labeling not less than 25 percent of the pieces of a bundled unit.

R323.3 Fasteners. Fasteners for pressure preservative and fire-retardant-treated wood shall be of hot-dipped galvanized steel, stainless steel, silicon bronze or copper.

Exception: One-half-inch (12.7 mm) diameter or greater steel bolts.

SECTION R324
PROTECTION AGAINST TERMITES

R324.1 Subterranean termite control. In areas favorable to termite damage as established by Table R301.2(1), methods of protection shall be by chemical soil treatment, pressure preservatively treated wood in accordance with the AWPA standards listed in Section R323.1, naturally termite-resistant wood or physical barriers (such as metal or plastic termite shields), or any combination of these methods.

R324.2 Chemical soil treatment. The concentration, rate of application and treatment method of the termiticide shall be consistent with and never less than the termiticide label.

R324.3 Pressure preservatively treated and naturally resistant wood. Heartwood of redwood and eastern red cedar shall be considered termite resistant. Pressure preservatively treated wood and naturally termite-resistant wood shall not be used as a physical barrier unless a barrier can be inspected for any termite shelter tubes around the inside and outside edges and joints of a barrier.

R324.3.1 Field treatment. Field cut ends, notches and drilled holes of pressure preservatively treated wood shall be retreated in the field in accordance with AWPA M4.

R324.4 Foam plastic protection. In areas where the probability of termite infestation is "very heavy" as indicated in Figure R301.2(6), extruded and expanded polystyrene, polyisocyanurate and other foam plastics shall not be installed on the exterior face or under interior or exterior foundation walls or slab foundations located below grade. The clearance between foam plastics installed above grade and exposed earth shall be at least 6 inches (152 mm).

Exceptions:

1. Buildings where the structural members of walls, floors, ceilings and roofs are entirely of noncombustible materials or pressure preservatively treated wood.

2. When in addition to the requirements of R324.1, an approved method of protecting the foam plastic and structure from subterranean termite damage is provided.

3. On the interior side of basement walls.

SECTION R325
SITE ADDRESS

R325.1 Premises identification. Approved numbers or addresses shall be provided for all new buildings in such a position as to be plainly visible and legible from the street or road fronting the property.

SECTION R326
ACCESSIBILITY

R326.1 Scope. Accessible dwelling units shall comply with Chapter 11 of the *International Building Code* as applicable.

SECTION R327
FLOOD-RESISTANT CONSTRUCTION

R327.1 General. All buildings and structures erected in areas prone to flooding as identified in Table R301.2(1) and classified as either flood hazard areas (including A Zones) or coastal high hazard areas (including V-Zones) shall be constructed and elevated as required by the provisions contained in this section.

Exception: All buildings and structures erected in identified floodways as established in Table R301.2(1) shall be designed and constructed as stipulated in the *International Building Code.*

R327.1.1 Structural systems. All structural systems of all buildings and structures shall be designed, connected and anchored to resist flotation, collapse or permanent lateral movement due to structural loads and stresses from flooding equal to the design flood elevation.

R327.1.2 Flood-resistant construction. All buildings and structures erected in areas prone to flooding shall be constructed by methods and practices that minimize flood damage.

R327.1.3 Establishing the design flood elevation. The design flood elevation shall be used to define areas prone to flooding, and shall describe, at a minimum, the base flood elevation at the depth of peak elevation of flooding (including wave height) which has a 1 percent (100-year flood) or greater chance of being equaled or exceeded in any given year.

R327.1.4 Lowest floor. The lowest floor shall be the floor of the lowest enclosed area, including basement, but excluding any unfinished flood-resistant enclosure that is useable solely for vehicle parking, building access or limited storage provided that such enclosure is not built so as to render the building or structure in violation of this section.

R327.1.5 Protection of mechanical and electrical systems. New and replacement electrical equipment, heating, ventilating, air conditioning, plumbing connections, and other service equipment shall be located at or above the design flood elevation. Electrical wiring and outlets, switches, junction boxes and panels shall be elevated to or above the design flood elevation unless they conform to the provisions of the electrical part of this code for location of such items in wet locations. Duct systems shall not be installed below the design flood elevation.

R327.1.6 Protection of water supply and sanitary sewage systems. New and replacement water supply systems shall be designed to minimize infiltration of flood waters into the systems in accordance with the plumbing provisions of this code. New and replacement sanitary sewage systems shall be designed to minimize infiltration of floodwaters into systems and discharges from systems into floodwaters in accordance with the plumbing provisions of this code and Chapter 3 of the *International Private Sewage Disposal Code.*

R327.1.7 Flood-resistant materials. Building materials used below the design flood elevation shall comply with the following:

1. All wood, including floor sheathing, shall be pressure preservatively treated in accordance with AWPA C1, C2, C3, C4, C9, C15, C18, C22, C23, C24, C28, P1, P2 and P3 or decay-resistant heartwood or redwood, black locust, or cedars.

2. Materials and installation methods used for flooring and interior and exterior walls shall conform to the provisions of FEMA/FIA-TB-2.

R327.1.8 Manufactured housing. New or replacement manufactured housing shall be elevated in accordance with Section R327.2 and the anchor and tie-down requirements of Sections AE604 and AE605 of Appendix E shall apply. The foundation and anchorage of manufactured housing to be located in identified flood ways as established in Table R301.2(1) shall be designed and constructed in accordance with the applicable provisions in the *International Building Code*.

R327.1.9 As-built elevation certifications. A licensed land surveyor or registered design professional shall certify that the building or structure is in compliance with the elevation requirements of Section R327.2 or R327.3.

R327.2 Flood hazard areas (including A Zones). All areas that have been determined to be prone to flooding but not subject to high velocity wave action shall be designated as flood hazard areas. All buildings and structures erected in flood hazard areas shall be designed and constructed in accordance with Sections R327.2.1 through R327.2.3.

R327.2.1 Elevation requirements.

1. Buildings and structures shall have the lowest floors elevated to or above the design flood elevation.

2. In areas of shallow flooding (AO Zones), buildings and structures shall have the lowest floor (including basement) elevated at least as high above the highest adjacent grade as the depth number specified in feet (mm) on the FIRM, or at least 2 feet (51 mm) if a depth number is not specified.

3. Basement floors that are below grade on all sides shall be elevated to or above the design flood elevation.

Exception: Enclosed areas below the design flood elevation, including basements whose floors are not below grade on all sides, shall meet the requirements of Section R327.2.2.

R327.2.2 Enclosed area below design flood elevation. Enclosed areas, including crawl spaces, that are below the design flood elevation shall:

1. Be used solely for parking of vehicles, building access or storage.

2. Be provided with flood openings which shall meet the following criteria:

    2.1. There shall be a minimum of two openings on different sides of each enclosed area; if a building has more than one enclosed area below the design flood elevation, each area shall have openings on exterior walls.

    2.2. The total net area of all openings shall be at least 1 square inch for each square foot (275 mm for each square meter) of enclosed area.

    2.3. The bottom of each opening shall be 1 foot (305 mm) or less above the adjacent ground level.

    2.4. Openings shall be at least 3 inches (76 mm) in diameter.

    2.5. Any louvers, screens or other opening covers shall allow the automatic flow of floodwaters into and out of the enclosed area.

    2.6. Openings installed in doors and windows, that meet requirements 2.1 through 2.5, are acceptable; however, doors and windows without

installed openings do not meet the requirements of this section.

R327.2.3 Foundation design and construction. Foundation walls for all buildings and structures erected in flood hazard areas shall meet the requirements of Chapter 4.

Exception: Unless designed in accordance with Section 404:

1. The unsupported height of 6 inches (152 mm) plain masonry walls shall be no greater than 3 feet (914 mm).

2. The unsupported height of 8 inches (203 mm) plain masonry walls shall be no greater than 4 feet (1219 mm).

3. The unsupported height of 8 inches (203 mm) reinforced masonry walls shall be no greater than 8 feet (2438 mm).

For the purpose of this exception, unsupported height is the distance from the finished grade of the under-floor space and the top of the wall.

R327.3 Coastal high hazard areas (including V Zones). Areas that have been determined to be subject to wave heights in excess of 3 feet (914 mm) or subject to high velocity wave action or wave-induced erosion shall be designated as coastal high hazard areas. All buildings and structures erected in coastal high hazard areas shall be designed and constructed in accordance with Sections R327.3.1 through R327.3.5.

R327.3.1 Elevation requirements.

1. All buildings and structures erected within coastal high hazard areas shall be elevated so that the lowest portion of all structural members supporting the lowest floor, with the exception of mat or raft foundations, piling, pile caps, columns, grade beams and bracing, is located at or above the design flood elevation.

2. Basement floors that are below grade on all sides are prohibited.

3. The use of fill for structural support is prohibited.

4. The placement of fill beneath buildings and structures is prohibited.

Exception: Walls and partitions enclosing areas below the design flood elevation shall meet the requirements of Sections R327.3.3 and R327.3.4.

R327.3.2 Foundations. All buildings and structures erected in coastal high hazard areas shall be supported on pilings or columns and shall be adequately anchored to such pilings or columns. Piling shall have adequate soil penetrations to resist the combined wave and wind loads (lateral and uplift). Water loading values used shall be those associated with the design flood. Wind loading values shall be those required by this code. Pile embedment shall include consideration of decreased resistance capacity caused by scour of soil strata surrounding the piling. Pile systems design and installation shall be certified in accordance with Section R327.3.5. Mat, raft or other foundations that support columns shall not be permitted where soil investigations that are required in accordance with Section R401.4 indicate that soil material under the mat, raft or other foundation is subject to scour or erosion from wave-velocity flow conditions.

R327.3.3 Walls below design flood elevation. Walls and partitions are permitted below the elevated floor, provided that such walls and partitions are not part of the structural support of the building or structure and:

1. Are constructed with insect screening or open lattice.

2. Designed to break away or collapse without causing collapse, displacement or other structural damage to the elevated portion of the building or supporting foundation system. Such walls, framing and connections shall have a design safe loading resistance of not less than 10 pounds per square foot (0.48 kN/m^2) and no more than 20 pounds per square foot (0.96 kN/m^2); or

3. Where wind loading values of this code exceed 20 pounds per square foot (0.96 kN/m^2), a registered design professional shall certify the following:

   3.1. Collapse of walls and partitions below the design flood elevation shall result from a water load less than that which would occur during the design flood.

   3.2. The elevated portion of the building and supporting foundation system shall not be subject to collapse, displacement, or other structural damage due to the effects of wind and flood loads acting simultaneously on all building components (structural and nonstructural). Water loading values used shall be those associated with the design flood. Wind loading values used shall be those required by this code.

R327.3.4 Enclosed areas below design flood elevation. Enclosed areas below the design flood elevation shall be used solely for parking of vehicles, building access or storage.

R327.3.5 Design certificate. A registered design professional shall certify that the design and methods of construction to be used meet the applicable criteria of this section.

CHAPTER 4
FOUNDATIONS

SECTION R401
GENERAL

R401.1 Application. The provisions of this chapter shall control the design and construction of the foundation and foundation spaces for all buildings. Wood foundations shall be designed and installed in accordance with AF&PA Report No. 7.

Exceptions:

1. The provisions of this chapter shall be permitted to be used for wood foundations only in the following situations:

    1.1. In buildings that have no more than two floors and a roof.

    1.2. When no dimension in a basement room or crawl space area exceeds the smaller of either the building width or length.

2. In addition to the provisions of this chapter, the design and construction of foundations in areas prone to flooding as established by Table R301.2(1) shall meet the provisions of Section R327.

Wood foundations in Seismic Design Categories D_1 and D_2 shall be designed in accordance with accepted engineering practice.

R401.2 Requirements. Foundation construction shall be capable of accommodating all loads according to Section R301 and of transmitting the resulting loads to the supporting soil. Fill soils that support footings and foundations shall be designed, installed and tested in accordance with accepted engineering practice. Gravel fill used as footings for wood foundations shall comply with Section R403.

R401.3 Drainage. Surface drainage shall be diverted to a storm sewer conveyance or other approved point of collection so as to not create a hazard. Lots shall be graded so as to drain surface water away from foundation walls. The grade away from foundation walls shall fall a minimum of 6 inches (152 mm) within the first 10 feet (3048 mm).

Exception: Where lot lines, walls, slopes or other physical barriers prohibit 6 inches (152 mm) of fall within 10 feet (3048 mm), drains or swales shall be provided to ensure drainage away from the structure.

R401.4 Soil tests. In areas likely to have expansive, compressible, shifting or other unknown soil characteristics, the building official shall determine whether to require a soil test to determine the soil's characteristics at a particular location. This test shall be made by an approved agency using an approved method.

R401.4.1 Geotechnical evaluation. In lieu of a complete geotechnical evaluation, the load-bearing values in Table R401.4.1 shall be assumed.

TABLE R401.4.1
PRESUMPTIVE LOAD-BEARING VALUES OF FOUNDATION MATERIALS[a]

CLASS OF MATERIAL	LOAD-BEARING PRESSURE (pounds per square foot)
Crystalline bedrock	12,000
Sedimentary and foliated rock	4,000
Sandy gravel and/or gravel (GW and GP)	3,000
Sand, silty sand, clayey sand, silty gravel and clayey gravel (SW, SP, SM, SC, GM and GC)	2,000
Clay, sandy clay, silty clay, clayey silt, silt and sandy silt (CI, ML, MH and CH)	1,500[b]

For SI: 1 pound per square foot = 0.0479 kN/m^2.

a. When soil tests are required by Section R401.4, the allowable bearing capacities of the soil shall be part of the recommendations.

b. Where the building official determines that in-place soils with an allowable bearing capacity of less than 1,500 psf are likely to be present at the site, the allowable bearing capacity shall be determined by a soils investigation.

R401.5 Compressible or shifting soil. When top or subsoils are compressible or shifting, such soils shall be removed to a depth and width sufficient to assure stable moisture content in each active zone and shall not be used as fill or stabilized within each active zone by chemical, dewatering, or presaturation.

SECTION R402
MATERIALS

R402.1 Wood foundations. Wood foundation systems shall be designed and installed in accordance with the provisions of this code.

R402.1.1 Fasteners. Fasteners used below grade to attach plywood to the exterior side of exterior basement or crawl-space wall studs, or fasteners used in knee wall construction, shall be of Type 304 or 316 stainless steel. Fasteners used above grade to attach plywood and all lumber-to-lumber fasteners except those used in knee wall construction shall be of Type 304 or 316 stainless steel, silicon bronze, copper, hot-dipped galvanized (zinc coated) steel nails, or hot-tumbled galvanized (zinc coated) steel nails. Electrogalvanized steel nails and galvanized (zinc coated) steel staples shall not be permitted.

R402.1.2 Wood treatment. All lumber and plywood shall be treated in accordance with AWPA C22, and shall bear the label of an accredited agency showing 0.60 retention. Where lumber and/or plywood is cut or drilled after treatment, the treated surface shall be field treated with Copper Napthenate, the concentration of which shall contain a minimum of 2 percent copper metal, by repeated brushing, dipping or soaking until the wood absorbs no more preservative.

R402.2 Concrete. Concrete shall have a minimum specified compressive strength as shown in Table R402.2. Concrete subject to weathering as indicated in Table R301.2(1) shall be air entrained as specified in Table R402.2. The maximum weight of fly ash, other pozzolans, silica fume, or slag that is included in concrete mixtures for garage floor slabs and for exterior porches, carport slabs, and steps that will be exposed to deicing chemicals shall not exceed the percentages of the total weight of cementitious materials. Materials used to produce concrete and testing thereof shall comply with the applicable standards listed in ACI 318. In addition to the cements permitted by ACI 318, cement complying with ASTM C 1157 is permitted.

SECTION R403
FOOTINGS

R403.1 General. All exterior walls shall be supported on continuous solid or fully grouted masonry or concrete footings, wood foundations, or other approved structural systems which shall be of sufficient design to accommodate all loads according to Section R301 and to transmit the resulting loads to the soil within the limitations as determined from the character of the soil. Footings shall be supported on undisturbed natural soils or engineered fill.

R403.1.1 Minimum size. Minimum sizes for concrete and masonry footings shall be as set forth in Table R403.1 and Figure R403.1(1). The footing width, W, shall be based on the load-bearing value of the soil in accordance with Table R401.4.1. Spread footings shall be at least 6 inches (152 mm) in thickness. Footing projections, P, shall be at least 2 inches (51 mm) and shall not exceed the thickness of the footing. The size of footings supporting piers and columns shall be based on the tributary load and allowable soil pressure in accordance with Table R401.4.1. Footings for wood foundations shall be in accordance with the details set forth in Section R403.2, and Figures R403.1(2) and R403.1(3).

R403.1.2 Continuous footings in Seismic Design Categories D_1 and D_2. The braced wall panels at exterior walls of all buildings located in Seismic Design Categories D_1 and D_2 shall be supported by continuous footings. All required interior braced wall panels in buildings with plan dimensions greater than 50 feet (15 240 mm) shall also be supported by continuous footings.

R403.1.3 Seismic reinforcing. Concrete footings located in Seismic Design Categories D_1 and D_2, as established in Table R301.2(1), shall have minimum reinforcement. Bottom reinforcement shall be located a minimum of 3 inches (76 mm) clear from the bottom of the footing.

In Seismic Design Categories D_1 and D_2 where a construction joint is created between a concrete footing and stem wall, a minimum of one No. 4 bar shall be provided at not more than 4 feet (1219 mm) on center. The vertical bar shall extend to 3 inches (76 mm) clear of the bottom of the footing, have a standard hook and extend a minimum of 14 inches (357 mm) into the stem wall.

In Seismic Design Categories D_1 and D_2 where a grouted masonry stem wall is supported on a concrete footing and stem wall, a minimum of one No. 4 bar shall be provided at not more than four feet on center. The vertical bar shall extend to 3 inches (76 mm) clear of the bottom of the footing and have a standard hook.

In Seismic Design Categories D_1 and D_2 masonry stem walls without solid grout and vertical reinforcing shall not be permitted.

Exception: In detached one and two family dwellings which are three stories or less in height and constructed with stud bearing walls, plain concrete footings without longitudinal reinforcement supporting walls and isolated plain concrete footings supporting columns or pedestals are permitted.

R403.1.3.1 Foundations with stemwalls. Foundations with stemwalls shall be provided with a minimum of one No. 4 bar at the top of the wall and one No. 4 bar at the bottom of the footing.

R403.1.3.2 Slabs-on-ground with turned-down footings. Slabs-on-ground with turned down footings shall have a minimum of one No. 4 bar at the top and bottom of the footing.

Exception: For slabs–on–ground cast monolithically with a footing, one No. 5 bar or two No. 4 bars shall be located in the middle third of the footing depth.

R403.1.4 Minimum depth. All exterior footings and foundation systems shall extend below the frost line specified in Table R301.2(1). All exterior footings shall be placed at least 12 inches (305 mm) below the undisturbed ground.

Exception: Frost-protected footings constructed in accordance with Section R403.3 and footings and foundations erected on solid rock shall not be required to extend below the frost line.

In Seismic Design Categories D_1 and D_2, interior footings supporting bearing or bracing walls and cast monolithically with a slab on grade shall extend to a depth of not less than 12 inches (325 mm) below the top of slab.

R403.1.5 Slope. The top surface of footings shall be level. The bottom surface of footings shall not have a slope exceeding one unit vertical in 10 units horizontal (10-percent slope). Footings shall be stepped where it is necessary to change the elevation of the top surface of the footings or where the slope of the bottom surface of the footings will exceed one unit vertical in ten units horizontal (10-percent slope).

TABLE R402.2
MINIMUM SPECIFIED COMPRESSIVE STRENGTH OF CONCRETE

TYPE OR LOCATIONS OF CONCRETE CONSTRUCTION	MINIMUM SPECIFIED COMPRESSIVE STRENGTH[a] (f'_c)		
	Weathering potential[b]		
	Negligible	Moderate	Severe
Basement walls, foundations and other concrete not exposed to the weather	2,500	2,500	2,500[c]
Basement slabs and interior slabs on grade, except garage floor slabs	2,500	2,500	2,500[c]
Basement walls, foundation walls, exterior walls and other vertical concrete work exposed to the weather	2,500	3,000[d]	3,000[d]
Porches, carport slabs and steps exposed to the weather, and garage floor slabs	2,500	3,000[d,e]	3,500[d,e]

For SI: 1 pound per square inch = 6.895 kPa.

a. At 28 days psi.

b. See Table R301.2(1) for weathering potential.

c. Concrete in these locations that may be subject to freezing and thawing during construction shall be air-entrained concrete in accordance with Footnote d.

d. Concrete shall be air entrained. Total air content (percent by volume of concrete) shall not be less than 5 percent or more than 7 percent.

e. See Section R402.2 for minimum cement content.

TABLE R403.1
MINIMUM WIDTH OF CONCRETE OR MASONRY FOOTINGS (inches)

	LOAD-BEARING VALUE OF SOIL (psf)					
	1,500	2,000	2,500	3,000	3,500	4,000
Conventional light-frame construction						
1-story	16	12	10	8	7	6
2-story	19	15	12	10	8	7
3-story	22	17	14	11	10	9
4-inch brick veneer over light frame or 8-inch hollow concrete masonry						
1-story	19	15	12	10	8	7
2-story	25	19	15	13	11	10
3-story	31	23	19	16	13	12
8-inch solid or fully grouted masonry						
1-story	22	17	13	11	10	9
2-story	31	23	19	16	13	12
3-story	40	30	24	20	17	15

For SI: 1 inch = 25.4 mm, 1 pound per square foot = 0.0479 kN/m².

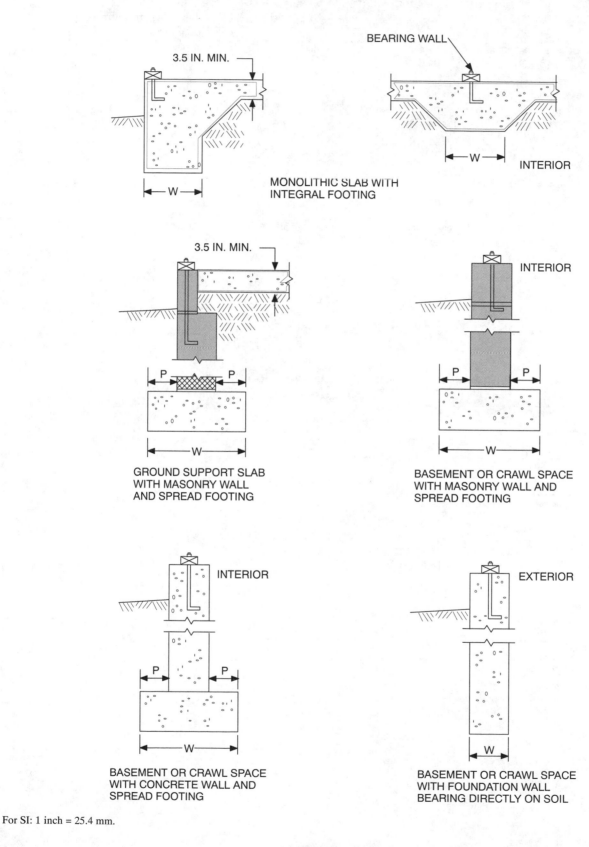

For SI: 1 inch = 25.4 mm.

FIGURE R403.1(1)
CONCRETE AND MASONRY FOUNDATION DETAILS

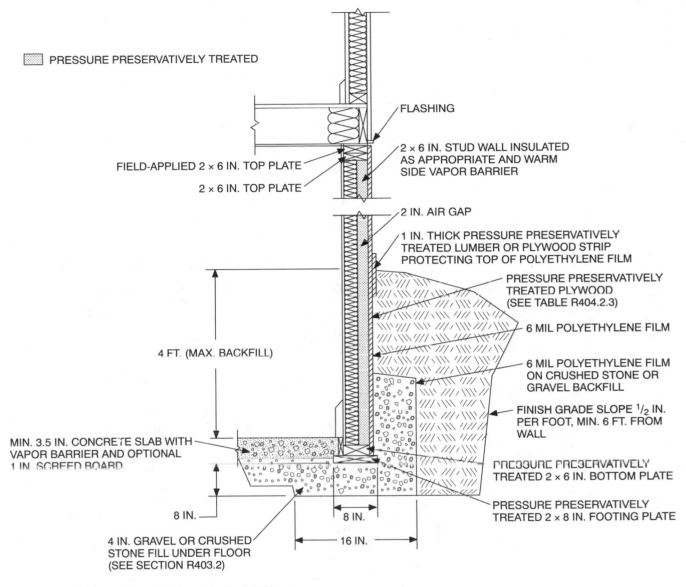

□ PRESSURE PRESERVATIVELY TREATED

FLASHING

FIELD-APPLIED 2 × 6 IN. TOP PLATE

2 × 6 IN. TOP PLATE

2 × 6 IN. STUD WALL INSULATED AS APPROPRIATE AND WARM SIDE VAPOR BARRIER

2 IN. AIR GAP

1 IN. THICK PRESSURE PRESERVATIVELY TREATED LUMBER OR PLYWOOD STRIP PROTECTING TOP OF POLYETHYLENE FILM

PRESSURE PRESERVATIVELY TREATED PLYWOOD (SEE TABLE R404.2.3)

6 MIL POLYETHYLENE FILM

6 MIL POLYETHYLENE FILM ON CRUSHED STONE OR GRAVEL BACKFILL

4 FT. (MAX. BACKFILL)

FINISH GRADE SLOPE 1/2 IN. PER FOOT, MIN. 6 FT. FROM WALL

MIN. 3.5 IN. CONCRETE SLAB WITH VAPOR BARRIER AND OPTIONAL 1 IN. SCREED BOARD

PRESSURE PRESERVATIVELY TREATED 2 × 6 IN. BOTTOM PLATE

PRESSURE PRESERVATIVELY TREATED 2 × 8 IN. FOOTING PLATE

8 IN.

8 IN.

16 IN.

4 IN. GRAVEL OR CRUSHED STONE FILL UNDER FLOOR (SEE SECTION R403.2)

For SI: 1 inch = 25.4 mm, 1 foot = 304.8 mm, 1 mil = 0.0254 mm.

**FIGURE R403.1(2)
PERMANENT WOOD FOUNDATION BASEMENT WALL SECTION**

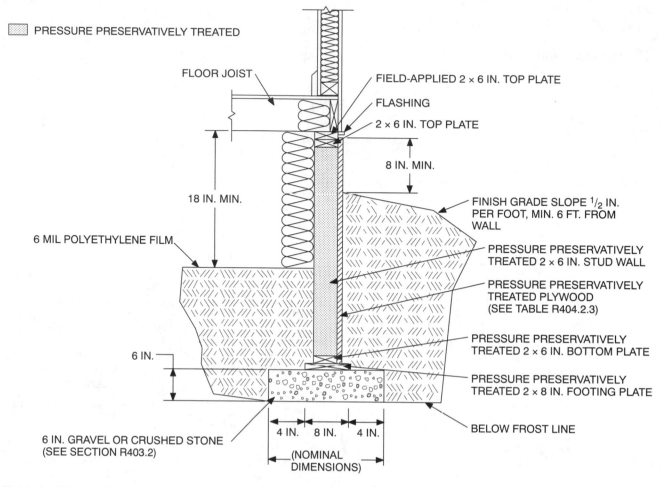

□ PRESSURE PRESERVATIVELY TREATED

FLOOR JOIST

FIELD-APPLIED 2 × 6 IN. TOP PLATE

FLASHING

2 × 6 IN. TOP PLATE

8 IN. MIN.

18 IN. MIN.

6 MIL POLYETHYLENE FILM

FINISH GRADE SLOPE $1/2$ IN. PER FOOT, MIN. 6 FT. FROM WALL

PRESSURE PRESERVATIVELY TREATED 2 × 6 IN. STUD WALL

PRESSURE PRESERVATIVELY TREATED PLYWOOD (SEE TABLE R404.2.3)

PRESSURE PRESERVATIVELY TREATED 2 × 6 IN. BOTTOM PLATE

PRESSURE PRESERVATIVELY TREATED 2 × 8 IN. FOOTING PLATE

BELOW FROST LINE

6 IN.

6 IN. GRAVEL OR CRUSHED STONE (SEE SECTION R403.2)

4 IN.   8 IN.   4 IN.

(NOMINAL DIMENSIONS)

For SI: 1 inch = 25.4 mm, 1 foot = 304.8 mm, 1 mil = 0.0254 mm.

**FIGURE R403.1(3)
PERMANENT WOOD FOUNDATION CRAWL SPACE SECTION**

R403.1.6 Foundation anchorage. When braced wall panels are supported directly on continuous foundations, the wall wood sill plate or cold-formed steel bottom track shall be anchored to the foundation in accordance with this section.

The wood sole plate at exterior walls on monolithic slabs and wood sill plate shall be anchored to the foundation with anchor bolts spaced a maximum of 6 feet (1829 mm) on center. Anchor bolts shall also be located within 12 inches (305 mm) from the ends of each plate section. Bolts shall be at least $1/2$ inch (12.7 mm) in diameter and shall extend a minimum of 7 inches (178 mm) into masonry or concrete. Interior bearing wall sole plates on monolithic slab foundations shall be positively anchored with approved fasteners. A nut and washer shall be tightened on each bolt to the plate. Sills and sole plates shall be protected against decay and termites where required by Sections R322 and R323. Cold-formed steel framing systems shall be fastened to the wood sill plates or anchored directly to the foundation as required in Section R505.3.1 or R603.1.1. When vertical reinforcing is required by other sections of this code, the foundation anchor bolts shall align with the reinforcing. All anchor bolts

installed in masonry shall be grouted in place with at least 1 inch (25.4 mm) of grout between the bolt and the masonry.

Exception: Foundation anchor straps, spaced as required to provide equivalent anchorage to $1/2$-inch-diameter (12.7 mm) anchor bolts. When vertical reinforcing is required by other sections of this code, the foundation anchor straps shall align with the reinforcing.

R403.1.6.1 Foundation anchorage in Seismic Design Categories D_1 and D_2. In addition to the requirements of Section R403.1.6, the following requirements shall apply to light-wood frame structures in Seismic Design Categories D_1 and D_2. Anchor bolts shall be located within 12 inches (305 mm) from the ends of each plate section at interior bearing walls, interior braced wall lines and at all exterior walls. Plate washers a minimum of 2 inches by 2 inches by $3/16$ inch (51 mm by 51 mm by 4.8 mm) thick shall be used on each bolt. The maximum anchor bolt spacing shall be 4 feet (1219 mm) for two-story structures.

R403.1.7 Footings on or adjacent to slopes. The placement of buildings and structures on or adjacent to slopes steeper than 1 unit vertical in 3 units horizontal (33.3-percent slope) shall conform to Sections R403.1.7.1 through R403.1.7.4.

R403.1.7.1 Building clearances from ascending slopes. In general, buildings below slopes shall be set a sufficient distance from the slope to provide protection from slope drainage, erosion and shallow failures. Except as provided in Section R403.1.7.4 and Figure R403.1.7.1, the following criteria will be assumed to provide this protection. Where the existing slope is steeper than one unit vertical in one unit horizontal (100-percent slope), the toe of the slope shall be assumed to be at the intersection of a horizontal plane drawn from the top of the foundation and a plane drawn tangent to the slope at an angle of 45 degrees (0.79 rad) to the horizontal. Where a retaining wall is constructed at the toe of the slope, the height of the slope shall be measured from the top of the wall to the top of the slope.

R403.1.7.2 Footing setback from descending slope surfaces. Footings on or adjacent to slope surfaces shall be founded in material with an embedment and setback from the slope surface sufficient to provide vertical and lateral support for the footing without detrimental settlement. Except as provided for in Section R403.1.7.4 and Figure R403.1.7.1, the following setback is deemed adequate to meet the criteria. Where the slope is steeper than one unit vertical in one unit horizontal (100-percent slope), the required setback shall be measured from an imaginary plane 45 degrees (0.79 rad) to the horizontal, projected upward from the toe of the slope.

R403.1.7.3 Foundation elevation. On graded sites, the top of any exterior foundation shall extend above the elevation of the street gutter at point of discharge or the inlet of an approved drainage device a minimum of 12 inches (305 mm) plus 2 percent. Alternate elevations are permitted subject to the approval of the building official, provided it can be demonstrated that required

drainage to the point of discharge and away from the structure is provided at all locations on the site.

R403.1.7.4 Alternate setback and clearances. Alternate setbacks and clearances are permitted, subject to the approval of the building official. The building official is permitted to require an investigation and recommendation of a qualified engineer to demonstrate that the intent of this section has been satisfied. Such an investigation shall include consideration of material, height of slope, slope gradient, load intensity and erosion characteristics of slope material.

R403.1.8 Foundations on expansive soils. Foundation and floor slabs for buildings located on expansive soils shall be designed in accordance with Section 1805.8 of the *International Building Code*.

Exception: Slab-on-ground and other foundation systems which have performed adequately in soil conditions similar to those encountered at the building site are permitted subject to the approval of the building official.

R403.1.8.1 Expansive soils classifications. Soils meeting all four of the following provisions shall be considered expansive, except that tests to show compliance with Items 1, 2 and 3 shall not be required if the test prescribed in Item 4 is conducted:

1. Plasticity Index (PI) of 15 or greater, determined in accordance with ASTM D 4318.

2. More than 10 percent of the soil particles pass a No. 200 sieve (75 μm), determined in accordance with ASTM D 422.

3. More than 10 percent of the soil particles are less than 5 micrometers in size, determined in accordance with ASTM D 422.

4. Expansion Index greater than 20, determined in accordance with UBC Standard 18-1.

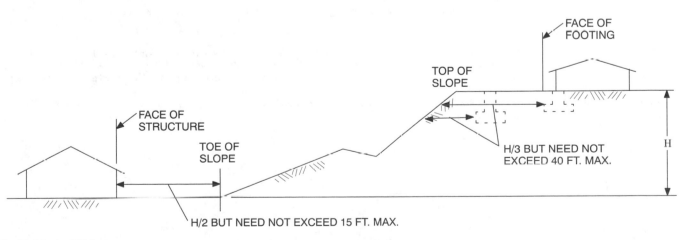

For SI: 1 foot = 304.8 mm.

**FIGURE R403.1.7.1
FOUNDATION CLEARANCE FROM SLOPES**

R403.2 Footings for wood foundations. Footings for wood foundations shall be in accordance with Figures R403.1(2) and R403.1(3). Gravel shall be washed and well graded. The maximum size stone shall not exceed $^3/_4$ inch (19.1 mm). Gravel shall be free from organic, clayey or silty soils. Sand shall be coarse, not smaller than $^1/_{16}$-inch (1.6 mm) grains and shall be free from organic, clayey or silty soils. Crushed stone shall have a maximum size of $^1/_2$ inch (12.7 mm).

R403.3 Frost protected shallow foundations. For buildings where the monthly mean temperature of the building is maintained at a minimum of 64°F (18°C), footings are not required to extend below the frost line when protected from frost by insulation in accordance with Figure R403.3(1) and Table R403.3.

Exceptions:

1. No foundation not so protected may be attached to frost-protected shallow foundations.

2. Unheated garages, porches, utility rooms and carports shall not be permitted to be attached to dwelling units with frost-protected shallow foundation.

Materials used below grade for the purpose of insulating footings against frost shall be labeled as complying with ASTM C 578.

R403.3.1 Protection of horizontal insulation below gound. Horizontal insulation placed less than 12 inches (305 mm) below the ground surface or that portion of horizontal insulation extending outward more than 24 inches (610 mm) from the foundation edge shall be protected against damage by use of a concrete slab or asphalt paving on the ground surface directly above the insulation or by cementitious board, plywood rated for below-ground use, or other approved materials placed below ground, directly above the top surface of the insulation.

R403.3.2 Drainage. Final grade shall be sloped in accordance with Section R401.3. In other than Group I Soils, as detailed in Table R405.1, gravel or crushed stone beneath horizontal insulation below ground shall drain to daylight or into an approved sewer system.

R403.3.3 Termite damage. The use of foam plastic in areas of "very heavy" termite infestation probability shall be in accordance with Section R324.4.

TABLE R403.3
MINIMUM INSULATION REQUIREMENTS FOR FROST-PROTECTED FOOTINGS IN HEATED BUILDINGS[a]

AIR FREEZING INDEX (°F-days)[b]	VERTICAL INSULATION R-VALUE[c,d]	HORIZONTAL INSULATION R-VALUE[c,e]		HORIZONTAL INSULATION DIMENSIONS PER FIGURE R403.3(1) (inches)		
		Along walls	At corners	A	B	C
1,500 or less	4.5	NR	NR	NR	NR	NR
2,000	5.6	NR	NR	NR	NR	NR
2,500	6.7	1.7	4.9	12	24	40
3,000	7.8	6.5	8.6	12	24	40
3,500	9.0	8.0	11.2	24	30	60
4,000	10.1	10.5	13.1	24	36	60

For SI: 1 inch = 25.4 mm, °C = [(°F)-32]/1.8.

a. Insulation requirements are for protection against frost damage in heated buildings. Greater values may be required to meet energy conservation standards. Interpolation between values is permissible.

b. See Figure R403.3(2) for Air Freezing Index values.

c. Insulation materials shall provide the stated minimum R-values under long-term exposure to moist, below-ground conditions in freezing climates. The following R-values shall be used to determine insulation thicknesses required for this application: Type II expanded polystyrene—2.4R per inch; Type IV extruded polystyrene—4.5R per inch; Type VI extruded polystyrene—4.5R per inch; Type IX expanded polystyrene—3.2R per inch; Type X extruded polystyrene—4.5R per inch. NR denotes "not required."

d. Vertical insulation shall be expanded polystyrene insulation or extruded polystyrene insulation.

e. Horizontal insulation shall be extruded polystyrene insulation.

INSULATION DETAIL

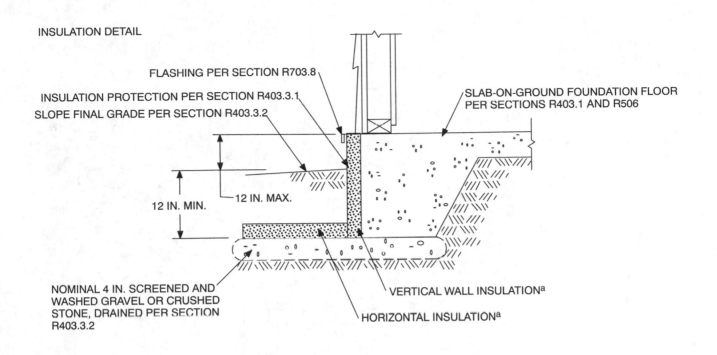

FLASHING PER SECTION R703.8

INSULATION PROTECTION PER SECTION R403.3.1

SLOPE FINAL GRADE PER SECTION R403.3.2

SLAB-ON-GROUND FOUNDATION FLOOR
PER SECTIONS R403.1 AND R506

12 IN. MIN.

12 IN. MAX.

NOMINAL 4 IN. SCREENED AND
WASHED GRAVEL OR CRUSHED
STONE, DRAINED PER SECTION
R403.3.2

VERTICAL WALL INSULATION[a]

HORIZONTAL INSULATION[a]

HORIZONTAL INSULATION PLAN

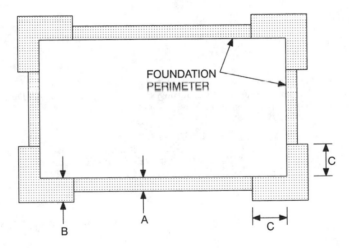

FOUNDATION
PERIMETER

A

B

C

For SI: 1 inch = 25.4 mm.

a. See Table R403.3 for required dimensions and *R*-values for vertical and horizontal insulation.

FIGURE R403.3(1)
INSULATION PLACEMENT FOR FROST-PROTECTED FOOTINGS IN HEATED BUILDINGS

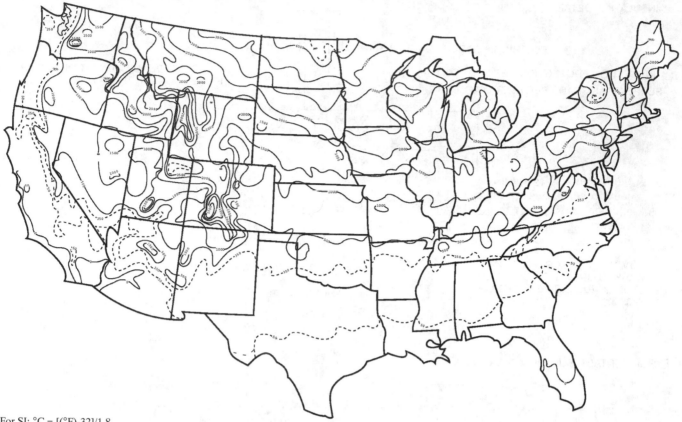

For SI: °C = [(°F)-32]/1.8.

Note: The air-freezing index is defined as cumulative degree days below 325°F. It is used as a measure of the combined magnitude and duration of air temperature below freezing. The index was computed over a 12-month period (July-June) for each of the 3,044 stations used in the above analysis. Data from the 1951-80 period were fitted to a Weibull probability distribution to produce an estimate of the 100-year return period.

FIGURE R403.3(2)
AIR-FREEZING INDEX
AN ESTIMATE OF THE 100-YEAR RETURN PERIOD

SECTION R404
FOUNDATION WALLS

R404.1 Concrete and masonry foundation walls. Concrete and masonry foundation walls shall be selected and constructed in accordance with the provisions of this section or in accordance with ACI 318, NCMA TR68-A or ACI 530/ASCE 5/TMS 402 or other approved structural standards. When ACI 318 or ACI 530/ASCE 5/TMS 402 or the provisions of this section are used to design concrete or masonry foundation walls, project drawings, typical details and specifications are not required to bear the seal of the architect or engineer responsible for design, unless otherwise required by the state law of the jurisdiction having authority.

R404.1.1 Masonry foundation walls. Concrete masonry and clay masonry foundation walls shall be constructed as set forth in Tables R404.1.1(2), R404.1.1(3) and R404.1.1(4) and shall also comply with the provisions of this section and the applicable provisions of Sections R606, R607 and R608. If foundation walls are parallel to floor framing, solid blocking or diagonal bracing must be installed at the anchor bolt locations in the first two joist or truss spaces.

R404.1.2 Concrete foundation walls. Concrete foundation walls shall be constructed as set forth in Tables R404.1.1(2), R404.1.1(3) and R404.1.1(4), and shall also comply with the provisions of this section and the applicable provisions of Section R402.2. If foundation walls are parallel to floor framing, solid blocking or diagonal bracing must be installed at the anchor bolt locations in the first two joist or truss spaces.

R404.1.3 Design required. A design in accordance with accepted engineering practice shall be provided for concrete or masonry foundation walls when any of the following conditions exist:

1. Walls are subject to hydrostatic pressure from groundwater.

2. Walls supporting more than 48 inches (1219 mm) of unbalanced backfill that do not have permanent lateral support at the top and bottom.

R404.1.4 Seismic Design Categories D₁ and D₂. In addition to the requirements of Table R404.1.1(1), plain concrete and plain masonry foundation walls located in Seismic Design Categories D_1 and D_2, as established in Table R301.2(1), shall comply with the following:

1. Minimum reinforcement shall consist of one No. 4 (No. 13) horizontal bar located in the upper 12 inches (305 mm) of the wall,

2. Wall height shall not exceed 8 feet (2438 mm),

3. Height of unbalanced backfill shall not exceed 4 feet (1219 mm), and

4. A minimum thickness of 7.5 inches (191 mm) is required for plain concrete foundation walls except that a minimum thickness of 6 inches (152 mm) shall be permitted for plain concrete foundation walls with a maximum height of 4 feet, 6 inches (1372 mm).

5. Plain masonry foundation walls shall be a minimum of 8 inches (203 mm) thick.

Vertical reinforcement for masonry stem walls shall be tied to the horizontal reinforcement in the footings. Masonry stem walls located in Seismic Design Categories D_1 and D_2 shall have a minimum vertical reinforcement of one No. 3 bar located a maximum of 4 feet (1220 mm) on center in grouted cells.

Foundation walls located in Seismic Design Categories D_1 and D_2, as established in Table R301.2(1), supporting more than 4 feet (1219 mm) of unbalanced backfill or exceeding 8 feet (2438 mm) in height shall be constructed in accordance with Table R404.1.1(2), R404.1.1(3) or R404.1.1(4) and shall have two No. 4 (No. 13) horizontal bars located in the upper 12 inches (305 mm) of the wall.

TABLE R404.1.1(1)
PLAIN CONCRETE AND PLAIN MASONRY FOUNDATION WALLS

Not adopted by the State of Minnesota.

TABLE R404.1.1(2)
REINFORCED CONCRETE AND MASONRY[a] FOUNDATION WALLS

MAXIMUM WALL HEIGHT (feet)	MAXIMUM UNBALANCED BACKFILL HEIGHT[e] (feet)	MINIMUM VERTICAL REINFORCEMENT SIZE AND SPACING[b, c] FOR 8-INCH NOMINAL WALL THICKNESS		
		Soil classes[d]		
		GW, GP, SW and SP soils	GM, GC, SM, SM-SC and ML soils	SC, MH, ML-CL and inorganic CL soils
6	5	#4 at 48″ o.c.	#4 at 48″ o.c.	#4 at 48″ o.c.
	6	#4 at 48″ o.c.	#4 at 40″ o.c.	#5 at 48″ o.c.
7	4	#4 at 48″ o.c.	#4 at 48″ o.c.	#4 at 48″ o.c.
	5	#4 at 48″ o.c.	#4 at 48″ o.c.	#4 at 40″ o.c.
	6	#4 at 48″ o.c.	#5 at 48″ o.c.	#5 at 40″ o.c.
	7	#4 at 40″ o.c.	#5 at 40″ o.c.	#6 at 48″ o.c.
8	5	#4 at 48″ o.c.	#4 at 48″ o.c.	#4 at 40″ o.c.
	6	#4 at 48″ o.c.	#5 at 48″ o.c.	#5 at 40″ o.c.
	7	#5 at 48″ o.c.	#6 at 48″ o.c.	#6 at 40″ o.c.
	8	#5 at 40″ o.c.	#6 at 40″ o.c.	#6 at 24″ o.c.
9	5	#4 at 48″ o.c.	#4 at 48″ o.c.	#5 at 48″ o.c.
	6	#4 at 48″ o.c.	#5 at 48″ o.c.	#6 at 48″ o.c.
	7	#5 at 48″ o.c.	#6 at 48″ o.c.	#6 at 32″ o.c.
	8	#5 at 40″ o.c.	#6 at 32″ o.c.	#6 at 24″ o.c.
	9	#6 at 40″ o.c.	#6 at 24″ o.c.	#6 at 16″ o.c.

For SI: 1 inch = 25.4 mm, 1 foot = 304.8 mm.

a. Mortar shall be Type M or S and masonry shall be laid in running bond.

b. Alternative reinforcing bar sizes and spacings having an equivalent cross-sectional area of reinforcement per lineal foot of wall shall be permitted provided the spacing of the reinforcement does not exceed 72 inches.

c. Vertical reinforcement shall be Grade 60 minimum. The distance from the face of the soil side of the wall to the center of vertical reinforcement shall be at least 5 inches.

d. Soil classes are in accordance with the Unified Soil Classification System. Refer to Table R405.1.

e. Unbalanced backfill height is the difference in height of the exterior and interior finish ground levels. Where an interior concrete slab is provided, the unbalanced backfill height shall be measured from the exterior finish ground level to the top of the interior concrete slab.

TABLE R404.1.1(3)
REINFORCED CONCRETE AND MASONRY[a] FOUNDATION WALLS

MAXIMUM WALL HEIGHT (feet)	MAXIMUM UNBALANCED BACKFILL HEIGHT[e] (feet)	VERTICAL REINFORCEMENT SIZE AND SPACING[b,c] FOR 12-INCH NOMINAL WALL THICKNESS		
		Soil classes[d]		
		GW, GP, SW and SP soils	GM, GC, SM, SM-SC and ML soils	SC, MH, ML-CL and inorganic CL soils
7	4	#4 at 72″ o.c.	#4 at 72″ o.c.	#4 at 72″ o.c.
	5	#4 at 72″ o.c.	#4 at 72″ o.c.	#4 at 72″ o.c.
	6	#4 at 72″ o.c.	#4 at 64″ o.c.	#4 at 48″ o.c.
	7	#4 at 72″ o.c.	#4 at 48″ o.c.	#5 at 56″ o.c.
8	5	#4 at 72″ o.c.	#4 at 72″ o.c.	#4 at 72″ o.c.
	6	#4 at 72″ o.c.	#4 at 56″ o.c.	#5 at 72″ o.c.
	7	#4 at 64″ o.c.	#5 at 64″ o.c.	#4 at 32″ o.c.
	8	#4 at 48″ o.c.	#4 at 32″ o.c.	#5 at 40″ o.c.
9	5	#4 at 72″ o.c.	#4 at 72″ o.c.	#4 at 72″ o.c.
	6	#4 at 72″ o.c.	#4 at 56″ o.c.	#5 at 64″ o.c.
	7	#4 at 56″ o.c.	#4 at 40″ o.c.	#6 at 64″ o.c.
	8	#4 at 64″ o.c.	#6 at 64″ o.c.	#6 at 48″ o.c.
	9	#5 at 56″ o.c.	#7 at 72″ o.c.	#6 at 40″ o.c.

For SI: 1 inch = 25.4 mm, 1 foot = 304.8 mm.

a. Mortar shall be Type M or S and masonry shall be laid in running bond.

b. Alternative reinforcing bar sizes and spacing having an equivalent cross-sectional area of reinforcement per lineal foot of wall shall be permitted provided the spacing of the reinforcement does not exceed 72 inches.

c. Vertical reinforcement shall be Grade 60 minimum. The distance from the face of the soil side of the wall to the center of vertical reinforcement shall be at least 8.75 inches.

d. Soil classes are in accordance with the Unified Soil Classification System. Refer to Table R405.1.

e. Unbalanced backfill height is the difference in height of the exterior and interior finish ground levels. Where an interior concrete slab is provided, the unbalanced backfill height shall be measured from the exterior finish ground level to the top of the interior concrete slab.

TABLE R404.1.1(4)
REINFORCED CONCRETE AND MASONRY[a] FOUNDATION WALLS

MAXIMUM WALL HEIGHT (feet)	MAXIMUM UNBALANCED BACKFILL HEIGHT[e] (feet)	MINIMUM VERTICAL REINFORCEMENT SIZE AND SPACING[b,c] FOR 10-INCH NOMINAL WALL THICKNESS		
		Soil Classes[d]		
		GW, GP, SW and SP soils	GM, GC, SM, SM-SC and ML soils	SC, MH, ML-CL and inorganic CL soils
7	4	#4 at 56″ o.c.	#4 at 56″ o.c.	#4 at 56″ o.c
	5	#4 at 56″ o.c	#4 at 56″ o.c.	#4 at 56″ o.c.
	6	#4 at 56″ o.c.	#4 at 48″ o.c	#4 at 40″ o.c.
	7	#4 at 56″ o.c.	#5 at 56″ o.c.	#5 at 40″ o.c.
8	5	#4 at 56″ o.c.	#4 at 56″ o.c.	#4 at 48″ o.c.
	6	#4 at 56″ o.c	#4 at 48″ o.c	#5 at 56″ o.c
	7	#4 at 48″ o.c.	#4 at 32″ o.c.	#6 at 56″ o.c.
	8	#5 at 56″ o.c.	#5 at 40″ o.c.	#7 at 56″ o.c.
9	5	#4 at 56″ o.c.	#4 at 56″ o.c.	#4 at 48″ o.c.
	6	#4 at 56″ o.c	#4 at 40″ o.c	#4 at 32″ o.c
	7	#4 at 56″ o.c.	#5 at 48″ o.c.	#6 at 48″ o.c.
	8	#4 at 32″ o.c.	#6 at 48″ o.c.	#4 at 16″ o.c.
	9	#5 at 40″ o.c.	#6 at 40″ o.c.	#7 at 40″ o.c.

For SI: 1 inch = 25.4 mm, 1 foot = 304.8 mm.

a. Mortar shall be Type M or S and masonry shall be laid in running bond.

b. Alternative reinforcing bar sizes and spacings having an equivalent cross-sectional area of reinforcement per lineal foot of wall shall be permitted provided the spacing of the reinforcement does not exceed 72 inches.

c. Vertical reinforcement shall be Grade 60 minimum. The distance from the face of the soil side of the wall to the center of vertical reinforcement shall be at least 6.75 inches.

d. Soil classes are in accordance with the Unified Soil Classification System. Refer to Table R405.1.

e. Unbalanced backfill height is the difference in height of the exterior and interior finish ground levels. Where an interior concrete slab is provided, the unbalanced backfill height shall be measured from the exterior finish ground level to the top of the interior concrete slab.

R404.1.5 Foundation wall thickness based on walls supported. The thickness of concrete and masonry foundation walls shall not be less than the thickness of the wall supported, except that foundation walls of at least 8-inch (203 mm) nominal thickness shall be permitted under brick-veneered frame walls and under 10-inch-wide (254 mm) cavity walls where the total height of the wall supported, including gables, is not more than 20 feet (6096 mm), provided the requirements of Sections R404.1.1 and R404.1.2 are met.

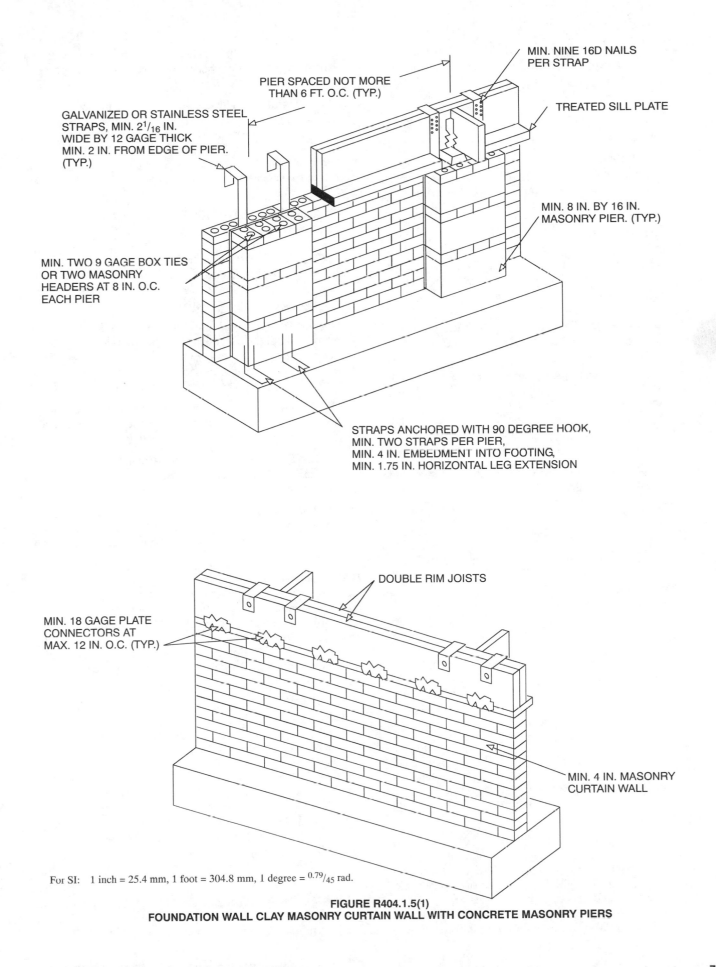

MIN. NINE 16D NAILS
PER STRAP

PIER SPACED NOT MORE
THAN 6 FT. O.C. (TYP.)

TREATED SILL PLATE

GALVANIZED OR STAINLESS STEEL
STRAPS, MIN. 2$^1/_{16}$ IN.
WIDE BY 12 GAGE THICK
MIN. 2 IN. FROM EDGE OF PIER.
(TYP.)

MIN. 8 IN. BY 16 IN.
MASONRY PIER. (TYP.)

MIN. TWO 9 GAGE BOX TIES
OR TWO MASONRY
HEADERS AT 8 IN. O.C.
EACH PIER

STRAPS ANCHORED WITH 90 DEGREE HOOK,
MIN. TWO STRAPS PER PIER,
MIN. 4 IN. EMBEDMENT INTO FOOTING,
MIN. 1.75 IN. HORIZONTAL LEG EXTENSION

DOUBLE RIM JOISTS

MIN. 18 GAGE PLATE
CONNECTORS AT
MAX. 12 IN. O.C. (TYP.)

MIN. 4 IN. MASONRY
CURTAIN WALL

For SI: 1 inch = 25.4 mm, 1 foot = 304.8 mm, 1 degree = $^{0.79}/_{45}$ rad.

FIGURE R404.1.5(1)
FOUNDATION WALL CLAY MASONRY CURTAIN WALL WITH CONCRETE MASONRY PIERS

R404.1.5.1 Pier and curtain wall foundations. Except in Seismic Design Categories D and E, pier and curtain wall foundations shall be permitted to be used to support light-frame construction not more than two stories in height, provided the following requirements are met:

1. All load-bearing walls shall be placed on continuous concrete footings placed integrally with the exterior wall footings.

2. The minimum actual thickness of a load-bearing masonry wall shall be not less than 4 inches (102 mm) nominal or $3^3/_8$ inches (92 mm) actual thickness, and shall be bonded integrally with piers spaced in accordance with R606.8.

3. Piers shall be constructed in accordance with Section R606.5 and Section R606.5.1, and shall be bonded into the load-bearing masonry wall in accordance with Section R608.1.1 or Section R608.1.1.2.

4. The maximum height of a 4-inch (102 mm) load-bearing masonry foundation wall supporting wood framed walls and floors shall not be more than 4 feet (1219 mm) in height.

5. Anchorage shall be in accordance with Section R403.1.6 or as specified by engineered design accepted by the building official.

6. The unbalanced fill for 4-inch (102 mm) foundation walls shall not exceed 24 inches (610 mm) for solid masonry or 12 inches (305 mm) for hollow masonry.

R404.1.6 Height above finished grade. Concrete and masonry foundation walls shall extend above the finished grade adjacent to the foundation at all points a minimum of 4 inches (102 mm) where masonry veneer is used and a minimum of 6 inches (152 mm) elsewhere.

R404.1.7 Backfill placement. Backfill shall not be placed against the wall until the wall has sufficient strength and has been anchored to the floor above, or has been sufficiently braced to prevent damage by the backfill.

Exception: Such bracing is not required for walls supporting less than 4 feet (1219 mm) of unbalanced backfill.

R404.1.8 Rubble stone masonry. Rubble stone masonry foundation walls shall have a minimum thickness of 16 inches (406 mm), shall not support an unbalanced backfill exceeding 8 feet (2438 mm) in height, shall not support a soil pressure greater than 30 psf (481 kg/m^2), and shall not be constructed in Seismic Design Categories D_1 or D_2 as established in Figure R301.2(2).

R404.2 Wood foundation walls. Wood foundation walls shall be constructed in accordance with the provisions of Sections R404.2.1 through R404.2.6 and with the details shown in Figures R403.1(2) and R403.1(3).

R404.2.1 Wood grade. All load-bearing lumber shall be identified by the grade mark of a lumber grading or inspection agency which has been approved by an accreditation body that complies with DOC PS 20. In lieu of a grade mark, a certificate of inspection issued by a lumber grading or inspection agency meeting the requirements of this section shall be accepted. Wood structural panels shall conform to DOC PS 1 or DOC PS 2 and shall be identified by a grade mark or certificate of inspection issued by an approved agency.

R404.2.2 Stud size. The studs used in foundation walls shall be 2-inch-by-6-inch (51 mm by 152 mm) members. When spaced 16 inches (406 mm) on center, a wood species with an F_b value of not less than 1,250 (8612 kPa) as listed in AF&PA/NDS shall be used. When spaced 12 inches (305 mm) on center, an F_b of not less than 875 (6029 kPa) shall be required.

R404.2.3 Height of backfill. For wood foundations built in accordance with the provisions of this code, the height of backfill against a foundation wall shall not exceed 4 feet (1219 mm). When the height of fill is more than 12 inches (305 mm) above the interior grade of a crawl space or floor of a basement, the thickness of the plywood sheathing shall meet the requirements of Table R404.2.3.

R404.2.4 Backfilling. Wood foundation walls shall not be backfilled until the basement floor and first floor have been constructed or the walls have been braced. For crawl space construction, backfill or bracing shall be installed on the interior of the walls prior to placing backfill on the exterior.

R404.2.5 Drainage and dampproofing. Wood foundation basements shall be drained and dampproofed in accordance with Sections R405 and R406, respectively.

R404.2.6 Fastening. Wood structural panel foundation wall sheathing shall be attached to framing in accordance with Table R602.3(1) and Section R402.1.1.

R404.3 Wood sill plates. Wood sill plates shall be a minimum of 2-inch by 4-inch (51 mm by 102 mm) nominal lumber. Sill plate anchorage shall be in accordance with Sections R403.1.6 and R602.11.

R404.4 Insulating concrete form foundation walls. Insulating concrete form (ICF) foundation walls shall be designed and constructed in accordance with the provisions of this section or in accordance with the provisions of ACI 318. When ACI 318 or the provisions of this section are used to design insulating concrete form foundation walls, project drawings, typical details and specifications are not required to bear the seal of the architect or engineer responsible for design unless otherwise required by the state law of the jurisdiction having authority.

R404.4.1 Applicability limits. The provisions of this section shall apply to the construction of insulating concrete form foundation walls for buildings not greater than 60 feet (18 288 mm) in plan dimensions, and floors not greater than 32 feet (9754 mm) or roofs not greater than 40 feet (12 192 mm) in clear span. Buildings shall not exceed two stories in height above-grade with each story not greater than 10 feet (3048 mm) high. Foundation walls constructed in accordance with the provisions of this section shall be limited to buildings subjected to a maximum ground snow load of 70 psf (3.35 kN/m^2) and located in Seismic Design Category A, B or C.

R404.4.2 Flat insulating concrete form wall systems. Flat ICF wall systems shall comply with Figure R611.3, shall have a minimum concrete thickness of 5.5 inches (140 mm), and shall have reinforcement in accordance with Table R404.4(1), R404.4(2) or R404.4(3).

R404.4.3 Waffle grid insulating concrete form wall systems. Waffle-grid wall systems shall have a minimum nominal concrete thickness of 6 inches (152 mm) for the horizontal and vertical concrete members (cores) and shall be reinforced in accordance with Table R404.4(4). The minimum core dimension shall comply with Table R611.4(2) and Figure R611.4.

R404.4.4 Screen grid insulating concrete form wall systems. Screen-grid ICF wall systems shall have a minimum nominal concrete thickness of 6 inches (152 mm) for the horizontal and vertical concrete members (cores). The minimum core dimensions shall comply with Table R611.4(2) and Figure R611.5. Walls shall have reinforcement in accordance with Table R404.4(5).

R404.4.5 Concrete material. Ready-mixed concrete for insulating concrete form walls shall be in accordance with Section R402.2. Maximum slump shall not be greater than 6 inches (152 mm) as determined in accordance with ASTM C 143. Maximum aggregate size shall not be larger than $3/4$ inch (19.1 mm).

Exception: Concrete mixes conforming to the ICF manufacturer's recommendations.

TABLE R404.2.3[d]
PLYWOOD GRADE AND THICKNESS FOR WOOD FOUNDATION CONSTRUCTION
(30 pcf equivalent-fluid weight soil pressure)

HEIGHT OF FILL (inches)	STUD SPACING (inches)	FACE GRAIN ACROSS STUDS			FACE GRAIN PARALLEL TO STUDS		
		Grade[a]	Minimum thickness (inches)	Span rating	Grade[a]	Minimum thickness (inches)[b,c]	Span rating
24	12	B	$15/32$	32/16	A	$15/32$	32/16
					B	$15/32$[c]	32/16
	16	B	$15/32$	32/16	A	$15/32$[c]	32/16
					B	$19/32$[c] (4, 5 ply)	40/20
36	12	B	$15/32$	32/16	A	$15/32$	32/16
					B	$15/32$[c] (4, 5 ply)	32/16
					B	$19/32$ (4, 5 ply)	40/20
	16	B	$15/32$[c]	32/16	A	$19/32$	40/20
					B	$23/32$	48/24
48	12	B	$15/32$	32/16	A	$15/32$[c]	32/16
					B	$19/32$[c] (4, 5 ply)	40/20
	16	B	$19/32$	40/20	A	$19/32$[c]	40/20
					A	$23/32$	48/24

For SI: 1 inch = 25.4 mm, 1 foot = 304.8 mm, 1 pound per cubic foot = 0.1572 kN/m^3.

a. Plywood shall be of the following minimum grades in accordance with DOC PS 1 or DOC PS 2:

    1. DOC PS 1 Plywood grades marked:

        1.1. Structural I C-D (Exposure 1)

        1.2. C-D (Exposure 1)

    2. DOC PS 2 Plywood grades marked:

        2.1. Structural I Sheathing (Exposure 1)

        2.2. Sheathing (Exposure 1)

    3. Where a major portion of the wall is exposed above ground and a better appearance is desired, the following plywood grades marked exterior are suitable:

        3.1. Structural I A-C, Structural I B-C or Structural I C-C (Plugged) in accordance with DOC PS 1

        3.2. A-C Group 1, B-C Group 1, C-C (Plugged) Group 1 or MDO Group 1 in accordance with DOC PS 1

        3.3. Single Floor in accordance with DOC PS 1 or DOC PS 2

b. Minimum thickness $15/32$ inch, except crawl space sheathing may be $3/8$ inch for face grain across studs 16 inches on center and maximum 2-foot depth of unequal fill.

c. For this fill height, thickness and grade combination, panels that are continuous over less than three spans (across less than three stud spacings) require blocking 16 inches above the bottom plate. Offset adjacent blocks and fasten through studs with two 16d corrosion-resistant nails at each end.

d. Fastening shall be in accordance with Section R323.3.

e. This table is not intended to prohibit the use of a manufacturer's or a national association's tables that are based on engineering analysis in accordance with AF&PA Report No. 7 and AF&PA NDS.

TABLE R404.4(1)
5.5-INCH THICK FLAT ICF FOUNDATION WALLS[a, b, c]

HEIGHT OF BASEMENT WALL (feet)	MAXIMUM UNBALANCED BACKFILL HEIGHT[d] (feet)	MINIMUM VERTICAL REINFORCEMENT SIZE AND SPACING[e]		
		Soil group I[e]	Soil group II[e]	Soil group III[e]
8	4	#4@48"	#4@48"	#4@48"
	5	#4@48"	#3@12"; #4@22"; #5@32"	#3@8"; #4@14"; #5@20"; #6@26"
	6	#3@12"; #4@22"; #5@30";	#3@8"; #4@14"; #5@20"; #6@24"	#3@6"; #4@10": #5@14"; #6@20"
	7	#3@8"; #4@14"; #5@22"; #6@26"	#3@5"; #4@10"; #5@14"; #6@18"	#3@4"; #4@6"; #5@10"; #6@14"
9	4	#4@48"	#4@48"	#4@48"
	5	#4@48"	#3@12"; #4@20"; #5@28"; #6@36"	#3@8"; #4@14"; #5@20"; #6@22"
	6	#3@10"; #4@20"; #5@28"; #6@34"	#3@6"; #4@12"; #5@18"; #6@20"	#4@8"; #5@14"; #6@16"
	7	#3@8"; #4@14"; #5@20"; #6@22"	#4@8"; #5@12"; #6@16"	#4@6"; #5@10"; #6@12"
	8	#3@6"; #4@10"; #5@14"; #6@16"	#4@6"; #5@10"; #6@12"	#4@4"; #5@6"; #6@8"
10	4	#4@48"	#4@48"	#4@48"
	5	#4@48"	#3@10"; #4@18"; #5@26"; #6@30"	#3@6"; #4@14"; #5@18"; #6@20"
	6	#3@10"; #4@18"; #5@24"; #6@30"	#3@6"; #4@12"; #5@16"; #6@18"	#3@4"; #4@8"; #5@12"; #6@14"
	7	#3@6"; #4@12"; #5@16"; #6@18"	#3@4"; #4@8"; #5@12"	#4@6"; #5@8"; #6@10"
	8	#4@8"; #5@12"; #6@14"	#4@6"; #5@8"; #6@12"	#4@4"; #5@6"; #6@8"
	9	#4@6"; #5@10"; #6@12"	#4@4"; #5@6"; #6@8"	#5@4"; #6@6"

For SI: 1 inch = 25.4 mm, 1 foot = 304.8 mm, 1 pound per square inch = 6.895 kPa.

a. This table is based on concrete with a minimum specified compressive strength of 2,500 psi, reinforcing steel with a minimum yield strength of 40,000 psi and an assumed equivalent rectangular cross-section. This table is not intended to prohibit the use of an ICF manufacturer's tables based on engineering analysis in accordance with ACI 318.

b. Deflection criteria: $L/240$.

c. Interpolation between rebar sizes and spacing is not permitted.

d. Unbalanced backfill height is the difference in height of the exterior and interior finished ground. Where an interior concrete slab is provided, the unbalanced backfill height shall be measured from the exterior finished ground level to the top of the interior concrete slab.

e. Soil classes are in accordance with the Unified Soil Classification System. Refer to Table R405.1.

TABLE R404.4(2)
7.5-INCH THICK FLAT ICF FOUNDATION WALLS[a, b, c, d]

HEIGHT OF BASEMENT WALL (feet)	MAXIMUM UNBALANCED BACKFILL HEIGHT[e] (feet)	MINIMUM VERTICAL REINFORCEMENT SIZE AND SPACING[f]		
		Soil group I[f]	Soil group II[f]	Soil group III[f]
8	6	N/R	N/R	N/R
	7	N/R	#3@8"; #4@14"; #5@20"; #6@28"	#3@6"; #4@10"; #5@16"; #6@20"
9	6	N/R	N/R	#3@8"; #4@14"; #5@20"; #6@28"
	7	N/R	#3@6"; #4@12"; #5@18"; #6@26"	#3@4"; #4@8"; #5@14"; #6@18"
	8	#3@8"; #4@14"; #5@22"; #6@28"	#3@4"; #4@8"; #5@14"; #6@18"	#3@4"; #4@6"; #5@10"; #6@14"
10	6	N/R	N/R	#3@6"; #4@12"; #5@18"; #6@26"
	7	N/R	#3@6"; #4@12"; #5@18"; #6@24"	#3@4"; #4@8"; #5@12"; #6@18"
	8	#3@6"; #4@12"; #5@20"; #6@26"	#3@4"; #4@8"; #5@12"; #6@16"	#3@4"; #4@6"; #5@8"; #6@12"
	9	#3@6"; #4@10"; #5@14"; #6@20"	#3@4"; #4@6"; #5@10"; #6@12"	#4@4"; #5@6"; #6@10"

For SI: 1 inch = 25.4 mm, 1 foot = 304.8 mm, 1 pound per square inch = 6.895 kPa.

a. This table is based on concrete with a minimum specified compressive strength of 2,500 psi, reinforcing steel with a minimum yield strength of 40,000 psi and an assumed equivalent rectangular cross-section. This table is not intended to prohibit the use of an ICF manufacturer's tables based on engineering analysis in accordance with ACI 318.

b. N/R denotes "design required."

c. Deflection criteria: $L/240$.

d. Interpolation between rebar sizes and spacing is not permitted.

e. Unbalanced backfill height is the difference in height of the exterior and interior finished ground. Where an interior concrete slab is provided, the unbalanced backfill height shall be measured from the exterior finished ground level to the top of the interior concrete slab.

f. Soil classes are in accordance with the Unified Soil Classification System. Refer to Table R405.1.

TABLE R404.4(3)
9.5-INCH THICK FLAT ICF FOUNDATION WALLS[a, b, c, d]

HEIGHT OF BASEMENT WALL (feet)	MAXIMUM UNBALANCED BACKFILL HEIGHT[e] (feet)	MINIMUM VERTICAL REINFORCEMENT SIZE AND SPACING[f]		
		Soil I[f]	Soil II[f]	Soil III[f]
8	7	N/R	N/R	N/R
9	6	N/R	N/R	N/R
	7	N/R	N/R	#3@6"; #4@12"; #5@18"; #6@26"
	8	N/R	#3@6"; #4@12"; #5@18"; #6@26"	#3@4"; #4@8"; #5@14"; #6@18"
10	5	N/R	N/R	N/R
	6	N/R	N/R	#3@10"; #4@18"; #5@26"; #6@36"
	7	N/R	N/R	#3@6"; #4@10"; #5@18"; #6@24"
	8	N/R	#3@6"; #4@12"; #5@16"; #6@24"	#3@4"; #4@8"; #5@12"; #6@16"
	9	N/R	#3@4"; #4@8"; #5@12"; #6@18"	#3@4"; #4@6"; #5@10"; #6@12"

For SI: 1 inch = 25.4 mm, 1 foot = 304.8 mm, 1 pound per square inch = 6.895 kPa.

a. This table is based on concrete with a minimum specified compressive strength of 2,500 psi, reinforcing steel with a minimum yield strength of 40,000 psi and an assumed equivalent rectangular cross-section. This table is not intended to prohibit the use of an ICF manufacturer's tables based on engineering analysis in accordance with ACI 318.

b. N/R denotes "design required."

c. Deflection criteria: $L/240$.

d. Interpolation between rebar sizes and spacing is not permitted.

e. Unbalanced backfill height is the difference in height of the exterior and interior finished ground. Where an interior concrete slab is provided, the unbalanced backfill height shall be measured from the exterior finished ground level to the top of the interior concrete slab.

f. Soil classes are in accordance with the Unified Soil Classification System. Refer to Table R405.1.

TABLE R404.4(4)
WAFFLE GRID ICF FOUNDATION WALLS[a,b,c,d]

MINIMUM NOMINAL WALL THICKNESS[e] (inches)	HEIGHT OF BASEMENT WALL (feet)	MAXIMUM UNBALANCED BACKFILL HEIGHT[e] (feet)	MINIMUM VERTICAL REINFORCEMENT SIZE AND SPACING		
			Soil group I[f]	Soil group II[f]	Soil group III[f]
6	8	4	#4@48"	#3@12"; #4@24"	#3@12"
		5	#3@12"; #5@24"	#4@12"	#7@12"
		6	#4@12"	Design required	Design required
		7	#7@12"	Design required	Design required
	9	4	#4@48"	#3@12"; #5@24"	#3@12"
		5	#3@12"	#4@12"	Design required
		6	#5@12"	Design required	Design required
		7	Design required	Design required	Design required
	10	4	#4@48"	#4@12"	#5@12"
		5	#3@12"	Design required	Design required
		6	Design required	Design required	Design required
		7	Design required	Design required	Design required
8	8	4	N/R	N/R	N/R
		5	N/R	#3@12"; #4@24"; #5@36"	#3@12"; #5@24"
		6	#3@12"; #4@24"; #5@36"	#4@12"; #5@24"	#4@12"
		7	#3@12"; #6@24"	#4@12"	#5@12"
	9	4	N/R	N/R	N/R
		5	N/R	#3@12"; #5@24"	#3@12"; #5@24"
		6	#3@12"; #4@24"	#4@12"	#4@12"
		7	#4@12"; #5@24"	#5@12"	#5@12"
		8	#4@12"	#5@12"	#8@12"
	10	4	N/R	#3@12"; #4@24"; #6@36"	#3@12"; #5@24"
		5	N/R	#3@12"; #4@24"; #6@36"	#4@12"; #5@24"
		6	#3@12"; #5@24"	#4@12"	#5@12"
		7	#4@12"	#5@12"	#6@12"
		8	#4@12"	#6@12"	Design required
		9	#5@12"	Design required	Design required

For SI: 1 inch = 25.4 mm, 1 foot = 304.8 mm, 1 pound per square foot = 0.0479 kN/m^2.

a. N/R denotes "design required."

b. Deflection criteria: $L/240$.

c. Interpolation between rebar sizes and spacing is not permitted.

d. Refer to Table R611.4(2) for wall dimensions.

e. Unbalanced backfill height is the difference in height of the exterior and interior finished ground. Where an interior concrete slab is provided, the unbalanced backfill height shall be measured from the exterior finished ground level to the top of the interior concrete slab.

f. Soil classes are in accordance with the Unified Soil Classification System. Refer to Table R405.1.

TABLE R404.4(5)
SCREEN-GRID ICF FOUNDATION WALLS[a,b,c]

MINIMUM NOMINAL WALL THICKNESS[d] (inches)	MAXIMUM WALL HEIGHT (feet)	MAXIMUM UNBALANCED BACKFILL HEIGHT[e] (feet)	MINIMUM VERTICAL REINFORCEMENT SIZE AND SPACING		
			Soil classes		
			Soil group I[f]	Soil group II[f]	Soil group III[f]
6	8	4	#4@48″	#3@12″; #4@24″; #5@36″	#3@12″; #5@24″
		5	#3@12″; #4@24″	#3@12″	#4@12″
		6	#4@12″	#5@12″	Design required
		7	#4@12″	Design required	Design required
	9	4	#4@48″	#3@12″; #4@24″	#3@12″; #6@24″
		5	#3@12″; #5@24″	#4@12″	#7@12″
		6	#4@12″	Design required	Design required
		7	Design required	Design required	Design required
		8	Design required	Design required	Design required
	10	4	#4@48″	#3@12″; #5@24″	#3@12″
		5	#3@12″	#4@12″	#7@12″
		6	#4@12″	Design required	Design required
		7	Design required	Design required	Design required
		8	Design required	Design required	Design required

For SI: 1 inch = 25.4 mm, 1 foot = 304.8 mm, 1 pound per square foot = 0.0479 kN/m².

a. N/R denotes "not required."

b. Deflection criteria: L/240.

c. Interpolation between rebar sizes and spacing is not permitted.

d. Refer to Table R611.4(2) for wall dimensions.

e. Unbalanced backfill height is the difference in height of the exterior and interior finished ground. Where an interior concrete slab is provided, the unbalanced backfill height shall be measured from the exterior finished ground level to the top of the interior concrete slab.

f. Soil classes are in accordance with the Unified Soil Classification System. Refer to Table R405.1.

R404.4.6 Reinforcing steel.

R404.4.6.1 General. Reinforcing steel shall meet the requirements of ASTM A 615, A 616, A 617 or A 706. The minimum yield strength of reinforcing steel shall be 40,000 psi (Grade 40) (276 MPa). Vertical and horizontal wall reinforcements shall be placed no closer to the outside face of the wall than one-half the wall thickness. Steel reinforcement for foundation walls shall have concrete cover in accordance with ACI 318.

Exception: Where insulated concrete forms are used and the form remains in place as cover for the concrete, the minimum concrete cover for the reinforcing steel is permitted to be reduced to ³/₄ inch (19.1 mm).

R404.4.6.2 Horizontal reinforcement. When vertical reinforcement is required, ICF foundation walls shall have horizontal reinforcement in accordance with this section. ICF foundation walls up to 8 feet (2438 mm) in height shall have a minimum of one continuous No. 4 horizontal reinforcing bar placed at 48 inches (1219 mm) on center with one bar located within 12 inches (305 mm) of the top of the wall story. ICF Foundation walls greater than 8 feet (2438 mm) in height shall have a minimum of one continuous No. 4 horizontal reinforcing bar placed at 36 inches (914 mm) on center with one bar located within 12 inches (305 mm) of the top of the wall story.

R404.4.6.3 Wall openings. Vertical wall reinforcement required by Section R404.4.2, R404.4.3 or R404.4.4 that is interrupted by wall openings shall have additional vertical reinforcement of the same size placed within 12 inches (305 mm) of each side of the opening.

R404.4.7 Foam plastic insulation. Foam plastic insulation in insulating concrete foam construction shall comply with this section.

R404.4.7.1 Material. Insulating concrete form material shall meet the surface burning characteristics of Section R318.1.1. A thermal barrier shall be provided on the building interior in accordance with Section R318.1.2.

R404.4.7.2 Termite hazards. In areas where hazard of termite damage is very heavy in accordance with Figure R301.2(6), foam plastic insulation shall be permitted below grade on foundation walls in accordance with one of the following conditions:

1. When in addition to the requirements in Section R324.1, an approved method of protecting the foam plastic and structure from subterranean termite damage is provided.

2. The structural members of walls, floors, ceilings and roofs are entirely of noncombustible materials or pressure preservatively treated wood.

3. On the interior side of basement walls.

R404.4.8 Foundation wall thickness based on walls supported. The thickness of ICF foundation walls shall not be less than the thickness of the wall supported above.

R404.4.9 Height above finished ground. ICF foundation walls shall extend above the finished ground adjacent to the foundation at all points a minimum of 4 inches (102 mm) where masonry veneer is used and a minimum of 6 inches (152 mm) elsewhere.

R404.4.10 Backfill placement. Backfill shall be placed in accordance with Section R404.1.7.

R404.4.11 Drainage and dampproofing/waterproofing. ICF foundation basements shall be drained and dampproofed/waterproofed in accordance with Sections R405 and R406.

SECTION R405
FOUNDATION DRAINAGE

R405.1 Concrete or masonry foundations. Drains shall be provided around all concrete or masonry foundations that retain earth and enclose habitable or usable spaces located below grade. Drainage tiles, gravel or crushed stone drains, perforated pipe or other approved systems or materials shall be installed at or below the area to be protected and shall discharge by gravity or mechanical means into an approved drainage system. Gravel or crushed stone drains shall extend at least 1 foot (305 mm) beyond the outside edge of the footing and 6 inches (153 mm) above the top of the footing and be covered with an approved filter membrane material. The top of open joints of drain tiles shall be protected with strips of building paper, and the drainage tiles or perforated pipe shall be placed on a minimum of 2 inches (51 mm) of washed gravel or crushed rock at least one sieve size larger than the tile joint opening or perforation and covered with not less than 6 inches (153 mm) of the same material.

Exception: A drainage system is not required when the foundation is installed on well-drained ground or sand-gravel mixture soils according to the Unified Soil Classification System, Group I Soils, as detailed in Table R405.1.

R405.2 Wood foundations. Wood foundations enclosing habitable or usable spaces located below grade shall be adequately drained in accordance with Sections R405.2.1 through R405.2.3.

TABLE R405.1
PROPERTIES OF SOILS CLASSIFIED ACCORDING TO THE UNIFIED SOIL CLASSIFICATION SYSTEM

SOIL GROUP	UNIFIED SOIL CLASSIFICATION SYSTEM SYMBOL	SOIL DESCRIPTION	DRAINAGE CHARACTERISTICS[a]	FROST HEAVE POTENTIAL	VOLUME CHANGE POTENTIAL EXPANSION[b]
Group I	GW	Well-graded gravels, gravel sand mixtures, little or no fines.	Good	Low	Low
	GP	Poorly graded gravels or gravel sand mixtures, little or no fines.	Good	Low	Low
	SW	Well-graded sands, gravelly sands, little or no fines.	Good	Low	Low
	SP	Poorly graded sands or gravelly sands, little or no fines.	Good	Low	Low
	GM	Silty gravels, gravel-sand-silt mixtures.	Good	Medium	Low
	SM	Silty sand, sand-silt mixtures.	Good	Medium	Low
Group II	GC	Clayey gravels, gravel-sand-clay mixtures.	Medium	Medium	Low
	SC	Clayey sands, sand-clay mixture.	Medium	Medium	Low
	ML	Inorganic silts and very fine sands, rock flour, silty or clayey fine sands or clayey silts with slight plasticity.	Medium	High	Low
	CL	Inorganic clays of low to medium plasticity, gravelly clays, sandy clays, silty clays, lean clays.	Medium	Medium	Medium to Low
Group III	CH	Inorganic clays of high plasticity, fat clays.	Poor	Medium	High
	MH	Inorganic silts, micaceous or diatomaceous fine sandy or silty soils, elastic silts.	Poor	High	High
Group IV	OL	Organic silts and organic silty clays of low plasticity.	Poor	Medium	Medium
	OH	Organic clays of medium to high plasticity, organic silts.	Unsatisfactory	Medium	High
	Pt	Peat and other highly organic soils.	Unsatisfactory	Medium	High

For SI: 1 inch = 25.4 mm.

a. The percolation rate for good drainage is over 4 inches per hour, medium drainage is 2 inches to 4 inches per hour, and poor is less than 2 inches per hour.

b. Soils with a low potential expansion typically have a plasticity index (PI) of 0 to 15, soils with a medium potential expansion have a PI of 10 to 35 and soils with a high potential expansion have a PI greater than 20.

R405.2.1 Base. A porous layer of gravel, crushed stone or coarse sand shall be placed to a minimum thickness of 4 inches (102 mm) under the basement floor. Provision shall be made for automatic draining of this layer and the gravel or crushed stone wall footings.

R405.2.2 Moisture barrier. A 6-mil-thick (0.15 mm) polyethylene moisture barrier shall be applied over the porous layer with the basement floor constructed over the polyethylene.

R405.2.3 Drainage system. In other than Group I soils, a sump shall be provided to drain the porous layer and footings. The sump shall be at least 24 inches (610 mm) in diameter or 20 inches square (0.0129 m^2), shall extend at least 24 inches (610 mm) below the bottom of the basement floor and shall be capable of positive gravity or mechanical drainage to remove any accumulated water. The drainage system shall discharge into an approved sewer system or to daylight.

SECTION R406
FOUNDATION WATERPROOFING
AND DAMPPROOFING

R406.1 Concrete and masonry foundation dampproofing. Except where required to be waterproofed by Section R406.2, foundation walls that retain earth and enclose habitable or usable spaces located below grade shall be dampproofed from the top of the footing to the finished grade. Masonry walls shall have not less than $^3/_8$ inch (9.5 mm) portland cement parging applied to the exterior of the wall. The parging shall be dampproofed with a bituminous coating, 3 pounds per square yard (1.63 kg/m^2) of acrylic modified cement, $^1/_8$-inch (3.2 mm) coat of surface-bonding mortar complying with ASTM C 887 or any material permitted for waterproofing in Section R406.2. Concrete walls shall be dampproofed by applying any one of the above listed dampproofing materials or any one of the waterproofing materials listed in Section R406.2 to the exterior of the wall.

R406.2 Concrete and masonry foundation waterproofing. In areas where a high water table or other severe soil-water conditions are known to exist, exterior foundation walls that retain earth and enclose habitable or usable spaces located below grade shall be waterproofed with a membrane extending from the top of the footing to the finished grade. The membrane shall consist of 2-ply hot-mopped felts, 55 pound (25 kg) roll roofing, 6-mil (0.15 mm) polyvinyl chloride, 6-mil (0.15 mm) polyethylene or 40-mil (1 mm) polymer-modified asphalt. The joints in the membrane shall be lapped and sealed with an adhesive compatible with the waterproofing membrane.

Exception: Organic solvent based products such as hydrocarbons, chlorinated hydrocarbons, ketons and esters shall not be used for ICF walls with expanded polystyrene form material. Plastic roofing cements, acrylic coatings, latex coatings, mortars and pargings are permitted to be used to seal ICF walls. Cold setting asphalt or hot asphalt shall conform to type C of ASTM D 449. Hot asphalt shall be applied at a temperature of less than 200 degrees.

R406.3 Dampproofing for wood foundations. Wood foundations enclosing habitable or usable spaces located below grade shall be dampproofed in accordance with Sections R406.3.1 through R406.3.4.

R406.3.1 Panel joint sealed. Plywood panel joints in the foundation walls shall be sealed full length with a caulking compound capable of producing a moisture-proof seal under the conditions of temperature and moisture content at which it will be applied and used.

R406.3.2 Below grade moisture barrier. A 6-mil-thick (0.15 mm) polyethylene film shall be applied over the below-grade portion of exterior foundation walls prior to backfilling. Joints in the polyethylene film shall be lapped 6 inches (152 mm) and sealed with adhesive. The top edge of the polyethylene film shall be bonded to the sheathing to form a seal. Film areas at grade level shall be protected from mechanical damage and exposure by a pressure preservatively treated lumber or plywood strip attached to the wall several inches above finish grade level and extending approximately 9 inches (229 mm) below grade. The joint between the strip and the wall shall be caulked full length prior to fastening the strip to the wall. Other coverings appropriate to the architectural treatment may also be used. The polyethylene film shall extend down to the bottom of the wood footing plate but shall not overlap or extend into the gravel or crushed stone footing.

R406.3.3 Porous fill. The space between the excavation and the foundation wall shall be backfilled with the same material used for footings, up to a height of 1 foot (305 mm) above the footing for well-drained sites, or one-half the total backfill height for poorly drained sites. The porous fill shall be covered with strips of 30-pound (13.6 kg) asphalt paper or 6-mil (0.15 mm) polyethylene to permit water seepage while avoiding infiltration of fine soils.

R406.3.4 Backfill. The remainder of the excavated area shall be backfilled with the same type of soil as was removed during the excavation.

SECTION R407
COLUMNS

R407.1 Wood column protection. Wood columns shall be protected against decay as set forth in Section R323.

R407.2 Steel column protection. All surfaces (inside and outside) of steel columns shall be given a shop coat of rust-inhibitive paint, except for corrosion-resistant steel and steel treated with coatings to provide corrosion resistance.

R407.3 Structural requirements. The columns shall be restrained to prevent lateral displacement at the bottom end. Wood columns shall not be less in nominal size than 4 inches by 4 inches (102 mm by 102 mm) and steel columns shall not be less than 3-inch-diameter (76 mm) standard pipe or approved equivalent.

Exception: In Seismic Design Categories A, B and C columns no more than 48 inches (1219 mm) in height on a pier or footing are exempt from the bottom end lateral displacement requirement within underfloor areas enclosed by a continuous foundation.

SECTION R408
UNDER-FLOOR SPACE

R408.1 Ventilation. The under-floor space between the bottom of the floor joists and the earth under any building (except space occupied by a basement or cellar) shall be provided with ventilation openings through foundation walls or exterior walls. The minimum net area of ventilation openings shall not be less than 1 square foot for each 150 square feet (0.67 m^2 for each 100 m^2) of under-floor space area. One such ventilating opening shall be within 3 feet (914 mm) of each corner of said building.

R408.2 Openings for under-floor ventilation. The minimum net area of ventilation openings shall not be less than 1 square foot (0.0929 m^2) for each 150 square feet (100 m^2) of underfloor space area. One such ventilating opening shall be within 3 feet (914 mm) of each corner of the building. Ventilation openings shall be covered for their height and width with any of the following materials provided that the least dimension of the covering shall not exceed $^1/_4$ inch (6.4 mm):

1. Perforated sheet metal plates not less than 0.070 inch (1.8 mm) thick.
2. Expanded sheet metal plates not less than 0.047 inch (1.2 mm) thick.
3. Cast iron grills or grating.
4. Extruded load-bearing brick vents.
5. Hardware cloth of 0.035 inch (0.89 mm) wire or heavier.
6. Corrosion-resistant wire mesh, with the least dimension being $^1/_8$ inch (3.2 mm).

Exceptions:

1. Where warranted by climatic conditions, ventilation openings to the outdoors are not required if ventilation openings to the interior are provided.
2. The total area of ventilation openings may be reduced to 1/1,500 of the under-floor area where the ground surface is treated with an approved vapor retarder material and the required openings are placed so as to provide cross-ventilation of the space. The installation of operable louvers shall not be prohibited.
3. Under-floor spaces used as supply plenums for distribution of heated and cooled air shall comply with the requirements of Minnesota Rules, Chapter 1346.
4. Ventilation openings are not required where continuously operated mechanical ventilation is provided at a rate of 1.0 cfm (10 m^2) for each 50 square feet (1.02 L/s) of underfloor space floor area and ground surface is covered with an approved vapor retarder material.
5. Ventilation openings are not required when the ground surface is covered with an approved vapor retarder material, the space is supplied with conditioned air and the perimeter walls are insulated in accordance with Minnesota Statute 16B.617, Minnesota Energy Code.

R408.3 Access. An access opening 18 inches by 24 inches (457 mm by 610 mm) shall be provided to the under-floor space. See Minnesota Rules, Chapter 1346 for access requirements where mechanical equipment is located under floors.

R408.4 Removal of debris. The under-floor grade shall be cleaned of all vegetation and organic material. All wood forms used for placing concrete shall be removed before a building is occupied or used for any purpose. All construction materials shall be removed before a building is occupied or used for any purpose.

R408.5 Finished grade. The finished grade of under-floor surface may be located at the bottom of the footings; however, where there is evidence that the groundwater table can rise to within 6 inches (152 mm) of the finished floor at the building perimeter or where there is evidence that the surface water does not readily drain from the building site, the grade in the underfloor space shall be as high as the outside finished grade, unless an approved drainage system is provided.

R408.6 Flood resistance. For buildings located in areas prone to flooding as established in Table R301.2(1), the walls enclosing the underfloor space shall be provided with flood openings in accordance with Section R327.2.2.

CHAPTER 5

FLOORS

SECTION R501
GENERAL

R501.1 Application. The provisions of this chapter shall control the design and construction of the floors for all buildings including the floors of attic spaces used to house mechanical and/or plumbing fixtures and equipment.

R501.2 Requirements. Floor construction shall be capable of accommodating all loads according to Section R301 and of transmitting the resulting loads to the supporting structural elements.

SECTION R502
WOOD FLOOR FRAMING

R502.1 General. Load-bearing dimension lumber for joists, beams and girders shall be identified by a grade mark of a lumber grading or inspection agency that has been approved by an accreditation body that complies with DOC PS 20. In lieu of a grade mark, a certificate of inspection issued by a lumber grading or inspection agency meeting the requirements of this section shall be accepted.

R502.1.1 Preservatively treated lumber. Preservatively treated dimension lumber shall also be identified as required by Section R323.1.

R502.1.2 Blocking and subflooring. Blocking shall be a minimum of utility grade lumber. Subflooring may be a minimum of utility grade lumber or No. 4 common grade boards.

R502.1.3 End-jointed lumber. Approved end-jointed lumber identified by a grade mark conforming to Section R501.2 may be used interchangeably with solid-sawn members of the same species and grade.

R502.1.4 Prefabricated wood I-joists. Structural capacities and design provisions for prefabricated wood I-joists shall be established and monitored in accordance with ASTM D 5055.

R502.2 Design and construction. Floors shall be designed and constructed in accordance with the provisions of this chapter, Figure R502.2 and Sections R323 and R324 or in accordance with AF&PA/NDS.

R502.2.1 Decks. Where supported by attachment to an exterior wall, decks shall be positively anchored to the primary structure and designed for both vertical and lateral loads as applicable. Such attachment shall not be accomplished by the use of toenails or nails subject to withdrawal. Where positive connection to the primary building structure cannot be verified during inspection, decks shall be self-supporting. For decks with cantilevered framing members, connections to exterior walls or other framing members, shall be designed and constructed to resist uplift resulting from the full live load specified in Table R301.4 acting on the cantilevered portion of the deck.

R502.3 Allowable joist spans. Spans for floor joists shall be in accordance with Tables R502.3.1(1) and R502.3.1(2). For other grades and species and for other loading conditions, refer to the AF&PA Span Tables for Joists and Rafters.

R502.3.1 Sleeping areas and attic joists. Table R502.3.1(1) shall be utilized to determine the maximum allowable span of floor joists that support sleeping areas and attics that are accessed by means of a fixed stairway provided that the design live load does not exceed 30 psf (1.44 kN/m^2) and the design dead load does not exceed 10 psf (0.48 kN/m^2). The allowable span of ceiling joists that support attics utilized for limited storage or no storage shall be determined in accordance with Section R802.4.

R502.3.2 Other floor joists. Table R502.3.1(2) shall be utilized to determine the maximum allowable span of floor joists that support all areas of the building, other than sleeping and attics, provided that the design live load does not exceed 40 psf (1.92 kN/m^2) and the design dead load does not exceed 10 psf (0.48 kN/m^2).

R502.4 Joists under bearing partitions. Joists under parallel bearing partitions shall be doubled or a beam of adequate size to support the load shall be provided. Double joists that are separated to permit the installation of piping or vents shall be full depth solid blocked with lumber not less than 2 inches (51 mm) in nominal thickness spaced not more than 4 feet (1219 mm) on center.

R502.5 Allowable girder spans. The allowable spans of girders fabricated of dimension lumber shall not exceed the values set forth in Tables R502.5(1) and R502.5(2).

R502.6 Bearing. The ends of each joist, beam or girder shall have not less than 1.5 inches (38 mm) of bearing on wood or metal and not less than 3 inches (76 mm) on masonry or concrete except where supported on a 1-inch-by-4-inch (25.4 mm by 102 mm) ribbon strip and nailed to the adjacent stud or by the use of approved joist hangers.

R502.6.1 Floor systems. Joists framing from opposite sides over a bearing support shall lap a minimum of 3 inches (76 mm) and shall be nailed together with a minimum three 10d face nails. A wood or metal splice with strength equal to or greater than that provided by the nailed lap is permitted.

R502.6.2 Joist framing. Joists framing into the side of a wood girder shall be supported by approved framing anchors or on ledger strips not less than nominal 2 inches by 2 inches (51 mm by 51 mm).

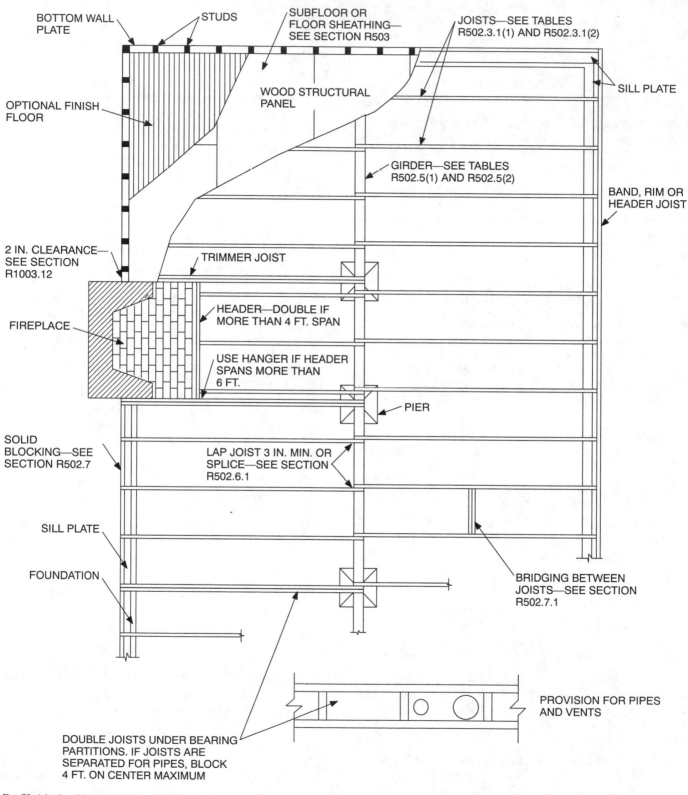

FIGURE R502.2
FLOOR CONSTRUCTION

For SI: 1 inch = 25.4 mm, 1 foot = 304.8 mm.

TABLE R502.3.1(1)
FLOOR JOIST SPANS FOR COMMON LUMBER SPECIES
(Residential sleeping areas, live load=30 psf, L/Δ=360)

JOIST SPACING (inches)	SPECIE AND GRADE		DEAD LOAD = 10 psf				DEAD LOAD = 20 psf			
			2x6	2x8	2x10	2x12	2x6	2x8	2x10	2x12
			Maximum floor joist spans							
			(ft.- in.)	(ft.- in.)	(ft.- in.)	(ft.- in.)	(ft.- in.)	(ft.- in.)	(ft.- in.)	(ft.- in.)
12	Douglas fir-larch	SS	12-6	16-6	21-0	25-7	12-6	16-6	21-0	25-7
	Douglas fir-larch	#1	12-0	15-10	20-3	24-8	12-0	15-7	19-0	22-0
	Douglas fir-larch	#2	11-10	15-7	19-10	23-0	11-6	14-7	17-9	20-7
	Douglas fir-larch	#3	9-8	12-4	15-0	17-5	8-8	11-0	13-5	15-7
	Hem-fir	SS	11-10	15-7	19-10	24-2	11-10	15-7	19-10	24-2
	Hem-fir	#1	11-7	15-3	19-5	23-7	11-7	15-2	18-6	21-6
	Hem-fir	#2	11-0	14-6	18-6	22-6	11-0	14-4	17-6	20-4
	Hem-fir	#3	9-8	12-4	15-0	17-5	8-8	11-0	13-5	15-7
	Southern pine	SS	12-3	16-2	20-8	25-1	12-3	16-2	20-8	25-1
	Southern pine	#1	12-0	15-10	20-3	24-8	12-0	15-10	20-3	24-8
	Southern pine	#2	11-10	15-7	19-10	18-8	11-10	15-7	18-7	21-9
	Southern pine	#3	10-5	13-3	15-8	18-8	9-4	11-11	14-0	16-8
	Spruce-pine-fir	SS	11-7	15-3	19-5	23-7	11-7	15-3	19-5	23-7
	Spruce-pine-fir	#1	11-3	14-11	19-0	23-0	11-3	14-7	17-9	20-7
	Spruce-pine-fir	#2	11-3	14-11	19-0	23-0	11-3	14-7	17-9	20-7
	Spruce-pine-fir	#3	9-8	12-4	15-0	17-5	8-8	11-0	13-5	15-7
16	Douglas fir-larch	SS	11-4	15-0	19-1	23-3	11-4	15-0	19-1	23-0
	Douglas fir-larch	#1	10-11	14-5	18-5	21-4	10-8	13-6	16-5	19-1
	Douglas fir-larch	#2	10-9	14-1	17-2	19-11	9-11	12-7	15-5	17-10
	Douglas fir-larch	#3	8-5	10-8	13-0	15-1	7-6	9-6	11-8	13-6
	Hem-fir	SS	10-9	14-2	18-0	21-11	10-9	14-2	18-0	21-11
	Hem-fir	#1	10-6	13-10	17-8	20-9	10-4	13-1	16-0	18-7
	Hem-fir	#2	10-0	13-2	16-10	19-8	9-10	12-5	15-2	17-7
	Hem-fir	#3	8-5	10-8	13-0	15-1	7-6	9-6	11-8	13-6
	Southern pine	SS	11-2	14-8	18-9	22-10	11-2	14-8	18-9	22-10
	Southern pine	#1	10-11	14-5	18-5	22-5	10-11	14-5	17-11	21-4
	Southern pine	#2	10-9	14-2	18-0	21-1	10-5	13-6	16-1	18-10
	Southern pine	#3	9-0	11-6	13-7	16-2	8-1	10-3	12-2	14-6
	Spruce-pine-fir	SS	10-6	13-10	17-8	21-6	10-6	13-10	17-8	21-4
	Spruce-pine-fir	#1	10-3	13-6	17-2	19-11	9-11	12-7	15-5	17-10
	Spruce-pine-fir	#2	10-3	13-6	17-2	19-11	9-11	12-7	15-5	17-10
	Spruce-pine-fir	#3	8-5	10-8	13-0	15-1	7-6	9-6	11-8	13-6
19.2	Douglas fir-larch	SS	10-8	14-1	18-0	21-10	10-8	14-1	18-0	21-0
	Douglas fir-larch	#1	10-4	13-7	16-9	19-6	9-8	12-4	15-0	17-5
	Douglas fir-larch	#2	10-1	12-10	15-8	18-3	9-1	11-6	14-1	16-3
	Douglas fir-larch	#3	7-8	9-9	11-10	13-9	6-10	8-8	10-7	12-4
	Hem-fir	SS	10-1	13-4	17-0	20-8	10-1	13-4	17-0	20-7
	Hem-fir	#1	9-10	13-0	16-4	19-0	9-6	12-0	14-8	17-0
	Hem-fir	#2	9-5	12-5	15-6	17-1	8-11	11-4	13-10	16-1
	Hem-fir	#3	7-8	9-9	11-10	13-9	6-10	8-8	10-7	12-4
	Southern pine	SS	10-6	13-10	17-8	21-6	10-6	13-10	17-8	21-6
	Southern pine	#1	10-4	13-7	17-4	21-1	10-4	13-7	16-4	19-6
	Southern pine	#2	10-1	13-4	16-5	19-3	9-6	12-4	14-8	17-2
	Southern pine	#3	8-3	10-6	12-5	14-9	7-4	9-5	11-1	13-2
	Spruce-pine-fir	SS	9-10	13-0	16-7	20-2	9-10	13-0	16-7	19-6
	Spruce-pine-fir	#1	9-8	12-9	15-8	18-3	9-1	11-6	14-1	16-3
	Spruce-pine-fir	#2	9-8	12-9	15-8	18-3	9-1	11-6	14-1	16-3
	Spruce-pine-fir	#3	7-8	9-9	11-10	13-9	6-10	8-8	10-7	12-4
24	Douglas fir-larch	SS	9-11	13-1	16-8	20-3	9-11	13-1	16-2	18-9
	Douglas fir-larch	#1	9-7	12-4	15-0	17-5	8-8	11-0	13-5	15-7
	Douglas fir-larch	#2	9-1	11-6	14-1	16-3	8-1	10-3	12-7	14-7
	Douglas fir-larch	#3	6-10	8-8	10-7	12-4	6-2	7-9	9-6	11-0
	Hem-fir	SS	9-4	12-4	15-9	19-2	9-4	12-4	15-9	18-5
	Hem-fir	#1	9-2	12-0	14-8	17-0	8-6	10-9	13-1	15-2
	Hem-fir	#2	8-9	11-4	13-10	16-1	8-0	10-2	12-5	14-4
	Hem-fir	#3	6-10	8-8	10-7	12-4	6-2	7-9	9-6	11-0
	Southern pine	SS	9-9	12-10	16-5	19-11	9-9	12-10	16-5	19-11
	Southern pine	#1	9-7	12-7	16-1	19-6	9-7	12-4	14-7	17-5
	Southern pine	#2	9-4	12-4	14-8	17-2	8-6	11-0	13-1	15-5
	Southern pine	#3	7-4	9-5	11-1	13-2	6-7	8-5	9-11	11-10
	Spruce-pine-fir	SS	9-2	12-1	15-5	18-9	9-2	12-1	15-0	17-5
	Spruce-pine-fir	#1	8-11	11-6	14-1	16-3	8-1	10-3	12-7	14-7
	Spruce-pine-fir	#2	8-11	11-6	14-1	16-3	8-1	10-3	12-7	14-7
	Spruce-pine-fir	#3	6-10	8-8	10-7	12-4	6-2	7-9	9-6	11-0

For SI: 1 inch = 25.4 mm, 1 foot = 304.8 mm, 1 pound per square foot = 0.0479 kN/m^2.

NOTE: Check sources for availability of lumber in lengths greater than 20 feet.

TABLE R502.3.1(2)
FLOOR JOIST SPANS FOR COMMON LUMBER SPECIES (Residential living areas, live load=40 psf, L/Δ=360)

JOIST SPACING (inches)	SPECIE AND GRADE		DEAD LOAD = 10 psf				DEAD LOAD = 20 psf			
			2x6	2x8	2x10	2x12	2x6	2x8	2x10	2x12
			Maximum floor joist spans							
			(ft.- in.)	(ft.- in.)	(ft.- in.)	(ft.- in.)	(ft.- in.)	(ft.- in.)	(ft.- in.)	(ft.- in.)
12	Douglas fir-larch	SS	11- 4	15- 0	19- 1	23- 3	11- 4	15- 0	19- 1	23- 3
	Douglas fir-larch	#1	10-11	14- 5	18- 5	22- 0	10-11	14- 2	17- 4	20- 1
	Douglas fir-larch	#2	10- 9	14- 2	17- 9	20- 7	10- 6	13- 3	16- 3	18-10
	Douglas fir-larch	#3	8- 8	11- 0	13- 5	15- 7	7-11	10- 0	12- 3	14- 3
	Hem-fir	SS	10- 9	14- 2	18- 0	21-11	10- 9	14- 2	18- 0	21-11
	Hem-fir	#1	10- 6	13-10	17- 8	21- 6	10- 6	13-10	16-11	19- 7
	Hem-fir	#2	10- 0	13- 2	16-10	20- 4	10- 0	13- 1	16- 0	18- 6
	Hem-fir	#3	8- 8	11- 0	13- 5	15- 7	7-11	10- 0	12- 3	14- 3
	Southern pine	SS	11- 2	14- 8	18- 9	22-10	11- 2	14- 8	18- 9	22-10
	Southern pine	#1	10-11	14- 5	18- 5	22- 5	10-11	14- 5	18- 5	22- 5
	Southern pine	#2	10- 9	14- 2	18- 0	21- 9	10- 9	14- 2	16-11	19-10
	Southern pine	#3	9- 4	11-11	14- 0	16- 8	8- 6	10-10	12-10	15- 3
	Spruce-pine-fir	SS	10- 6	13-10	17- 8	21- 6	10- 6	13-10	17- 8	21- 6
	Spruce-pine-fir	#1	10- 3	13- 6	17- 3	20- 7	10- 3	13- 3	16- 3	18-10
	Spruce-pine-fir	#2	10- 3	13- 6	17- 3	20- 7	10- 3	13- 3	16- 3	18-10
	Spruce-pine-fir	#3	8- 8	11- 0	13- 5	15- 7	7-11	10- 0	12- 3	14- 3
16	Douglas fir-larch	SS	10- 4	13- 7	17- 4	21- 1	10- 4	13- 7	17- 4	21- 0
	Douglas fir-larch	#1	9-11	13- 1	16- 5	19- 1	9- 8	12- 4	15- 0	17- 5
	Douglas fir-larch	#2	9- 9	12- 7	15- 5	17-10	9- 1	11- 6	14- 1	16- 3
	Douglas fir-larch	#3	7- 6	9- 6	11- 8	13- 6	6-10	8- 8	10- 7	12- 4
	Hem-fir	SS	9- 9	12-10	16- 5	19-11	9- 9	12-10	16- 5	19-11
	Hem-fir	#1	9- 6	12- 7	16- 0	18- 7	9- 6	12- 0	14- 8	17- 0
	Hem-fir	#2	9- 1	12- 0	15- 2	17- 7	8-11	11- 4	13-10	16- 1
	Hem-fir	#3	7- 6	9- 6	11- 8	13- 6	6-10	8- 8	10- 7	12- 4
	Southern pine	SS	10- 2	13- 4	17- 0	20- 9	10- 2	13- 4	17- 0	20- 9
	Southern pine	#1	9-11	13- 1	16- 9	20- 4	9-11	13- 1	16- 4	19- 6
	Southern pine	#2	9- 9	12-10	16- 1	18-10	9- 6	12- 4	14- 8	17- 2
	Southern pine	#3	8- 1	10- 3	12- 2	14- 6	7- 4	9- 5	11- 1	13- 2
	Spruce-pine-fir	SS	9- 6	12- 7	16- 0	19- 6	9- 6	12- 7	16- 0	19- 6
	Spruce-pine-fir	#1	9- 4	12- 3	15- 5	17-10	9- 1	11- 6	14- 1	16- 3
	Spruce-pine-fir	#2	9- 4	12- 3	15- 5	17-10	9- 1	11- 6	14- 1	16- 3
	Spruce-pine-fir	#3	7- 6	9- 6	11- 8	13- 6	6-10	8- 8	10- 7	12- 4
19.2	Douglas fir-larch	SS	9- 8	12-10	16- 4	19-10	9- 8	12-10	16- 4	19- 2
	Douglas fir-larch	#1	9- 4	12- 4	15- 0	17- 5	8-10	11- 3	13- 8	15-11
	Douglas fir-larch	#2	9- 1	11- 6	14- 1	16- 3	8- 3	10- 6	12-10	14-10
	Douglas fir-larch	#3	6-10	8- 8	10- 7	12- 4	6- 3	7-11	9- 8	11- 3
	Hem-fir	SS	9- 2	12- 1	15- 5	18- 9	9- 2	12- 1	15- 5	18- 9
	Hem-fir	#1	9- 0	11-10	14- 8	17- 0	8- 8	10-11	13- 4	15- 6
	Hem-fir	#2	8- 7	11- 3	13-10	16- 1	8- 2	10- 4	12- 8	14- 8
	Hem-fir	#3	6-10	8- 8	10- 7	12- 4	6- 3	7-11	9- 8	11- 3
	Southern pine	SS	9- 6	12- 7	16- 0	19- 6	9- 6	12- 7	16- 0	19- 6
	Southern pine	#1	9- 4	12- 4	15- 9	19- 2	9- 4	12- 4	14-11	17- 9
	Southern pine	#2	9- 2	12- 1	14- 8	17- 2	8- 8	11- 3	13- 5	15- 8
	Southern pine	#3	7- 4	9- 5	11- 1	13- 2	6- 9	8- 7	10- 1	12- 1
	Spruce-pine-fir	SS	9- 0	11-10	15- 1	18- 4	9- 0	11-10	15- 1	17- 9
	Spruce-pine-fir	#1	8- 9	11- 6	14- 1	16- 3	8- 3	10- 6	12-10	14-10
	Spruce-pine-fir	#2	8- 9	11- 6	14- 1	16- 3	8- 3	10- 6	12-10	14-10
	Spruce-pine-fir	#3	6-10	8- 8	10- 7	12- 4	6- 3	7-11	9- 8	11- 3
24	Douglas fir-larch	SS	9- 0	11-11	15- 2	18- 5	9- 0	11-11	14- 9	17- 1
	Douglas fir-larch	#1	8- 8	11- 0	13- 5	15- 7	7-11	10- 0	12- 3	14- 3
	Douglas fir-larch	#2	8- 1	10- 3	12- 7	14- 7	7- 5	9- 5	11- 6	13- 4
	Douglas fir-larch	#3	6- 2	7- 9	9- 6	11- 0	5- 7	7- 1	8- 8	10- 1
	Hem-fir	SS	8- 6	11- 3	14- 4	17- 5	8- 6	11- 3	14- 4	16-10a
	Hem-fir	#1	8- 4	10- 9	13- 1	15- 2	7- 9	9- 9	11-11	13-10
	Hem-fir	#2	7-11	10- 2	12- 5	14- 4	7- 4	9- 3	11- 4	13- 1
	Hem-fir	#3	6- 2	7- 9	9- 6	11- 0	5- 7	7- 1	8- 8	10- 1
	Southern pine	SS	8-10	11- 8	14-11	18- 1	8-10	11- 8	14-11	18- 1
	Southern pine	#1	8- 8	11- 5	14- 7	17- 5	8- 8	11- 3	13- 4	15-11
	Southern pine	#2	8- 6	11- 0	13- 1	15- 5	7- 9	10- 0	12- 0	14- 0
	Southern pine	#3	6- 7	8- 5	9-11	11-10	6- 0	7- 8	9- 1	10- 9
	Spruce-pine-fir	SS	8- 4	11- 0	14- 0	17- 0	8- 4	11- 0	13- 8	15-11
	Spruce-pine-fir	#1	8- 1	10- 3	12- 7	14- 7	7- 5	9- 5	11- 6	13- 4
	Spruce-pine-fir	#2	8- 1	10- 3	12- 7	14- 7	7- 5	9- 5	11- 6	13- 4
	Spruce-pine-fir	#3	6- 2	7- 9	9- 6	11- 0	5- 7	7- 1	8- 8	10- 1

Check sources for availability of lumber in lengths greater than 20 feet.

For SI:　1 inch = 25.4 mm, 1 foot = 308.4 mm, 1 pound per square foot = 0.0479 kN/m.

a. End bearing length shall be increased to 2 inches.

TABLE R502.5(1)
GIRDER SPANS[a] AND HEADER SPANS[a] FOR EXTERIOR BEARING WALLS
(Maximum header spans for douglas fir-larch, hem-fir, southern pine and spruce-pine-fir[b] and required number of jack studs)

HEADERS SUPPORTING	SIZE	GROUND SNOW LOAD (psf)[e]											
		30						50					
		Building width[c] (feet)											
		20		28		36		20		28		36	
		Span	NJ[d]	Span	NJ[d]	Span	NJ[d]	Span	NJ[d]	Span	NJ[d]	Span	NJ[d]
Roof and ceiling	2-2×4	3-6	1	3-2	1	2-10	1	3-2	1	2-9	1	2-6	1
	2-2×6	5-5	1	4-8	1	4-2	1	4-8	1	4-1	1	3-8	2
	2-2×8	6-10	1	5-11	2	5-4	2	5-11	2	5-2	2	4-7	2
	2-2×10	8-5	2	7-3	2	6-6	2	7-3	2	6-3	2	5-7	2
	2-2×12	9-9	2	8-5	2	7-6	2	8-5	2	7-3	2	6-6	2
	3-2×8	8-4	1	7-5	1	6-8	1	7-5	1	6-5	2	5-9	2
	3-2×10	10-6	1	9-1	2	8-2	2	9-1	2	7-10	2	7-0	2
	3-2×12	12-2	2	10-7	2	9-5	2	10-7	2	9-2	2	8-2	2
	4-2×8	7-0	1	6-1	2	5-5	2	6-1	2	5-3	2	4-8	2
	4-2×10	11-8	1	10-6	1	9-5	2	10-6	1	9-1	2	8-2	2
	4-2×12	14-1	1	12-2	2	10-11	2	12-2	2	10-7	2	9-5	2
Roof, ceiling and one center-bearing floor	2-2×4	3-1	1	2-9	1	2-5	1	2-9	1	2-5	1	2-2	1
	2-2×6	4-6	1	4-0	1	3-7	2	4-1	1	3-7	2	3-3	2
	2-2×8	5-9	2	5-0	2	4-6	2	5-2	2	4-6	2	4-1	2
	2-2×10	7-0	2	6-2	2	5-6	2	6-4	2	5-6	2	5-0	2
	2-2×12	8-1	2	7-1	2	6-5	2	7-4	2	6-5	2	5-9	3
	3-2×8	7-2	1	6-3	2	5-8	2	6-5	2	5-8	2	5-1	2
	3-2×10	8-9	2	7-8	2	6-11	2	7-11	2	6-11	2	6-3	2
	3-2×12	10-2	2	8-11	2	8-0	2	9-2	2	8-0	2	7-3	2
	4-2×8	5-10	2	5-2	2	4-8	2	5-3	2	4-7	2	4-2	2
	4-2×10	10-1	1	8-10	2	8-0	2	9-1	2	8-0	2	7-2	2
	4-2×12	11-9	2	10-3	2	9-3	2	10-7	2	9-3	2	8-4	2
Roof, ceiling and one clear span floor	2-2×4	2-8	1	2-4	1	2-1	1	2-7	1	2-3	1	2-0	1
	2-2×6	3-11	1	3-5	2	3-0	2	3-10	2	3-4	2	3-0	2
	2-2×8	5-0	2	4-4	2	3-10	2	4-10	2	4-2	2	3-9	2
	2-2×10	6-1	2	5-3	2	4-8	2	5-11	2	5-1	2	4-7	3
	2-2×12	7-1	2	6-1	3	5-5	3	6-10	2	5-11	3	5-4	3
	3-2×8	6-3	2	5-5	2	4-10	2	6-1	2	5-3	2	4-8	2
	3-2×10	7-7	2	6-7	2	5-11	2	7-5	2	6-5	2	5-9	2
	3-2×12	8-10	2	7-8	2	6-10	2	8-7	2	7-5	2	6-8	2
	4-2×8	5-1	2	4-5	2	3-11	2	4-11	2	4-3	2	3-10	2
	4-2×10	8-9	2	7-7	2	6-10	2	8-7	2	7-5	2	6-7	2
	4-2×12	10-2	2	8-10	2	7-11	2	9-11	2	8-7	2	7-8	2
Roof, ceiling and two center-bearing floors	2-2×4	2-7	1	2-3	1	2-0	1	2-6	1	2-2	1	1-11	1
	2-2×6	3-9	2	3-3	2	2-11	2	3-8	2	3-2	2	2-10	2
	2-2×8	4-9	2	4-2	2	3-9	2	4-7	2	4-0	2	3-8	3
	2-2×10	5-9	2	5-1	2	4-7	3	5-8	2	4-11	2	4-5	3
	2-2×12	6-8	2	5-10	3	5-3	3	6-6	2	5-9	3	5-2	3
	3-2×8	5-11	2	5-2	2	4-8	2	5-9	2	5-1	2	4-7	2
	3-2×10	7-3	2	6-4	2	5-8	2	7-1	2	6-2	2	5-7	2
	3-2×12	8-5	2	7-4	2	6-7	2	8-2	2	7-2	2	6-5	3
	4-2×8	4-10	2	4-3	2	3-10	2	4-9	2	4-2	2	3-9	2
	4-2×10	8-4	2	7-4	2	6-7	2	8-2	2	7-2	2	6-5	2
	4-2×12	9-8	2	8-6	2	7-8	2	9-5	2	8-3	2	7-5	2

For SI: 1 inch = 25.4 mm, 1 pound per square foot = 0.0479 kN/m².

a. Spans are given in feet and inches.

b. Tabulated values assume #2 grade lumber.

c. Building width is measured perpendicular to the ridge. For widths between those shown, spans are permitted to be interpolated.

d. NJ - Number of jack studs required to support each end. Where the number of required jack studs equals one, the header is permitted to be supported by an approved framing anchor attached to the full-height wall stud and to the header.

e. Use 30 psf ground snow load for cases in which ground snow load is less than 30 psf and the roof live load is equal to or less than 20 psf.

TABLE R502.5(2)
GIRDER SPANS[a] AND HEADER SPANS[a] FOR INTERIOR BEARING WALLS
(Maximum header spans for douglas fir-larch, hem-fir, southern pine and spruce-pine-fir[b] and required number of jack studs)

HEADERS AND GIRDERS SUPPORTING	SIZE	BUILDING WIDTH[c] (feet)					
		20		28		36	
		Span	NJ[d]	Span	NJ[d]	Span	NJ[d]
One floor only	2-2×4	3-1	1	2-8	1	2-5	1
	2-2×6	4-6	1	3-11	1	3-6	1
	2-2×8	5-9	1	5-0	2	4-5	2
	2-2×10	7-0	2	6-1	2	5-5	2
	2-2×12	8-1	2	7-0	2	6-3	2
	3-2×8	7-2	1	6-3	1	5-7	2
	3-2×10	8-9	1	7-7	2	6-9	2
	3-2×12	10-2	2	8-10	2	7-10	2
	4-2×8	5-10	1	5-1	2	4-6	2
	4-2×10	10-1	1	8-9	1	7-10	2
	4-2×12	11-9	1	10-2	2	9-1	2
Two floors	2-2×4	2-2	1	1-10	1	1-7	1
	2-2×6	3-2	2	2-9	2	2-5	2
	2-2×8	4-1	2	3-6	2	3-2	2
	2-2×10	4-11	2	4-3	2	3-10	3
	2-2×12	5-9	2	5-0	3	4-5	3
	3-2×8	5-1	2	4-5	2	3-11	2
	3-2×10	6-2	2	5-4	2	4-10	2
	3-2×12	7-2	2	6-3	2	5-7	3
	4-2×8	4-2	2	3-7	2	3-2	2
	4-2×10	7-2	2	6-2	2	5-6	2
	4-2×12	8-4	2	7-2	2	6-5	2

For SI: 1 inch = 25.4 mm, 1 foot = 304.8 mm.

a. Spans are given in feet and inches.

b. Tabulated values assume #2 grade lumber.

c. Building width is measured perpendicular to the ridge. For widths between those shown, spans are permitted to be interpolated.

d. NJ - Number of jack studs required to support each end. Where the number of required jack studs equals one, the headers are permitted to be supported by an approved framing anchor attached to the full-height wall stud and to the header.

R502.7 Lateral restraint at supports. Joists shall be supported laterally at the ends by full-depth solid blocking not less than 2 inches (51 mm) nominal in thickness; or by attachment to a header, band, or rim joist, or to an adjoining stud; or shall be otherwise provided with lateral support to prevent rotation.

Exception: In Seismic Design Categories D_1 and D_2, lateral restraint shall also be provided at each intermediate support.

R502.7.1 Bridging. Joists exceeding a nominal 2 by 12 shall be supported laterally by solid blocking, diagonal bridging (wood or metal), or a continuous 1-inch-by-3-inch (25 mm by 76 mm) strip nailed across the bottom of joists perpendicular to joists at intervals not exceeding 8 feet (2438 mm).

R502.8 Drilling and notching. Structural floor members shall not be cut, bored or notched in excess of the limitations specified in this section. See Figure R502.8.

R502.8.1 Sawn lumber. Notches in solid lumber joists, rafters and beams shall not exceed one-sixth of the depth of the member, shall not be longer than one-third of the depth of the member and shall not be located in the middle one-third of the span. Notches at the ends of the member shall not exceed one-fourth the depth of the member. The tension side of members 4 inches (102 mm) or greater in nominal thickness shall not be notched except at the ends of the members. The diameter of holes bored or cut into members shall not exceed one-third the depth of the member. Holes shall not be closer than 2 inches (51 mm) to the top or bottom of the member, or to any other hole located in the member. Where the member is also notched, the hole shall not be closer than 2 inches (51 mm) to the notch.

R502.8.2 Engineered wood products. Cuts, notches and holes bored in trusses, laminated veneer lumber, glue-laminated members or I-joists are not permitted unless the effects of such penetrations are specifically considered in the design of the member.

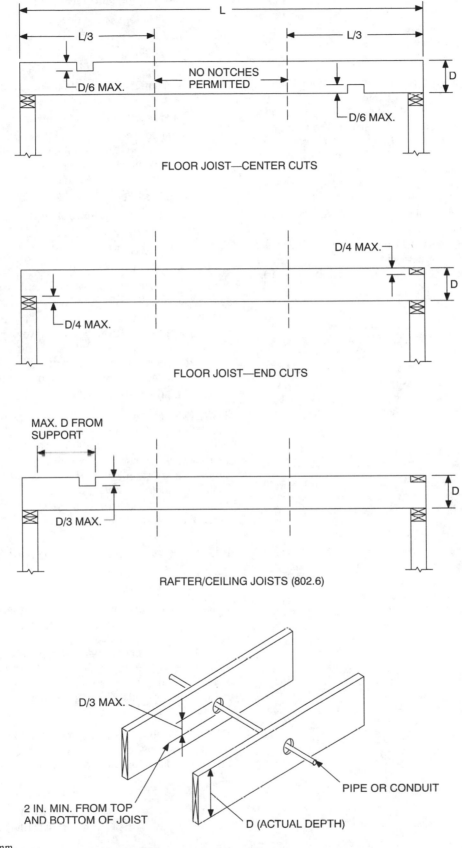

FLOOR JOIST—CENTER CUTS

FLOOR JOIST—END CUTS

RAFTER/CEILING JOISTS (802.6)

For SI: 1 inch = 25.4 mm.

FIGURE R502.8
CUTTING, NOTCHING AND DRILLING

R502.9 Fastening. Floor framing shall be nailed in accordance with Table R602.3(1). Where posts and beam or girder construction is used to support floor framing, positive connections shall be provided to ensure against uplift and lateral displacement.

R502.10 Framing of openings. Openings in floor framing shall be framed with a header and trimmer joists. When the header joist span does not exceed 4 feet (1219 mm), the header joist may be a single member the same size as the floor joist. Single trimmer joists may be used to carry a single header joist that is located within 3 feet (914 mm) of the trimmer joist bearing. When the header joist span exceeds 4 feet (1219 mm), the trimmer joists and the header joist shall be doubled and of sufficient cross section to support the floor joists framing into the header. Approved hangers shall be used for the header joist to trimmer joist connections when the header joist span exceeds 6 feet (1829 mm). Tail joists over 12 feet (3658 mm) long shall be supported at the header by framing anchors or on ledger strips not less than 2 inches by 2 inches (51 mm by 51 mm).

R502.11 Wood trusses.

R502.11.1 Design. Wood trusses shall be designed in accordance with approved engineering practice. The design and manufacture of metal plate connected wood trusses shall comply with ANSI/TPI 1. The truss design drawings shall be prepared by a registered professional where required by the statutes of the jurisdiction in which the project is to be constructed in accordance with Minnesota Rules, Chapter 1300.

R502.11.2 Bracing. Trusses shall be braced to prevent rotation and provide lateral stability in accordance with the requirements specified in the construction documents for the building and on the individual truss design drawings. In the absence of specific bracing requirements, trusses shall be braced in accordance with the TPI, HIB.

R502.11.3 Alterations to trusses. Truss members and components shall not be cut, notched, spliced or otherwise altered in any way without the approval of a registered design professional. Alterations resulting in the addition of load (e.g. HVAC equipment, water heater, etc.), that exceed the design load for the truss, shall not be permitted without verification that the truss is capable of supporting the additional loading.

R502.11.4 Truss design drawings. Truss design drawings, prepared in compliance with Section R502.11.1, shall be provided to the building official and approved prior to installation. Truss design drawing shall be provided with the shipment of trusses delivered to the jobsite. Truss design drawings shall include, at a minimum, the information specified below:

1. Slope or depth, span, and spacing.
2. Location of all joints.
3. Required bearing widths.
4. Design loads as applicable.
   4.1. Top chord live load (including snow loads).
   4.2. Top chord dead load.
   4.3. Bottom chord live load.
   4.4. Bottom chord dead load.
   4.5. Concentrated loads and their points of application.
   4.6. Controlling wind and earthquake loads.
5. Adjustments to lumber and joint connector design values for conditions of use.
6. Each reaction force and direction.
7. Joint connector type and description (e.g., size, thickness or gauge); and the dimensioned location of each joint connector except where symmetrically located relative to the joint interface.
8. Lumber size, species and grade for each member.
9. Connection requirements for:
   9.1. Truss-to-truss girder.
   9.2. Truss ply-to-ply.
   9.3. Field splices.
10. Calculated deflection ratio and/or maximum description for live and total load.
11. Maximum axial compression forces in the truss members to enable the building designer to design the size, connections and anchorage of the permanent continuous lateral bracing. Forces shall be shown on the truss drawing or on supplemental documents.
12. Required permanent truss member bracing location.

R502.12 Draftstopping required. When there is usable space both above and below the concealed space of a floor/ceiling assembly, draftstops shall be installed so that the area of the concealed space does not exceed 1,000 square feet (92.9 m^2). Draftstopping shall divide the concealed space into approximately equal areas. Where the assembly is enclosed by a floor membrane above and a ceiling membrane below draftstopping shall be provided in floor/ceiling assemblies under the following circumstances:

1. Ceiling is suspended under the floor framing.
2. Floor framing is constructed of truss-type open-web or perforated members.

R502.12.1 Materials. Draftstopping materials shall not be less than $^1/_2$-inch (12.7 mm) gypsum board, $^3/_8$-inch (9.5 mm) wood structural panels, $^3/_8$-inch (9.5 mm) Type 2-M-W particleboard or other approved materials adequately supported. Draftstopping shall be installed parallel to the floor framing members unless otherwise approved by the building official. The integrity of all draftstops shall be maintained.

R502.13 Fireblocking required. Fireblocking shall be provided in wood-frame floor construction and floor-ceiling assemblies in accordance with Section R602.8.

SECTION R503
FLOOR SHEATHING

R503.1 Lumber sheathing. Maximum allowable spans for lumber used as floor sheathing shall conform to Tables R503.1, R503.2.1.1(1) and R503.2.1.1(2).

TABLE R503.1
MINIMUM THICKNESS OF LUMBER FLOOR SHEATHING

JOIST OR BEAM SPACING (inches)	MINIMUM NET THICKNESS	
	Perpendicular to joist	Diagonal to joist
24	$^{11}/_{16}$	$^3/_4$
16	$^5/_8$	$^5/_8$
48[a]		
54[b]	$1^1/_2$ T & G	N/A
60[c]		

For SI: 1 inch = 25.4 mm, 1 pound per square inch = 6.895 kPa.

a. For this support spacing, lumber sheathing shall have a minimum F_b of 675 and minimum E of 1,100,000 (see AF&PA/NDS).

b. For this support spacing, lumber sheathing shall have a minimum F_b of 765 and minimum E of 1,400,000 (see AF&PA/NDS).

c. For this support spacing, lumber sheathing shall have a minimum F_b of 855 and minimum E of 1,700,000 (see AF&PA/NDS).

R503.1.1 End joints. End joints in lumber used as subflooring shall occur over supports unless end-matched lumber is used, in which case each piece shall bear on at least two joists. Subflooring may be omitted when joist spacing does not exceed 16 inches (406 mm) and a 1-inch (25.4 mm) nominal tongue-and-groove wood strip flooring is applied perpendicular to the joists.

R503.2 Wood structural panel sheathing.

R503.2.1 Identification and grade. Wood structural panel sheathing used for structural purposes shall conform to DOC PS 1, DOC PS 2 or, when manufactured in Canada, CSA 0437 or CSA 0325. All panels shall be identified by a grade mark of certificate of inspection issued by an approved agency.

R503.2.1.1 Subfloor and combined subfloor underlayment. Where used as subflooring or combination subfloor underlayment, wood structural panels shall be of one of the grades specified in Table R503.2.1.1(1). When sanded plywood is used as combination subfloor underlayment, the grade shall be as specified in Table R503.2.1.1(2).

TABLE R503.2.1.1(1)
ALLOWABLE SPANS AND LOADS FOR WOOD STRUCTURAL PANELS FOR ROOF AND SUBFLOOR SHEATHING AND COMBINATION SUBFLOOR UNDERLAYMENT[a,b,c]

SPAN RATING	MINIMUM NOMINAL PANEL THICKNESS (inch)	MAXIMUM SPAN (inches)[d]		LOAD (pounds per square foot, at maximum span)		MAXIMUM SPAN (inches)
		With edge support	Without edge support	Total load	Live load	
Sheathing[e]		Roof[f]				Subfloor[j]
12/0	$^5/_{16}$	12	12	40	30	0
16/0	$^5/_{16}$	16	16	40	30	0
20/0	$^5/_{16}$	20	20	40	30	0
24/0	$^3/_8$	24	20[g]	40	30	0
24/16	$^7/_{16}$	24	24	50	40	16
32/16	$^{15}/_{32}$, $^1/_2$	32	28	40	30	16[h]
40/20	$^{19}/_{32}$, $^5/_8$	40	32	40	30	20[h,i]
48/24	$^{23}/_{32}$, $^3/_{48}$	48	36	45	35	24
60/32	$^7/_8$	60	48	45	35	32
Underlayment, C-C plugged, single floor[e]		Roof[f]				Combination subfloor underlayment[k]
16 o.c.	$^{19}/_{32}$, $^5/_8$	24	24	50	40	16[i]
20 o.c.	$^{19}/_{32}$, $^5/_8$	32	32	40	30	20[i,j]
24 o.c.	$^{23}/_{32}$, $^3/_4$	48	36	35	25	24
32 o.c.	$^7/_8$	48	40	50	40	32
48 o.c.	$^{13}/_{32}$, $1^1/_8$	60	48	50	40	48

For SI: 1 inch = 25.4 mm, 1 pound per square foot = 0.0479 kN/m².

a. The allowable total loads were determined using a dead load of 10 psf. If the dead load exceeds 10 psf, then the live load shall be reduced accordingly.

b. Panels continuous over two or more spans with long dimension perpendicular to supports. Spans shall be limited to values shown because of possible effect of concentrated loads.

c. Applies to panels 24 inches or wider.

d. Lumber blocking, panel edge clips (one midway between each support, except two equally spaced between supports when span is 48 inches), tongue-and-groove panel edges, or other approved type of edge support.

e. Includes Structural 1 panels in these grades.

f. Uniform load deflection limitation: $^1/_{180}$ of span under live load plus dead load, $^1/_{240}$ of span under live load only.

g. Maximum span 24 inches for $^{15}/_{32}$- and $^1/_2$-inch panels.

h. Maximum span 24 inches where $^3/_4$-inch wood finish flooring is installed at right angles to joists.

i. Maximum span 24 inches where 1.5 inches of lightweight concrete or approved cellular concrete is placed over the subfloor.

j. Unsupported edges shall have tongue-and-groove joints or shall be supported with blocking unless minimum nominal $^1/_4$-inch thick underlayment with end and edge joints offset at least 2 inches or 1.5 inches of lightweight concrete or approved cellular concrete is placed over the subfloor, or $^3/_4$-inch wood finish flooring is installed at right angles to the supports. Allowable uniform live load at maximum span, based on deflection of $^1/_{360}$ of span, is 100 psf.

k. Unsupported edges shall have tongue-and-groove joints or shall be supported by blocking unless nominal $^1/_4$-inch-thick underlayment with end and edge joints offset at least 2 inches or $^3/_4$-inch wood finish flooring is installed at right angles to the supports. Allowable uniform live load at maximum span, based on deflection of $^1/_{360}$ of span, is 100 psf, except panels with a span rating of 48 on center are limited to 65 psf total uniform load at maximum span.

TABLE R503.2.1.1(2)
ALLOWABLE SPANS FOR PLYWOOD COMBINATION SUBFLOOR UNDERLAYMENT[a]

IDENTIFICATION	SPACING OF JOISTS (inches)		
	16	20	24
Species group[b]			
1	$1/2$	$5/8$	$3/4$
2, 3	$5/8$	$3/4$	$7/8$
4	$3/4$	$7/8$	1

For SI: 1 inch = 25.4 mm, 1 pound per square foot = 0.0479 kN/m^2.

a. Plywood continuous over two or more spans and face grain perpendicular to supports. Unsupported edges shall be tongue-and-groove or blocked except where nominal $1/4$-inch-thick underlayment or $3/4$-inch wood finish floor is used. Allowable uniform live load at maximum span based on deflection of $1/360$ of span is 100 psf.

b. Applicable to all grades of sanded exterior-type plywood.

R503.2.2 Allowable spans. The maximum allowable span for wood structural panels used as subfloor or combination subfloor underlayment shall be as set forth in Table R503.2.1.1(1). The maximum span for sanded plywood combination subfloor underlayment shall be as set forth in Table R503.2.1.1(2).

R503.2.3 Installation. Wood structural panels used as subfloor or combination subfloor underlayment shall be attached to wood framing in accordance with Table R602.3(1) and shall be attached to cold-formed steel framing in accordance with Table R505.3.1(2).

R503.3 Particleboard.

R503.3.1 Identification and grade. Particleboard shall conform to ANSI A208.1 and shall be so identified by a grade mark or certificate of inspection issued by an approved agency.

R503.3.2 Floor underlayment. Particleboard floor underlayment shall conform to Type PBU and shall not be less than $1/4$ inch (6.4 mm) in thickness.

R503.3.3 Installation. Particleboard underlayment shall be installed in accordance with the recommendations of the manufacturer and attached to framing in accordance with Table R602.3(1).

SECTION R504
PRESSURE PRESERVATIVELY TREATED-WOOD FLOORS (ON GROUND)

R504.1 General. Pressure preservatively treated-wood basement floors and floors on ground shall be designed to withstand axial forces and bending moments resulting from lateral soil pressures at the base of the exterior walls and floor live and dead loads. Floor framing shall be designed to meet joist deflection requirements in accordance with Section R301.

R504.1.1 Unbalanced soil loads. Unless special provision is made to resist sliding caused by unbalanced lateral soil loads, wood basement floors shall be limited to applications where the differential depth of fill on opposite exterior foundation walls is 2 feet (610 mm) or less.

R504.1.2 Construction. Joists in wood basement floors shall bear tightly against the narrow face of studs in the foundation wall or directly against a band joist that bears on the studs. Plywood subfloor shall be continuous over lapped joists or over butt joints between in-line joists. Sufficient blocking shall be provided between joists to transfer lateral forces at the base of the end walls into the floor system.

R504.1.3 Uplift and buckling. Where required, resistance to uplift or restraint against buckling shall be provided by interior bearing walls or properly designed stub walls anchored in the supporting soil below.

R504.2 Site preparation. The area within the foundation walls shall have all vegetation, topsoil and foreign material removed, and any fill material that is added shall be free of vegetation and foreign material. The fill shall be compacted to assure uniform support of the pressure preservatively treated-wood floor sleepers.

R504.2.1 Base. A minimum 4-inch-thick (102 mm) granular base of gravel having a maximum size of $3/4$ inch (19.1 mm) or crushed stone having a maximum size of $1/2$ inch (12.7 mm) shall be placed over the compacted earth.

R504.2.2 Moisture barrier. Polyethylene sheeting of minimum 6-mil (0.15 mm) thickness shall be placed over the granular base. Joints shall be lapped 6 inches (152 mm) and left unsealed. The polyethylene membrane shall be placed over the pressure preservatively treated-wood sleepers and shall not extend beneath the footing plates of the exterior walls.

R504.3 Materials. All framing materials, including sleepers, joists, blocking and plywood subflooring, shall be pressure preservatively treated and dried after treatment in accordance with AWPA C22.

SECTION R505
STEEL FLOOR FRAMING

R505.1 Cold-formed steel floor framing. Elements shall be straight and free of any defects that would significantly affect structural performance. Cold-formed steel floor framing members shall comply with the requirements of this section.

R505.1.1 Applicability limits. The provisions of this section shall control the construction of steel floor framing for buildings not greater than 60 feet (18 288 mm) in length perpendicular to the joist span, not greater than 36 feet (10 973 mm) in width parallel to the joist span, and not greater than two stories in height with each story not greater than 10 feet (3048 mm) high. Steel floor framing constructed in accordance with the provisions of this section shall be limited to sites subjected to a maximum design wind speed of 130 miles per hour (209 km/hr) Exposure A, B or C and a maximum ground snow load of 70 pounds per square foot (3.35 kN/m^2).

R505.1.2 In-line framing. When supported by steel-framed walls in accordance with Section R603, steel floor framing shall be constructed with floor joists located directly in-line with load-bearing studs located below the joists with a maximum tolerance of $^3/_4$ inch (19.1 mm) between the center lines of the joist and the stud.

R505.2 Structural framing. Load-bearing floor framing members shall comply with Figure R505.2(1) and with the dimensional and minimum thickness requirements specified in Tables R505.2(1) and R505.2(2). Tracks shall comply with Figure R505.2(2) and shall have a minimum flange width of $1^1/_4$ inches (32 mm). The maximum inside bend radius for members shall be the greater of $^3/_{32}$ inch (2.4 mm) or twice the uncoated steel thickness. Holes in joist webs shall conform to Figure R505.2(3) and to the dimensional requirements specified in Table R505.2(3). Holes shall be permitted only along the centerline of the web of the framing member. Holes for 800S162-33, 1000S162-43, 1200S162-43 and 1200S162-54 nominal joist sizes located less than 10 inches (254 mm) from the edge of load-bearing surface shall be patched in accordance with Section R505.3.6.

TABLE R505.2(1)
COLD-FORMED STEEL JOIST SIZES

MEMBER DESIGNATION[a]	WEB DEPTH (inches)	MINIMUM FLANGE WIDTH (inches)	MAXIMUM FLANGE WIDTH (inches)	MINIMUM LIP SIZE (inches)
550S162-t	5.5	1.625	2	0.5
800S162-t	8	1.625	2	0.5
1000S162-t	10	1.625	2	0.5
1200S162-t	12	1.625	2	0.5

For SI: 1 inch = 25.4 mm.

a. The member designation is defined by the first number representing the member depth in $^1/_{100}$ inches, the letter "S" representing a stud or joist member, the second number representing the flange width in $^1/_{100}$ inches, and the letter "t" shall be a number representing the minimum base metal thickness in mils [See Table R505.2(2)].

TABLE R505.2(2)
MINIMUM THICKNESS OF COLD-FORMED STEEL MEMBERS

DESIGNATION (mils)	MINIMUM UNCOATED THICKNESS (inches)	REFERENCE GAGE NUMBER
33	0.033	20
43	0.043	18
54	0.054	16
68	0.068	14

For SI: 1 inch = 25.4 mm, 1 mil = 0.0254 mm.

TABLE R505.2(3)
MAXIMUM HOLE DIMENSIONS AND SPACING IN JOIST WEBS

NOMINAL MEMBER SIZE	MAXIMUM HOLE DEPTH[a] (inches)	MAXIMUM HOLE LENGTH[b] (inches)	MINIMUM HOLE SPACING (inches)	MINIMUM HOLE EDGE DISTANCE[c] (inches)
550S162-33	2	5.25	16.5	10
550S162-43	2	5.25	16.5	10
550S162-54	2	5.25	16.5	10
550S162-68	2	5.25	16.5	10
800S162-33	1.5	4	24	10
800S162-43	3	6	24	10
800S162-54	3	6	24	10
800S162-68	3	6	24	10
1000S162-43	1.5	4	24	10
1000S162-54	4	6	24	10
1000S162-68	4	6	24	10
1200S162-43	1.5	4	24	10
1200S162-54	1.5	4	24	10
1200S162-68	4.75	6	24	10

For SI: 1 inch = 25.4 mm.

a. The dimension of the hole measured across the depth of the joist web.

b. The dimension of the hole measured along the length of the joist.

c. Edge distance is measured from the edge of the hole to the edge of bearing support.

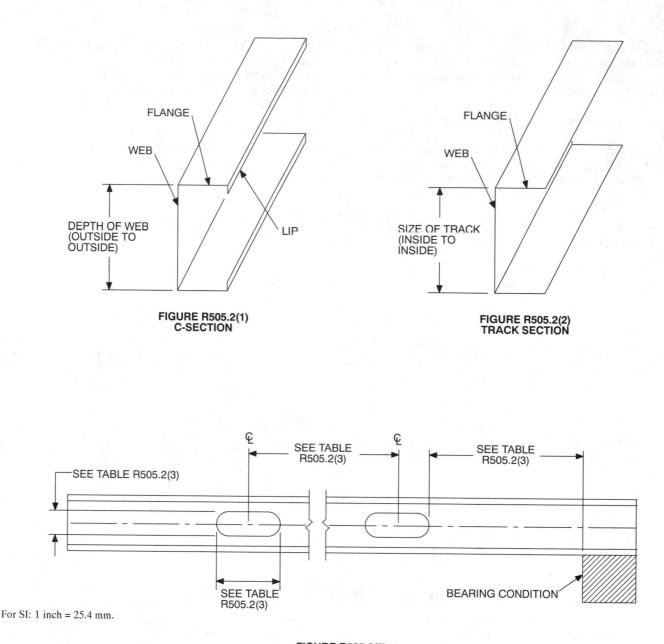

FIGURE R505.2(1)
C-SECTION

FIGURE R505.2(2)
TRACK SECTION

For SI: 1 inch = 25.4 mm.

FIGURE R505.2(3)
FLOOR JOIST WEB HOLES

R505.2.1 Material. Load-bearing members utilized in steel floor construction shall be cold formed to shape from structural quality sheet steel complying with the requirements of one of the following:

1. ASTM A 653: Grades 33, 37, 40 and 50 (Class 1 and 3).

2. ASTM A 792: Grades 33, 37, 40 and 50A.

3. ASTM A 875: Grades 33, 37, 40 and 50 (Class 1 and 3).

4. Steels that comply with ASTM A 653, except for tensile and elongation, shall be permitted provided the ratio of tensile strength to yield point is at least 1.08 and the total elongation is at least 10 percent for a 2-inch (51 mm) gage length or 7 percent for an 8-inch (203 mm) gage length.

R505.2.2 Identification. Load-bearing steel framing members shall have a legible label, stencil, stamp or embossment with the following information as a minimum:

1. Manufacturer's identification.

2. Minimum uncoated steel thickness in inches (mm).

3. Minimum coating designation.

4. Minimum yield strength, in kips per square inch (ksi) (kPa).

R505.2.3 Corrosion protection. Load-bearing steel framing shall have a metallic coating complying with one of the following:

1. A minimum of G 60 in accordance with ASTM A 653.

2. A minimum of AZ 50 in accordance with ASTM A 792.

3. A minimum of GF 60 in accordance with ASTM A 875.

R505.2.4 Fastening requirements. Screws for steel-to-steel connections shall be installed with a minimum edge distance and center-to-center spacing of 0.5 inch (12.7 mm), shall be self-drilling tapping, and shall conform to SAE J78. Floor sheathing shall be attached to steel joists with minimum No. 8 self-drilling tapping screws that conform to SAE J78. Screws attaching floor-sheathing-to-steel joists shall have a minimum head diameter of 0.292 inch (7.4 mm) with countersunk heads and shall be installed with a minimum edge distance of 0.375 inch (9.5 mm). Gypsum board ceilings shall be attached to steel joists with minimum No. 6 screws conforming to ASTM C 954 and shall be installed in accordance with Section R702. For all connections, screws shall extend through the steel a minimum of three exposed threads. All self-drilling tapping screws conforming to SAE J78 shall have a Type II coating in accordance with ASTM B 633.

Where No. 8 screws are specified in a steel to steel connection the required number of screws in the connection is permitted to be reduced in accordance with the reduction factors in Table R505.2.4 when larger screws are used or when one of the sheets of steel being connected is thicker than 33 mils (0.84 mm). When applying the reduction factor the resulting number of screws shall be rounded up.

TABLE R505.2.4
SCREW SUBSTITUTION FACTOR

SCREW SIZE	THINNEST CONNECTED STEEL SHEET (mils)	
	33	43
#8	1.0	0.67
#10	0.93	0.62
#12	0.86	0.56

For SI: 1 mil = 0.0254 mm.

R505.3 Floor construction. Cold-formed steel floors shall be constructed in accordance with this section and Figure R505.3.

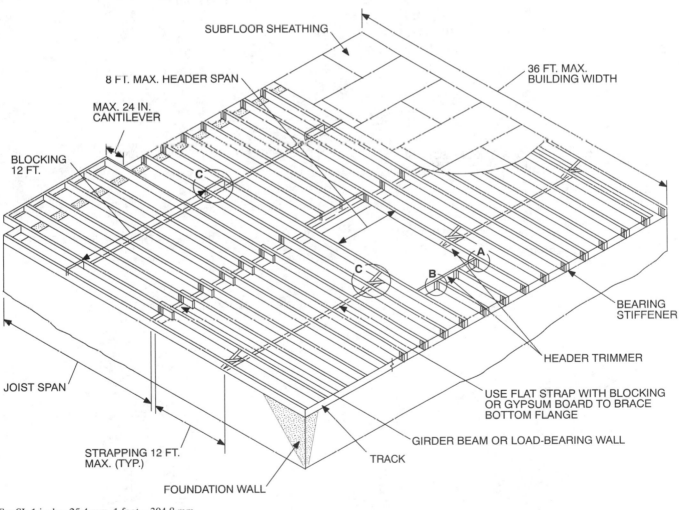

For SI: 1 inch = 25.4 mm, 1 foot = 304.8 mm.

FIGURE R505.3
STEEL FLOOR CONSTRUCTION
(continued)

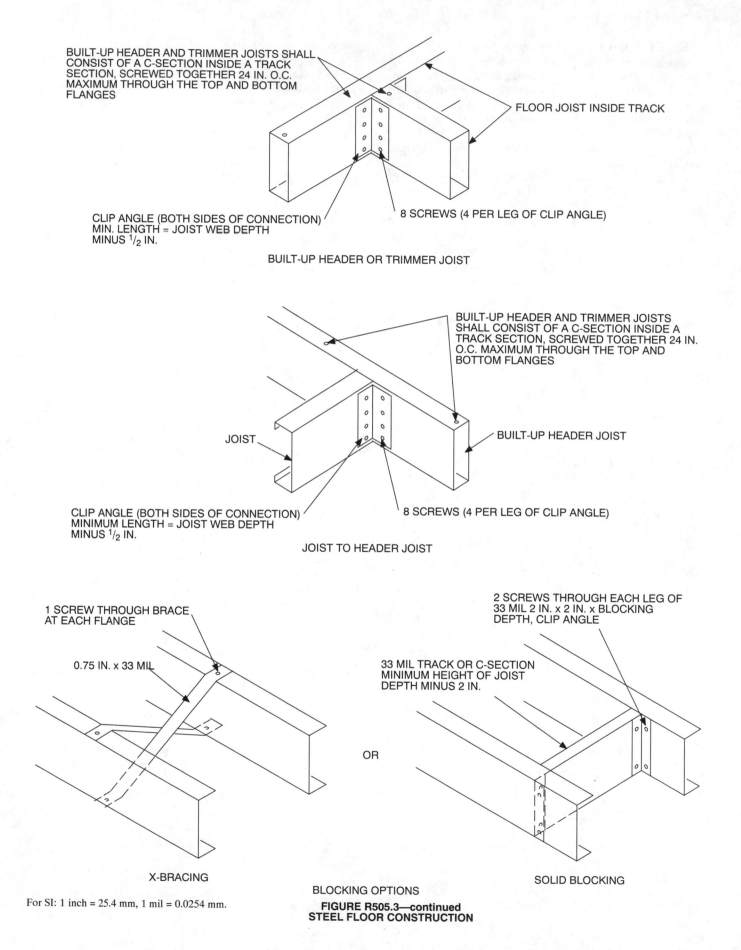

BUILT-UP HEADER AND TRIMMER JOISTS SHALL CONSIST OF A C-SECTION INSIDE A TRACK SECTION, SCREWED TOGETHER 24 IN. O.C. MAXIMUM THROUGH THE TOP AND BOTTOM FLANGES

FLOOR JOIST INSIDE TRACK

CLIP ANGLE (BOTH SIDES OF CONNECTION) MIN. LENGTH = JOIST WEB DEPTH MINUS 1/2 IN.

8 SCREWS (4 PER LEG OF CLIP ANGLE)

BUILT-UP HEADER OR TRIMMER JOIST

BUILT-UP HEADER AND TRIMMER JOISTS SHALL CONSIST OF A C-SECTION INSIDE A TRACK SECTION, SCREWED TOGETHER 24 IN. O.C. MAXIMUM THROUGH THE TOP AND BOTTOM FLANGES

JOIST

BUILT-UP HEADER JOIST

CLIP ANGLE (BOTH SIDES OF CONNECTION) MINIMUM LENGTH = JOIST WEB DEPTH MINUS 1/2 IN.

8 SCREWS (4 PER LEG OF CLIP ANGLE)

JOIST TO HEADER JOIST

1 SCREW THROUGH BRACE AT EACH FLANGE

0.75 IN. x 33 MIL

2 SCREWS THROUGH EACH LEG OF 33 MIL 2 IN. x 2 IN. x BLOCKING DEPTH, CLIP ANGLE

33 MIL TRACK OR C-SECTION MINIMUM HEIGHT OF JOIST DEPTH MINUS 2 IN.

X-BRACING

OR

SOLID BLOCKING

BLOCKING OPTIONS

For SI: 1 inch = 25.4 mm, 1 mil = 0.0254 mm.

FIGURE R505.3—continued
STEEL FLOOR CONSTRUCTION

R505.3.1 Floor to foundation or bearing wall connections. Cold-formed steel floors shall be anchored to foundations, wood sills or load-bearing walls in accordance with Table R505.3.1(1) and Figure R505.3.1(1), R505.3.1(2), R505.3.1(3), R505.3.1(4), R505.3.1(5) or R505.3.1(6). Continuous steel joists supported by interior load-bearing walls shall be constructed in accordance with Figure R505.3.1(7). Lapped steel joists shall be constructed in accordance with Figure R505.3.1(8). Fastening of steel joists to other framing members shall be in accordance with Table R505.3.1(2).

TABLE R505.3.1(1)
FLOOR TO FOUNDATION OR BEARING WALL CONNECTION REQUIREMENTS [a,b,c]

FRAMING CONDITION	WIND SPEED (mph) AND EXPOSURE		
	Up to 110 A/B or 85 C or Seismic Design Categories A, B, C and D_1	Up to 130 B or 110 C or Seismic Design Category D_2	Up to 130C
Floor joist to wall track of exterior steel load-bearing wall per Figure R505.3.1(1)	2-No. 8 screws	3-No. 8 screws	4-No. 8 screws
Floor joist track to wood sill per Figure R505.3.1(2)	Steel plate spaced at 3' o.c., with 4-No. 8 screws and 4-10d or 6-8d common nails	Steel plate, spaced at 2' o.c., with 4-No. 8 screws and 4-10d or 6-8d common nails	Steel plate spaced at 1' o.c. with 4-No. 8 screws and 4-10d or 6-8d common nails
Floor joist track to foundation per Figure R505.3.1(3)	$1/2''$ minimum diameter anchor bolt and clip angle spaced at 6' o.c. with 8-No. 8 screws	$1/2''$ minimum diameter anchor bolt and clip angle spaced at 4' o.c. with 8-No. 8 screws	$1/2''$ minimum diameter anchor bolt and clip angle spaced at 2' o.c. with 8-No. 8 screws
Joist cantilever to wall track per Figure R505.3.1(4)	2-No. 8 screws per stiffener or bent plate	3-No. 8 screws per stiffener or bent plate	$1/2''$ minimum diameter anchor bolt and clip angle spaced at 2' o.c. with 8-No. 8 screws
Joist cantilever to wood sill per Figure R505.3.1(5)	Steel plate spaced at 3' o.c., with 4-No. 8 screws and 4-10d or 6-8d common nails	Steel plate spaced at 2' o.c., with 4-No. 8 screws and 4-10d or 6-8d common nails	Steel plate spaced at 1' o.c. with 4-No. 8 screws and 4-10d or 6-8d common nails
Joist cantilever to foundation per Figure R505.3.1(6)	$1/2''$ minimum diameter anchor bolt and clip angle spaced at 6' o.c. with 8-No. 8 screws	$1/2''$ minimum diameter anchor bolt and clip angle spaced at 4' o.c. with 8-No. 8 screws	$1/2''$ minimum diameter anchor bolt and clip angle spaced at 2' o.c. with 8-No. 8 screws

For SI: 1 inch = 25.4 mm, 1 foot = 304.8 mm, 1 mile per hour = 1.609 km/h.

a. Anchor bolts shall be located not more than 12 inches from corners or the termination of bottom tracks (e.g., at door openings). Bolts shall extend a minimum of 15 inches into masonry or 7 inches into concrete.

b. All screw sizes shown are minimum.

c. In Seismic Design Category D_1 and D_2 or where the basic wind speed equals or exceeds 110 mph, connection shall comply with requirements in Section R603.8, but shall be no less than the minimum required herein.

TABLE R505.3.1(2)
FLOOR FASTENING SCHEDULE[a]

DESCRIPTION OF BUILDING ELEMENTS	NUMBER AND SIZE OF FASTENERS	SPACING OF FASTENERS
Floor joist to track of an interior load-bearing wall per Figures R505.3.1(7) and R505.3.1(8)	2 No. 8 screws	Each joist
Floor joist to track at end of joist	2 No. 8 screws	One per flange or two per bearing stiffener
Subfloor to floor joists	No. 8 screws	6" o.c. on edges and 10" o.c. at intermediate supports

For SI: 1 inch = 25.4 mm.

a. All screw sizes shown are minimum.

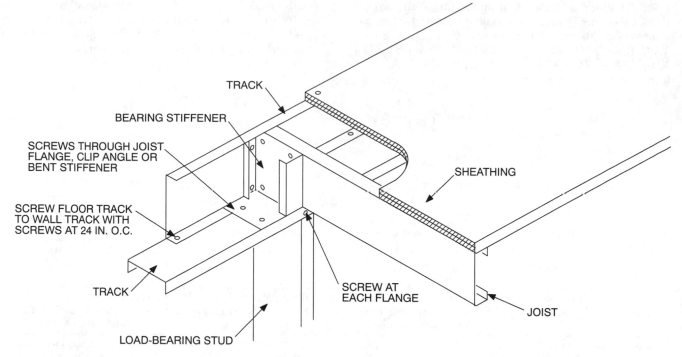

TRACK

BEARING STIFFENER

SCREWS THROUGH JOIST FLANGE, CLIP ANGLE OR BENT STIFFENER

SCREW FLOOR TRACK TO WALL TRACK WITH SCREWS AT 24 IN. O.C.

TRACK

LOAD-BEARING STUD

SHEATHING

SCREW AT EACH FLANGE

JOIST

For SI: 1 inch = 25.4 mm, 1 mil = 0.0254 mm.

FIGURE R505.3.1(1)
FLOOR TO LOAD-BEARING WALL STUD CONNECTION

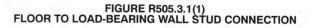

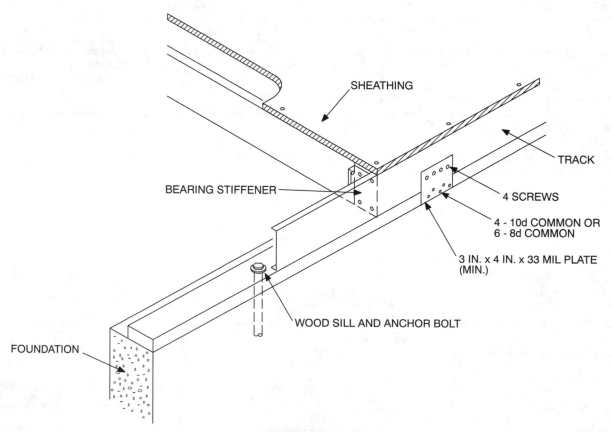

SHEATHING

BEARING STIFFENER

TRACK

4 SCREWS

4 - 10d COMMON OR
6 - 8d COMMON

3 IN. x 4 IN. x 33 MIL PLATE (MIN.)

WOOD SILL AND ANCHOR BOLT

FOUNDATION

For SI: 1 inch = 25.4 mm, 1 mil = 0.0254 mm.

FIGURE R505.3.1(2)
FLOOR TO WOOD SILL CONNECTION

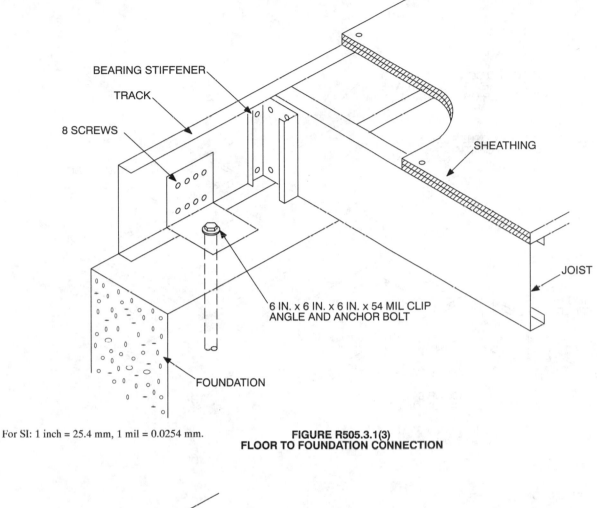

BEARING STIFFENER

TRACK

8 SCREWS

SHEATHING

JOIST

6 IN. x 6 IN. x 6 IN. x 54 MIL CLIP ANGLE AND ANCHOR BOLT

FOUNDATION

For SI: 1 inch = 25.4 mm, 1 mil = 0.0254 mm.

FIGURE R505.3.1(3)
FLOOR TO FOUNDATION CONNECTION

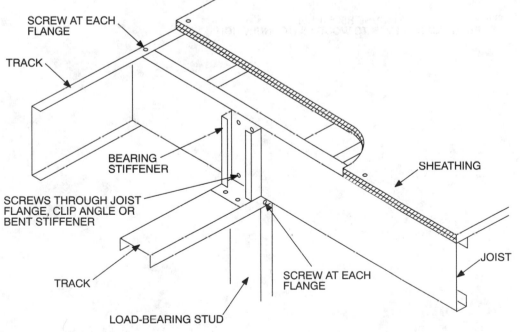

SCREW AT EACH FLANGE

TRACK

BEARING STIFFENER

SCREWS THROUGH JOIST FLANGE, CLIP ANGLE OR BENT STIFFENER

TRACK

LOAD-BEARING STUD

SCREW AT EACH FLANGE

SHEATHING

JOIST

FIGURE R505.3.1(4)
FLOOR CANTILEVER TO LOAD-BEARING WALL CONNECTION

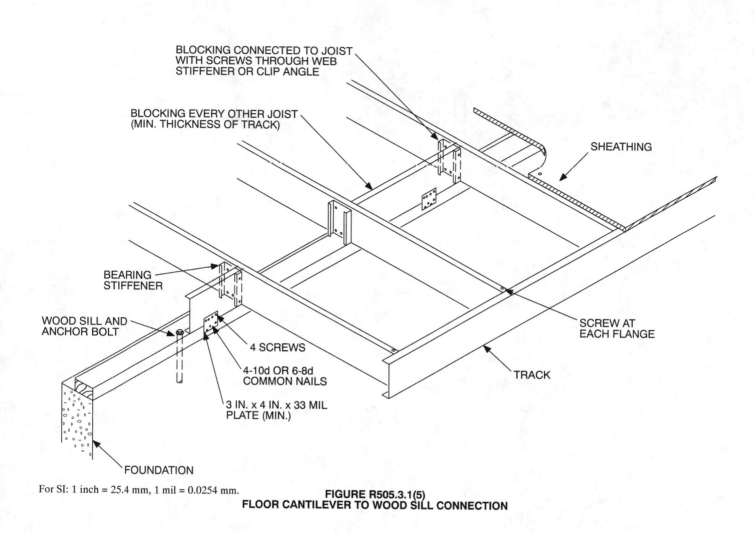

BLOCKING CONNECTED TO JOIST
WITH SCREWS THROUGH WEB
STIFFENER OR CLIP ANGLE

BLOCKING EVERY OTHER JOIST
(MIN. THICKNESS OF TRACK)

SHEATHING

BEARING
STIFFENER

WOOD SILL AND
ANCHOR BOLT

4 SCREWS

4-10d OR 6-8d
COMMON NAILS

3 IN. x 4 IN. x 33 MIL
PLATE (MIN.)

SCREW AT
EACH FLANGE

TRACK

FOUNDATION

For SI: 1 inch = 25.4 mm, 1 mil = 0.0254 mm.

**FIGURE R505.3.1(5)
FLOOR CANTILEVER TO WOOD SILL CONNECTION**

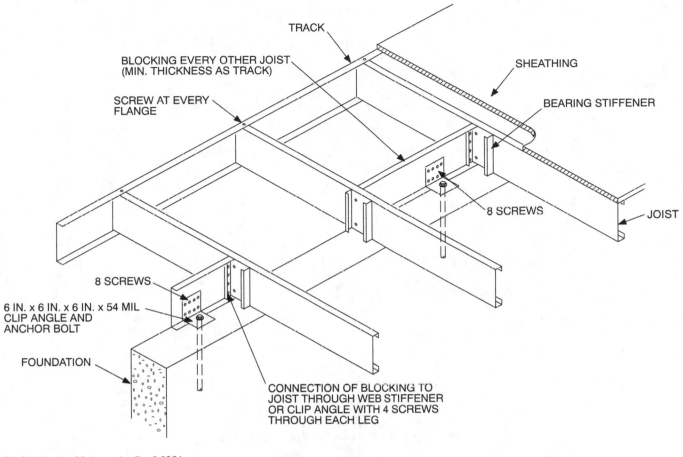

For SI: 1 inch = 25.4 mm, 1 mil = 0.0254 mm.

FIGURE R505.3.1(6)
FLOOR CANTILEVER TO FOUNDATION CONNECTION

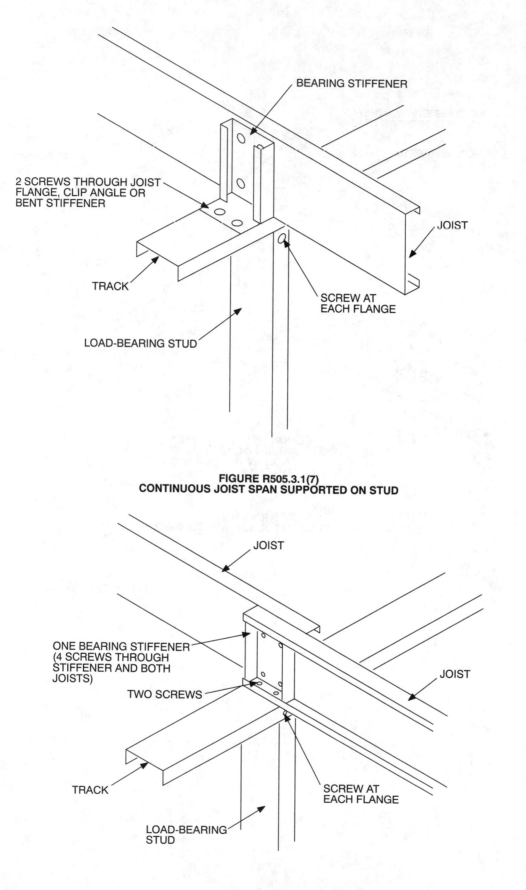

FIGURE R505.3.1(7)
CONTINUOUS JOIST SPAN SUPPORTED ON STUD

FIGURE R505.3.1(8)
LAPPED JOISTS SUPPORTED ON STUD

R505.3.2 Allowable joist spans. The clear span of cold-formed steel floor joists shall not exceed the limits set forth in Table R505.3.2. Floor joists shall have a minimum bearing length of 1.5 inches (38 mm). When continuous joists are used the interior bearing supports shall be located within 2 feet (610 mm) of mid span of the steel joists, and the individual spans shall not exceed the spans in Table R505.3.2. Bearing stiffeners shall be installed at each bearing location in accordance with Section R505.3.4 and as shown in Figure R505.3.

R505.3.3 Joist bracing. The top flanges of steel joists shall be laterally braced by the application of floor sheathing fastened to the joists in accordance with Table R505.3.1(2). Floor joists with spans that exceed 12 feet (3658 mm) shall have the bottom flanges laterally braced in accordance with one of the following:

1. Gypsum board installed with minimum No. 6 screws in accordance with Section R702.
2. Continuous steel strapping installed in accordance with Figure R505.3. Steel straps shall be at least 1.5 inches (38 mm) in width and 33 mils (0.84 mm) in thickness. Straps shall be fastened to the bottom flange at each joist with at least one No. 8 screw and shall be fastened to blocking with at least two No. 8 screws. Blocking or bridging (X-bracing) shall be installed between joists in-line with straps at a maximum spacing of 12 feet (3658 mm) measured perpendicular to the joist run and at the termination of all straps.

R505.3.4 Bearing stiffeners. Bearing stiffeners shall be installed at all bearing locations for steel floor joists. A bearing stiffener shall be fabricated from a minimum 33 mil (0.84 mm) C-section or 43 mil (1.09 mm) track section. Each stiffener shall be fastened to the web of the joist with a minimum of four No. 8 screws equally spaced as shown in Figure R505.3.4. Stiffeners shall extend across the full depth of the web and shall be installed on either side of the web.

R505.3.5 Cutting and notching. Flanges and lips of load-bearing steel floor framing members shall not be cut or notched.

R505.3.6 Hole patching. Web holes for 800S162-33, 1000S162-43, 1200S162-43 and 1200S162-54 nominal joist sizes with dimensions conforming to Section R505.2 that are closer than 10 inches (305 mm) from the edge of the hole to the edge of the bearing surface shall be patched with a solid steel plate, C-section or track section in accordance with Figure R505.3.6. The steel patch shall be of a minimum thickness as the receiving member and shall extend at least 1 inch (25.4 mm) beyond all edges of the hole. The steel patch shall be fastened to the web with No. 8 screws (minimum) spaced no greater than 1 inch (25.4 mm) center-to-center along the edges of the patch, with a minimum edge distance of 0.5 inch (12.7 mm).

R505.3.7 Floor cantilevers. Floor cantilevers shall not exceed 24 inches (610 mm) as illustrated in Figure R505.3. The cantilever back-span shall extend a minimum of 6 feet (1830 mm) within the building, and shall be fastened to a bearing condition in accordance with Section R505.3.1. Floor cantilevers shall be permitted only on the second floor of a two-story building or the first floor of a one-story building. Floor framing that is cantilevered and supports the cantilevered floor only shall consist of single joist members in accordance with Section R505.3.2. Floor framing that is cantilevered and supports the cantilevered floor and the roof framing load above shall consist of double joist members of the same size and material thickness as that for single joist members in accordance with Section R505.3.2, and shall be fastened web-to-web with minimum No. 8 screws at 24 inches (610 mm) maximum on-center spacing top and bottom. Built-up floor framing consisting of a C-section inside a track section, fastened at the top and bottom flanges by minimum No. 8 screws at 24 inches (610 mm) maximum on center spacing, is permitted in lieu of the web-to-web double joist method.

TABLE R505.3.2
ALLOWABLE SPANS FOR COLD-FORMED STEEL JOISTS[a,b]

| NOMINAL JOIST SIZE | 30 PSF LIVE LOAD | | 40 PSF LIVE LOAD | |
| | Spacing (inches) | | Spacing (inches) | |
	16	24	16	24
550S162-33	10'-7"	9'-1"	9'-7"	8'-1"
550S162-43	11'-6"	10'-0"	10'-5"	9'-1"
550S162-54	12'-4"	10'-9"	11'-2"	9'-9"
550S162-68	13'-2"	11'-6"	12'-0"	10'-6"
800S162-33	13'-3"	8'-10"	10'-7"	7'-1"
800S162-43	15'-6"	13'-7"	14'-1"	12'-3"
800S162-54	16'-8"	14'-7"	15'-2"	13'-3"
800S162-68	17'-11"	15'-7"	16'-3"	14'-2"
1000S162-43	18'-8"	15'-3"	16'-8"	13'-1"
1000S162-54	20'-1"	17'-6"	18'-3"	15'-11"
1000S162-68	21'-6"	18'-10"	19'-7"	17'-1"
1200S162-43	20'-3"	14'-1"	16'-10"	11'-3"
1200S162-54	23'-4"	19'-7"	21'-3"	17'-6"
1200S162-68	25'-1"	21'-11"	22'-10"	19'-11"

For SI: 1 inch = 25.4 mm, 1 foot = 304.8 mm, 1 pound per square foot = 0.0479 kN/m².
a. Deflection criteria: $L/480$ for live loads, $L/360$ for total loads.
b. Floor dead load = 10 psf.

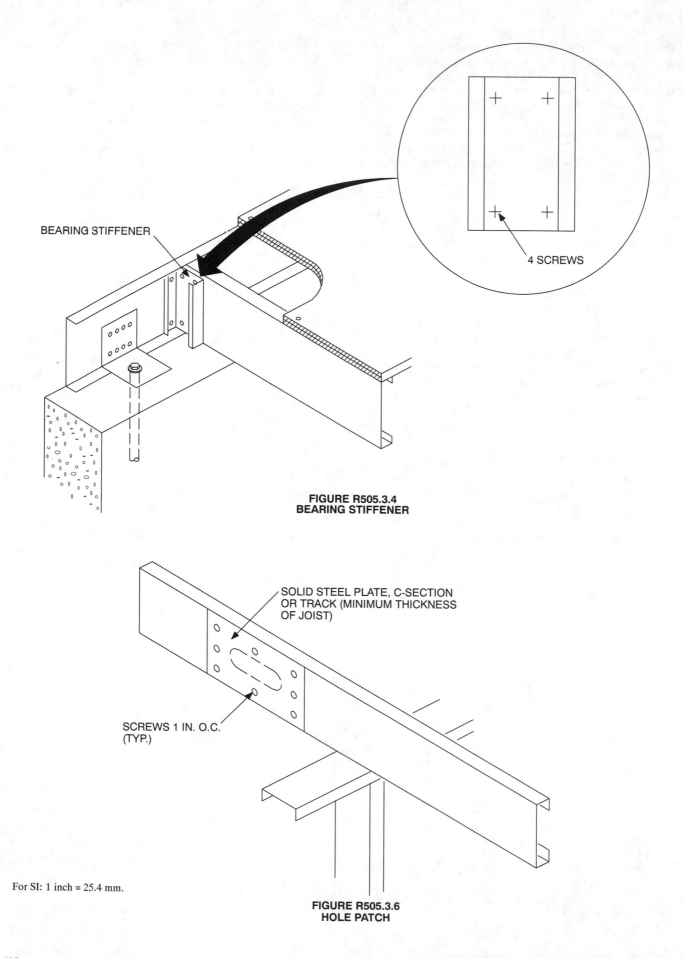

BEARING STIFFENER

4 SCREWS

FIGURE R505.3.4
BEARING STIFFENER

SOLID STEEL PLATE, C-SECTION
OR TRACK (MINIMUM THICKNESS
OF JOIST)

SCREWS 1 IN. O.C.
(TYP.)

For SI: 1 inch = 25.4 mm.

FIGURE R505.3.6
HOLE PATCH

R505.3.8 Splicing. Joists and other structural members shall not be spliced. Splicing of tracks shall conform with Figure R505.3.8.

R505.3.9 Framing of openings. Openings in floor framing shall be framed with header and trimmer joists. Header joist spans shall not exceed 8 feet (2438 mm). Header and trimmer joists shall be fabricated from joist and track sections, which shall be of a minimum size and thickness as the adjacent floor joists and shall be installed in accordance with Figure R505.3. Each header joist shall be connected to trimmer joists with a minimum of four 2-inch-by-2-inch (51 mm by 51 mm) clip angles. Each clip angle shall be fastened to both the header and trimmer joists with four No. 8 screws, evenly spaced, through each leg of the clip angle. The clip angles shall have a steel thickness not less than that of the floor joist.

SECTION R506
CONCRETE FLOORS (ON GROUND)

R506.1 General. Concrete slab-on-ground floors shall be a minimum 3.5 inches (89 mm) thick (for expansive soils, see Section R403.1.8). The specified compressive strength of concrete shall be as set forth in Section R402.2.

R506.2 Site preparation. The area within the foundation walls shall have all vegetation, top soil and foreign material removed.

R506.2.1 Fill. Fill material shall be free of vegetation and foreign material. The fill shall be compacted to assure uniform support of the slab, and except where approved, the fill depths shall not exceed 24 inches (610 mm) for clean sand or gravel and 8 inches (203 mm) for earth.

R506.2.2 Base. A 4-inch-thick (102 mm) base course consisting of clean graded sand, gravel, crushed stone or crushed blast-furnace slag passing a 2-inch (51 mm) sieve shall be placed on the prepared subgrade when the slab is below grade.

Exception: A base course is not required when the concrete slab is installed on well-drained or sand-gravel mixture soils classified as Group I according to the United Soil Classification System in accordance with Table R405.1.

R506.2.3 Vapor retarder. An approved vapor retarder with joints lapped not less than 6 inches (153 mm) shall be placed between the concrete floor slab and the base course or the prepared subgrade where no base course exists.

Exception: The vapor retarder may be omitted:

1. From garages, utility buildings and other unheated accessory structures.
2. From driveways, walks, patios and other flatwork not likely to be enclosed and heated at a later date.
3. Where approved by the building official, based on local site conditions.

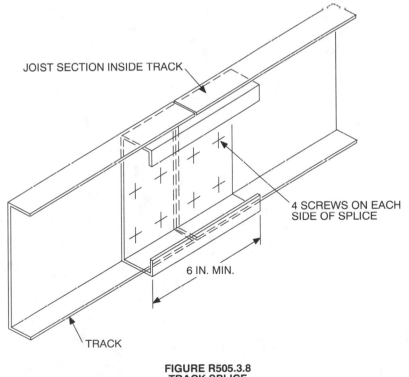

JOIST SECTION INSIDE TRACK

4 SCREWS ON EACH
SIDE OF SPLICE

6 IN. MIN.

TRACK

For SI: 1 inch = 25.4 mm.

FIGURE R505.3.8
TRACK SPLICE

CHAPTER 6
WALL CONSTRUCTION

SECTION R601
GENERAL

R601.1 Application. The provisions of this chapter shall control the design and construction of all walls and partitions for all buildings.

R601.2 Requirements. Wall construction shall be capable of accommodating all loads imposed according to Section R301 and of transmitting the resulting loads to the supporting structural elements.

R601.2.1 Compressible floor-covering materials. Compressible floor-covering materials that compress more than $1/32$ inch (0.794 mm) when subjected to 50 pounds (23 kg) applied over 1 inch square (645 mm) of material and are greater than $1/8$ inch (3.2 mm) in thickness in the uncompressed state shall not extend beneath walls, partitions or columns, which are fastened to the floor.

SECTION R602
WOOD WALL FRAMING

R602.1 Identification. Load-bearing dimension lumber for studs, plates and headers shall be identified by a grade mark of a lumber grading or inspection agency that has been approved by an accreditation body that complies with DOC PS 20. In lieu of a grade mark, a certification of inspection issued by a lumber grading or inspection agency meeting the requirements of this section shall be accepted.

R602.1.1 End-jointed lumber. Approved end-jointed lumber identified by a grade mark conforming to Section R602.1 may be used interchangeably with solid-sawn members of the same species and grade.

R602.2 Grade. Studs shall be a minimum No. 3, standard or stud grade lumber.

Exception: Bearing studs not supporting floors and nonbearing studs may be utility grade lumber, provided the studs are spaced in accordance with Table R602.3(5).

R602.3 Design and construction. Exterior walls of wood-frame construction shall be designed and constructed in accordance with the provisions of this chapter and Figures R602.3(1) and R602.3(2) or in accordance with AF&PA's NDS. Components of exterior walls shall be fastened in accordance with Tables R602.3(1) through R602.3(4).

R602.3.1 Stud spacing. In bearing walls, studs that are not more than 10 feet (3048 mm) in length shall be spaced not more than is specified in Table R602.3(5). In bearing walls, studs that are more than 10 feet (3048 mm) in height shall be spaced not more than specified in Table R602.3.1.

R602.3.2 Top plate. Wood stud walls shall be capped with a double top plate installed to provide overlapping at corners and intersections with bearing partitions. End joints in top plates shall be offset at least 24 inches (610 mm).

Exception: A single top plate may be installed in stud walls, provided the plate is adequately tied at joints, corners and intersecting walls by a minimum 3-inch-by-6-inch by a 0.036-inch-thick (76 mm by 152 mm by 0.914 mm) galvanized steel plate that is nailed to each wall or segment of wall by six 8d nails on each side, provided the rafters or joists are centered over the studs with a tolerance of no more than 1 inch (25.4 mm). The top plate may be omitted over lintels that are adequately tied to adjacent wall sections with steel plates or equivalent as previously described.

R602.3.3 Bearing studs. Where joists, trusses or rafters are spaced more than 16 inches (406 mm) on center and the bearing studs below are spaced 24 inches (610 mm) on center, such members shall bear within 5 inches (127 mm) of the studs beneath.

Exceptions:

1. The top plates are two 2-inch by 6-inch (38 mm by 140 mm) or two 3-inch by 4-inch (64 mm by 89 mm) members.

2. A third top plate is installed.

3. Solid blocking equal in size to the studs is installed to reinforce the double top plate.

R602.3.4 Bottom (sole) plate. Studs shall have full bearing on a nominal 2 by (38 mm) or larger plate or sill having a width at least equal to the width of the studs.

R602.4 Interior load-bearing walls. Interior load-bearing walls shall be constructed, framed and fireblocked as specified for exterior walls.

R602.5 Interior nonbearing walls. Interior nonbearing walls shall be permitted to be constructed with 2-inch-by-3-inch (51 mm by 76 mm) studs spaced 24 inches (610 mm) on center or, when not part of a braced wall line, 2-inch-by-4-inch (51 mm by 102 mm) flat studs spaced at 16 inches (406 mm) on center. Interior nonbearing walls shall be capped with at least a single top plate. Interior nonbearing walls shall be fireblocked in accordance with Section R602.8.

TABLE R602.3(1)
FASTENER SCHEDULE FOR STRUCTURAL MEMBERS

DESCRIPTION OF BUILDING ELEMENTS	NUMBER AND TYPE OF FASTENER[a,b,c,d]	SPACING OF FASTENERS
Joist to sill or girder, toe nail	3-8d	—
1″ × 6″ subfloor or less to each joist, face nail	2-8d	—
	2 staples, 1¾	—
2″ subfloor to joist or girder, blind and face nail	2-16d	—
Sole plate to joist or blocking, face nail	16d	16″ o.c.
Top or sole plate to stud, end nail	2-16d	—
Stud to sole plate, toe nail	3-8d or 2-16d	—
Double studs, face nail	10d	24″ o.c.
Double top plates, face nail	10d	24″ o.c.
Sole plate to joist or blocking at braced wall panels	3-16d	16″ o.c.
Double top plates, minimum 48-inch offset of end joints, face nail in lapped area	8-16d	—
Blocking between joists or rafters to top plate, toe nail	3-8d	—
Rim joist to top plate, toe nail	8d	6″ o.c.
Top plates, laps at corners and intersections, face nail	2-10d	—
Built-up header, two pieces with ½″ spacer	16d	16″ o.c. along each edge
Continued header, two pieces	16d	16″ o.c. along each edge
Ceiling joists to plate, toe nail	3-8d	—
Continuous header to stud, toe nail	4-8d	—
Ceiling joist, laps over partitions, face nail	3-10d	—
Ceiling joist to parallel rafters, face nail	3-10d	—
Rafter to plate, toe nail	2-16d	—
1″ brace to each stud and plate, face nail	2-8d	—
	2 staples, 1¾	—
1″ x 6″ sheathing to each bearing, face nail	2-8d	—
	2 staples, 1¾	—
1″ x 8″ sheathing to each bearing, face nail	2-8d	—
	3 staples, 1¾	—
Wider than 1″ x 8″ sheathing to each bearing, face nail	3-8d	—
	4 staples, 1¾	—
Built-up corner studs	10d	24″ o.c.
Built-up girders and beams, 2-inch lumber layers	10d	Nail each layer as follows: 32″ o.c. at top and bottom and staggered. Two nails at ends and at each splice.
2″ planks	2-16d	At each bearing
Roof rafters to ridge, valley or hip rafters: toe nail / face nail	4-16d / 3-16d	—
Rafter ties to rafters, face	3-8d	—
Wood structural panels, subfloor, roof and wall sheathing to framing, and particleboard wall sheathing to framing		
5/16-1/2	6d common nail (subfloor, wall) 8d common nail (roof)[f]	6	12[g]
19/32 -1	8d common nail	6	12[g]
1⅛-1¼	10d common nail or 8d deformed nail	6	12

(continued)

TABLE R602.3(1)—continued
FASTENER SCHEDULE FOR STRUCTURAL MEMBERS

DESCRIPTION OF BUILDING MATERIALS	DESCRIPTION OF FASTENER[b,c,d,e]	SPACING OF FASTENERS	
		Edges (inches)[i]	Intermediate supports[c,e] (inches)
Other wall sheathing[h]			
$1/2''$ regular cellulosic fiberboardsheathing	$1^1/_2$ galvanized roofing nail 6d common nail staple 16 ga., $1^1/_2$ long	3	6
$1/2$ structural cellulosic fiberboard sheathing	$1^1/_2$ galvanized roofing nail 8d common nail staple 16 ga., $1^1/_2$ long	3	6
$25/_{32}$ structural cellulosic fiberboard sheathing	$1^3/_4$ galvanized roofing nail 8d common nail staple 16 ga., $1^3/_4$ long	3	6
$1/2$ gypsum sheathing	$1^1/_2$ galvanized roofing nail; 6d common nail; staple galvanized, $1^1/_2$ long; $1^1/_4$ screws, Type W or S	4	8
$5/_8$ gypsum sheathing	$1^3/_4$ galvanized roofing nail; 8d common nail; staple galvanized, $1^5/_8$ long; $1^5/_8$ screws, Type W or S	4	8
Wood structural panels, combination subfloor underlayment to framing			
$3/_4$ and less	6d deformed nail or 8d common nail	6	12
$7/_8$-1	8d common nail or 8d deformed nail	6	12
$1^1/_8$-$1^1/_4$	10d common nail or 8d deformed nail	6	12

For SI: 1 inch = 25.4 mm, 1 foot = 304.8 mm, 1 mile per hour = 1.609 km/h.

a. All nails are smooth-common, box or deformed shanks except where otherwise stated.

b. Staples are 16 gage wire and have a minimum $7/_{16}$-inch on diameter crown width.

c. Nails shall be spaced at not more than 6 inches on center at all supports where spans are 48 inches or greater.

d. Four-foot-by-8-foot or 4-foot-by-9-foot panels shall be applied vertically.

e. Spacing of fasteners not included in this table shall be based on Table R602.3(1).

f. For regions having basic wind speed of 110 mph or greater, 8d deformed nails shall be used for attaching plywood and wood structural panel roof sheathing to framing within minimum 48-inch distance from gable end walls, if mean roof height is more than 25 feet, up to 35 feet maximum.

g. For regions having basic wind speed of 100 mph or less, nails for attaching wood structural panel roof sheathing to gable end wall framing shall be spaced 6 inches on center When basic wind speed is greater than 100 mph, nails for attaching panel roof sheathing to intermediate supports shall be spaced 6 inches on center for minimum 48-inch distance from ridges, eaves and gable end walls; and 4 inches on center to gable end wall framing.

h. Gypsum sheathing shall conform to ASTM C 79 and shall be installed in accordance with GA 253. Fiberboard sheathing shall conform to either AHA 194.1 or ASTM C 208.

i. Spacing of fasteners on floor sheathing panel edges applies to panel edges supported by framing members and at all floor perimeters only. Spacing of fasteners on roof sheathing panel edges applies to panel edges supported by framing members and at all roof plane perimeters. Blocking of roof or floor sheathing panel edges perpendicular to the framing members shall not be required except at intersection of adjacent roof planes. Floor and roof perimeter shall be supported by framing members or solid blocking.

TABLE R602.3(2)
ALTERNATE ATTACHMENTS

NOMINAL MATERIAL THICKNESS (inches)	DESCRIPTION[a, b] OF FASTENER AND LENGTH (inches)	SPACING[c] OF FASTENERS	
		Edges (inches)	Intermediate supports (inches)
Wood structural panels subfloor, roof and wall sheathing to framing and particleboard wall sheathing to framing[f]			
$5/16$	0.097 - 0.099 Nail $1^1/_2$ Staple 15 ga. $1^3/_8$ Staple 16 ga. $1^3/_4$	6	12
$3/8$	Staple 15 ga. $1^3/_8$	6	12
	0.097 - 0.099 Nail $1^1/_2$	4	10
	Staple 16 ga. $1^3/_4$	6	12
$15/_{32}$ and $1/_2$	Staple 15 ga. $1^1/_2$	6	12
	0.097 - 0.099 Nail $1^5/_8$	3	6
	Staple 16 ga. $1^3/_4$	6	12
$19/_{32}$ and $5/_8$	0.113 Nail $1^7/_8$ Staple 15 and 16 ga. $1^5/_8$	6	12
	0.097 - 0.099 Nail $1^3/_4$	3	6
$23/_{32}$ and $3/_4$	Staple 14 ga. $1^3/_4$	6	12
	Staple 15 ga. $1^3/_4$	5	10
	0.097 - 0.099 Nail $1^7/_8$	3	6
	Staple 16 ga. 2	4	8
1	Staple 14 ga. 2	5	10
	0.113 Nail $2^1/_4$, Staple 15 ga. 2	4	8
	0.097 - 0.099 Nail $2^1/_8$	3	6

NOMINAL MATERIAL THICKNESS (inches)	DESCRIPTION[a,b] OF FASTENER AND LENGTH	SPACING[c] OF FASTENERS	
		Edges (inches)	Body of panel (inches)
Floor underlayment; plywood-hardboard-particleboard[f]			
Plywood			
$1/_4$ and $5/16$	$1^1/_4$ ring or screw shank nail—minimum $12^1/_2$ ga. (0.099") shank diameter	3	6
	Staple 18 ga., $7/_8$, $3/16$ crown width	2	5
$11/_{32}$, $3/_8$, $15/_{32}$ and $1/_2$	$1^1/_4$ ring or screw shank nail—minimum $12^1/_2$ ga. (0.099) shank diameter	6	8[e]
$19/_{32}$, $5/_8$, $23/_{32}$ and $3/_4$	$1^1/_2$ ring or screw shank nail—minimum $12^1/_2$ ga. (0.099) shank diameter	6	12
	Staple 16 ga. $1^1/_4$	6	8
Hardboard[f]			
0.200	$1^1/_2$ long ring-grooved underlayment nail	6	6
	4d cement-coated sinker nail	6	6
	Staple 18 ga., $7/_8$ long (plastic coated)	3	6
Particleboard			
$1/_4$	4d ring-grooved underlayment nail	3	6
	Staple 18 ga., $7/_8$ long, $3/16$ crown	3	6
$3/_8$	6d ring-grooved underlayment nail	6	10
	Staple 16 ga., $1^1/_8$ long, $3/_8$ crown	3	6
$1/_2$, $5/_8$	6d ring-grooved underlayment nail	6	10
	Staple 16 ga., $1^5/_8$ long, $3/_8$ crown	3	6

For SI: 1 inch = 25.4 mm.

a. Nail is a general description and may be T-head, modified round head or round head.

b. Staples shall have a minimum crown width of $7/_{16}$-inch on diameter except as noted.

c. Nails or staples shall be spaced at not more than 6 inches on center at all supports where spans are 48 inches or greater. Nails or staples shall be spaced at not more than 12 inches on center at intermediate supports for floors.

d. Fasteners shall be placed in a grid pattern throughout the body of the panel.

e. For 5-ply panels, intermediate nails shall be spaced not more than 12 inches on center each way.

f. Hardboard underlayment shall conform to ANSI/AHA A135.4.

TABLE R602.3(3)
ALLOWABLE STUD SPACING FOR WOOD STRUCTURAL PANEL WALL SHEATHING

PANEL SPAN RATING	PANEL NOMINAL THICKNESS (inch)	MAXIMUM STUD SPACING (inches)	
		Siding nailed to:[a]	
		Stud	Sheathing
12/0, 16/0, 20/0, or wall —16 o.c.	$^5/_{16}$, $^3/_8$	16	16[b]
24/0, 24/16, 32/16 or wall—24 o.c.	$^3/_8$, $^7/_{16}$, $^{15}/_{32}$, $^1/_2$	24	24[c]

For SI: 1 inch = 25.4 mm.

a. Blocking of horizontal joints shall not be required.

b. Plywood sheathing $^3/_8$-inch thick or less shall be applied with long dimension across studs.

c. Three-ply plywood panels shall be applied with long dimension across studs.

TABLE R602.3(4)
ALLOWABLE SPANS FOR PARTICLEBOARD WALL SHEATHING[a]

THICKNESS (Inch)	GRADE	STUD SPACING (inches)	
		When siding is nailed to studs	When siding is nailed to sheathing
$^3/_8$	M-1 Exterior glue	16	—
$^1/_2$	M-2 Exterior glue	16	16

For SI: 1 inch – 25.4 mm.

a. Wall sheathing not exposed to the weather. If the panels are applied horizontally, the end joints of the panel shall be offset so that four panels corners will not meet. All panel edges must be supported. Leave a $^1/_{16}$-inch gap between panels and nail no closer than $^3/_8$ inch from panel edges.

TABLE R602.3(5)
MAXIMUM STUD SPACING

STUD SIZE (inches)	SUPPORTING ROOF AND CEILING ONLY (inches)	SUPPORTING ONE FLOOR ROOF AND CEILING (inches)	SUPPORTING TWO FLOORS ROOF AND CEILING (inches)	SUPPORTING ONE FLOOR ONLY (inches)
2 × 4	24[a]	16	—	24[a]
3 × 4	24[a]	24	16	24
2 × 5	24	24	—	24
2 × 6	24	24	16	24

For SI: 1 inch = 25.4 mm.

a. Shall be reduced to 16 inches if utility grade studs are used.

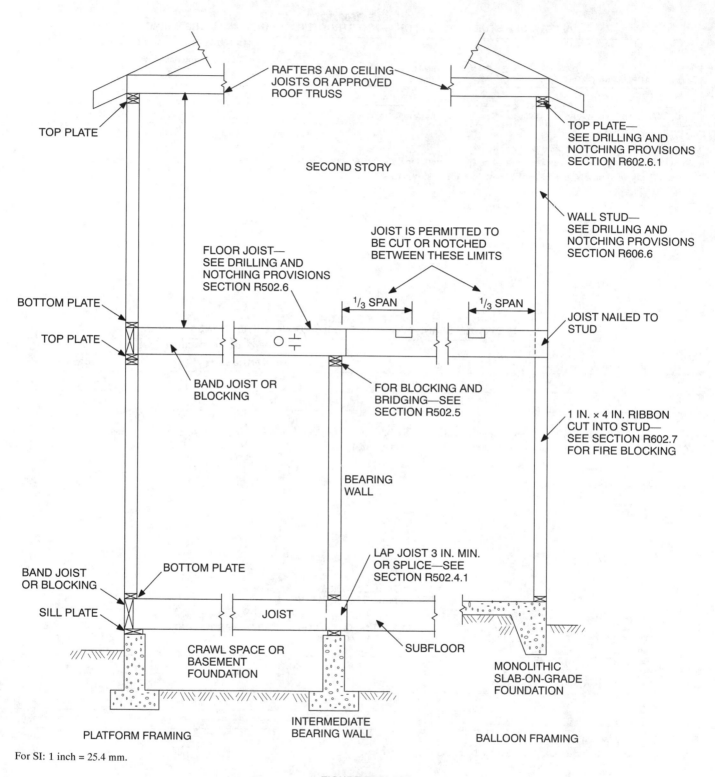

RAFTERS AND CEILING JOISTS OR APPROVED ROOF TRUSS

TOP PLATE

TOP PLATE— SEE DRILLING AND NOTCHING PROVISIONS SECTION R602.6.1

SECOND STORY

WALL STUD— SEE DRILLING AND NOTCHING PROVISIONS SECTION R606.6

FLOOR JOIST— SEE DRILLING AND NOTCHING PROVISIONS SECTION R502.6

JOIST IS PERMITTED TO BE CUT OR NOTCHED BETWEEN THESE LIMITS

$^1/_3$ SPAN

$^1/_3$ SPAN

BOTTOM PLATE

TOP PLATE

JOIST NAILED TO STUD

BAND JOIST OR BLOCKING

FOR BLOCKING AND BRIDGING—SEE SECTION R502.5

1 IN. × 4 IN. RIBBON CUT INTO STUD— SEE SECTION R602.7 FOR FIRE BLOCKING

BEARING WALL

LAP JOIST 3 IN. MIN. OR SPLICE—SEE SECTION R502.4.1

BAND JOIST OR BLOCKING

BOTTOM PLATE

SILL PLATE

JOIST

SUBFLOOR

CRAWL SPACE OR BASEMENT FOUNDATION

MONOLITHIC SLAB-ON-GRADE FOUNDATION

PLATFORM FRAMING

INTERMEDIATE BEARING WALL

BALLOON FRAMING

For SI: 1 inch = 25.4 mm.

FIGURE R602.3(1)
TYPICAL WALL, FLOOR AND ROOF FRAMING

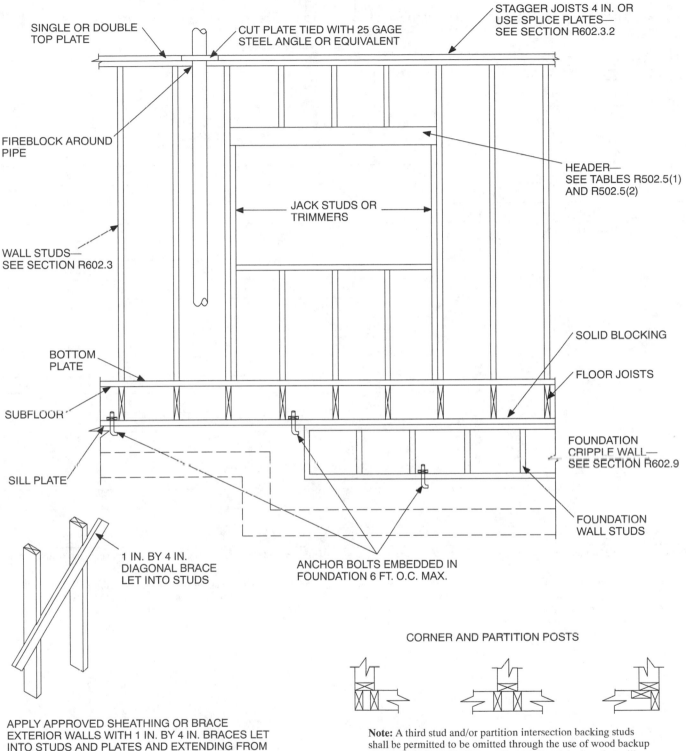

SINGLE OR DOUBLE TOP PLATE

CUT PLATE TIED WITH 25 GAGE STEEL ANGLE OR EQUIVALENT

STAGGER JOISTS 4 IN. OR USE SPLICE PLATES—SEE SECTION R602.3.2

FIREBLOCK AROUND PIPE

HEADER—SEE TABLES R502.5(1) AND R502.5(2)

JACK STUDS OR TRIMMERS

WALL STUDS—SEE SECTION R602.3

SOLID BLOCKING

BOTTOM PLATE

FLOOR JOISTS

SUBFLOOR

SILL PLATE

FOUNDATION CRIPPLE WALL—SEE SECTION R602.9

FOUNDATION WALL STUDS

1 IN. BY 4 IN. DIAGONAL BRACE LET INTO STUDS

ANCHOR BOLTS EMBEDDED IN FOUNDATION 6 FT. O.C. MAX.

CORNER AND PARTITION POSTS

APPLY APPROVED SHEATHING OR BRACE EXTERIOR WALLS WITH 1 IN. BY 4 IN. BRACES LET INTO STUDS AND PLATES AND EXTENDING FROM BOTTOM PLATE TO TOP PLATE, OR OTHER APPROVED METAL STRAP DEVICES INSTALLED IN ACCORDANCE WITH THE MANUFACTURER'S SPECIFICATIONS. SEE SECTION R602.10.

Note: A third stud and/or partition intersection backing studs shall be permitted to be omitted through the use of wood backup cleats, metal drywall clips or other approved devices that will serve as adequate backing for the facing materials.

For SI: 1 inch = 25.4 mm, 1 foot = 304.8 mm.

**FIGURE R602.3(2)
FRAMING DETAILS**

TABLE R602.3.1
MAXIMUM ALLOWABLE LENGTH OF WOOD WALL STUDS EXPOSED TO WIND SPEEDS OF 100 MPH OR LESS IN SEISMIC DESIGN CATEGORIES A, B, C and D[a,b,c]

HEIGHT (feet)	ON-CENTER SPACING (inches)			
	24	16	12	8
Supporting a roof only				
>10	2×4	2×4	2×4	2×4
12	2×6	2×4	2×4	2×4
14	2×6	2×6	2×6	2×4
16	2×6	2×6	2×6	2×4
18	NA[a]	2×6	2×6	2×6
20	NA[a]	NA[a]	2×6	2×6
24	NA[a]	NA[a]	NA[a]	2×6
Supporting one floor and a roof				
>10	2×6	2×4	2×4	2×4
12	2×6	2×6	2×6	2×4
14	2×6	2×6	2×6	2×6
16	NA[a]	2×6	2×6	2×6
18	NA[a]	2×6	2×6	2×6
20	NA[a]	NA[a]	2×6	2×6
24	NA[a]	NA[a]	NA[a]	2×6
Supporting two floors and a roof				
>10	2×6	2×6	2×4	2×4
12	2×6	2×6	2×6	2×6
14	2×6	2×6	2×6	2×6
16	NA[a]	NA[a]	2×6	2×6
18	NA[a]	NA[a]	2×6	2×6
20	NA[a]	NA[a]	NA[a]	2×6
22	NA[a]	NA[a]	NA[a]	NA[a]
24	NA[a]	NA[a]	NA[a]	NA[a]

For SI: 1 inch = 25.4 mm, 1 foot = 304.8 mm, 1 pound per square foot = 0.0479 kN/m^2, 1 pound per square inch = 6.895 kPa, 1 mile per hour = 1.609 km/h.

a. Design required.

b. Applicability of this table assumes the following: Snow load not exceeding 25 psf, but not less than 1310 psi determined by multiplying the AF&PA NDS tabular base design value by the repetitive use factor, and by the size factor for all species except southern pine, E not less than 1.6 by 10^6 psi, tributary dimensions for floors and roofs not exceeding 6 feet, maximum span for floors and roof not exceeding 12 feet, eaves not greater than 2 feet in dimension and exterior sheathing. Where the conditions are not within these parameters, design is required.

c. Utility, standard, stud and No. 3 grade lumber of any species are not permitted.

(continued)

TABLE R602.3.1—continued
MAXIMUM ALLOWABLE LENGTH OF WOOD WALL STUDS EXPOSED TO WIND SPEEDS OF 100 MPH OR LESS IN SEISMIC DESIGN CATEGORIES A, B, C and D_1

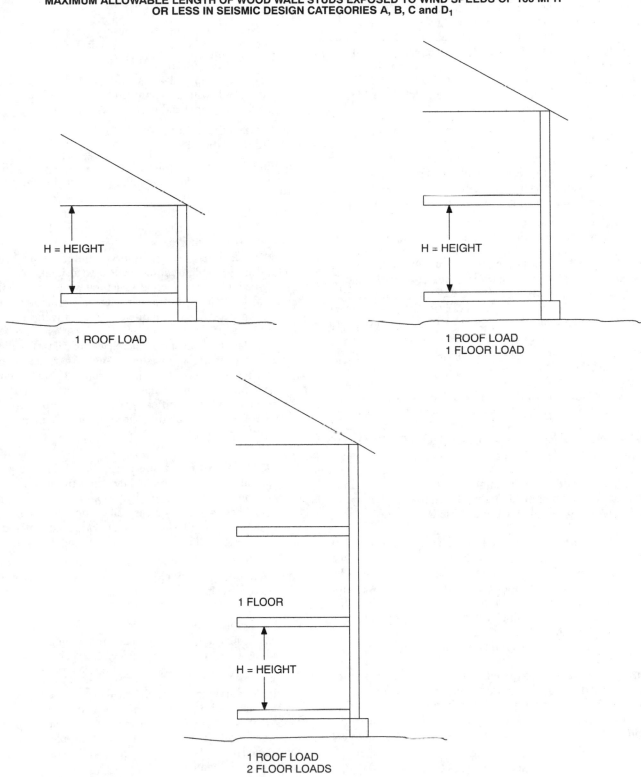

H = HEIGHT

1 ROOF LOAD

H = HEIGHT

1 ROOF LOAD
1 FLOOR LOAD

1 FLOOR

H = HEIGHT

1 ROOF LOAD
2 FLOOR LOADS

R602.6 Drilling and notching—studs. Any stud in an exterior wall or bearing partition may be cut or notched to a depth not exceeding 25 percent of its width. Studs in nonbearing partitions may be notched to a depth not to exceed 40 percent of a single stud width. Any stud may be bored or drilled, provided that the diameter of the resulting hole is no greater than 40 percent of the stud width, the edge of the hole is no closer than $^5/_8$ inch (15.9 mm) to the edge of the stud, and the hole is not located in the same section as a cut or notch. See Figures R602.6(1) and R602.6(2).

Exceptions:

1. A stud may be bored to a diameter not exceeding 60 percent of its width, provided that such studs located in exterior walls or bearing partitions are doubled and that not more than two successive studs are bored.

2. Approved stud shoes may be used when installed in accordance with the manufacturer's recommendation.

R602.6.1 Drilling and notching of top plate. When piping or ductwork is placed in or partly in an exterior wall or interior, braced or load-bearing wall, necessitating a cutting of the top plate by more than 50 percent of its width, a galvanized metal tie not less than 0.054 inch thick (1.37 mm) (16 gage) and 1.5 inches (38 mm) wide shall be fastened to each plate across and to each side of the opening with not less than six 16d nails. (See Figure R602.6.1.)

Exception: When the entire side of the wall with the notch or cut is covered by wood structural panel sheathing.

R602.7 Headers. For header spans see Tables R502.5(1) and R502.5(2).

R602.7.1 Wood structural panel box headers. Wood structural panel box headers shall be constructed in accordance with Figure R602.7.2 and Table R602.7.2.

R602.7.2 Nonbearing walls. Load-bearing headers are not required in interior or exterior nonbearing walls. A single flat 2-inch-by-4-inch (51 mm by 102 mm) member may be used as a header in interior or exterior nonbearing walls for openings up to 8 feet (2438 mm) in width if the vertical distance to the parallel nailing surface above is not more than 24 inches (610 mm). For such nonbearing headers, no cripples or blocking are required above the header.

R602.8 Fireblocking required. Fireblocking shall be provided to cut off all concealed draft openings (both vertical and horizontal) and to form an effective fire barrier between stories, and between a top story and the roof space. Fireblocking shall be provided in wood-frame construction in the following locations:

1. In concealed spaces of stud walls and partitions, including furred spaces, at the ceiling and floor level and at 10 foot (3048 mm) intervals both vertical and horizontal. Batts or blankets of mineral or glass fiber or other approved nonrigid materials shall be allowed as fireblocking in walls constructed using parallel rows of studs or staggered studs.

2. At all interconnections between concealed vertical and horizontal spaces such as occur at soffits, drop ceilings and cove ceilings.

3. In concealed spaces between stair stringers at the top and bottom of the run. Enclosed spaces under stairs shall comply with Section R314.8.

4. At openings around vents, pipes, and ducts at ceiling and floor level, with an approved material to resist the free passage of flame and products of combustion.

5. For the fireblocking of chimneys and fireplaces, see Section R1001.16.

6. Fireblocking of cornices of a two-family dwelling is required at the line of dwelling unit separation.

R602.8.1 Materials. Except as provided in Section R602.8, Item 4, fireblocking shall consist of 2-inch (51 mm) nominal lumber, or two thicknesses of 1-inch (25.4 mm) nominal lumber with broken lap joints, or one thickness of $^{23}/_{32}$-inch (19.8 mm) wood structural panels with joints backed by $^{23}/_{32}$-inch (19.8 mm) wood structural panels or one thickness of $^3/_4$-inch (19.1 mm) particleboard with joints backed by $^3/_4$-inch (19.1 mm) particleboard, $^1/_2$-inch (12.7 mm) gypsum board, or $^1/_4$-inch (6.4 mm) cement-based millboard. Batts or blankets of mineral wool or glass fiber or other approved materials installed in such a manner as to be securely retained in place shall be permitted as an acceptable fire block. Loose-fill insulation material shall not be used as a fire block unless specifically tested in the form and manner intended for use to demonstrate its ability to remain in place and to retard the spread of fire and hot gases.

R602.8.1.1 Unfaced fiberglass. Unfaced fiberglass batt insulation used as fireblocking shall fill the entire cross section of the wall cavity to a minimum height of 16 inches (406 mm) measured vertically. When piping, conduit or similar obstructions are encountered, the insulation shall be packed tightly around the obstruction.

R602.8.1.2 Fireblocking integrity. The integrity of all fireblocks shall be maintained.

R602.9 Cripple walls. Foundation cripple walls shall be framed of studs not less in size than the studding above. When exceeding 4 feet (1219 mm) in height, such walls shall be framed of studs having the size required for an additional story.

Cripple walls with a stud height less than 14 inches (356 mm) shall be sheathed on at least one side with a wood structural panel that is fastened to both the top and bottom plates in accordance with Table R602.3(1), or the cripple walls shall be constructed of solid blocking. Cripple walls shall be supported on continuous foundations.

R602.10 Wall bracing. Walls shall be braced in accordance with this section. For buildings in Seismic Design Categories D_1 and D_2, walls shall be constructed in accordance with the additional requirements of Sections R602.10.9, R602.10.11 and R602.11.

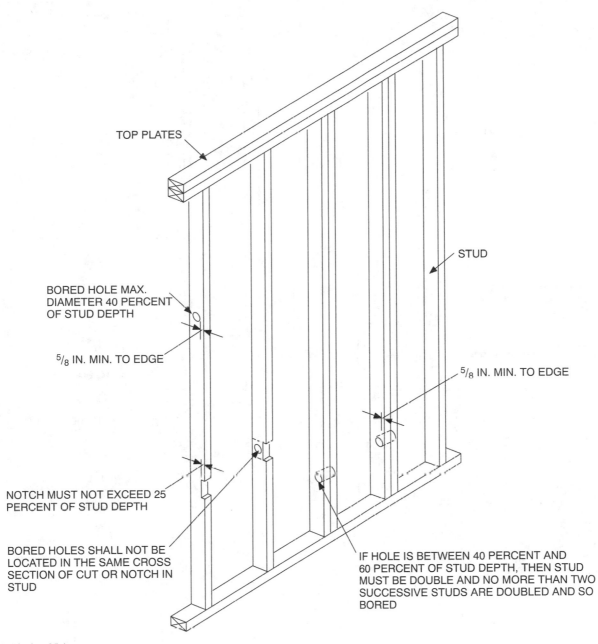

TOP PLATES

STUD

BORED HOLE MAX.
DIAMETER 40 PERCENT
OF STUD DEPTH

$\frac{5}{8}$ IN. MIN. TO EDGE

$\frac{5}{8}$ IN. MIN. TO EDGE

NOTCH MUST NOT EXCEED 25
PERCENT OF STUD DEPTH

BORED HOLES SHALL NOT BE
LOCATED IN THE SAME CROSS
SECTION OF CUT OR NOTCH IN
STUD

IF HOLE IS BETWEEN 40 PERCENT AND
60 PERCENT OF STUD DEPTH, THEN STUD
MUST BE DOUBLE AND NO MORE THAN TWO
SUCCESSIVE STUDS ARE DOUBLED AND SO
BORED

For SI: 1 inch = 25.4 mm.

Note: Condition for exterior and bearing walls.

FIGURE R602.6(1)
NOTCHING AND BORED HOLE LIMITATIONS FOR EXTERIOR WALLS AND BEARING WALLS

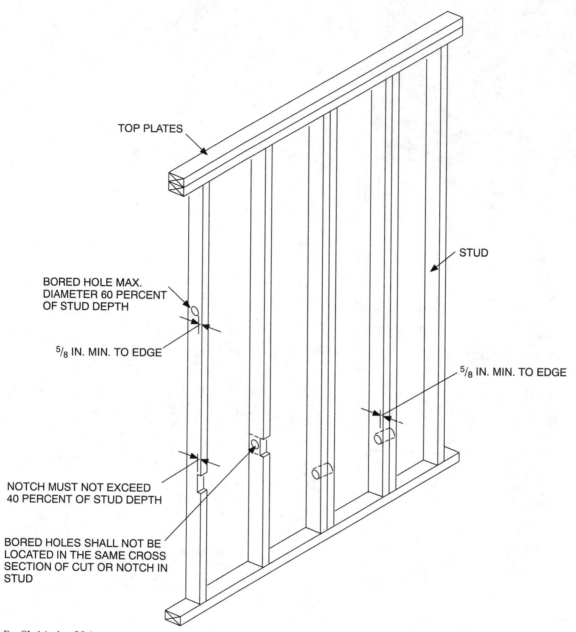

TOP PLATES

STUD

BORED HOLE MAX.
DIAMETER 60 PERCENT
OF STUD DEPTH

$^5/_8$ IN. MIN. TO EDGE

$^5/_8$ IN. MIN. TO EDGE

NOTCH MUST NOT EXCEED
40 PERCENT OF STUD DEPTH

BORED HOLES SHALL NOT BE
LOCATED IN THE SAME CROSS
SECTION OF CUT OR NOTCH IN
STUD

For SI: 1 inch = 25.4 mm.

FIGURE R602.6(2)
NOTCHING AND BORED HOLE LIMITATIONS FOR INTERIOR NONBEARING WALLS

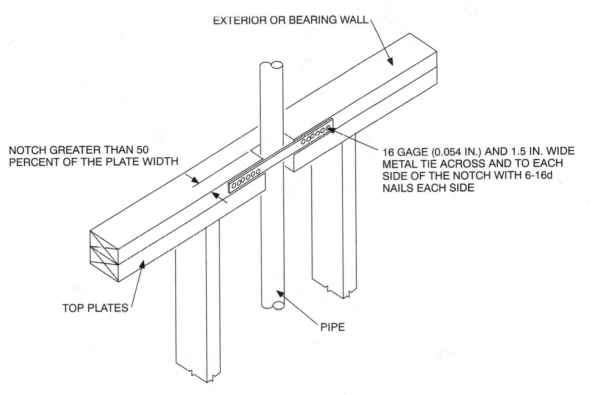

EXTERIOR OR BEARING WALL

NOTCH GREATER THAN 50
PERCENT OF THE PLATE WIDTH

16 GAGE (0.054 IN.) AND 1.5 IN. WIDE
METAL TIE ACROSS AND TO EACH
SIDE OF THE NOTCH WITH 6-16d
NAILS EACH SIDE

TOP PLATES

PIPE

For SI: 1 inch = 25.4 mm.

FIGURE R602.6.1
TOP PLATE FRAMING TO ACCOMMODATE PIPING

TABLE R602.7.2
MAXIMUM SPANS FOR WOOD STRUCTURAL PANEL BOX HEADERS[a]

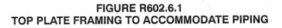

HEADER CONSTRUCTION[b]	HEADER DEPTH (inches)	HOUSE DEPTH (feet)				
		24	26	28	30	32
Wood structural panel—one side	9	4	4	3	3	—
	15	5	5	4	3	3
Wood structural panel—both sides	9	7	5	5	4	3
	15	8	8	7	7	6

For SI: 1 inch = 25.4 mm, 1 foot = 304.8 mm.

a. Spans are based on single story with clear-span trussed roof or two-story with floor and roof supported by interior-bearing walls.

b. See Figure R602.7.2 for construction details.

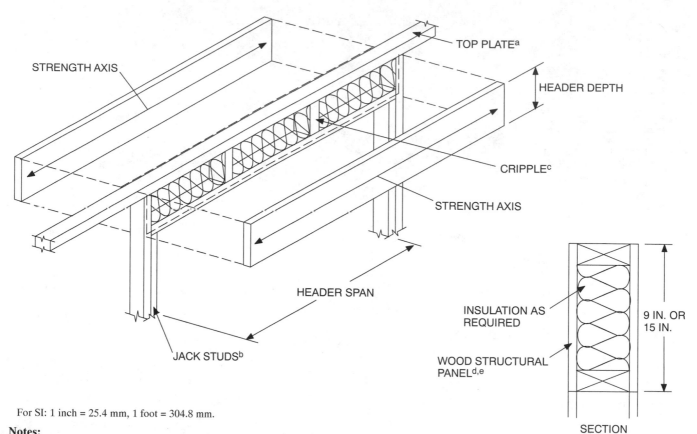

For SI: 1 inch = 25.4 mm, 1 foot = 304.8 mm.

Notes:
a. The top plate shall be continuous over header.
b. Jack studs shall be used for spans over 4 feet.
c. Cripple spacing shall be the same as for studs.
d. Wood structural panel faces shall be single pieces of $^{15}/_{32}$-inch-thick Exposure 1 (exterior glue) or thicker, installed on the interior or exterior or both sides of the header.
e. Wood structural panel faces shall be nailed to framing and cripples with 8d common or galvanized box nails spaced 3 inches on center, staggering alternate nails $^1/_2$ inch.
f. Galvanized nails shall be hot-dipped or tumbled.

FIGURE R602.7.2
TYPICAL WOOD STRUCTURAL PANEL BOX HEADER CONSTRUCTION

R602.10.1 Braced wall lines. Braced wall lines shall consist of braced wall panel construction methods in accordance with Section R602.10.3. The amount and location of bracing shall be in accordance with Table R602.10.1 and the amount of bracing shall be the greater of that required by the Seismic Design Category or the design wind speed. Braced wall panels shall begin no more than 12.5 feet (3810 mm) from each end of a braced wall line. Braced wall panels that are counted as part of a braced wall line shall be in line, except that offsets out-of-plane of up to 4 feet (1219 mm) shall be permitted provided that the total out-to-out offset dimension in any braced wall line is not more than 8 feet (2438 mm).

A designed collector shall be provided if the bracing begins more than 12 feet (3658 mm) from each end of a braced wall line.

R602.10.2 Cripple wall bracing. Cripple walls shall be braced with an amount and type of bracing as required for the wall above in accordance with Table R602.10.1 with the following modifications for the cripple wall bracing:

1. The percent bracing amount as determined from Table R602.10.3 shall be increased by 15 percent.

2. The wall panel spacing shall be decreased to 18 feet (5486 mm) instead of 25 feet (7620 mm).

R602.10.3 Braced wall panel construction methods. The construction of braced wall panels shall be in accordance with one of the following methods:

1. Nominal 1-inch-by-4-inch (25.4 mm by 102 mm) continuous diagonal braces let in to the top and bottom plates and the intervening studs or approved metal strap devices installed in accordance with the manufacturer's specifications. The let-in bracing shall be placed at an angle not more than 60 degrees (1.06 rad) or less than 45 degrees (0.79 rad) from the horizontal.

2. Wood boards of $^5/_8$ inch (15.9 mm) net minimum thickness applied diagonally on studs spaced a maximum of 24 inches (610 mm). Diagonal boards shall be attached to studs in accordance with Table R602.3(1).

3. Wood structural panel sheathing with a thickness not less than $^5/_{16}$ inch (7.9 mm) for 16-inch (406 mm) stud spacing and not less than $^3/_8$ inch (9.5 mm) for 24-inch (610 mm) stud spacing. Wood structural panels shall be installed in accordance with Table R602.3(3).

4. One-half-inch (12.7 mm) or $^{25}/_{32}$-inch (19.8 mm) thick structural fiberboard sheathing applied vertically on studs spaced a maximum of 16 inches (406 mm) on center. Structural fiberboard sheathing shall be installed in accordance with Table R602.3(1).

5. Gypsum board with minimum $^1/_2$-inch (12.7 mm) thickness placed on studs spaced a maximum of 24 inches (610 mm) on center and fastened at 7 inches (178 mm) on center with nails in accordance with Table R602.3(1).

6. Particleboard wall sheathing panels installed in accordance with Table R602.3(4).

7. Portland cement plaster on studs spaced a maximum of 16 inches (406 mm) on center and installed in accordance with Section R703.6.

8. Hardboard panel siding when installed in accordance with Table R703.4.

Exception: Alternate braced wall panels constructed in accordance with Section R602.10.6 shall be permitted to replace any of the above methods of braced wall panels.

R602.10.4 Length of braced panels. For Methods 2, 3, 4, 6 and 7 above, each braced wall panel shall be at least 48 inches (1219 mm) in length, covering a minimum of three stud spaces where studs are spaced 16 inches (406 mm) on center and covering a minimum of two stud spaces where studs are spaced 24 inches (610 mm) on center. For Method 5 above, each braced wall panel shall be at least 96 inches (2438 mm) in length where applied to one face of a braced wall panel and at least 48 inches (1219 mm) where applied to both faces.

Exceptions:

1. Lengths of braced wall panels for continuous wood structural panel sheathing shall be in accordance with Section R602.10.5.

2. Lengths of alternate braced wall panels shall be in accordance with Section R602.10.6.

R602.10.5 Continuous structural panel sheathing. When continuous wood structural panel sheathing is provided in accordance with Method 3 of Section R602.10.3, including areas above and below openings, braced wall panel lengths shall be in accordance with Table R602.10.5. Wood structural panel sheathing at corners shall be installed in accordance with Figure R602.10.5. The bracing amounts in Table R602.10.3 for Method 3 shall be permitted to be multiplied by a factor of 0.9 for walls with a maximum opening height that does not exceed 85 percent of the wall height or a factor of 0.8 for walls with a maximum opening height that does not exceed 67 percent of the wall height.

R602.10.6 Alternate braced wall panels. Alternate braced wall lines constructed in accordance with one of the following provisions shall be permitted to replace each 4 feet (1219 mm) of braced wall panel as required by Section R602.10.4:

1. In one-story buildings, each panel shall have a length of not less than 2 feet, 8 inches (813 mm) and a height of not more than 10 feet (3048 mm). Each panel shall be sheathed on one face with $^3/_8$-inch-minimum-thickness (9.5 mm) wood structural panel sheathing nailed with 8d common or galvanized box nails in accordance with Table R602.3(1) and blocked at all wood structural panel sheathing edges. Two anchor bolts installed in accordance with Figure R403.1(1) shall be provided in each panel. Anchor bolts shall be placed at panel quarter points. Each panel end stud shall have a tie-down device fastened to the foundation, capable of providing an uplift capacity of at least 1,800 pounds (816.5 kg). The tie-down device shall be installed in accordance with the manufacturer's recommendations. The panels shall be supported directly on a foundation or on floor framing supported directly on a foundation which is continuous across the entire length of the braced wall line. This foundation shall be reinforced with not less than one No. 4 bar top and bottom. When the continuous foundation is required to have a depth greater than 12 inches (305 mm), a minimum 12-inch-by-12-inch (305 mm by 305 mm) continuous footing or turned down slab edge is permitted at door openings in the braced wall line. This continuous footing or turned down slab edge shall be reinforced with not less than one No. 4 bar top and bottom. This reinforcement shall be lapped 15 inches (381 mm) with the reinforcement required in the continuous foundation located directly under the braced wall line.

2. In the first story of two-story buildings, each braced wall panel shall be in accordance with Item 1 above, except that the wood structural panel sheathing shall be provided on both faces, at least three anchor bolts shall be placed at one-fifth points, and tie-down device uplift capacity shall not be less than 3,000 pounds (1360.8 kg).

R602.10.7 Panel joints. All vertical joints of panel sheathing shall occur over studs. Horizontal joints in braced wall panels shall occur over blocking of a minimum of $1^1/_2$ inch (38 mm) thickness.

Exception: Blocking is not required behind horizontal joints where permitted by the manufacturer's installation requirements for the specific sheathing material.

R602.10.8 Connections. Braced wall panel sole plates shall be fastened to the floor framing and top plates shall be connected to the framing above in accordance with Table R602.3(1). Sills shall be fastened to the foundation or slab in accordance with Sections R403.1.6 and R602.11. Where joists are perpendicular to the braced wall lines above, blocking shall be provided under and in line with the braced wall panels.

TABLE R602.10.3
WALL BRACING

SEISMIC DESIGN CATEGORY OR WIND SPEED	CONDITION	TYPE OF BRACE[b,c]	AMOUNT OF BRACING[a,d,e]
Category A and B ($S_s \leq 0.35g$ and $S_{ds} \leq 0.33g$) or 100 mph and less	One story Top of two or three story	Methods 1, 2, 3, 4, 5, 6, 7 or 8	Located at each end and at least every 25 feet on center but not less than 16% of braced wall line.
	First story of two story Second story of three story	Methods 1, 2, 3, 4, 5, 6, 7 or 8	Located at each end and at least every 25 feet on center but not less than 16% of braced wall line for Method 3 and 25% of braced wall line for Methods 2, 4, 5, 6, 7 or 8.
	First story of three story	Methods 2, 3, 4, 5, 6, 7 or 8	Minimum 48-inch-wide panels located at each end and at least every 25 feet on center but not less than 25% of braced wall line for method 3 and 35% of braced wall line for Methods 2, 4, 5, 6, 7 or 8.
Category C ($S_s \leq 0.6g$ and $S_{ds} \leq 0.53g$) or less than 110 mph	One story Top of two or three story	Methods 1, 2, 3, 4, 5, 6, 7 or 8	Located at each end and at least every 25 feet on center but not less than 16% of braced wall line for Method 3 and 25% of braced wall line for Methods 2, 4, 5, 6, 7 or 8.
	First story of two story Second story of three story	Methods 2, 3, 4, 5, 6, 7 or 8	Located at each end and at least every 25 feet on center but not less than 30% of braced wall line for Method 3 and 45% of braced wall line for Methods 2, 4, 5, 6, 7 or 8.
	First story of three story	Methods 2, 3, 4, 5, 6, 7 or 8	Located at each end and at least every 25 feet on center but not less than 45% of braced wall line for Method 3 and 60% of braced wall line for Methods 2, 4, 5, 6, 7 or 8.
Category D_1 ($S_s \leq 1.25g$ and $S_{ds} \leq 0.83g$) or less than 110 mph	One story Top of two or three story	Methods 2, 3, 4, 5, 6, 7 or 8	Located at each end and at least every 25 feet on center but not less than 20% of braced wall line for Method 3 and 30% of braced wall line for Methods 2, 4, 5, 6, 7 or 8.
	First story of two story Second story of three story	Methods 2, 3, 4, 5, 6, 7 or 8	Located at each end and not more than 25 feet on center but not less than 45% of braced wall line for Method 3 and 60% of braced wall line for Methods 2, 4, 5, 6, 7 or 8.
	First story of three story	Methods 2, 3, 4, 5, 6, 7 or 8	Located at each end and not more than 25 feet on center but not less than 60% of braced wall line for Method 3 and 85% of braced wall line for Method 2, 4, 5, 6, 7 or 8.
Category D_2 or less than 110 mph	One story Top of two story	Methods 2, 3, 4, 5, 6, 7 or 8	Located at each end and at least every 25 feet on center but not less than 25% of braced wall line for Method 3 and 40% of braced wall line for Methods 2, 4, 5, 6, 7 or 8.
	First story of two story	Methods 2, 3, 4, 5, 6, 7 or 8	Located at each end and not more than 25 feet on center but not less than 55% of braced wall line for Method 3 and 75% of braced wall line for Methods 2, 4, 5, 6, 7 or 8.
	Cripple walls	Method 3	Located at each end and not more than 25 feet on center but not less than 75% of braced wall line.

For SI: 1 inch = 25.4 mm, 1 foot = 304.8 mm, 1 pound per square foot = 0.0479 kN/m², 1 mile per hour = 1.609 km/h.

a. Wall bracing amounts are based on a soil site class "D." Interpolation of bracing amounts between the S_{ds} values associated with the Seismic Design Categories shall be permitted when a site specific S_{ds} value is determined in accordance with Section 1615 of the *International Building Code.*

b. Foundation cripple wall panels shall be braced in accordance with Section R602.10.2.

c. Methods of bracing shall be as described in Section R602.10.3. The alternate braced wall panels described in Section R602.10.6 shall also be permitted.

d. The bracing amounts for Seismic Design Categories are based on a 15 psf wall dead load. For walls with a dead load of 8 psf or less, the bracing amounts shall be permitted to be multiplied by 0.85 provided that the adjusted bracing amount is not less than that required for the site's wind speed. The minimum length of braced panel shall not be less than required by Section R602.10.3.

e. When the dead load of the roof/ceiling exceeds 15 psf, the bracing amounts shall be increased in accordance with Section R301.2.2.4. Bracing required for a site's wind speed shall not be adjusted.

TABLE R602.10.5
LENGTH REQUIREMENTS FOR BRACED WALL PANELS IN A CONTINUOUSLY SHEATHED WALL[a,b]

LENGTH OF BRACED WALL PANEL (inches)			MAXIMUM OPENING HEIGHT NEXT TO THE BRACED WALL PANEL (% of wall height)
8-foot wall	9-foot wall	10-foot wall	
48	54	60	100%
32	36	40	85%
24	27	30	65%

For SI: 1 inch = 25.4 mm, 1 foot = 305 mm, 1 pound per square foot = 0.0479 kN/m².

a. Linear interpolation shall be permitted.

b. Full-height sheathed wall segments to either side of garage openings that support light frame roofs with roof covering dead loads of 3 psf or less shall be permitted to have a 4:1 aspect ratio.

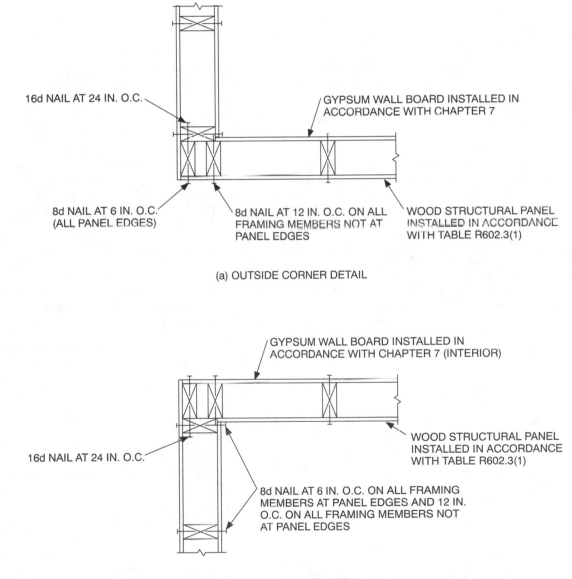

16d NAIL AT 24 IN. O.C.

GYPSUM WALL BOARD INSTALLED IN ACCORDANCE WITH CHAPTER 7

8d NAIL AT 6 IN. O.C. (ALL PANEL EDGES)

8d NAIL AT 12 IN. O.C. ON ALL FRAMING MEMBERS NOT AT PANEL EDGES

WOOD STRUCTURAL PANEL INSTALLED IN ACCORDANCE WITH TABLE R602.3(1)

(a) OUTSIDE CORNER DETAIL

GYPSUM WALL BOARD INSTALLED IN ACCORDANCE WITH CHAPTER 7 (INTERIOR)

WOOD STRUCTURAL PANEL INSTALLED IN ACCORDANCE WITH TABLE R602.3(1)

16d NAIL AT 24 IN. O.C.

8d NAIL AT 6 IN. O.C. ON ALL FRAMING MEMBERS AT PANEL EDGES AND 12 IN. O.C. ON ALL FRAMING MEMBERS NOT AT PANEL EDGES

(b) INSIDE CORNER DETAIL

For SI: 1 inch = 25.4 mm.

FIGURE R602.10.5
EXTERIOR CORNER FRAMING

R602.10.9 Interior braced wall support. In one-story buildings located in Seismic Design Category D_2, interior braced wall lines shall be supported on continuous foundations at intervals not exceeding 50 feet (15 240 mm). In two story buildings located in Seismic Design Category D_2, all interior braced wall panels shall be supported on continuous foundations.

Exception: Two-story buildings shall be permitted to have interior braced wall lines supported on continuous foundations at intervals not exceeding 50 feet (15 240 mm) provided that:

1. The height of cripple walls does not exceed 4 feet (1219 mm).
2. First-floor braced wall panels are supported on doubled floor joists, continuous blocking or floor beams.
3. The distance between bracing lines does not exceed twice the building width measured parallel to the braced wall line.

R602.10.10 Design of structural elements. Where a building, or portion thereof, does not comply with one or more of the bracing requirements in this section, those portions shall be designed and constructed in accordance with accepted engineering practice.

R602.10.11 Bracing in Seismic Design Categories D_1 and D_2. Structures located in Seismic Design Categories D_1 and D_2 shall be provided with exterior and interior braced wall lines. Spacing between braced wall lines in each story shall not exceed 25 feet (7620 mm) on center in both the longitudinal and transverse directions.

Exception: In one- and two-story buildings, spacing between braced wall lines shall not exceed 35 feet (10 363 mm) on center in order to accommodate one single room not exceeding 900 square feet (83.61 m^2) in each dwelling unit. The length of wall bracing in braced wall lines spaced greater or less other than 25 feet (7620 mm) apart shall be the length required by Table R602.10.1 multiplied by the appropriate adjustment factor from Table R602.10.11.

Exterior braced wall lines shall have a braced wall panel located at each end of the braced wall line.

Exception: For braced wall panel construction Method 3 of Section R602.10.3, the braced wall panel shall be permitted to begin no more than 12 feet (3810 mm) from each end of the braced wall line provided one of the following is satisfied:

1. A minimum 24-inch-wide (610 mm) panel is applied to each side of the building corner and the two 24-inch-wide (610 mm) panels at the corner shall be attached to framing in accordance with Figure R602.10.5 or,
2. The end of each braced wall panel closest to the corner shall have a tie-down device fastened to the stud at the edge of the braced wall panel closest to the corner and to the foundation or framing below. The tie-down device shall be capable of providing an uplift allowable design value of at least 1,800 pounds

(816.5 kg). The tie-down device shall be installed in accordance with the manufacturer's recommendations.

A designed collector shall be provided if the bracing is not located at each end of a braced wall line as indicated above or more than 8 feet (2438 mm) from each end of a braced wall line as indicated in the exception.

TABLE R602.10.11
ADJUSTMENT OF BRACING AMOUNTS FOR INTERIOR BRACED WALL LINES ACCORDING TO BRACED WALL LINE SPACING[a,b]

BRACED WALL LINE SPACING (feet)	MULTIPLY BRACING AMOUNT IN TABLE R602.10.3 BY:
15 or less	0.6
20	0.8
25	1.0
30	1.2
35	1.4

For SI: 1 foot = 304.8 mm.

a. Linear interpolation is permissible.

b. The adjustment is limited to the larger spacing between braced wall lines to either side of an interior braced wall line.

R602.10.11.1 Cripple wall bracing. In addition to the requirements of Section R602.10.2, where interior braced wall lines occur without a continuous foundation below, the length of parallel exterior cripple wall bracing shall be one and one-half times the length required by Table R602.10.3. Where cripple walls braced using Method 3 of Section R602.10.3 cannot provide this additional length, the capacity of the sheathing shall be increased by reducing the spacing of fasteners along the perimeter of each piece of sheathing to 4 inches (102 mm) on center.

R602.10.11.2 Sheathing attachment. Adhesive attachment of wall sheathing shall not be permitted in Seismic Design Categories C, D_1 and D_2.

R602.11 Framing and connections for Seismic Design Categories D_1 and D_2. The framing and connection details of buildings located in Seismic Design Categories D_1 and D_2 shall be in accordance with Sections R602.11.1 through R602.11.3.

R602.11.1 Wall anchorage. Braced wall line sills shall be anchored to concrete or masonry foundations in accordance with Sections R403.1.6 and R602.11. Plate washers, a minimum of $^3/_{16}$ inch by 2 inches by 2 inches (6.4 mm by 51 mm) in size, shall be provided between the foundation sill plate and the nut.

R602.11.2 Interior braced wall panel connections. Interior braced wall lines shall be fastened to floor and roof framing in accordance with Table R602.3(1), to required foundations in accordance with Section R602.11.1, and in accordance with the following requirements:

1. Floor joists parallel to the top plate shall be toe-nailed to the top plate with at least 8d nails spaced a maximum of 6 inches (150 mm) on center.
2. Top plate laps shall be face-nailed with at least eight 16d nails on each side of the splice.

R602.11.3 Stepped foundations. Where stepped foundations occur, the following requirements apply:

1. Where the height of a required braced wall panel that extends from foundation to floor above varies more than 4 feet (1220 mm), the braced wall panel shall be constructed in accordance with Figure R602.11.3.

2. Where the lowest floor framing rests directly on a sill bolted to a foundation not less than 8 feet (2440 mm) in length along a line of bracing, the line shall be considered as braced. The double plate of the cripple stud wall beyond the segment of footing that extends to the lowest framed floor shall be spliced by extending the upper top plate a minimum of 4 feet (1219 mm) along the foundation. Anchor bolts shall be located a maximum of 1 foot and 3 feet (305 and 914 mm) from the step in the foundation.

3. Where cripple walls occur between the top of the foundation and the lowest floor framing, the bracing requirements for a story shall apply.

4. Where only the bottom of the foundation is stepped and the lowest floor framing rests directly on a sill bolted to the foundations, the requirements of Section R602.11.1 shall apply.

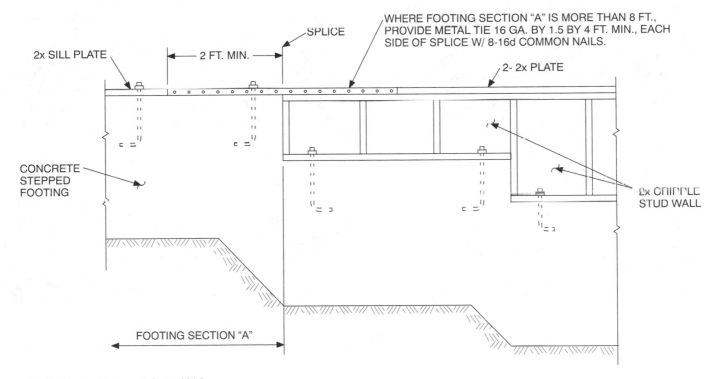

For SI: 1 inch = 25.4 mm, 1 foot = 304.8 mm.

Note: Where footing Section "A" is less than 8 feet long in a 25 feet total length wall, provide bracing at cripple stud wall.

FIGURE R602.11.3
STEPPED FOUNDATION CONSTRUCTION

SECTION R603
STEEL WALL FRAMING

R603.1 General. Elements shall be straight and free of any defects that would significantly affect structural performance. Cold-formed steel wall framing members shall comply with the requirements of this section.

R603.1.1 Applicability limits. The provisions of this section shall control the construction of exterior steel wall framing and interior load-bearing steel wall framing for buildings not greater than 60 feet (18 288 mm) in length perpendicular to the joist or truss span, not greater than 36 feet (10 973 mm) in width parallel to the joist span or truss, and not greater than two stories in height with each story not greater than 10 feet (3048 mm) high. All exterior walls installed in accordance with the provisions of this section shall be considered as load-bearing walls. Steel walls constructed in accordance with the provisions of this section shall be limited to sites subjected to a maximum design wind speed of 130 miles per hour (209 km/h) Exposure A, B or C and a maximum ground snow load of 70 pounds per foot (3.35 kN/m^2).

R603.1.1.1 Additional limits in high wind and high seismic regions. Braced wall lines and diaphragms in regions with wind speeds greater than or equal to 110 miles per hour (177 km/hr) or in Seismic Design Category D$_1$ or greater shall be permitted to have offsets of no greater than 4 feet (1219 mm). When offsets exceed 4 feet (1219 mm) the wall to either side shall be considered as a separate braced wall line with bracing amounts in accordance with Table R603.7.

R603.1.2 In-line framing. Load-bearing steel studs constructed in accordance with Section R603 shall be located directly in-line with joists, trusses and rafters with a maximum tolerance of $^3/_4$ inch (19.1 mm) between their center lines. Interior load-bearing steel stud walls shall be supported on foundations or shall be located directly above load-bearing walls with a maximum tolerance of $^3/_4$ inch (19.1 mm) between the centerline of the studs.

R603.2 Structural framing. Load-bearing steel wall framing members shall comply with Figure R603.2(1) and the dimensional and minimum thickness requirements specified in Tables R603.2(1) and R603.2(2). Tracks shall comply with Figure R603.2(2) and shall have a minimum flange width of $1^1/_4$ inches (32 mm). The maximum inside bend radius for load-bearing members shall be the greater of $^3/_{32}$ inch (2.4 mm) or twice the uncoated steel thickness. Holes in wall studs and other structural members shall not exceed 1.5 inches (38 mm) in width or 4 inches (102 mm) in length as shown in Figure R603.2(3). Holes shall be permitted only along the centerline of the web of the framing member. Holes shall not be less than 24 inches (610 mm) center to center and shall not be located less than 10 inches (254 mm) from edge of hole to end of member unless patched in accordance with Section R603.3.5.

TABLE R603.2(1)
LOAD-BEARING COLD-FORMED STEEL STUD SIZES

MEMBER DESIGNATION[a]	WEB DEPTH (inches)	MINIMUM FLANGE WIDTH (inches)	MAXIMUM FLANGE WIDTH (inches)	MINIMUM LIP SIZE (inches)
350S162-t	3.5	1.625	2	0.5
550S162-t	5.5	1.625	2	0.5

For SI: 1 inch = 25.4 mm.

a. The member designation is defined by the first number representing the member depth in $^1/_{100}$ inches, the letter "S" representing a stud or joist member, the second number representing the flange width in $^1/_{100}$ inches, and the letter "t" shall be a number representing the minimum base metal thickness in mils [See Table R603.2(2)].

TABLE R603.2(2)
MINIMUM THICKNESS OF COLD-FORMED STEEL STUDS

DESIGNATION (mils)	MINIMUM UNCOATED THICKNESS (inches)	REFERENCE GAGE NUMBER
33	0.033	20
43	0.043	18
54	0.054	16
68	0.068	14

For SI: 1 inch = 25.4 mm, 1 mil = 0.0254 mm.

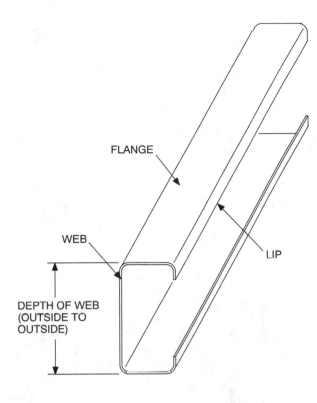

FLANGE

WEB

DEPTH OF WEB
(OUTSIDE TO
OUTSIDE)

LIP

FIGURE R603.2(1)
C-SECTION

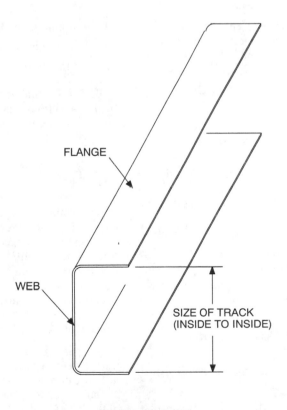

FLANGE

WEB

SIZE OF TRACK
(INSIDE TO INSIDE)

FIGURE R603.2(2)
TRACK SECTION

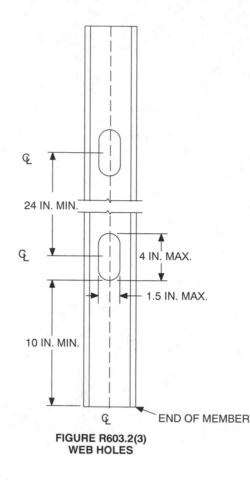

For SI: 1 inch = 25.4 mm.

FIGURE R603.2(3)
WEB HOLES

R603.2.1 Material. Load-bearing steel framing members shall be cold-formed to shape from structural quality sheet steel complying with the requirements of one of the following:

1. ASTM A 653: Grades 33, 37, 40 and 50 (Classes 1 and 3).
2. ASTM A 792: Grades 33, 37, 40 and 50A.
3. ASTM A 875: Grades 33, 37, 40 and 50 (Classes 1 and 3).
4. Steels that comply with ASTM A 653, except for tensile and elongation, shall be permitted, provided the ratio of tensile strength to yield point is at least 1.08 and the total elongation is at least 10 percent for a 2-inch (51 mm) gage length or 7 percent for an 8-inch (203 mm) gage length.

R603.2.2 Identification. Load-bearing steel framing members shall have a legible label, stencil, stamp or embossment with the following information as a minimum:

1. Manufacturer's identification.
2. Minimum uncoated steel thickness in inches (mm).
3. Minimum coating designation.
4. Minimum yield strength, in kips per square inch (ksi) (kPa).

R603.2.3 Corrosion protection. Load-bearing steel framing shall have a metallic coating complying with one of the following:

1. A minimum of G 60 in accordance with ASTM A 653.
2. A minimum of AZ 50 in accordance with ASTM A 792.
3. A minimum of GF 60 in accordance with ASTM A 875.

R603.2.4 Fastening requirements. Screws for steel-to-steel connections shall be installed with a minimum edge distance and center-to-center spacing of $^1/_2$ inch (12.7 mm), shall be self-drilling tapping and shall conform to SAE J 78. Structural sheathing shall be attached to steel studs with minimum No. 8 self-drilling tapping screws that conform to SAE J78. Screws for attaching structural sheathing to steel wall framing shall have a minimum head diameter of 0.292 inch (7.4 mm) with countersunk heads and shall be installed with a minimum edge distance of $^3/_8$ inch (9.5 mm). Gypsum board shall be attached to steel wall framing with minimum No. 6 screws conforming to ASTM C 954 and shall be installed in accordance with Section R702. For all connections, screws shall extend through the steel a minimum of three exposed threads. All self-drilling tapping screws conforming to SAE J 78 shall have a Type II coating in accordance with ASTM B 633.

Where No. 8 screws are specified in a steel to steel connection the required number of screws in the connection is permitted to be reduced in accordance with the reduction factors in Table R505.2.4, when larger screws are used or when one of the sheets of steel being connected is thicker than 33 mils (0.84 mm). When applying the reduction factor the resulting number of screws shall be rounded up.

TABLE R603.2.4
SCREW SUBSTITUTION FACTOR

SCREW SIZE	THINNEST CONNECTED STEEL SHEET (mils)	
	33	43
#8	1.0	0.67
#10	0.93	0.62
#12	0.86	0.56

For SI: 1 mil = 0.0254 mm.

R603.3 Wall construction. All exterior steel framed walls and interior load-bearing steel framed walls shall be constructed in accordance with the provisions of this section and Figure R603.3.

R603.3.1 Wall to foundation or floor connections. Steel framed walls shall be anchored to foundations or floors in accordance with Table R603.3.1 and Figure R603.3.1(1) or R603.3.1(2).

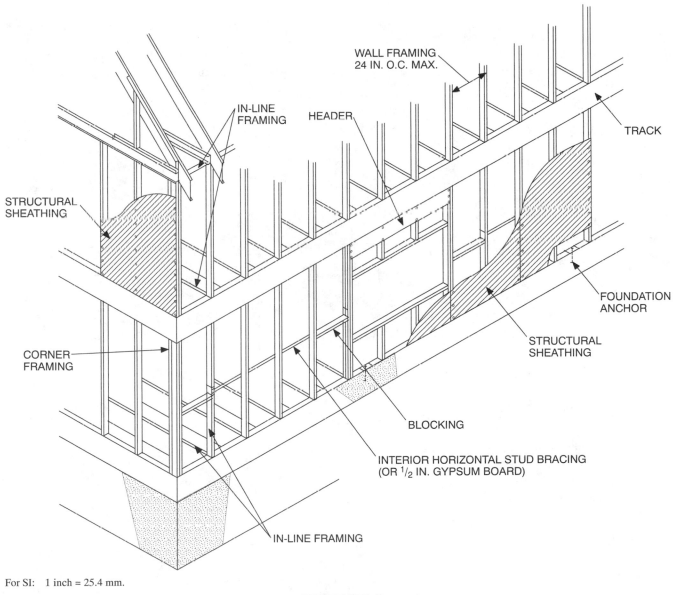

For SI: 1 inch = 25.4 mm.

FIGURE R603.3
STEEL WALL CONSTRUCTION

TABLE R603.3.1
WALL TO FOUNDATION OR FLOOR CONNECTION REQUIREMENTS[a,b,c]

FRAMING CONDITION	BASIC WIND SPEED (mph) AND EXPOSURE		
	85 A/B or Seismic Design Categories A, B and C	85 C or less than 110 A/B	Less than 110 C
Wall bottom track to floor joist or track	1-No. 8 screw at 12″ o.c.	1-No. 8 screw at 12″ o.c.	2-No. 8 screw at 12″ o.c.
Wall bottom track to wood sill per Figure R603.3.1(2)	Steel plate spaced at 4′ o.c., with 4-No. 8 screws and 4-10d or 6-8d common nails	Steel plate spaced at 3′ o.c., with 4-No. 8 screws and 4-10d or 6-8d common nails	Steel plate spaced at 2′ o.c., with 4-No. 8 screws and 4-10d or 6-8d common nails
Wall bottom track to foundation per Figure R603.3.1(1)	$1/2$″ minimum diameter anchor bolt at 6′ o.c.	$1/2$″ minimum diameter anchor bolt at 6′ o.c.	$1/2$″ minimum diameter anchor bolt at 4′ o.c.
Wind uplift connector capacity for 16-inch stud spacing[c]	N/R	N/R	65 lbs.
Wind uplift connector capacity for 24-inch stud spacing[c]	N/R	N/R	100 lbs.

For SI: 1 inch = 25.4 mm, 1 foot = 304.8 mm, 1 mile per hour = 1.609 km/hr, 1 pound = 4.4 N.

a. Anchor bolts shall be located not more than 12 inches from corners or the termination of bottom tracks (e.g. at door openings or corners). Bolts shall extend a minimum of 7 inches into concrete or masonry.

b. All screw sizes shown are minimum.

c. N/R = uplift connector not required. Uplift connectors are in addition to other connection requirements and shall be applied in accordance with Section R603.8.

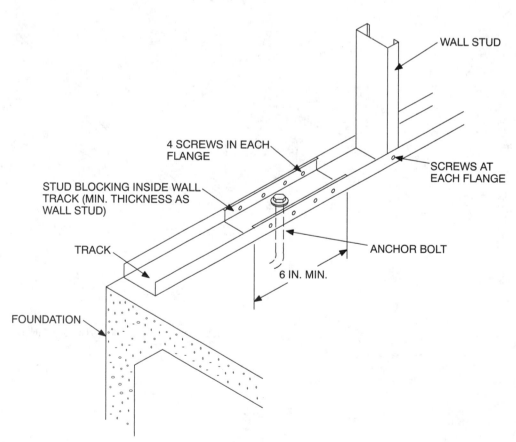

For SI: 1 inch = 25.4 mm.

FIGURE R603.3.1(1)
WALL TO FOUNDATION CONNECTION

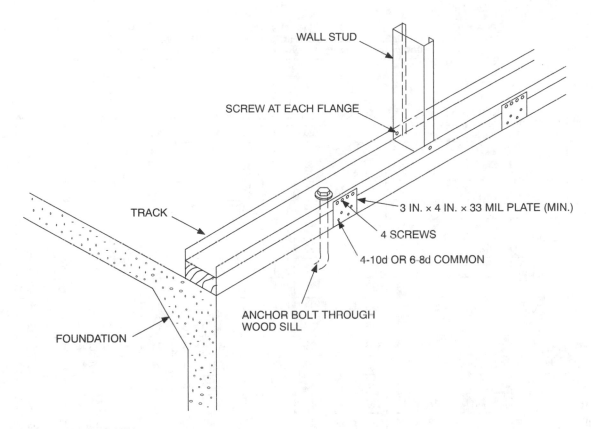

WALL STUD

SCREW AT EACH FLANGE

TRACK

3 IN. × 4 IN. × 33 MIL PLATE (MIN.)

4 SCREWS

4-10d OR 6-8d COMMON

ANCHOR BOLT THROUGH WOOD SILL

FOUNDATION

For SI: 1 inch = 25.4 mm, 1 mil = 0.0254 mm.

FIGURE R603.3.1(2)
WALL TO WOOD SILL CONNECTION

R603.3.2 Load-bearing walls. Steel studs shall comply with Tables R603.3.2(2) through R603.3.2(7) for steels with minimum yield strength of 33 ksi (227.7 MPa) and Tables R603.3.2(8) through R603.3.2(13) for steels with minimum yield strength of 50 ksi (345 MPa). Fastening requirements shall be in accordance with Section R603.2.4 and Table R603.3.2(1). Tracks shall have the same minimum steel thickness as the wall studs. Exterior walls with a minimum of $1/2$-inch (12.7 mm) gypsum board installed in accordance with Section R702 on the interior surface and wood structural panels of minimum $7/16$-inch-thick (11.1 mm) oriented strand board or $15/32$-inch-thick (11.9 mm) plywood installed in accordance with Table R603.3.2(1) on the outside surface shall be permitted to use the next thinner stud, from Tables R603.3.2(2) through R603.3.2(13) but not less than 33 mils (0.84 mm). Interior load-bearing walls with a minimum of $1/2$-inch (12.7 mm) gypsum board installed in accordance with Section R702 on both sides of the wall shall be permitted to use the next thinner stud, from Tables R603.3.2(2) through R603.3.2(13) but not less than 33 mils (0.84 mm).

TABLE R603.3.2(1)
WALL FASTENING SCHEDULE[a]

DESCRIPTION OF BUILDING ELEMENT	NUMBER AND SIZE OF FASTENERS[a]	SPACING OF FASTENERS
Floor joist to track of load-bearing wall	2-No. 8 screws	Each joist
Wall stud to top or bottom track	2-No. 8 screws	Each end of stud, one per flange
Structural sheathing to wall studs	No. 8 screws	6″ o.c. on edges and 12″ o.c. at intermediate supports
Roof framing to wall	Approved design or tie down in accordance with Section R802.11	

For SI: 1 inch = 25.4 mm.

a. All screw sizes shown are minimum.

TABLE R603.3.2(2)
COLD-FORMED STEEL STUD THICKNESS FOR 8-FOOT WALLS
Studs supporting roof and ceiling only (one-story building or second floor of a two-story building) 33 ksi steel

WIND SPEED Exp. A/B	Exp. C	MEMBER SIZE[c]	MEMBER SPACING (inches)	STUD THICKNESS (mils)[a,b] Building width (feet)[d] 24 Ground snow load (psf) 20	30	50	70	28 Ground snow load (psf) 20	30	50	70	32 Ground snow load (psf) 20	30	50	70	36 Ground snow load (psf) 20	30	50	70
85 mph	—	350S162	16	33	33	33	33	33	33	33	33	33	33	33	33	33	33	33	33
			24	33	33	33	33	33	33	33	33	33	33	33	33	33	33	33	43
		550S162	16	33	33	33	33	33	33	33	33	33	33	33	33	33	33	33	33
			24	33	33	33	33	33	33	33	33	33	33	33	33	33	33	33	33
100 mph	85 mph	350S162	16	33	33	33	33	33	33	33	33	33	33	33	33	33	33	33	33
			24	33	33	33	33	33	33	33	33	33	33	33	43	33	33	43	43
		550S162	16	33	33	33	33	33	33	33	33	33	33	33	33	33	33	33	33
			24	33	33	33	33	33	33	33	33	33	33	33	33	33	33	33	33
110 mph	100 mph	350S162	16	33	33	33	33	33	33	33	33	33	33	33	33	33	33	33	33
			24	33	33	43	43	33	33	43	43	33	43	43	43	43	43	43	43
		550S162	16	33	33	33	33	33	33	33	33	33	33	33	33	33	33	33	33
			24	33	33	33	33	33	33	33	33	33	33	33	33	33	33	33	33
120 mph	110 mph	350S162	16	33	33	33	33	33	33	33	33	33	33	33	33	33	33	33	33
			24	43	43	43	43	43	43	43	54	43	43	54	54	43	43	54	54
		550S162	16	33	33	33	33	33	33	33	33	33	33	33	33	33	33	33	33
			24	33	33	33	33	33	33	33	33	33	33	33	33	33	33	33	33
130 mph	120 mph	350S162	16	33	33	43	43	33	43	43	43	43	43	43	43	43	43	43	43
			24	54	54	54	54	54	54	54	68	54	54	68	68	54	54	68	68
		550S162	16	33	33	33	33	33	33	33	33	33	33	33	33	33	33	33	33
			24	33	33	33	33	33	33	33	43	33	33	33	43	33	33	43	43
—	130 mph	350S162	16	43	43	43	43	43	43	43	43	43	43	43	54	43	43	43	54
			24	68	68	68	68	68	68	68	68	68	68	68	68	68	68	68	(d)
		550S162	16	33	33	33	33	33	33	33	33	33	33	33	33	33	33	33	33
			24	33	43	43	43	43	43	43	43	43	43	43	43	43	43	43	43

For SI: 1 inch = 25.4 mm, 1 foot = 304.8 mm, 1 mil = 0.0254 mm, 1 mile per hour = 1.609 km/h, 1 pound per square foot = 0.0479 kN/m², 1 kilogram per square inch = 6.895 MPa.

a. Deflection criteria: $L/240$.

b. Building width is in the direction of horizontal framing members supported by the wall studs.

c. Design load assumptions:
   Roof dead load is 12 psf.
   Attic live load is 10 psf.

d. 68-mil-thick stud is allowed if wall is fully sheathed per Section R603.3.2.

TABLE R603.3.2(3)
COLD-FORMED STEEL STUD THICKNESS FOR 8-FOOT WALLS
Studs supporting one floor, roof and ceiling (first story of a two-story building) 33 ksi steel

WIND SPEED		MEMBER SIZE[c]	MEMBER SPACING (inches)	STUD THICKNESS (mils)[a,b]															
				Building width (feet)[d]															
				24				28				32				36			
				Ground snow load (psf)				Ground snow load (psf)				Ground snow load (psf)				Ground snow load (psf)			
Exp. A/B	Exp. C			20	30	50	70	20	30	50	70	20	30	50	70	20	30	50	70
85 mph	—	350S162	16	33	33	33	33	33	33	33	33	33	33	33	43	33	33	33	43
			24	43	43	43	43	43	43	43	43	43	43	43	54	43	43	54	54
		550S162	16	33	33	33	33	33	33	33	33	33	33	33	33	33	33	33	33
			24	33	33	33	33	33	33	33	43	33	33	43	43	33	43	43	54
100 mph	85 mph	350S162	16	33	33	33	33	33	33	33	33	33	33	33	43	33	33	43	43
			24	43	43	43	54	43	43	54	54	54	54	54	54	54	54	54	54
		550S162	16	33	33	33	33	33	33	33	33	33	33	33	33	33	33	33	43
			24	33	33	33	33	33	33	33	43	33	33	43	43	43	43	43	54
110 mph	100 mph	350S162	16	33	33	33	33	33	33	43	43	43	43	43	43	43	43	43	43
			24	54	54	54	54	54	54	54	54	54	54	54	68	54	54	68	68
		550S162	16	33	33	33	33	33	33	33	33	33	33	33	33	33	33	33	33
			24	33	33	33	33	33	33	43	43	43	43	43	43	43	43	43	54
120 mph	110 mph	350S162	16	43	43	43	43	43	43	43	43	43	43	43	43	43	43	43	54
			24	54	54	54	68	54	68	68	68	68	68	68	68	68	68	68	68
		550S162	16	33	33	33	33	33	33	33	33	33	33	33	33	33	33	33	33
			24	33	43	43	43	43	43	43	43	43	43	43	43	43	43	43	54
130 mph	120 mph	350S162	16	43	43	43	54	43	54	54	54	54	54	54	54	54	54	54	54
			24	68	68	68	68	68	68	(d)	(d)	(d)	(d)	(d)	(d)	(d)	(d)	(d)	(d)
		550S162	16	33	33	33	33	33	33	33	33	33	33	33	33	33	33	33	43
			24	43	43	43	43	43	43	43	54	43	43	54	54	54	54	54	54
—	130 mph	350S162	16	54	54	54	54	54	54	54	54	54	54	54	68	54	54	68	68
			24	(d)	(d)	(d)	(d)	(d)	(d)	(d)	(d)	(d)	(d)	(d)	(d)	(d)	(d)	(d)	(d)
		550S162	16	33	33	33	33	33	33	33	43	33	33	43	43	43	43	43	43
			24	43	43	54	54	54	54	54	54	54	54	54	54	54	54	54	54

For SI: 1 inch = 25.4 mm, 1 foot = 304.8 mm, 1 mil = 0.0254 mm, 1 mile per hour = 1.609 km/h, 1 pound per square foot = 0.0479 kN/m², 1 kilogram per square inch = 6.895 MPa.

a. Deflection criteria: $L/240$.

b. Building width is in the direction of horizontal framing members supported by the wall studs.

c. Design load assumptions:
   Roof dead load is 12 psf.
   Attic live load is 10 psf.

d. 68-mil-thick stud is allowed used if wall is fully sheathed per Section R603.3.2.

TABLE R603.3.2(4)
COLD-FORMED STEEL STUD THICKNESS FOR 9-FOOT WALLS
Studs supporting roof and ceiling only (one-story building or second floor of a two-story building) 33 ksi steel

WIND SPEED		MEMBER SIZE[c]	MEMBER SPACING (inches)	STUD THICKNESS (mils)[a,b] Building width (feet)[d]															
				24				28				32				36			
Exp. A/B	Exp. C			Ground snow load (psf)				Ground snow load (psf)				Ground snow load (psf)				Ground snow load (psf)			
				20	30	50	70	20	30	50	70	20	30	50	70	20	30	50	70
85 mph	—	350S162	16	33	33	33	33	33	33	33	33	33	33	33	33	33	33	33	33
			24	33	33	33	33	33	33	33	33	33	33	33	33	33	33	33	43
		550S162	16	33	33	33	33	33	33	33	33	33	33	33	33	33	33	33	33
			24	33	33	33	33	33	33	33	33	33	33	33	33	33	33	33	33
100 mph	85 mph	350S162	16	33	33	33	33	33	33	33	33	33	33	33	33	33	33	33	33
			24	33	33	43	43	33	33	43	43	33	43	43	43	43	43	43	43
		550S162	16	33	33	33	33	33	33	33	33	33	33	33	33	33	33	33	33
			24	33	33	33	33	33	33	33	33	33	33	33	33	33	33	33	33
110 mph	100 mph	350S162	16	33	33	33	33	33	33	33	33	33	33	33	33	33	33	33	33
			24	43	43	43	43	43	43	43	43	43	43	43	54	43	43	43	54
		550S162	16	33	33	33	33	33	33	33	33	33	33	33	33	33	33	33	33
			24	33	33	33	33	33	33	33	33	33	33	33	33	33	33	33	33
120 mph	110 mph	350S162	16	33	33	33	33	33	33	33	43	33	33	43	43	33	33	43	43
			24	54	54	54	54	54	54	54	54	54	54	54	54	54	54	54	68
		550S162	16	33	33	33	33	33	33	33	33	33	33	33	33	33	33	33	33
			24	33	33	33	33	33	33	33	33	33	33	33	33	33	33	33	43
130 mph	120 mph	350S162	16	43	43	43	43	43	43	43	43	43	43	43	54	43	43	43	54
			24	68	68	68	68	68	68	68	68	68	68	68	68	68	68	68	(d)
		550S162	16	33	33	33	33	33	33	33	33	33	33	33	33	33	33	33	33
			24	33	43	43	43	43	43	43	43	43	43	43	43	43	43	43	43
—	130 mph	350S162	16	54	54	54	54	54	54	54	54	54	54	54	54	54	54	54	54
			24	(d)	(d)	(d)	(d)	(d)	(d)	(d)	(d)	(d)	(d)	(d)	(d)	(d)	(d)	(d)	(d)
		550S162	16	33	33	33	33	33	33	33	33	33	33	33	33	33	33	33	33
			24	43	43	43	43	43	43	43	43	43	43	43	54	43	43	43	54

For SI:　1 inch = 25.4 mm, 1 foot = 304.8 mm, 1 mil = 0.0254 mm, 1 mile per hour = 1.609 km/h, 1 pound per square foot = 0.0479 kN/m², 1 kilogram per square inch = 6.895 MPa.

a. Deflection criteria: $L/240$.

b. Building width is in the direction of horizontal framing members supported by the wall studs.

c. Design load assumptions:

　　Roof dead load is 12 psf.

　　Attic live load is 10 psf.

d. 68-mil-thick stud is allowed if wall is fully sheathed per Section R603.3.2.

TABLE R603.3.2(5)
COLD-FORMED STEEL STUD THICKNESS FOR 9-FOOT WALLS
Studs supporting one floor, roof and ceiling (first story of a two-story building) 33 ksi steel

WIND SPEED Exp. A/B	Exp. C	MEMBER SIZE[c]	MEMBER SPACING (inches)	Building width (feet)[d] 24 Ground snow load (psf) 20	30	50	70	28 Ground snow load (psf) 20	30	50	70	32 Ground snow load (psf) 20	30	50	70	36 Ground snow load (psf) 20	30	50	70
85 mph	—	350S162	16	33	33	33	33	33	33	33	33	33	33	33	33	33	33	33	43
			24	43	43	43	43	43	43	43	54	43	43	54	54	54	54	54	54
		550S162	16	33	33	33	33	33	33	33	33	33	33	33	33	33	33	33	33
			24	33	33	33	33	33	33	33	43	33	33	43	43	33	33	43	43
100 mph	85 mph	350S162	16	33	33	33	33	33	33	33	43	33	43	43	43	43	43	43	43
			24	43	54	54	54	54	54	54	54	54	54	54	54	54	54	68	68
		550S162	16	33	33	33	33	33	33	33	33	33	33	33	33	33	33	33	33
			24	33	33	33	33	33	33	33	43	33	33	43	43	43	43	43	43
110 mph	100 mph	350S162	16	43	43	43	43	43	43	43	43	43	43	43	43	43	43	43	43
			24	54	54	54	54	54	54	54	54	54	54	54	54	54	54	68	68
		550S162	16	33	33	33	33	33	33	33	33	33	33	33	33	33	33	33	33
			24	33	33	43	43	43	43	43	43	43	43	43	43	43	43	43	54
120 mph	110 mph	350S162	16	43	43	43	43	43	43	43	54	43	43	54	54	54	54	54	54
			24	68	68	68	68	68	68	68	68	68	68	68	(d)	68	68	(d)	(d)
		550S162	16	33	33	33	33	33	33	33	33	33	33	33	33	33	33	33	33
			24	43	43	43	43	43	43	43	43	43	43	43	54	43	43	54	54
130 mph	120 mph	350S162	16	54	54	54	54	54	54	54	54	54	54	54	68	54	54	68	68
			24	(d)	(d)	(d)	(d)	(d)	(d)	(d)	(d)	(d)	(d)	(d)	(d)	(d)	(d)	(d)	(d)
		550S162	16	33	33	33	33	33	33	33	43	33	33	43	43	33	43	43	43
			24	43	43	54	54	54	54	54	54	54	54	54	54	54	54	54	54
—	130 mph	350S162	16	68	68	68	68	68	68	68	68	68	68	68	68	68	68	68	68
			24	(d)	(d)	(d)	(d)	(d)	(d)	(d)	—	(d)	(d)	—	—	—	—	—	—
		550S162	16	33	33	43	43	43	43	43	43	43	43	43	43	43	43	43	43
			24	54	54	54	54	54	54	54	54	54	54	54	68	54	54	68	68

For SI: 1 inch = 25.4 mm, 1 foot = 304.8 mm, 1 mil = 0.0254 mm, 1 mile per hour = 1.609 km/h, 1 pound per square foot = 0.0479 kN/m², 1 kilogram per square inch = 6.895 MPa.

a. Deflection criteria: $L/240$.

b. Building width is in the direction of horizontal framing members supported by the wall studs.

c. Design load assumptions:

    Roof dead load is 12 psf.

    Attic live load is 10 psf.

d. 68-mil-thick stud is allowed if wall is fully sheathed per Section R603.3.2.

TABLE R603.3.2(6)
COLD-FORMED STEEL STUD THICKNESS FOR 10-FOOT WALLS
Studs supporting roof and ceiling only (one-story building or second floor of a two-story building) 33 ksi steel

WIND SPEED		MEMBER SIZE[c]	MEMBER SPACING (inches)	STUD THICKNESS (mils)[a,b] Building width (feet)[d]															
				24				28				32				36			
				Ground snow load (psf)				Ground snow load (psf)				Ground snow load (psf)				Ground snow load (psf)			
Exp. A/B	Exp. C			20	30	50	70	20	30	50	70	20	30	50	70	20	30	50	70
85 mph	—	350S162	16	33	33	33	33	33	33	33	33	33	33	33	33	33	33	33	33
			24	33	33	33	43	33	33	43	43	33	33	43	43	33	43	43	43
		550S162	16	33	33	33	33	33	33	33	33	33	33	33	33	33	33	33	33
			24	33	33	33	33	33	33	33	33	33	33	33	33	33	33	33	33
100 mph	85 mph	350S162	16	33	33	33	33	33	33	33	33	33	33	33	33	33	33	33	33
			24	43	43	43	43	43	43	43	54	43	43	43	54	43	43	54	54
		550S162	16	33	33	33	33	33	33	33	33	33	33	33	33	33	33	33	33
			24	33	33	33	33	33	33	33	33	33	33	33	33	33	33	33	33
110 mph	100 mph	350S162	16	33	33	33	43	33	33	43	43	33	33	43	43	33	33	43	43
			24	54	54	54	54	54	54	54	54	54	54	54	54	54	54	54	68
		550S162	16	33	33	33	33	33	33	33	33	33	33	33	33	33	33	33	33
			24	33	33	33	33	33	33	33	33	33	33	33	33	33	33	33	43
120 mph	110 mph	350S162	16	43	43	43	43	43	43	43	43	43	43	43	43	43	43	43	54
			24	68	68	68	68	68	68	68	68	68	68	68	68	68	68	68	68
		550S162	16	33	33	33	33	33	33	33	33	33	33	33	33	33	33	33	33
			24	33	33	43	43	33	33	43	43	33	43	43	43	43	43	43	43
130 mph	120 mph	350S162	16	54	54	54	54	54	54	54	54	54	54	54	54	54	54	54	68
			24	(d)	(d)	(d)	(d)	(d)	(d)	(d)	(d)	(d)	(d)	(d)	(d)	(d)	(d)	(d)	(d)
		550S162	16	33	33	33	33	33	33	33	33	33	33	33	33	33	33	33	33
			24	43	43	43	43	43	43	43	54	43	43	54	54	43	43	54	54
—	130 mph	350S162	16	68	68	68	68	68	68	68	68	68	68	68	68	68	68	68	68
			24	(d)	(d)	(d)	—	(d)	(d)	—	—	(d)	(d)	—	—	(d)	—	—	—
		550S162	16	33	33	33	43	33	33	43	43	33	33	43	43	33	43	43	43
			24	54	54	54	54	54	54	54	54	54	54	54	54	54	54	54	68

For SI: 1 inch = 25.4 mm, 1 foot = 304.8 mm, 1 mil = 0.0254 mm, 1 mile per hour = 1.609 km/h, 1 pound per square foot = 0.0479 kN/m^2, 1 kilogram per square inch = 6.895 MPa.

a. Deflection criteria: $L/240$.

b. Building width is in the direction of horizontal framing members supported by the wall studs.

c. Design load assumptions:
   Roof dead load is 12 psf.
   Attic live load is 10 psf.

d. 68-mil-thick stud is allowed if wall is fully sheathed per Section R603.3.2.

TABLE R603.3.2(7)
COLD-FORMED STEEL STUD THICKNESS FOR 10-FOOT WALLS
Studs supporting one floor, roof and ceiling (first story of a two-story building) 33 ksi steel

WIND SPEED Exp. A/B	Exp. C	MEMBER SIZE[c]	MEMBER SPACING (inches)	24 Ground snow load (psf) 20	30	50	70	28 Ground snow load (psf) 20	30	50	70	32 Ground snow load (psf) 20	30	50	70	36 Ground snow load (psf) 20	30	50	70
85 mph	—	350S162	16	33	33	33	43	33	33	43	43	43	43	43	43	43	43	43	43
			24	54	54	54	54	54	54	54	54	54	54	54	68	54	54	68	68
		550S162	16	33	33	33	33	33	33	33	33	33	33	33	33	33	33	33	33
			24	33	33	33	33	33	33	33	43	33	33	43	43	43	43	43	54
100 mph	85 mph	350S162	16	43	43	43	43	43	43	43	43	43	43	43	43	43	43	43	54
			24	54	54	68	68	68	68	68	68	68	68	68	68	68	68	68	(d)
		550S162	16	33	33	33	33	33	33	33	33	33	33	33	33	33	33	33	33
			24	33	33	43	43	43	43	43	43	43	43	43	43	43	43	43	54
110 mph	100 mph	350S162	16	43	43	43	43	43	43	54	54	43	54	54	54	54	54	54	54
			24	68	68	68	68	68	68	68	(d)	68	68	(d)	(d)	(d)	(d)	(d)	(d)
		550S162	16	33	33	33	33	33	33	33	33	33	33	33	33	33	33	33	33
			24	43	43	43	43	43	43	43	43	43	43	43	54	43	43	54	54
120 mph	110 mph	350S162	16	54	54	54	54	54	54	54	54	54	54	54	54	54	54	54	54
			24	(d)	(d)	(d)	(d)	(d)	(d)	(d)	(d)	(d)	(d)	(d)	(d)	(d)	(d)	(d)	(d)
		550S162	16	33	33	33	33	33	33	33	33	33	33	33	43	33	33	43	43
			24	43	43	43	54	43	54	54	54	54	54	54	54	54	54	54	54
130 mph	120 mph	350S162	16	68	68	68	68	68	68	68	68	68	68	68	68	68	68	68	(4)
			24	(d)	(d)	—	—	—	—	—	—	—	—	—					
		550S162	16	43	43	43	43	43	43	43	43	43	43	43	43	43	43	43	43
			24	54	54	54	54	54	54	54	68	54	68	68	68	68	68	68	68
—	130 mph	350S162	16	68	(d)	(d)	(d)	(d)	(d)	(d)	(d)	(d)	(d)	(d)	(d)	(d)	(d)	(d)	(d)
			24	—	—	—	—	—	—	—	—	—	—	—	—	—	—	—	—
		550S162	16	43	43	43	43	43	43	43	43	43	43	43	54	43	43	54	54
			24	68	68	68	68	68	68	68	68	68	68	68	68	68	68	68	(d)

For SI: 1 inch = 25.4 mm, 1 foot = 304.8 mm, 1 mil = 0.0254 mm, 1 mile per hour = 1.609 km/h, 1 pound per square foot = 0.0479 kN/m², 1 kilogram per square inch = 6.895 MPa.

a. Deflection criteria: L/240.

b. Building width is in the direction of horizontal framing members supported by the wall studs.

c. Design load assumptions:
   Roof dead load is 12 psf.
   Attic live load is 10 psf.

d. 68-mil-thick stud is allowed if wall is fully sheathed per Section R603.3.2.

TABLE R603.3.2(8)
COLD-FORMED STEEL STUD THICKNESS FOR 8-FOOT WALLS
Studs supporting roof and ceiling only (one-story building or second floor of a two-story building) 50 ksi steel

WIND SPEED		MEMBER SIZE[c]	MEMBER SPACING (inches)	STUD THICKNESS (mils)[a,b]															
				Building width (feet)[d]															
				24				28				32				36			
Exp. A/B	Exp. C			Ground snow load (psf)				Ground snow load (psf)				Ground snow load (psf)				Ground snow load (psf)			
				20	30	50	70	20	30	50	70	20	30	50	70	20	30	50	70
85 mph	—	350S162	16	33	33	33	33	33	33	33	33	33	33	33	33	33	33	33	33
			24	33	33	33	33	33	33	33	33	33	33	33	33	33	33	33	33
		550S162	16	33	33	33	33	33	33	33	33	33	33	33	33	33	33	33	33
			24	33	33	33	33	33	33	33	33	33	33	33	33	33	33	33	33
100 mph	85 mph	350S162	16	33	33	33	33	33	33	33	33	33	33	33	33	33	33	33	33
			24	33	33	33	33	33	33	33	33	33	33	33	33	33	33	33	33
		550S162	16	33	33	33	33	33	33	33	33	33	33	33	33	33	33	33	33
			24	33	33	33	33	33	33	33	33	33	33	33	33	33	33	33	33
110 mph	100 mph	350S162	16	33	33	33	33	33	33	33	33	33	33	33	33	33	33	33	33
			24	33	33	33	33	33	33	33	33	33	33	33	33	33	33	33	43
		550S162	16	33	33	33	33	33	33	33	33	33	33	33	33	33	33	33	33
			24	33	33	33	33	33	33	33	33	33	33	33	33	33	33	33	33
120 mph	110 mph	350S162	16	33	33	33	33	33	33	33	33	33	33	33	33	33	33	33	33
			24	33	33	33	43	33	33	43	43	33	33	43	43	33	43	43	43
		550S162	16	33	33	33	33	33	33	33	33	33	33	33	33	33	33	33	33
			24	33	33	33	33	33	33	33	33	33	33	33	33	33	33	33	33
130 mph	120 mph	350S162	16	33	33	33	33	33	33	33	33	33	33	33	33	33	33	33	33
			24	43	43	43	43	43	43	43	43	43	43	43	54	43	43	43	54
		550S162	16	33	33	33	33	33	33	33	33	33	33	33	33	33	33	33	33
			24	33	33	33	33	33	33	33	33	33	33	33	33	33	33	33	33
—	130 mph	350S162	16	33	33	33	33	33	33	33	43	33	33	43	43	33	33	43	43
			24	43	54	54	54	54	54	54	54	54	54	54	54	54	54	54	54
		550S162	16	33	33	33	33	33	33	33	33	33	33	33	33	33	33	33	33
			24	33	33	33	33	33	33	33	33	33	33	33	33	33	33	33	33

For SI: 1 inch = 25.4 mm, 1 foot = 304.8 mm, 1 mil = 0.0254 mm, 1 mile per hour = 1.609 km/h, 1 pound per square foot = 0.0479 kN/m², 1 kilogram per square inch = 6.895 MPa.

a. Deflection criteria: $L/240$.

b. Building width is in the direction of horizontal framing members supported by the wall studs.

c. Design load assumptions:
   Roof dead load is 12 psf.
   Attic live load is 10 psf.

d. 68-mil-thick stud is allowed if wall is fully sheathed per Section R603.3.2.

TABLE R603.3.2(9)
COLD-FORMED STEEL STUD THICKNESS FOR 8-FOOT WALLS
Studs supporting one floor, roof and ceiling (first story of a two-story building) 50 ksi steel

WIND SPEED		MEMBER SIZE[c]	MEMBER SPACING (inches)	STUD THICKNESS (mils)[a,b]															
				Building width (feet)[d]															
				24				28				32				36			
				Ground snow load (psf)				Ground snow load (psf)				Ground snow load (psf)				Ground snow load (psf)			
Exp. A/B	Exp. C			20	30	50	70	20	30	50	70	20	30	50	70	20	30	50	70
85 mph	—	350S162	16	33	33	33	33	33	33	33	33	33	33	33	33	33	33	33	43
			24	33	33	33	43	33	33	43	43	43	43	43	43	43	43	43	54
		550S162	16	33	33	33	33	33	33	33	33	33	33	33	33	33	33	33	33
			24	33	33	33	33	33	33	33	33	33	33	33	43	33	33	43	43
100 mph	85 mph	350S162	16	33	33	33	33	33	33	33	33	33	33	33	33	33	33	33	43
			24	33	43	43	43	43	43	43	43	43	43	43	43	43	33	33	54
		550S162	16	33	33	33	33	33	33	33	33	33	33	33	33	33	33	33	43
			24	33	33	33	33	33	33	33	33	33	33	33	43	33	33	43	43
110 mph	100 mph	350S162	16	33	33	33	33	33	33	33	33	33	33	33	33	33	33	33	43
			24	43	43	43	43	43	43	43	43	43	43	54	54	43	54	54	54
		550S162	16	33	33	33	33	33	33	33	33	33	33	33	33	33	33	33	33
			24	33	33	33	33	33	33	33	33	33	33	33	43	33	33	43	43
120 mph	110 mph	350S162	16	33	33	33	33	33	33	33	43	33	33	43	43	33	43	43	43
			24	43	43	43	54	43	54	54	54	54	54	54	54	54	54	54	54
		550S162	16	33	33	33	33	33	33	33	33	33	33	33	33	33	33	33	33
			24	33	33	33	33	33	33	33	33	33	33	33	43	33	33	43	43
130 mph	120 mph	350S162	16	43	43	43	43	43	43	43	43	43	43	43	43	43	43	43	43
			24	54	54	54	54	54	54	54	68	54	54	68	68	68	68	68	68
		550S162	16	33	33	33	33	33	33	33	33	33	33	33	33	33	33	33	43
			24	33	33	33	43	33	43	43	43	43	43	43	43	43	43	43	43
—	130 mph	350S162	16	43	43	43	43	43	43	43	43	43	43	43	54	43	43	54	54
			24	54	68	68	68	68	68	68	68	68	68	68	68	68	68	68	68
		550S162	16	33	33	33	33	33	33	33	33	33	33	33	33	33	33	33	33
			24	43	43	43	43	43	43	43	43	43	43	43	43	43	43	43	43

For SI: 1 inch = 25.4 mm, 1 foot = 304.8 mm, 1 mil = 0.0254 mm, 1 mile per hour = 1.609 km/h, 1 pound per square foot = 0.0479 kN/m^2, 1 kilogram per square inch = 6.895 MPa.

a. Deflection criteria: $L/240$.

b. Building width is in the direction of horizontal framing members supported by the wall studs.

c. Design load assumptions:
   Roof dead load is 12 psf.
   Attic live load is 10 psf.

d. 68-mil-thick stud is allowed if wall is fully sheathed per Section R603.3.2.

TABLE R603.3.2(10)
COLD-FORMED STEEL STUD THICKNESS FOR 9-FOOT WALLS
Studs supporting roof and ceiling only (one-story building or second floor of a two-story building) 50 ksi steel

WIND SPEED		MEMBER SIZE[c]	MEMBER SPACING (inches)	STUD THICKNESS (mils)[a,b]															
				Building width (feet)[d]															
				24				28				32				36			
Exp. A/B	Exp. C			Ground snow load (psf)				Ground snow load (psf)				Ground snow load (psf)				Ground snow load (psf)			
				20	30	50	70	20	30	50	70	20	30	50	70	20	30	50	70
85 mph	—	350S162	16	33	33	33	33	33	33	33	33	33	33	33	33	33	33	33	33
			24	33	33	33	33	33	33	33	33	33	33	33	33	33	33	33	33
		550S162	16	33	33	33	33	33	33	33	33	33	33	33	33	33	33	33	33
			24	33	33	33	33	33	33	33	33	33	33	33	33	33	33	33	33
100 mph	85 mph	350S162	16	33	33	33	33	33	33	33	33	33	33	33	33	33	33	33	33
			24	33	33	33	33	33	33	33	33	33	33	33	33	33	33	33	33
		550S162	16	33	33	33	33	33	33	33	33	33	33	33	33	33	33	33	33
			24	33	33	33	33	33	33	33	33	33	33	33	33	33	33	33	33
110 mph	100 mph	350S162	16	33	33	33	33	33	33	33	33	33	33	33	33	33	33	33	33
			24	33	33	33	33	33	33	33	43	33	33	33	43	33	33	43	43
		550S162	16	33	33	33	33	33	33	33	33	33	33	33	33	33	33	33	33
			24	33	33	33	33	33	33	33	33	33	33	33	33	33	33	33	33
120 mph	110 mph	350S162	16	33	33	33	33	33	33	33	33	33	33	33	33	33	33	33	33
			24	43	43	43	43	43	43	43	43	43	43	43	43	43	43	43	43
		550S162	16	33	33	33	33	33	33	33	33	33	33	33	33	33	33	33	33
			24	33	33	33	33	33	33	33	33	33	33	33	33	33	33	33	33
130 mph	120 mph	350S162	16	33	33	33	33	33	33	33	33	33	33	33	43	33	33	43	43
			24	43	43	54	54	43	54	54	54	54	54	54	54	54	54	54	54
		550S162	16	33	33	33	33	33	33	33	33	33	33	33	33	33	33	33	33
			24	33	33	33	33	33	33	33	33	33	33	33	33	33	33	33	33
—	130 mph	350S162	16	43	43	43	43	43	43	43	43	43	43	43	43	43	43	43	43
			24	54	54	54	54	54	54	54	54	54	54	54	68	54	54	54	68
		550S162	16	33	33	33	33	33	33	33	33	33	33	33	33	33	33	33	33
			24	33	33	33	33	33	33	33	43	33	33	43	43	33	33	43	43

For SI:　1 inch = 25.4 mm, 1 foot = 304.8 mm, 1 mil = 0.0254 mm, 1 mile per hour = 1.609 km/h, 1 pound per square foot = 0.0479 kN/m², 1 kilogram per square inch = 6.895 MPa.

a. Deflection criteria: $L/240$.

b. Building width is in the direction of horizontal framing members supported by the wall studs.

c. Design load assumptions:
　　Roof dead load is 12 psf.
　　Attic live load is 10 psf.

d. 68-mil-thick stud is allowed if wall is fully sheathed per Section R603.3.2.

TABLE R603.3.2(11)
COLD-FORMED STEEL STUD THICKNESS FOR 9-FOOT WALLS
Studs supporting one floor, roof and ceiling (first story of a two-story building) 50 ksi steel

WIND SPEED Exp. A/B	Exp. C	MEMBER SIZE[c]	MEMBER SPACING (inches)	24				28				32				36			
				Ground snow load (psf)				Ground snow load (psf)				Ground snow load (psf)				Ground snow load (psf)			
				20	30	50	70	20	30	50	70	20	30	50	70	20	30	50	70
85 mph	—	350S162	16	33	33	33	33	33	33	33	33	33	33	33	33	33	33	33	33
			24	33	33	33	43	33	43	43	43	43	43	43	43	43	43	43	43
		550S162	16	33	33	33	33	33	33	33	33	33	33	33	33	33	33	33	33
			24	33	33	33	33	33	33	33	33	33	33	33	33	33	33	33	43
100 mph	85 mph	350S162	16	33	33	33	33	33	33	33	33	33	33	33	33	33	33	33	33
			24	43	43	43	43	43	43	43	43	43	43	43	43	43	43	54	54
		550S162	16	33	33	33	33	33	33	33	33	33	33	33	33	33	33	33	33
			24	33	33	33	33	33	33	33	33	33	33	33	33	33	33	33	43
110 mph	100 mph	350S162	16	33	33	33	33	33	33	33	33	33	33	43	33	33	33	43	43
			24	43	43	43	43	43	43	43	54	43	54	54	54	54	54	54	54
		550S162	16	33	33	33	33	33	33	33	33	33	33	33	33	33	33	33	33
			24	33	33	33	33	33	33	33	33	33	33	33	33	33	33	33	43
120 mph	110 mph	350S162	16	33	33	33	43	33	33	43	43	43	43	43	43	43	43	43	43
			24	54	54	54	54	54	54	54	54	54	54	54	54	54	54	54	68
		550S162	16	33	33	33	33	33	33	33	33	33	33	33	33	33	33	33	33
			24	33	33	33	33	33	33	33	43	33	33	43	43	43	43	43	43
130 mph	120 mph	350S162	16	43	43	43	43	43	43	43	43	43	43	43	43	43	43	43	54
			24	54	54	68	68	68	68	68	68	68	68	68	68	68	68	68	68
		550S162	16	33	33	33	33	33	33	33	33	33	33	33	33	33	33	33	33
			24	43	43	43	43	43	43	43	43	43	43	43	43	43	43	43	43
—	130 mph	350S162	16	43	43	43	54	43	43	54	54	54	54	54	54	54	54	54	54
			24	68	68	68	68	68	68	68	68	68	68	(d)	(d)	68	(d)	(d)	(d)
		550S162	16	33	33	33	33	33	33	33	33	33	33	33	33	33	33	33	33
			24	43	43	43	43	43	43	43	43	43	43	43	43	43	43	43	54

For SI: 1 inch = 25.4 mm, 1 foot = 304.8 mm, 1 mil = 0.0254 mm, 1 mile per hour = 1.609 km/h, 1 pound per square foot = 0.0479 kN/m², 1 kilogram per square inch = 6.895 MPa.

a. Deflection criteria. $L/240$.

b. Building width is in the direction of horizontal framing members supported by the wall studs.

c. Design load assumptions:
   Roof dead load is 12 psf.
   Attic live load is 10 psf.

d. 68-mil-thick stud is allowed if wall is fully sheathed per Section R603.3.2.

TABLE R603.3.2(12)
COLD-FORMED STEEL STUD THICKNESS FOR 10-FOOT WALLS
Studs supporting roof and ceiling only (one-story building or second floor of a two-story building) 50 ksi steel

WIND SPEED		MEMBER SIZE[c]	MEMBER SPACING (inches)	STUD THICKNESS (mils)[a,b] Building width (feet)[d]															
				24				28				32				36			
				Ground snow load (psf)				Ground snow load (psf)				Ground snow load (psf)				Ground snow load (psf)			
Exp. A/B	Exp. C			20	30	50	70	20	30	50	70	20	30	50	70	20	30	50	70
85 mph	—	350S162	16	33	33	33	33	33	33	33	33	33	33	33	33	33	33	33	33
			24	33	33	33	33	33	33	33	33	33	33	33	33	33	33	33	43
		550S162	16	33	33	33	33	33	33	33	33	33	33	33	33	33	33	33	33
			24	33	33	33	33	33	33	33	33	33	33	33	33	33	33	33	33
100 mph	85 mph	350S162	16	33	33	33	33	33	33	33	33	33	33	33	33	33	33	33	33
			24	33	33	33	43	33	33	33	43	33	33	43	43	33	33	43	43
		550S162	16	33	33	33	33	33	33	33	33	33	33	33	33	33	33	33	33
			24	33	33	33	33	33	33	33	33	33	33	33	33	33	33	33	33
110 mph	100 mph	350S162	16	33	33	33	33	33	33	33	33	33	33	33	33	33	33	33	33
			24	43	43	43	43	43	43	43	43	43	43	43	43	43	43	43	54
		550S162	16	33	33	33	33	33	33	33	33	33	33	33	33	33	33	33	33
			24	33	33	33	33	33	33	33	33	33	33	33	33	33	33	33	33
120 mph	110 mph	350S162	16	33	33	33	33	33	33	33	33	33	33	33	43	33	33	33	43
			24	43	43	54	54	43	43	54	54	43	54	54	54	54	54	54	54
		550S162	16	33	33	33	33	33	33	33	33	33	33	33	33	33	33	33	33
			24	33	33	33	33	33	33	33	33	33	33	33	33	33	33	33	33
130 mph	120 mph	350S162	16	43	43	43	43	43	43	43	43	43	43	43	43	43	43	43	43
			24	54	54	54	68	54	54	68	68	54	54	68	68	54	68	68	68
		550S162	16	33	33	33	33	33	33	33	33	33	33	33	33	33	33	33	33
			24	33	33	33	43	33	33	43	43	33	33	43	43	33	43	43	43
—	130 mph	350S162	16	43	43	54	54	43	43	54	54	43	54	54	54	54	54	54	54
			24	68	68	68	68	68	68	68	(d)	68	68	68	(d)	68	68	(d)	(d)
		550S162	16	33	33	33	33	33	33	33	33	33	33	33	33	33	33	33	33
			24	43	43	43	43	43	43	43	43	43	43	43	43	43	43	43	43

For SI: 1 inch = 25.4 mm, 1 foot = 304.8 mm, 1 mil = 0.0254 mm, 1 mile per hour = 1.609 km/h, 1 pound per square foot = 0.0479 kN/m^2, 1 kilogram per square inch = 6.895 MPa.

a. Deflection criteria: $L/240$.

b. Building width is in the direction of horizontal framing members supported by the wall studs.

c. Design load assumptions:

    Roof dead load is 12 psf.

    Attic live load is 10 psf.

d. 68-mil-thick stud is allowed if wall is fully sheathed per Section R603.3.2.

TABLE R603.3.2(13)
COLD-FORMED STEEL STUD THICKNESS FOR 10-FOOT WALLS
Studs supporting one floor, roof and ceiling (first story of a two-story building) 50 ksi steel

WIND SPEED		MEMBER SIZE[c]	MEMBER SPACING (inches)	STUD THICKNESS (mils)[a,b]															
				Building width (feet)[d]															
				24				28				32				36			
				Ground snow load (psf)				Ground snow load (psf)				Ground snow load (psf)				Ground snow load (psf)			
Exp. A/B	Exp. C			20	30	50	70	20	30	50	70	20	30	50	70	20	30	50	70
85 mph	—	350S162	16	33	33	33	33	33	33	33	33	33	33	33	33	33	33	33	43
			24	43	43	43	43	43	43	43	43	43	43	54	54	43	54	54	54
		550S162	16	33	33	33	33	33	33	33	33	33	33	33	33	33	33	33	33
			24	33	33	33	33	33	33	33	33	33	33	33	43	33	33	33	43
100 mph	85 mph	350S162	16	33	33	33	33	33	33	33	43	33	33	43	43	43	43	43	43
			24	43	43	54	54	54	54	54	54	54	54	54	54	54	54	54	54
		550S162	16	33	33	33	33	33	33	33	33	33	33	33	33	33	33	33	33
			24	33	33	33	33	33	33	33	33	33	33	33	43	33	33	43	43
110 mph	100 mph	350S162	16	33	33	43	43	43	43	43	43	43	43	43	43	43	43	43	43
			24	54	54	54	54	54	54	54	54	54	54	68	68	54	68	68	68
		550S162	16	33	33	33	33	33	33	33	33	33	33	33	33	33	33	33	33
			24	33	33	33	33	33	33	33	43	33	43	43	43	43	43	43	43
120 mph	110 mph	350S162	16	43	43	43	43	43	43	43	43	43	43	43	54	43	43	54	54
			24	54	54	68	68	68	68	68	68	68	68	68	68	68	68	68	(d)
		550S162	16	33	33	33	33	33	33	33	33	33	33	33	33	33	33	33	33
			24	43	43	43	43	43	43	43	43	43	43	43	43	43	43	43	43
130 mph	120 mph	350S162	16	54	54	54	54	54	54	54	54	54	54	54	54	54	54	54	54
			24	68	68	(d)	(d)	(d)	(d)	(d)	(d)	(d)	(d)	(d)	(d)	(d)	(d)	(d)	(d)
		550S162	16	33	33	33	33	33	33	33	33	33	33	33	33	33	33	33	43
			24	43	43	43	43	43	43	43	43	43	43	43	54	43	43	54	54
—	130 mph	350S162	16	54	54	54	54	54	54	54	54	54	54	68	68	54	68	68	68
			24	(d)	(d)	(d)	(d)	(d)	(d)	(d)	(d)	(d)	(d)	(d)	(d)	(d)	(d)	(d)	(d)
		550S162	16	33	33	33	33	33	33	43	43	33	43	43	43	43	43	43	43
			24	43	43	54	54	54	54	54	54	54	54	54	54	54	54	54	54

For SI: 1 inch = 25.4 mm, 1 foot = 304.8 mm, 1 mil = 0.0254 mm, 1 mile per hour = 1.609 km/h, 1 pound per square foot = 0.0479 kN/m², 1 kilogram per square inch = 6.895 MPa.

a. Deflection criteria: $L/240$.

b. Building width is in the direction of horizontal framing members supported by the wall studs.

c. Design load assumptions:
   Roof dead load is 12 psf.
   Attic live load is 10 psf.

d. 68-mil-thick stud is allowed if wall is fully sheathed per Section R603.3.2.

R603.3.3 Stud bracing. The flanges of steel studs shall be laterally braced in accordance with one of the following:

1. Gypsum board installed with minimum No. 6 screws in accordance with Section R702 or structural sheathing installed in accordance with Table R603.3.2.

2. Horizontal steel strapping installed in accordance with Figure R603.3 at mid-height for 8-foot (2438 mm) walls, and one-third points for 9-foot and 10-foot (2743 mm and 3048 mm) walls. Steel straps shall be at least 1.5 inches in width and 33 mils in thickness (38 mm by 0.836 mm). Straps shall be attached to the flanges of studs with at least one No. 8 screw. In-line blocking shall be installed between studs at the termination of all straps. Straps shall be fastened to the blocking with at least two No. 8 screws.

R603.3.4 Cutting and notching. Flanges and lips of steel studs and headers shall not be cut or notched.

R603.3.5 Hole patching. Stud web holes with dimensions conforming to Section R603.2 that are closer than 10 inches (305 mm) from the edge of the hole to the end of the member shall be patched with a solid steel plate, C-section or track section in accordance with Figure R603.3.5. The patch shall be of a minimum thickness as the stud member and shall extend at least 1 inch (25.4 mm) beyond all edges of the hole.

The patch shall be fastened to the web with No. 8 screws (minimum) spaced not greater than 1 inch (25.4 mm) center to center along the edges of the patch, with a minimum edge distance of $^{1}/_{2}$ inch (12.7 mm).

R603.3.6 Splicing. Steel studs and other structural members shall not be spliced. Tracks shall be spliced in accordance with Figure R603.3.6.

R603.4 Corner framing. Corner studs and the top tracks shall be installed in accordance with Figure R603.4.

R603.5 Exterior wall covering. The method of attachment of exterior wall covering materials to cold-formed steel stud wall framing shall conform to the manufacturer's installation instructions.

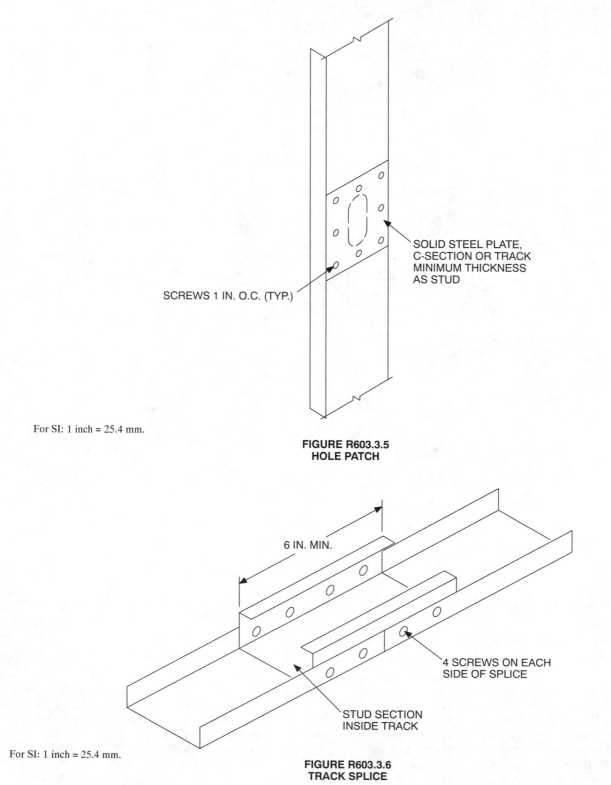

SOLID STEEL PLATE, C-SECTION OR TRACK MINIMUM THICKNESS AS STUD

SCREWS 1 IN. O.C. (TYP.)

For SI: 1 inch = 25.4 mm.

FIGURE R603.3.5
HOLE PATCH

6 IN. MIN.

4 SCREWS ON EACH SIDE OF SPLICE

STUD SECTION INSIDE TRACK

For SI: 1 inch = 25.4 mm.

FIGURE R603.3.6
TRACK SPLICE

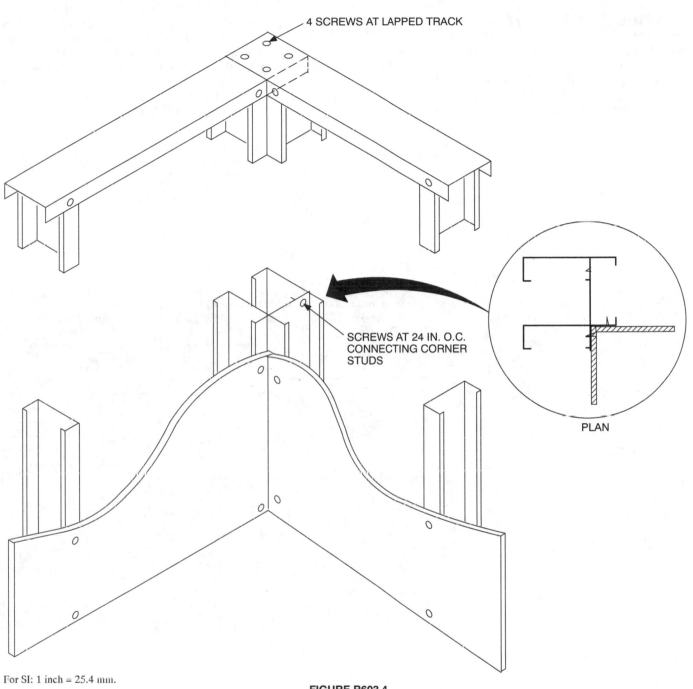

4 SCREWS AT LAPPED TRACK

SCREWS AT 24 IN. O.C.
CONNECTING CORNER
STUDS

PLAN

For SI: 1 inch = 25.4 mm.

**FIGURE R603.4
CORNER FRAMING**

R603.6 Headers. Headers shall be installed above wall openings in all exterior walls and interior load-bearing walls in accordance with Figure R603.6 and Tables R603.6(1), R603.6(2), and R603.6(3). The number of jack and king studs shall comply with Table R603.6(4). King and jack studs shall be of the same dimension and thickness as the adjacent wall studs. Headers shall be connected to king studs in accordance with Table R603.6(5). One-half of the total number of screws shall be applied to the header and one-half to the king stud by use of a minimum 2-inch by 2-inch (51 mm by 51 mm) clip angle or 4-inch (102 mm) wide steel plate. The clip angle or plate shall extend the depth of the header minus $1/2$ inch (12.7 mm) and shall have a minimum thickness of the header members or the wall studs, whichever is thicker.

TABLE R603.6(1)
ALLOWABLE HEADER SPANS[a,b]
Headers supporting roof and ceiling only (33 ksi steel)

NOMINAL MEMBER	GROUND SNOW LOAD (20 psf) Building width[c] (feet)				GROUND SNOW LOAD (30 psf) Building width[c] (feet)				GROUND SNOW LOAD (50 psf) Building width[c] (feet)				GROUND SNOW LOAD (70 psf) Building width[c] (feet)			
	24	28	32	36	24	28	32	36	24	28	32	36	24	28	32	36
2-350S162-33	3'-11"	3'-8"	3'-5"	3'-3"	3'-8"	3'-5"	3'-2"	2'-10"	3'-0"	2'-7"	2'-4"	2'-1"	2'-4"	2'-1"	—	—
2-350S162-43	4'-9"	4'-5"	4'-2"	4'-0"	4'-5"	4'-2"	3'-11"	3'-9"	3'-10"	3'-7"	3'-4"	3'-2"	3'-5"	3'-2"	3'-0"	2'-9"
2-350S162-54	5'-4"	5'-0"	4'-9"	4'-6"	5'-0"	4'-8"	4'-5"	4'-2"	4'-3"	4'-0"	3'-9"	3'-7"	3'-10"	3'-7"	3'-4"	3'-2"
2-350S162-68	6'-0"	5'-7"	5'-3"	5'-0"	5'-7"	5'-3"	4'-11"	4'-8"	4'-10"	4'-6"	4'-3"	4'-0"	4'-3"	4'-0"	3'-9"	3'-7"
2-550S162-33	3'-11"	3'-5"	3'-0"	2'-9"	3'-5"	3'-0"	2'-8"	2'-5"	2'-6"	2'-2"	—	—	—	—	—	—
2-550S162-43	6'-5"	6'-0"	5'-8"	5'-5"	6'-0"	5'-8"	5'-4"	5'-0"	5'-2"	4'-10"	4'-4"	3'-11"	4'-5"	3'-10"	3'-5"	3'-1"
2-550S162-54	7'-3"	6'-10"	6'-5"	6'-1"	6'-9"	6'-4"	6'-0"	5'-8"	5'-10"	5'-5"	5'-1"	4'-10"	5'-2"	4'-10"	4'-7"	4'-4"
2-550S162-68	8'-2"	7'-8"	7'-2"	6'-11"	7'-7"	7'-2"	6'-9"	6'-4"	6'-6"	6'-1"	5'-9"	5'-6"	5'-10"	5'-5"	5'-1"	4'-10"
2-800S162-33	3'-0"	2'-8"	2'-4"	2'-1"	2'-7"	2'-3"	—	—	—	—	—	—	—	—	—	—
2-800S162-43	6'-8"	5'-10"	5'-2"	4'-8"	5'-10"	5'-1"	4'-6"	4'-1"	4'-3"	3'-9"	3'-4"	3'-0"	3'-4"	2'-11"	2'-7"	2'-4"
2-800S162-54	9'-6"	8'-10"	8'-4"	7'-11"	8'-10"	8'-3"	7'-9"	7'-5"	7'-7"	7'-1"	6'-7"	5'-11"	6'-9"	5'-10"	5'-3"	4'-8"
2-800S162-68	10'-8"	10'-0"	9'-5"	8'-11"	9'-11"	9'-4"	8'-9"	8'-4"	8'-6"	8'-0"	7'-6"	7'-2"	7'-7"	7'-1"	6'-8"	6'-4"
2-1000S162-43	5'-7"	4'-10"	4'-4"	3'-11"	4'-10"	4'-3"	3'-9"	3'-5"	3'-7"	3'-1"	2'-9"	2'-6"	2'-10"	2'-6"	2'-2"	—
2-1000S162-54	10'-6"	9'-8"	8'-7"	7'-9"	9'-8"	8'-5"	7'-6"	6'-9"	7'-1"	6'-2"	5'-6"	4'-11"	5'-7"	4'-11"	4'-4"	3'-11"
2-1000S162-68	12'-7"	11'-9"	11'-1"	10'-6"	11'-9"	10'-12"	10'-4"	9'-10"	10'-1"	9'-5"	8'-10"	8'-5"	8'-11"	8'-4"	7'-11"	7'-6"
2-1200S162-43	—	—	—	—	—	—	—	—	—	—	—	—	—	—	—	—
2-1200S162-54	9'-6"	8'-3"	7'-4"	6'-7"	8'-3"	7'-3"	6'-5"	5'-9"	6'-1"	5'-4"	4'-9"	4'-3"	4'-10"	4'-2"	3'-9"	3'-4"
2-1200S162-68	13'-5"	12'-7"	11'-10"	11'-3"	12'-6"	11'-9"	11'-1"	10'-6"	10'-9"	10'-1"	9'-6"	8'-6"	9'-7"	8'-5"	7'-6"	6'-9"

For SI: 1 inch = 25.4 mm, 1 foot = 304.8 mm, 1 pound per square foot = 0.0479 kN/m², 1 kilogram per square inch = 6.895 MPa.

a. Deflection criteria: $L/360$ for live loads, $L/240$ for total loads.

b. Design load assumptions:

    Roof dead load is 7 psf.

    Ceiling dead load is 5 psf.

    Attic live load is 10 psf.

c. Building width is in the direction of horizontal framing members supported by the header.

TABLE R603.6(2)
ALLOWABLE HEADER SPANS[a,b]
Headers supporting one floor, roof and ceiling (33 ksi steel)

NOMINAL MEMBER	GROUND SNOW LOAD (20 psf) Building width[c] (feet)				GROUND SNOW LOAD (30 psf) Building width[c] (feet)				GROUND SNOW LOAD (50 psf) Building width[c] (feet)				GROUND SNOW LOAD (70 psf) Building width[c] (feet)			
	24	28	32	36	24	28	32	36	24	28	32	36	24	28	32	36
2-350S162-42	3'-3"	3'-1"	2'-11"	2'-8"	3'-2"	3'-0"	2'-9"	2'-6"	2'-11"	2'-8"	2'-4"	2'-2"	2'-10"	2'-6"	2'-3"	2'-1"
2-350S162-54	3'-8"	3'-6"	3'-3"	3'-2"	3'-6"	3'-4"	3'-2"	3'-0"	3'-4"	3'-1"	2'-11"	2'-9"	3'-3"	3'-0"	2'-10"	2'-9"
2-350S162-68	4'-2"	3'-11"	3'-8"	3'-6"	4'-0"	3'-9"	3'-6"	3'-4"	3'-8"	3'-6"	3'-3"	3'-1"	3'-7"	3'-5"	3'-2"	3'-1"
2-550S162-43	4'-1"	3'-8"	3'-3"	3'-0"	3'-10"	3'-4"	3'-0"	2'-9"	3'-3"	2'-11"	2'-7"	2'-4"	3'-2"	2'-9"	2'-6"	2'-3"
2-550S162-54	5'-0"	4'-9"	4'-6"	4'-3"	4'-10"	4'-6"	4'-3"	4'-1"	4'-6"	4'-2"	4'-0"	3'-9"	4'-4"	4'-1"	3'-11"	3'-8"
2-550S162-68	5'-7"	5'-4"	5'-0"	4'-9"	5'-5"	5'-1"	4'-10"	4'-7"	5'-0"	4'-9"	4'-6"	4'-3"	4'-11"	4'-7"	4'-4"	4'-2"
2-800S162-43	3'-2"	2'-10"	2'-6"	2'-3"	2'-11"	2'-7"	2'-4"	—	2'-6"	2'-3"	—	—	2'-5"	2'-2"	—	—
2-800S162-54	6'-3"	5'-7"	5'-0"	4'-6"	5'-10"	5'-2"	4'-7"	4'-2"	5'-0"	4'-5"	4'-0"	3'-7"	4'-10"	4'-3"	3'-10"	3'-5"
2-800S162-68	7'-4"	6'-11"	6'-7"	6'-3"	7'-1"	6'-8"	6'-3"	6'-0"	6'-7"	6'-2"	5'-10"	5'-7"	6'-5"	6'-0"	5'-8"	5'-5"
2-1000S162-43	2'-8"	2'-4"	—	—	2'-5"	—	—	—	—	—	—	—	—	—	—	—
2-1000S162-54	5'-3"	4'-8"	4'-2"	3'-9"	4'-10"	4'-3"	3'-10"	3'-6"	4'-2"	3'-8"	3'-4"	3'-0"	4'-0"	3'-6"	3'-2"	2'-10"
2-1000S162-68	8'-8"	8'-2"	7'-9"	7'-4"	8'-4"	7'-10"	7'-5"	7'-0"	7'-9"	7'-3"	6'-8"	6'-0"	7'-7"	7'-1"	6'-5"	5'-9"
2-1000S162-54	4'-6"	4'-0"	3'-7"	3'-3"	4'-2"	3'-8"	3'-3"	3'-0"	3'-7"	3'-2"	2'-10"	2'-7"	3'-5"	3'-0"	2'-9"	2'-5"
2-1000S162-68	9'-1"	8'-0"	7'-2"	6'-6"	8'-4"	7'-5"	6'-8"	6'-0"	7'-3"	6'-5"	5'-9"	5'-2"	6'-11"	6'-1"	5'-6"	4'-11"

For SI: 1 inch = 25.4 mm, 1 foot = 304.8 mm, 1 pound per square foot = 0.0479 kN/m², 1 kilogram per square inch = 6.895 MPa.

a. Deflection criteria: $L/360$ for live loads, $L/240$ for total loads.

b. Design load assumptions:
    Roof dead load is 7 psf.
    Ceiling dead load is 5 psf.
    Attic live load is 10 psf.
    Second floor live load is 30 psf.
    Second floor dead load is 10 psf.
    Second floor wall dead load is 10 psf.

c. Building width is in the direction of horizontal framing members supported by the header.

TABLE R603.6(3)
ALLOWABLE HEADER SPANS[a,b,c]
Headers supporting one floor, roof and ceiling first story of a two-story building with center load bearing beam (33 ksi steel)

NOMINAL MEMBER	GROUND SNOW LOAD (20 psf) Building width[c] (feet)				GROUND SNOW LOAD (30 psf) Building width[c] (feet)				GROUND SNOW LOAD (50 psf) Building width[c] (feet)				GROUND SNOW LOAD (70 psf) Building width[c] (feet)			
	24	28	32	36	24	28	32	36	24	28	32	36	24	28	32	36
2-350S162-33	2'-10"	2'-6"	2'-3"	—	2'-7"	2'-3"	—	—	2'-2"	—	—	—	—	—	—	—
2-350S162-43	3'-9"	3'-6"	3'-4"	3'-2"	3'-7"	3'-4"	3'-2"	3'-0"	3'-3"	3'-1"	2'-11"	2'-8"	3'-0"	2'-9"	2'-6"	2'-3"
2-350S162-54	4'-2"	4'-0"	3'-9"	3'-7"	4'-0"	3'-9"	3'-7"	3'-5"	3'-8"	3'-5"	3'-3"	3'-1"	3'-5"	3'-2"	3'-0"	2'-10"
2-350S162-68	4'-8"	4'-5"	4'-2"	4'-0"	4'-6"	4'-2"	4'-0"	3'-10"	4'-1"	3'-10"	3'-8"	3'-6"	3'-9"	3'-7"	3'-4"	3'-2"
2-550S162-33	2'-5"	2'-2"	—	—	2'-2"	—	—	—	—	—	—	—	—	—	—	—
2-550S162-43	5'-1"	4'-9"	4'-3"	3'-10"	4'-10"	4'-3"	3'-10"	3'-6"	4'-0"	3'-7"	3'-2"	2'-11"	3'-5"	3'-1"	2'-9"	2'-6"
2-550S162-54	5'-8"	5'-4"	5'-1"	4'-10"	5'-5"	5'-1"	4'-10"	4'-7"	4'-11"	4'-8"	4'-5"	4'-2"	4'-7"	4'-4"	4'-1"	3'-11"
2-550S162-68	6'-5"	6'-0"	5'-9"	5'-6"	6'-1"	5'-9"	5'-5"	5'-2"	5'-7"	5'-3"	4'-11"	4'-9"	5'-2"	4'-10"	4'-7"	4'-4"
2-800S162-33	4'-2"	3'-8"	3'-3"	3'-0"	3'-8"	3'-3"	2'-11"	2'-8"	3'-1"	2'-9"	2'-5"	2'-3"	2'-8"	2'-4"	—	—
2-800S162-43	7'-5"	7'-0"	6'-6"	6'-0"	7'-1"	6'-6"	5'-10"	5'-4"	6'-2"	5'-5"	4'-11"	4'-5"	5'-3"	4'-8"	4'-2"	3'-9"
2-800S162-54	8'-4"	7'-11"	7'-6"	7'-1"	7'-11"	7'-6"	7'-1"	6'-9"	7'-3"	6'-10"	6'-6"	6'-2"	6'-9"	6'-4"	6'-0"	5'-8"
2-800S162-68	10'-0"	9'-9"	9'-0"	8'-6"	9'-6"	9'-0"	8'-6"	8'-1"	8'-8"	8'-2"	7'-9"	7'-5"	8'-1"	7'-7"	7'-2"	6'-10"
2-1000S162-43	3'-5"	3'-0"	2'-9"	2'-6"	3'-1"	2'-9"	2'-6"	2'-3"	2'-7"	2'-3"	2'-1"	—	2'-3"	—	—	—
2-1000S162-54	6'-10"	6'-0"	5'-6"	5'-0"	6'-2"	5'-5"	4'-11"	4'-5"	5'-1"	4'-6"	4'-1"	3'-8"	4'-5"	3'-11"	3'-6"	3'-2"
2-1000S162-68	9'-10"	9'-4"	8'-10"	8'-5"	9'-4"	8'-10"	8'-4"	8'-0"	8'-7"	8'-1"	7'-8"	7'-3"	7'-	7'-6"	7'-0"	6'-4"
2-1200S162-43	2'-11"	2'-7"	2'-4"	2'-1"	2'-8"	2'-4"	—	—	2'-3"	—	—	—	—	—	—	—
2-1200S162-54	5'-10"	5'-2"	4'-8"	4'-3"	5'-3"	4'-8"	4'-2"	3'-10"	4'-5"	3'-11"	3'-6"	3'-2"	3'-9"	3'-4"	3'-0"	2'-8"
2-1200S162-68	10'-6"	10'-0"	9'-5"	8'-6"	9'-12"	9'-5"	8'-5"	7'-8"	8'-10"	7'-10"	7'-0"	6'-4"	7'-7"	6'-9"	6'-0"	5'-5"

For SI: 1 inch = 25.4 mm, 1 foot = 304.8 mm, 1 pound per square foot = 0.0479 kN/m², 1 kilogram per square inch = 6.895 MPa.

a. Deflection criteria: $L/360$ for live loads, $L/240$ for total loads.

b. Design load assumptions:
    Roof dead load is 7 psf.
    Ceiling dead load is 5 psf.
    Attic live load is 10 psf.
    Second floor live load is 30 psf.
    Second floor dead load is 10 psf.
    Second floor wall dead load is 10 psf.

c. Building width is in the direction of horizontal framing members supported by the header.

TABLE R603.6(4)
TOTAL NUMBER OF JACK AND KING STUDS REQUIRED
AT EACH END OF AN OPENING

SIZE OF OPENING (feet-inches)	24" O.C. STUD SPACING		16" O.C. STUD SPACING	
	No. of jack studs	No. of king studs	No. of jack studs	No. of king studs
Up to 3'-6"	1	1	1	1
>3'-6" to 5'-0"	1	2	1	2
>5'-0" to 5'-6"	1	2	2	2
>5'-6" to 8'-0"	1	2	2	2
>8'-0" to 10'-6"	2	2	2	3
>10'-6" to 12'-0"	2	2	3	3
>12'-0" to 13'-0"	2	3	3	3
>13'-0" to 14'-0"	2	3	3	4

For SI: 1 inch = 25.4 mm, 1 foot = 304.8 mm.

TABLE R603.6(5)
HEADER TO KING STUD CONNECTION REQUIREMENTS[a,b,c,d,e]

HEADER SPAN (feet)	BASIC WIND SPEED (mph), EXPOSURE		
	85 A/B or Seismic Design Categories A, B, C and D	85 C or less than 110 A/B	Less than 110 C
≤ 4'	4-No. 8 screws	4-No. 8 screws	6-No. 8 screws
> 4' to 8'	4-No. 8 screws	4-No. 8 screws	8-No. 8 screws
> 8' to 12'	4-No. 8 screws	6-No. 8 screws	10-No. 8 screws
> 12' to 16'	4-No. 8 screws	8-No. 8 screws	12-No. 8 screws

For SI: 1 inch = 25.4 mm, 1 foot = 304.8 mm, 1 mile per hour = 1.609 km/h, 1 pound = 0.454 kg.

a. All screw sizes shown are minimum.

b. For headers located on the first floor of a two-story building, the total number of screws may be reduced by two screws, but the total number of screws shall be no less than four.

c. For roof slopes of 6:12 or greater, the required number of screws may be reduced by half, but the total number of screws shall be no less than four.

d. Screws can be replaced by a up-lift connector which has a capacity of the number of screws multiplied by 164 pounds (e.g., 12-No. 8 screws can be replaced by an up-lift connector whose capacity exceeds 12 by 164 pounds = 1,968 pounds)

e. In Seismic Design Category D_1 and D_2 or where the basic wind speed equals or exceeds 110 miles per hour, connection shall comply with the requirements in Section R603.8, but shall be no less than the minimum required herein.

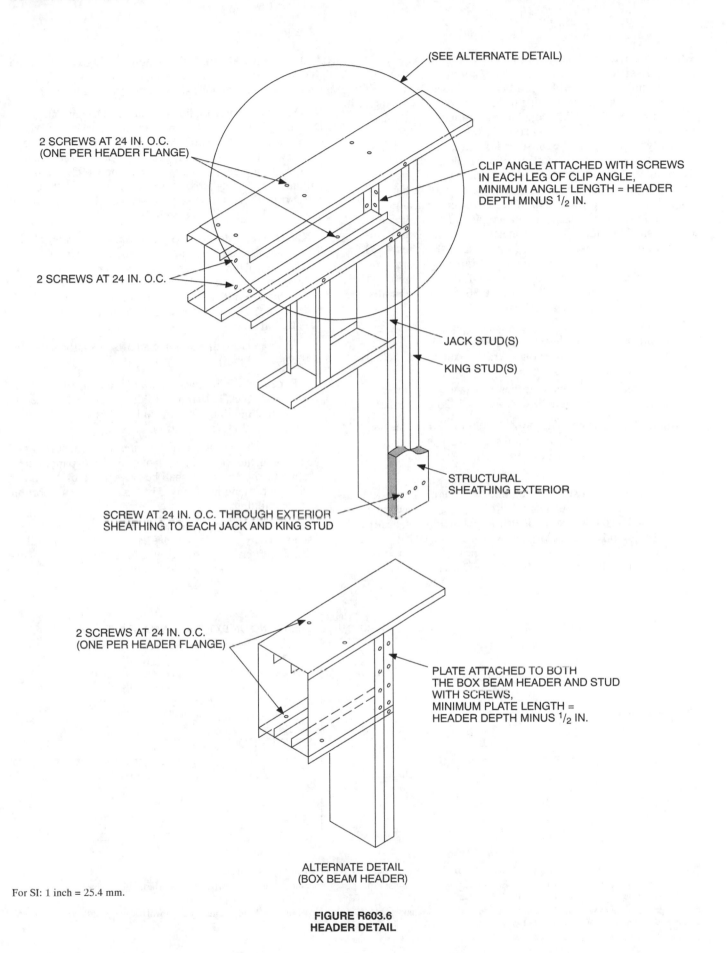

(SEE ALTERNATE DETAIL)

2 SCREWS AT 24 IN. O.C.
(ONE PER HEADER FLANGE)

CLIP ANGLE ATTACHED WITH SCREWS
IN EACH LEG OF CLIP ANGLE,
MINIMUM ANGLE LENGTH = HEADER
DEPTH MINUS $1/2$ IN.

2 SCREWS AT 24 IN. O.C.

JACK STUD(S)

KING STUD(S)

STRUCTURAL
SHEATHING EXTERIOR

SCREW AT 24 IN. O.C. THROUGH EXTERIOR
SHEATHING TO EACH JACK AND KING STUD

2 SCREWS AT 24 IN. O.C.
(ONE PER HEADER FLANGE)

PLATE ATTACHED TO BOTH
THE BOX BEAM HEADER AND STUD
WITH SCREWS,
MINIMUM PLATE LENGTH =
HEADER DEPTH MINUS $1/2$ IN.

ALTERNATE DETAIL
(BOX BEAM HEADER)

For SI: 1 inch = 25.4 mm.

**FIGURE R603.6
HEADER DETAIL**

R603.7 Structural sheathing. In areas where the basic wind speed is less than 110 miles per hour (177 km/h), wood structural sheathing panels shall be installed on all exterior walls of buildings in accordance with this section. Wood structural sheathing panels shall consist of minimum $^7/_{16}$-inch (11.1 mm) thick oriented strand board or $^{15}/_{32}$-inch (11.9 mm) thick plywood and shall be installed on all exterior wall surfaces in accordance with Section R603.7.1 and Figure R603.3. The minimum length of full height sheathing on exterior walls shall be determined in accordance with Table R603.7, but shall not be less than 20 percent of the braced wall length in any case. The minimum percentage of full height sheathing in Table R603.7 shall include only those sheathed wall sections, uninterrupted by openings, which are a minimum of 48 inches (1120 mm) wide. The minimum percentage of full-height structural sheathing shall be multiplied by 1.10 for 9-foot (2743 mm) high walls and multiplied by 1.20 for 10-foot (3048 mm) high walls. In addition, structural sheathing shall:

1. Be installed with the long dimension parallel to the stud framing and shall cover the full vertical height of studs, from the bottom of the bottom track to the top of the top track of each story.

2. Be applied to each end (corners) of each of the exterior walls with a minimum 48-inch-wide (1220 mm) panel.

R603.7.1 Structural sheathing fastening. All edges and interior areas of wood, structural sheathing panels shall be fastened to a framing member and tracks in accordance with Table R603.3.2(1).

R603.7.2 Hold-down requirements. The percent of structural sheathing, required in Table R603.7, is permitted to be multiplied by 0.6 where a hold down anchor with a capacity of 4,300 pounds (1952.2 kg) is provided at each end of exterior walls. A single hold down anchors is permitted to be installed at wall corners per Figure R603.8.1.3.

R603.8 Braced walls and diaphragms in high seismic and high wind regions. Braced walls and diaphragms in high seismic and high wind regions shall comply with this section.

R603.8.1 General. Buildings in Seismic Design Categories D_1 and D_2 and buildings in areas where the basic wind speed equals or exceeds 110 miles per hour (177 km/h) shall have braced wall lines and diaphragms constructed in accordance with the additional provisions of Section R603.8. Where a building, or portion thereof, does not comply with the provisions of this section, those portions shall be designed and constructed in compliance with Section R301.

R603.8.1.1 Building configuration. Floor and roof diaphragm plan aspect ratios shall not exceed four to one (4:1). The diaphragm aspect ratio shall be determined by dividing the length of the diaphragm between braced wall lines by the width of the diaphragm between braced wall lines. Braced wall lines shall be placed on all exterior walls and on interior walls as required.

Floor and roof diaphragm plan offsets shall not exceed 4 feet (1219 mm).

Exception: Buildings where diaphragm plan offsets exceed 4 feet (1219 mm), buildings shall be analyzed as separate buildings, separated by a braced wall line or lines (see Figure R603.8.1).

Where a braced wall line separates different portions of a building, the required length of braced wall panels separating the two portions shall be determined by summing the required lengths of braced wall panels for each portion of the building.

Vertical offsets in floor and roof diaphragms shall be supported by braced wall lines. Braced wall lines shall be in a single vertical plane from the foundation to the uppermost story in which they are required.

TABLE R603.7
MINIMUM PERCENTAGE OF FULL HEIGHT STRUCTURAL SHEATHING ON EXTERIOR WALLS[a,b,c,d,e]

WALL SUPPORTING	ROOF SLOPE	WIND SPEED (mph) AND EXPOSURE				
		85 A/B	100 A/B	110 A/B or 85 C	100 C	110 C
Roof and ceiling only	3:12	8	9	12	16	20
	6:12	12	15	20	26	35
	9:12	21	25	30	50	58
	12:12	30	35	40	66	75
One story, roof and ceiling	3:12	24	30	35	50	66
	6:12	25	30	40	58	74
	9:12	35	40	55	74	91
	12:12	40	50	65	100	115

For SI: 1 mile per hour = 1.609 km/h.

a. Linear interpolation shall be permitted.

b. Bracing amount shall not be less than 20 percent of the wall length after all applicable adjustments are made.

c. Minimum percentages are based on a building aspect ratio of 1:1. Minimum percentages for the shorter walls of a building shall be multiplied by a factor of 1.5 and 2.0 for building aspect ratios of 1.5:1 and 2:1 respectively.

d. For hip roofed homes with continuous structural sheathing, the amount of bracing shall be permitted to be multiplied by a factor of 0.95 for roof slopes not exceeding 7:12 and a factor of 0.9 for roof slopes greater than 7:12.

e. Sheathing percentage are permitted to be reduced in accordance with Section R603.7.2.

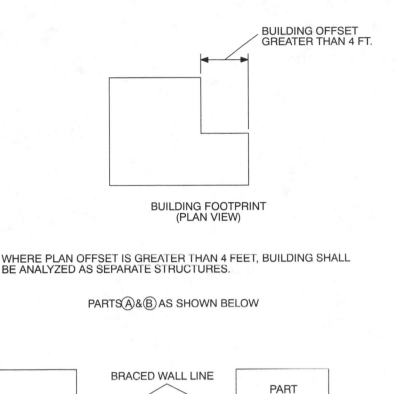

BUILDING FOOTPRINT
(PLAN VIEW)

WHERE PLAN OFFSET IS GREATER THAN 4 FEET, BUILDING SHALL
BE ANALYZED AS SEPARATE STRUCTURES.

PARTS Ⓐ & Ⓑ AS SHOWN BELOW

OPTION 1
(PLAN VIEW)

OPTION 2
(PLAN VIEW)

For SI: 1 foot = 304.8 mm.

**FIGURE R603.8.1
BUILDING CONFIGURATION**

R603.8.1.2 Braced wall lines. Braced wall lines shall be composed of either Type I braced wall panels or Type II (perforated) braced walls as shown in Figure R603.8.1.2. The required length of bracing shall be determined in accordance with the greater requirement for seismic or wind. Each braced wall line shall have not less than two full height braced wall panels, each meeting the minimum height to width aspect ratios in Sections R603.8.2 or R603.8.3. Braced wall panels shall begin not more than 8 feet (2438 mm) from each end.

Sheathing on Type I and Type II braced walls shall have wood structural sheathing panels one side and $^1/_2$-inch (12.7 mm) gypsum wallboard on the other. Wood structural sheathing panels shall be as specified in Section R603.7 and shall be attached to framing members with minimum No. 8 screws spaced as required by Table R603.8.1.2 on all edges and 12 inches (305 mm) in the field. Gypsum

wallboard shall be attached as required by Table R702.3.4. In braced wall lines, all edges of wood structural sheathing panels shall be attached to framing members or 2-inch-by-33-mil (51 mm by 0.84 mm) horizontal strapping. Where horizontal strapping is used to attach adjacent sheets of sheathing material, solid blocking as shown in Figure R603.3 shall not be required.

**TABLE R603.8.1.2
EDGE SCREW SPACING SHEARWALL LENGTH
ADJUSTMENT FACTORS**

EDGE SCREW SPACING (inches)			
6	4	3	2
Shearwall length adjustment factors			
1.00	0.72	0.60	0.56

For SI: 1 inch = 25.4 mm.

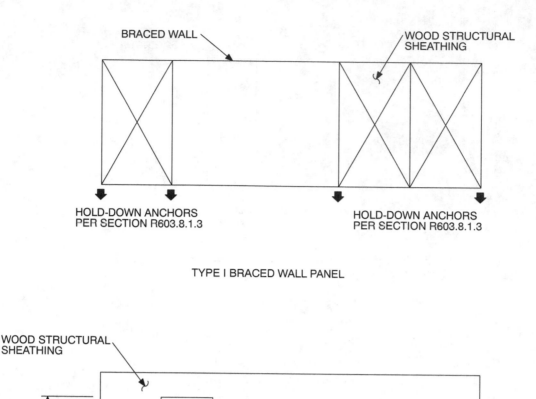

TYPE I BRACED WALL PANEL

TYPE II BRACED WALL

FIGURE R603.8.1.2
TYPE I AND TYPE II BRACED WALLS

R603.8.1.2.1 Type I braced wall panels. Type I braced wall panels shall have no openings and shall be continuous between hold-down anchors. Hold-down anchors shall be as required by Section R603.8.1.3. The required length of Type I braced wall panels shall be determined by Section R603.8.2 for seismic applications and Section R603.8.3 for wind applications. The required length is permitted to be adjusted by the edge screw spacing adjustment factors in Table R603.8.1.2. The total length of Type I braced wall panels on a braced wall line shall be the sum of the lengths of panels conforming to the minimum height to width aspect ratio herein.

R603.8.1.2.2 Type II braced wall lines. Type II braced wall lines are fully sheathed and are permitted to have openings. Where sheathing does not extend above and below window openings and above door openings, the height of unrestrained opening shall be defined as the full height of the wall.

The required length of full height sheathing panels in Type II braced wall lines shall be determined by multiplying the required length of Type I braced wall panels, including adjustments permitted by Tables R603.8.1.2 and R603.8.2.2, by the length adjustment factors in Table R603.8.1.2.2. The length adjustment factors in Table R603.8.1.2.2 are permitted only in seismic applications. For a segment to count toward the required length, it shall have a height to width ratio of two to one (2:1). Type II braced wall lines shall have hold-down anchors as required by Section R603.8.1.3 at each end, attached to wall segments meeting the minimum height-to-width ratio.

TABLE R603.8.1.2.2
TYPE II BRACED WALL LINE LENGTH ADJUSTMENT FACTORS

	MAXIMUM UNRESTRAINED OPENING HEIGHT (feet)					
Wall height H (feet)	$^1/_3$H	$^1/_2$H	$^2/_3$H	$^3/_4$H	$^5/_6$H	H
8	2.67	4.00	5.33	5.93	6.67	8.00
9	3.00	4.50	6.00	6.67	7.50	9.00
10	3.33	5.00	6.67	7.41	8.33	10.00
Percent fully sheathed wall	Type II braced wall line length adjustment factors					
0	1.00	1.50	2.00	2.22	2.50	3.00
20	1.00	1.36	1.67	1.79	1.92	2.14
40	1.00	1.25	1.43	1.49	1.56	1.67
60	1.00	1.15	1.25	1.28	1.32	1.36
80	1.00	1.07	1.11	1.12	1.14	1.15
100	1.00	1.00	1.00	1.00	1.00	1.00

For SI: 1 foot = 304.8 mm.

R603.8.1.3 Braced wall hold-down anchorage and support. Hold-down anchors shall be installed at each end of Type I braced wall panels and at each end of Type II braced wall lines. The required hold-down force shall be determined by Table R603.8.1.3. Hold-down anchors shall attach to the foundation or to framing members below. Where hold-down anchors are attached to framing members below, the required anchor force shall be transferred to the foundation. Where hold-down anchors from an upper story align with those in the lower story, the required lower-story anchor force shall be determined by summing the upper story anchor force and the lower-story anchor force. Hold-down anchors are permitted to be attached to blocking members provided the required hold-down forces are transferred to structural framing members. Hold-down anchors shall be attached to a minimum of two back-to-back, 33 mil (0.84 mm) studs in accordance with the anchor manufacturer's instructions.

A single hold-down anchor installed in accordance with Figure R603.8.1.3 is permitted at the corners of buildings.

Hold-down anchors shall be fastened to studs that have the required sheathing edge fastening. A minimum of two studs shall support end studs of Type I braced wall panel above. These supporting studs shall be in addition to load bearing studs required at the level below.

TABLE R603.8.1.3
REQUIRED HOLD-DOWN ANCHOR FORCE

	REQUIRED HOLD-DOWN ANCHOR FORCE (pounds)			
	Panel edge screw spacing (inches)			
Wall height (feet)	6	4	3	2
8	3440	4760	5720	6120
9	3870	5355	6435	6885
10	4300	5950	7150	7650

For SI: 1 inch = 25.4 mm, 1 foot = 304.8 mm, 1 pound = 4.4 N.

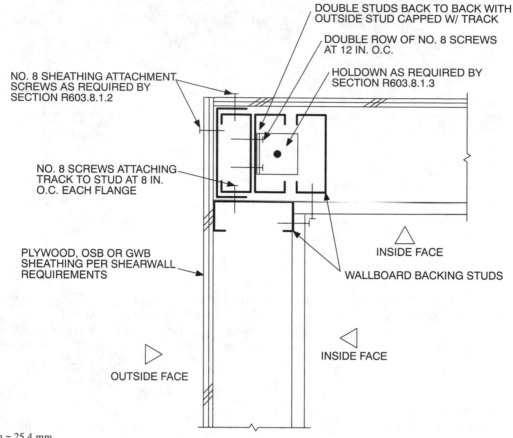

DOUBLE STUDS BACK TO BACK WITH
OUTSIDE STUD CAPPED W/ TRACK

DOUBLE ROW OF NO. 8 SCREWS
AT 12 IN. O.C.

HOLDOWN AS REQUIRED BY
SECTION R603.8.1.3

NO. 8 SHEATHING ATTACHMENT
SCREWS AS REQUIRED BY
SECTION R603.8.1.2

NO. 8 SCREWS ATTACHING
TRACK TO STUD AT 8 IN.
O.C. EACH FLANGE

INSIDE FACE

WALLBOARD BACKING STUDS

PLYWOOD, OSB OR GWB
SHEATHING PER SHEARWALL
REQUIREMENTS

INSIDE FACE

OUTSIDE FACE

For SI: 1 inch = 25.4 mm.

FIGURE R603.8.1.3
CORNER STUD HOLD-DOWN

**R603.8.1.4 Attachment of braced walls to foundations
and floor and roof diaphragms.** The top track of braced
wall lines shall be attached directly to the roof sheathing in
accordance with Figure R603.8.1.4(1) or shall have
blocking, installed in accordance with Figure
R603.8.1.4(2), connecting the top track to the roof sheathing at locations specified herein. Blocking shall be
installed at each end of braced wall lines. Continuous
blocking shall be installed above all Type I braced wall
panels and above full height sheathing panels in Type II
braced wall lines. Where the roof diaphragm spans more
than 40 feet (12 192 mm) between braced wall lines, continuous blocking shall also be installed in the middle one-
third of the braced wall lines.

Splices in top tracks in braced walls shall comply with
Figure R603.3.6 except the number of screws in the splice
shall be as shown in Table R603.8.1.4(1). Screws used to
attach blocking to the top track are permitted to be counted
toward the required number of track splice screws. Splices
in the top track and the strap at the roof sheathing shall not
occur in the same stud bay.

The top and bottom track of braced walls shall be
attached to floor diaphragms in accordance with Figure
R603.8.1.4.(3).

Splices in the floor track shall not occur in the same bay
as splices in the wall track immediately above or below the
floor track splice.

The bottom track of braced walls supported on foundations shall have anchor bolts installed in accordance with
Figure R603.3.1(1). Floor track or rim joists supporting
braced wall lines shall be attached to foundations in accordance with Figure R505.3.1(3). The maximum spacing
between anchor bolts shall be as shown in Table
R603.8.1.4(2). Anchor bolts shall extend 7 inches
(178 mm) into concrete or masonry. An anchor bolt shall
be located not more than 12 inches (305 mm) from wall
corners or the termination of bottom track sections.

In regions where the basic wind speed equals or exceeds 110 miles per hour (177 km/h), the bottom track in
exterior walls shall also comply with the provisions of
Section R603.8.3.2.6 for uplift.

TABLE R603.8.1.4(1)
TOP TRACK SPLICE SCREW SCHEDULE

UP TO 120 MPH OR SDC D1	UP TO 130 MPH OR SDC D2
6 #8 screws each side of splice	11 #8 screws each side of splice

For SI: 1 mile per hour = 1.609 km/h.
NOTE: SDC = Seismic Design Category.

TABLE R603.8.1.4(2)
REQUIRED SHEAR ANCHORAGE FOR BRACED WALLS

ANCHOR BOLT DIAMETER (inch)	REQUIRED ANCHOR BOLT SPACING (feet on center)			
	Panel edge screw spacing (inches)			
	6	4	3	2
$^1/_2$	4.5	3	3	2.5
$^5/_8$	5.5	4	3	3

For SI: 1 inch = 25.4 mm.

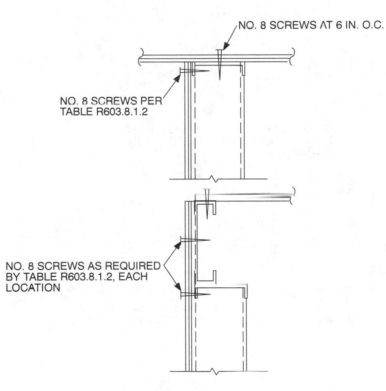

NO. 8 SCREWS AT 6 IN. O.C.

NO. 8 SCREWS PER TABLE R603.8.1.2

NO. 8 SCREWS AS REQUIRED BY TABLE R603.8.1.2, EACH LOCATION

For SI: 1 inch = 25.4 mm.

FIGURE R603.8.1.4(1)
GABLE ROOF SHEATHING ATTACHMENT TO BRACE WALLS

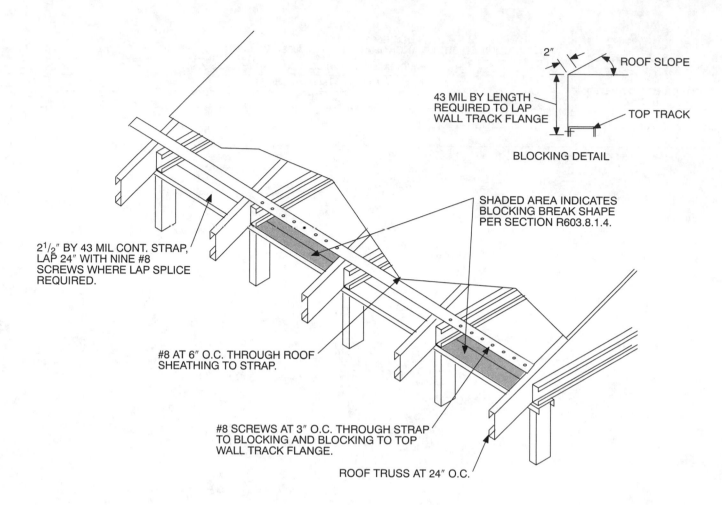

2" ROOF SLOPE

43 MIL BY LENGTH
REQUIRED TO LAP
WALL TRACK FLANGE

TOP TRACK

BLOCKING DETAIL

SHADED AREA INDICATES
BLOCKING BREAK SHAPE
PER SECTION R603.8.1.4.

$2^1/_2$" BY 43 MIL CONT. STRAP,
LAP 24" WITH NINE #8
SCREWS WHERE LAP SPLICE
REQUIRED.

#8 AT 6" O.C. THROUGH ROOF
SHEATHING TO STRAP.

#8 SCREWS AT 3" O.C. THROUGH STRAP
TO BLOCKING AND BLOCKING TO TOP
WALL TRACK FLANGE.

ROOF TRUSS AT 24" O.C.

LIGHT GAUGE STEEL BLOCKING

For SI: 1 inch = 25.4 mm, 1 mil = 0.0254 mm.

FIGURE R603.8.1.4(2)
STRAP AND BLOCKING DIAPHRAGM LOAD TRANSFER AT ROOF EAVE

SHEATHING SCREW SPACING IN WALL			
6 IN. O.C.	4 IN. O.C.	3 IN. O.C.	2 IN. O.C.
SCREW SPACING - WALL TRACK TO FRAMING BELOW			
4 NO. 8 AT 24 IN. O.C.	5 NO. 8 AT 24 IN. O.C.	7 NO. 8 AT 24 IN. O.C.	8 NO. 8 AT 24 IN. O.C.

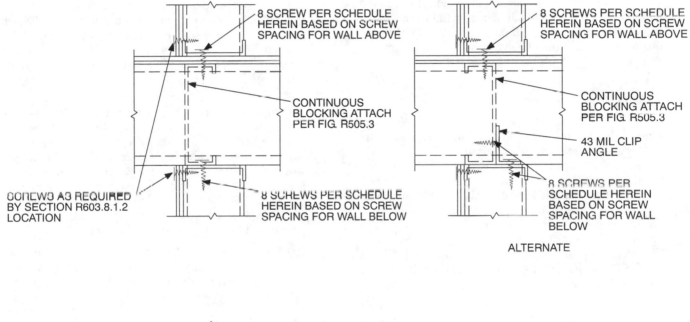

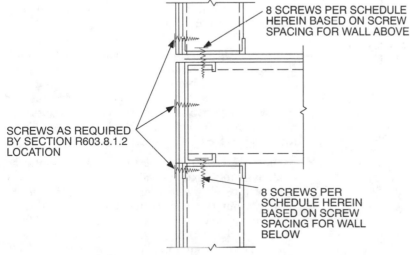

For SI: 1 inch = 25.4 mm, 1 mil = 0.0254 mm.

FIGURE R603.8.1.4(3)
FLOOR DIAPHRAGM—ATTACHMENT TO BRACED WALLS

R603.8.2 Seismic Design Categories D$_1$ and D$_2$.

R603.8.2.1 Limitations. The construction of buildings in Seismic Design Categories D$_1$ and D$_2$ shall comply with the provisions of this section. Buildings shall be limited to slab on grade or continuous concrete or masonry foundations and the weight of floors, roofs or walls shall not exceed the limits set forth in Section 301.2.2.4.

Exception: Buildings constructed in accordance with Section 301.1.

R603.8.2.2 Required length of Type I braced wall panels. For the purposes of this section, the diaphragm aspect ratio shall be taken as the dimension of the diaphragm perpendicular to the walls under consideration divided by the dimension of the diaphragm parallel to the walls under consideration, and shall be not less than one-quarter to one (0.25:1) nor more than four to one (4:1). The required length of Type I braced wall panels shall be determined from Figures R603.8.2(1) through R603.8.2(4) where the diaphragm span is the dimension of the diaphragm perpendicular to the walls under consideration.

Interpolation shall be permitted for determining diaphragm span values.

The required length of Type I braced wall panels is permitted to be adjusted by length adjustment factors in Table R603.8.2.2 where the dead weights of roof/ceiling assemblies and exterior walls are less than or equal to the unit weights specified therein. The required length of Type I braced wall panels shall be increased by length adjustment factors in Table R603.8.2.2 where the dead weights of roof/ceiling assemblies is greater than 15 psf (0.7185 kN/m^2) and less than or equal to 25 psf (1.1975 kN/m^2). The length adjustment factors in Tables R301.2.2.4 and R603.8.2.2 are permitted to be compounded with those in Table R603.8.1.2.

The height to width aspect ratio in Type I braced wall panels and full height sheathing segments in Type II braced walls shall be limited to two to one (2:1).

Exception: Type I braced wall panels on either side of garage openings, that support roofs only, are permitted to have an aspect ratio of four to one (4:1).

TABLE R603.8.2.2
LIGHT WEIGHT ROOF AND LIGHT WEIGHT EXTERIOR WALL TYPE I LENGTH ADJUSTMENT FACTORS

BRACED WALL SUPPORTING	LIGHT WEIGHT ROOF/CEILING —UNIT WEIGHT LESS THAN 11 PSF	LIGHT WEIGHT EXTERIOR WALLS—UNIT WEIGHT LESS THAN 7 PSF	BUILDINGS HAVING BOTH LIGHT WEIGHT WALLS AND ROOFS
Roof/ceiling only	0.80	0.95	0.70
One floor and roof/ceiling	0.90	0.90	0.75

For SI: 1 pound per square foot = 0.0479 kN/m^2.

R603.8.3 High wind requirements.

R603.8.3.1 Braced wall design. Buildings in areas where the basic wind speed is 110 miles per hour (177 km/h) or greater shall have braced wall lines complying with Section R603.8.1 as required by this section.

For the purpose of this section, the endwall shall be defined as the exterior wall of the building perpendicular to the roof ridge and the sidewall shall be defined as the exterior wall of the building parallel to the roof ridge. For the purposes of determining uplift and lateral bracing requirements, the attic shall be considered an additional story when the roof slope is 7 in 12 or greater.

The minimum and maximum allowable sidewall lengths shall be determined from Tables R603.8.3.1(1) and R603.8.3.1(2). The required length of Type I braced wall panels shall be determined from Tables R603.8.3.1(3) and R603.8.3.1(4).

Braced wall hold down anchors shall comply with Section R603.8.1.3. The height to width aspect ratio of Type I braced wall panels shall be limited to four to one (4:1). The height to width aspect ratio of full height sheathing segments in Type II braced walls shall be limited to two to one (2:1).

Exterior walls shall be sheathed with wood structural sheathing panels or other approved materials. Wood structural sheathing panels, and their attachments, shall comply with Section R603.8.1.2 except in regions where the basic wind speed exceeds 110 miles per hour (177 km/h) wood structural sheathing panels attached to framing spaced 24 inches (610 mm) on center shall be a minimum of $^{19}/_{32}$ inch (15.1 mm). Attachment of wall sheathing materials other than wood structural sheathing panels shall comply with the manufacturer's instructions.

R603.8.3.2 High wind connections. Connections, as required in this section, shall be provided to ensure a continuous load path capable of transferring shear and uplift loads from floors, studs and roof framing to the foundation.

R603.8.3.2.1 Uplift connection—roof rafter or truss to wall. Roof rafters and trusses shall be attached to their supporting wall assemblies by connections capable of resisting the uplift loads listed in Table R603.8.3.2.1(1). Alternatively, a 1.25-inch-by-minimum-33-mil (32 mm by 0.84 mm) steel uplift strap connecting the rafter or truss to the in-line framing stud below shall be permitted. Each end of the uplift strap shall be fastened with minimum No. 8 screws as required by Table R603.8.3.2.1(2).

R603.8.3.2.2 Uplift connection—wall assembly to wall assembly. Exterior wall studs in the upper story wall of a two-story building shall be attached to the in-line framing wall studs in the supporting wall below, with connections capable of resisting the uplift loads listed in Table R603.8.3.2.2(1). Alternatively, a 1.25-inch-by-33-mil (32 mm by 0.84 mm) steel uplift strap shall be permitted with minimum No. 8 screws attached to each stud, as required by Table R603.8.3.2.2(2).

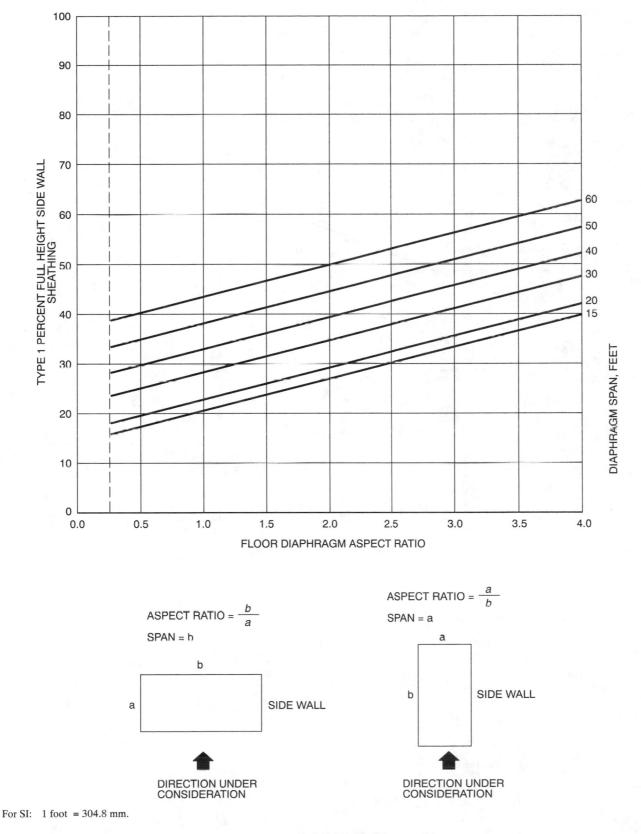

FIGURE R603.8.2(1)
SDC D$_1$ SINGLE STORY OR TOP OF TWO STORY

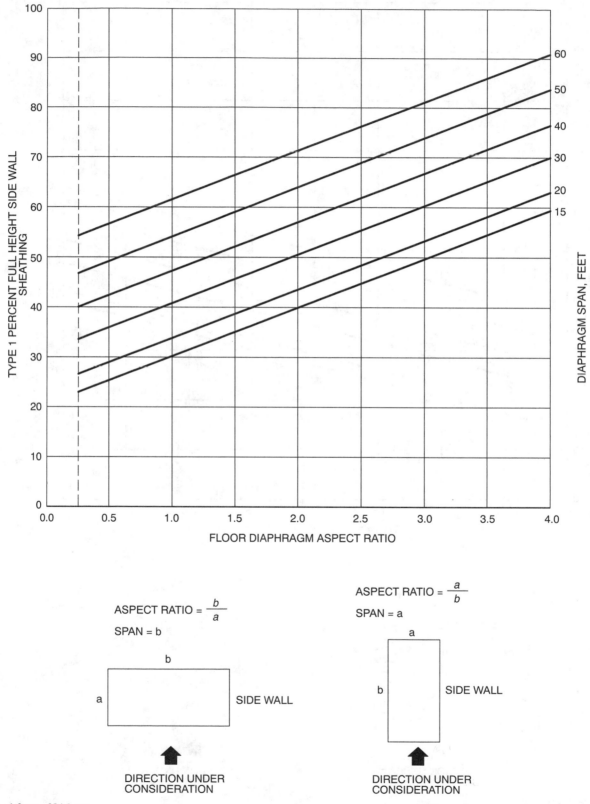

For SI: 1 foot = 304.8 mm.

FIGURE R603.8.2(2)
SDC D₁ BOTTOM OF TWO STORY

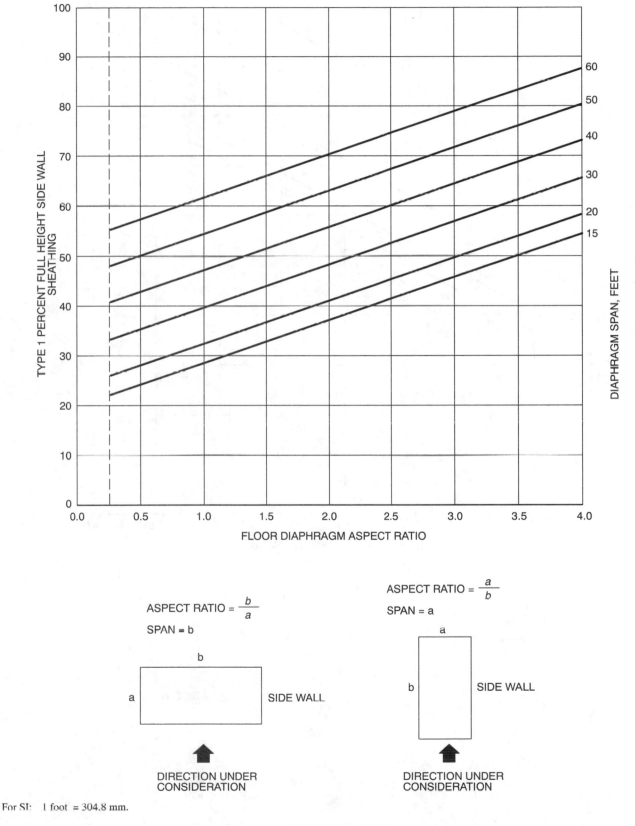

For SI: 1 foot = 304.8 mm.

FIGURE R603.8.2(3)
SDC D₂ SINGLE STORY OR TOP OF TWO STORY

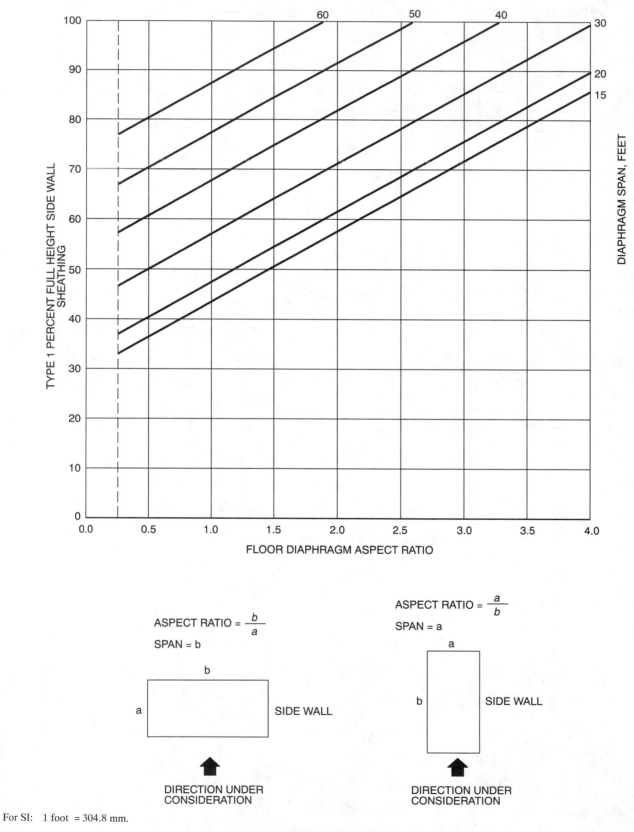

For SI: 1 foot = 304.8 mm.

FIGURE R603.8.2(4)
SDC D₂ BOTTOM OF TWO STORY

TABLE R603.8.3.1(1)
RANGE OF ALLOWABLE SIDEWALL LENGTHS ONE-STORY SLAB ON GRADE

FOUNDATION SUPPORTING	BUILDING ENDWALL WIDTH (FEET)	BASIC WIND SPEED (mph)					
		110		120		130	
		Allowable building sidewall length (feet)					
		Minimum	Maximum	Minimum	Maximum	Minimum	Maximum
One-story slab on grade	12	10	48	10	48	10	43
	16	10	60	10	60	10	58
	20	10	60	10	60	11	60
	24	10	60	11	60	13	60
	28	10	60	12	60	15	60
	32	11	60	14	60	17	60
	36	13	60	16	60	19	60

For SI: 1 foot = 304.8 mm, 1 mile per hour = 1.609 km/h.

TABLE R603.8.3.1(2)
RANGE OF ALLOWABLE SIDEWALL LENGTHS ALL OTHER CASES

FOUNDATION SUPPORTING	BUILDING ENDWALL WIDTH (feet)	BASIC WIND SPEED (mph)					
		110		120		130	
		Allowable building sidewall length (feet)					
		Minimum	Maximum	Minimum	Maximum	Minimum	Maximum
One to two stories	12	10	29	10	23	10	19
	16	10	38	10	31	10	26
	20	10	48	10	39	12	32
	24	10	58	12	47	14	39
	28	11	60	14	55	17	45
	32	13	60	16	60	19	51
	36	15	60	18	60	22	58

For SI: 1 foot = 304.8 mm, 1 mile per hour = 1.609 km/h.

TABLE R603.8.3.1(3)
TYPE I BRACED WALL PANEL SIDEWALL SHEATHING LENGTH REQUIREMENTS

BRACED WALL SUPPORTING	BUILDING ENDWALL LENGTH (W) (feet)	BASIC WIND SPEED (mph)		
		110	120	130
		Minimum length of full height sheathing on building sidewall (L)[a,b,c] (feet)		
Roof/ceiling only[d]	12	5	5	5
	16	5	5	5
	20	5	5	6
	24	5	6	7
	28	5	6	8
	32	6	7	9
	36	7	8	10
One floor and roof/ceiling[e]	20	8	10	11
	24	9	11	14
	28	11	13	16
	32	12	15	18
	36	14	17	20

For SI: 1 inch = 25.4 mm, 1 foot = 304.8 mm, 1 mile per hour = 1.609 km/h.

a. Tabulated sheathing lengths are based on 8-foot wall heights. For 9-foot wall heights, the tabulated values shall be multiplied by 1.13. For 10-foot wall heights, the tabulated values shall be multiplied by 1.25.

b. Tabulated sheathing lengths assume a mean roof height of 33 feet. For mean roof heights of 15 feet or less, the tabulated values shall be permitted to be multiplied by 0.8.

c. Tabulated sheathing lengths assume a 6-inch edge screw spacing. Required lengths shall be permitted to be multiplied by the adjustment factors in Table R603.8.1.2 for edge screw spacing other than 6 inches, but the resulting sheathing length shall not be less than 5 feet.

d. Applies to a one-story building or the top story of a two-story building.

e. Applies to the lower story of a two-story building.

TABLE R603.8.3.1(4)
TYPE I BRACED WALL PANEL ENDWALL SHEATHING LENGTH REQUIREMENTS

BRACED WALL SUPPORTING	BUILDING SIDEWALL LENGTH (W) (feet)	BASIC WIND SPEED (mph)		
		110	120	130
		Minimum length of full height sheathing on building endwall (L)[a,b,c] (feet)		
Roof/ceiling only[d]	12	5	5	5
	16	5	5	5
	20	5	5	5
	24	5	5	5
	28	5	5	5
	32	5	5	6
	36	5	6	7
	40	5	6	8
	50	6	8	9
	60	8	9	11
One floor and roof/ceiling[e]	20	8	10	12
	24	10	12	14
	28	11	14	17
	32	13	16	19
	36	14	18	21
	40	16	20	24
	50	20	24	29
	60	24	29	35

For SI: 1 inch = 25.4 mm, 1 foot = 304.8 mm, 1 mile per hour = 1.609 km/h.

a. Tabulated sheathing lengths are based on 8-foot wall heights. For 10-foot wall heights, the tabulated values shall be multiplied by 1.25.

b. Tabulated sheathing lengths are based on a mean roof height of 33 feet. For mean roof heights of 15 feet or less, the tabulated values shall be permitted to be multiplied by 0.8.

c. Tabulated sheathing lengths are based on a 6-inch edge screw spacing. Required lengths shall be permitted to be multiplied by the adjustment factors in Table R603.8.1.2 for edge screw spacing other than 6 inches, but the resulting sheathing length shall not be less than 5 feet.

d. Applies to a one-story building or the top story of a two-story building.

e. Applies to the lower story of a two-story building.

R603.8.3.2.3 Uplift connection—wall assembly to foundation or floor assembly. Exterior wall studs in bottom-story walls shall be attached to a wood sill plate or directly attached to the foundation by connections capable of resisting the uplift loads listed in Table R603.8.3.2.3(1). Alternatively, a continuous 1.25-inch-by-33-mil (32 mm by 0.84 mm) steel uplift strap is permitted when placed under the wood sill and attached to both flanges of the exterior stud as shown in Figure R603.8.3.2.3. The uplift strap shall be fastened to each flange with minimum No. 8 screws as required by Table R603.8.3.2.3(2).

R603.8.3.2.4 Ridge strap connection. Roof rafters shall be provided with a connection at the ridge line to transfer tension loads. The ridge connection shall be capable of resisting the unit loads listed in Table R804.3.3.1.1(1), multiplied by the appropriate spacing multiplier. Alternatively, steel ridge strap shall be provided with minimum No. 8 screws on each end of the strap as required in Table R804.3.3.1.1(1). The number of screws shall be increased to account for the spacing multipliers shown in the table. The width and thickness of the steel ridge strap shall be as shown in Table R804.3.3.1.1(2), based upon the required number of screws on one side of the strap.

R603.8.3.2.5 Header uplift connections.

R603.8.3.2.5.1 Single story or top story of a two-story building. Uplift connections shall be provided to fasten the rafter or roof trusses to the header by connectors capable of resisting the uplift loads listed in Table R603.8.3.2.1(1).

Uplift connections shall be provided to fasten the header to the jack studs by connectors capable of resisting the uplift loads listed in Table R603.8.3.2.1(1), multiplied by the number of framing members displaced, divided by two. An additional uplift strap shall be provided to fasten rafters or roof trusses to king studs that provide in-line framing support in accordance with Table R603.8.3.2.1(1).

Uplift connections shall be provided to fasten the jack studs to the foundation by connectors capable of resisting the uplift loads listed in Table R603.8.3.2.1(1), multiplied by the number of framing members displaced, divided by two.

R603.8.3.2.5.2 Bottom story of a two-story building. Uplift connections shall be provided to fasten the exterior wall studs in the upper story wall of a two-story building to the header below by connections capable of resisting the uplift loads listed in Table R603.8.3.2.2(1).

Uplift connections shall be provided to fasten the header to the jack studs by connectors capable of resisting the uplift loads listed in Table R603.8.3.2.2(1), multiplied by the number of framing members displaced, divided by two. An additional uplift strap shall be provided to fasten exterior wall studs in the upper story to king studs that provide in-line framing support in accordance with Table R603.8.3.2.2(1).

Uplift connections shall be provided to fasten the jack studs to the foundation by connectors capable of resisting the uplift loads listed in Table R603.8.3.2.2(1), multiplied by the number of framing members displaced, divided by two.

R603.8.3.2.6 Wall bottom track to foundation. The bottom track of exterior walls shall be connected to a wood sill plate as shown in Figure R603.3.1(2). The track shall be attached with steel plates spaced at 2 feet (610 mm) on center and fastened with four No. 8 screws with four 10d or six 8d common nails. The bottom track of interior braced walls shall be connected to supporting floors or foundations as required by Section R603.8.1.4.

The bottom track shall be connected to the foundation with $^1/_2$ inch (12.7 mm) anchor bolts extending 15 inches (381 mm) into masonry or 7 inches (178 mm) into concrete. An anchor bolt shall be located not more than 12 inches (305 mm) from wall corners or the termination of bottom track sections. Anchor bolts shall be spaced in accordance with Table R603.8.1.4(2), but shall be a maximum of 3 feet (915 mm) on center.

Exception: In regions with a wind speed of 120 miles per hour (193 km/h) or greater, anchor bolts located within the 8 feet (2438 mm) end zone shall be spaced a maximum of 2 feet (610 mm) on center.

TABLE R603.8.3.2.1(1)
REQUIRED UPLIFT CAPACITY ROOF TRUSS OR RAFTER TO WALL

| FRAMING SPACING[c] (inches) | ROOF SPAN (feet) | BASIC WIND SPEED (mph) | | |
| | | 110 | 120 | 130 |
		Required connection capacity[a,b] (pounds)		
12	24	245	336	435
	28	279	382	495
	32	312	428	555
	36	346	474	615
16	24	327	447	580
	28	371	509	660
	32	416	570	740
	36	461	632	820
19.2	24	392	536	696
	28	446	610	792
	32	499	684	888
	36	553	758	984
24	24	490	671	868
	28	557	763	990
	32	624	855	1110
	36	691	947	1230

For SI: 1 inch = 25.4 mm, 1 foot = 304.8 mm, 1 pound = 4.4 N, 1 mile per hour = 1.609 km/h, 1 pound per square foot = 0.0479 kN/m².

a. Uplift requirements assume a roof/ceiling dead load of 10 psf (2/3 by 15 psf).

b. Uplift connection requirements shall be permitted to be multiplied by 0.70 for framing not located within 8 feet of building corners.

c. The 12-inch and 19.2-inch framing spacing provides options for design, but shall not negate the in-line framing requirement of Section R603.1.2.

TABLE R603.8.3.2.1(2)
UPLIFT STRAP CONNECTION REQUIREMENTS ROOF RAFTER OR TRUSS TO WALL

| FRAMING SPACING[a] (inches) | ROOF SPAN (feet) | BASIC WIND SPEED (mph) | | |
| | | 110 | 120 | 130 |
		Number of #8 screws in each end of a 1 1/4 inch by 33 mil steel strap		
12	24	2	2	2
	28	2	2	3
	32	2	2	3
	36	2	3	3
16	24	2	3	3
	28	2	3	3
	32	2	3	4
	36	3	3	4
19.2	24	2	3	4
	28	3	3	4
	32	3	4	5
	36	3	4	5
24	24	3	4	4
	28	3	4	5
	32	3	4	6[b]
	36	4	5	6[b]

For SI: 1 inch = 25.4 mm, 1 foot = 304.8 mm, 1 mile per hour = 1.609 km/h, 1 mil = 0.0254 mm.

a. The 12-inch and 19.2-inch framing spacing provides options for design, but shall not negate the in-line framing requirement of Section R603.1.2.

b. Strap width shall be a minimum of 1.5 inches or thickness shall be a minimum of 0.043 inches.

TABLE R603.8.3.2.2(1)
REQUIRED UPLIFT CAPACITY WALL ASSEMBLY TO WALL ASSEMBLY

| FRAMING SPACING[c] (inches) | ROOF SPAN (feet) | BASIC WIND SPEED (mph) | | |
| | | 110 | 120 | 130 |
		Required connection capacity[a,b] (pounds)		
12	24	185	276	375
	28	219	322	435
	32	252	368	495
	36	286	414	555
16	24	242	362	495
	28	286	424	575
	32	331	485	655
	36	376	547	735
19.2	24	287	431	591
	28	341	505	687
	32	394	579	784
	36	448	653	879
24	24	355	536	733
	28	422	628	855
	32	489	720	975
	36	556	812	1095

For SI: 1 inch = 25.4 mm, 1 foot = 304.8 mm, 1 pound = 4.4 N, 1 mile per hour = 1.609 km/h, 1 pound per square foot = 0.0479 kN/m^2.

a. Uplift requirements assume a roof/ceiling dead load of 10 psf (^{2}/$_3$ by 15 psf).

b. Uplift connection requirements shall be permitted to be multiplied by 0.70 for framing not located within 8 feet of building corners.

c. The 12-inch and 19.2-inch framing spacing provides options for design, but shall not negate the in-line framing requirement of Section R603.1.2.

TABLE R603.8.3.2.2(2)
UPLIFT STRAP CONNECTION REQUIREMENTS WALL ASSEMBLY TO WALL ASSEMBLY

| FRAMING SPACING[a] (inches) | ROOF SPAN (feet) | BASIC WIND SPEED (mph) | | |
| | | 110 | 120 | 130 |
		Number of #8 screws in each of a 1^1/$_4$ inch by 33 mil steel strap		
12	24	2	2	2
	28	2	2	2
	32	2	2	3
	36	2	2	3
16	24	2	2	3
	28	2	2	3
	32	2	3	3
	36	2	3	4
19.2	24	2	2	3
	28	2	3	4
	32	2	3	4
	36	3	3	4
24	24	2	3	4
	28	2	3	4
	32	3	4	5
	36	3	4	5

For SI: 1 inch = 25.4 mm, 1 foot = 304.8 mm, 1 mile per hour = 1.609 km/h, 1 mil = 0.0254 mm.

a. The 12-inch and 19.2-inch framing spacing provides options for design, but shall not negate the in-line framing requirement of Section R603.1.2.

TABLE R603.8.3.2.3(1)
REQUIRED UPLIFT CAPACITY WALL ASSEMBLY TO FOUNDATION OR FLOOR ASSEMBLY

FRAMING SPACING[c] (inches)	ROOF SPAN (feet)	BASIC WIND SPEED (mph)		
		110	120	130
		Required connection capacity[a,b] (pounds)		
12	24	170	261	360
	28	204	307	420
	32	237	353	480
	36	271	399	540
16	24	227	347	480
	28	271	409	560
	32	316	470	640
	36	361	532	720
19.2	24	272	416	576
	28	326	490	672
	32	379	564	768
	36	433	638	864
24	24	340	521	718
	28	407	613	840
	32	474	705	960
	36	541	797	1080

For SI: 1 inch = 25.4 mm, 1 foot = 304.8 mm, 1 pound = 4.4 N, 1 mile per hour = 1.609 km/h, 1 pound per square foot = 0.0479 kN/m^2.

a. Uplift requirements assume a roof/ceiling dead load of 10 psf ($^2/_3$ by15 psf).

b. Uplift connection requirements shall be permitted to be multiplied by 0.70 for framing not located within 8 feet of building corners.

c. The 12-inch and 19.2-inch framing spacing provides options for design, but shall not negate the in-line framing requirement of Section R603.1.2.

TABLE R603.8.3.2.3(2)
UPLIFT STRAP CONNECTION REQUIREMENTS WALL ASSEMBLY TO FOUNDATION OR FLOOR ASSEMBLY

FRAMING SPACING[a] (inches)	ROOF SPAN (feet)	BASIC WIND SPEED (mph)		
		110	120	130
		Number of #8 screw in a 1.25 inch by 33 mil strap in each flange of studs (see Figure R603.8.3.2.3)		
12	24	1	1	1
	28	1	1	1
	32	1	1	2
	36	1	1	2
16	24	1	1	2
	28	1	1	2
	32	1	2	2
	36	1	2	2
19.2	24	1	1	2
	28	1	2	2
	32	1	2	2
	36	1	2	2
24	24	1	2	2
	28	1	2	2
	32	2	2	3
	36	2	2	3

For SI: 1 inch = 25.4 mm, 1 foot = 304.8 mm, 1 mile per hour = 1.609 km/h, 1 mil = 0.0254 mm.

a. The 12-inch and 19.2-inch framing spacing provides options for design, but shall not negate the in-line framing requirement of Section R603.1.2.

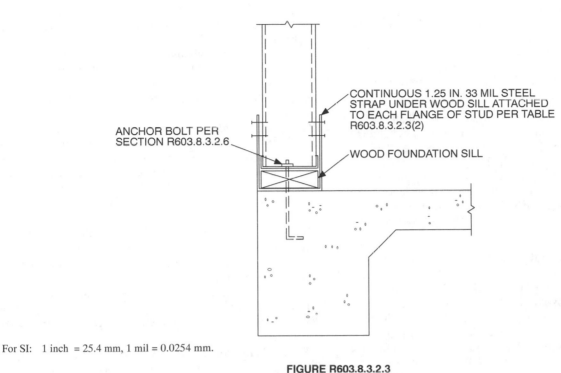

ANCHOR BOLT PER
SECTION R603.8.3.2.6

CONTINUOUS 1.25 IN. 33 MIL STEEL
STRAP UNDER WOOD SILL ATTACHED
TO EACH FLANGE OF STUD PER TABLE
R603.8.3.2.3(2)

WOOD FOUNDATION SILL

For SI: 1 inch = 25.4 mm, 1 mil = 0.0254 mm.

FIGURE R603.8.3.2.3
WIND UPLIFT CONNECTOR

SECTION R604
WOOD STRUCTURAL PANELS

R604.1 Identification and grade. Wood structural panels shall conform to DOC PS 1 or DOC PS 2. All panels shall be identified by a grade mark or certificate of inspection issued by an approved agency.

R604.2 Allowable spans. The maximum allowable spans for wood structural panel wall sheathing shall not exceed the values set forth in Table R602.3(3).

R604.3 Installation. Wood structural panel wall sheathing shall be attached to framing in accordance with Table R602.3(1). Wood structural panels marked Exposure 1 or Exterior are considered water-repellent sheathing under the code.

SECTION R605
PARTICLEBOARD

R605.1 Identification and grade. Particleboard shall conform to ANSI A208.1 and shall be so identified by a grade mark or certificate of inspection issued by an approved agency. Particleboard shall comply with the grades specified in Table R602.3(4).

SECTION R606
GENERAL MASONRY CONSTRUCTION

R606.1 General. Masonry construction shall be designed and constructed in accordance with the provisions of this section or in accordance with the provisions of ACI 530/ASCE 5/TMS 402.

R606.1.1 Professional registration not required. When the empirical design provisions of ACI 530/ASCE 5/TMS 402 Chapter 5 or the provisions of this section are used to design masonry, project drawings, typical details and specifications are not required to bear the seal of the architect or engineer responsible for design, unless otherwise required by the state law of the jurisdiction having authority.

R606.2 Thickness of masonry. The nominal thickness of masonry walls shall conform to the requirements of Sections R606.2.1 through R606.2.4.

R606.2.1 Minimum thickness. The minimum thickness of masonry bearing walls more than one story high shall be 8 inches (203 mm). Solid masonry walls of one-story dwellings and garages shall not be less than 6 inches (152 mm) in thickness when not greater than 9 feet (2743 mm) in height, provided that when gable construction is used, an additional 6 feet (1829 mm) is permitted to the peak of the gable. Masonry walls shall be laterally supported in either the horizontal or vertical direction at intervals as required by Section R606.8.

R606.2.2 Rubble stone masonry wall. The minimum thickness of rough, random or coursed rubble stone masonry walls shall be 16 inches (406 mm).

R606.2.3 Change in thickness. Where walls of masonry of hollow units or masonry bonded hollow walls are decreased in thickness, a course of solid masonry shall be constructed between the wall below and the thinner wall above, or special units or construction shall be used to transmit the loads from face shells or wythes above to those below.

R606.2.4 Parapet walls. Unreinforced solid masonry parapet walls shall not be less than 8 inches (203 mm) in thickness and their height shall not exceed four times their thickness. Unreinforced hollow unit masonry parapet walls shall be not less than 8 inches (203 mm) in thickness, and their height shall not exceed three times their thickness. Masonry parapet walls in areas subject to wind loads of 30 pounds per square foot (1.44 kN/m^2) or located in Seismic Design Category D$_1$ or D$_2$ shall be reinforced in accordance with Section R606.11.

R606.3 Corbeled masonry. Solid masonry units shall be used for corbeling. The maximum corbeled projection beyond the face of the wall shall not be more than one-half of the wall thickness or one-half the wythe thickness for hollow walls; the maximum projection of one unit shall not exceed one-half the height of the unit or one-third the thickness at right angles to the wall. The top course of corbels shall be a header course when the corbeled masonry is used to support floor or roof-framing members.

R606.3.1 Support conditions. Cavity wall or masonry veneer construction may be supported on an 8-inch (203 mm) foundation wall, provided the 8-inch (203 mm) wall is corbeled with solid masonry to the width of the wall system above. The total horizontal projection of the corbel shall not exceed 2 inches (51 mm) with individual corbels projecting not more than one-third the thickness of the unit or one-half the height of the unit. The top course of all corbels shall be a header course.

R606.4 Allowable stresses. Allowable compressive stresses in masonry shall not exceed the values prescribed in Table R606.4. In determining the stresses in masonry, the effects of all loads and conditions of loading and the influence of all forces affecting the design and strength of the several parts shall be taken into account.

R606.4.1 Combined units. In walls or other structural members composed of different kinds or grades of units, materials or mortars, the maximum stress shall not exceed the allowable stress for the weakest of the combination of units, materials and mortars of which the member is composed. The net thickness of any facing unit that is used to resist stress shall not be less than 1.5 inches (38 mm).

R606.5 Piers. The unsupported height of masonry piers shall not exceed ten times their least dimension. When structural clay tile or hollow concrete masonry units are used for isolated piers to support beams and girders, the cellular spaces shall be filled solidly with concrete or Type M or S mortar, except that unfilled hollow piers may be used if their unsupported height is not more than four times their least dimension. Where hollow masonry units are solidly filled with concrete or Type M, S or N mortar, the allowable compressive stress shall be permitted to be increased as provided in Table R606.4.

R606.5.1 Pier cap. Hollow piers shall be capped with 4 inches (102 mm) of solid masonry or concrete or shall have cavities of the top course filled with concrete or grout or other approved methods.

R606.6 Chases. Chases and recesses in masonry walls shall not be deeper than one-third the wall thickness, and the maximum length of a horizontal chase or horizontal projection shall not exceed 4 feet (1219 mm), and shall have at least 8 inches (203 mm) of masonry in back of the chases and recesses and between adjacent chases or recesses and the jambs of openings.

Chases and recesses in masonry walls shall be designed and constructed so as not to reduce the required strength or required fire resistance of the wall and in no case shall a chase or recess be permitted within the required area of a pier. Masonry directly above chases or recesses wider than 12 inches (305 mm) shall be supported on noncombustible lintels

R606.7 Stack bond. In unreinforced masonry where masonry units are laid in stack bond, longitudinal reinforcement consisting of not less than two continuous wires each with a minimum aggregate cross-sectional area of 0.017 square inch (11 mm^2) shall be provided in horizontal bed joints spaced not more than 16 inches (406 mm) on center vertically.

R606.8 Lateral support. Masonry walls shall be laterally supported in either the horizontal or the vertical direction. The maximum spacing between lateral supports shall not exceed the distances in Table R606.8. Lateral support shall be provided by cross walls, pilasters, buttresses or structural frame members when the limiting distance is taken horizontally, or by floors or roofs when the limiting distance is taken vertically.

R606.8.1 Horizontal lateral support. Lateral support in the horizontal direction provided by intersecting masonry walls shall be provided by one of the methods in Section R606.8.1.1 or Section R606.8.1.2.

R606.8.1.1 Bonding pattern. Fifty percent of the units at the intersection shall be laid in an overlapping masonry bonding pattern, with alternate units having a bearing of not less than 3 inches (76 mm) on the unit below.

R606.8.1.2 Metal reinforcement. Interior nonload-bearing walls shall be anchored at their intersections, at vertical intervals of not more than 16 inches (406 mm) with joint reinforcement of at least 9 gage, or $^1/_4$ inch (6.4 mm) galvanized mesh hardware cloth. Intersecting masonry walls, other than interior nonloadbearing walls, shall be anchored at vertical intervals of not more than 8 inches (203 mm) with joint reinforcement of at least 9 gage and shall extend at least 30 inches (762 mm) in each direction at the intersection. Other metal ties, joint reinforcement or anchors, if used, shall be spaced to provide equivalent area of anchorage to that required by this section.

R606.8.2 Vertical lateral support. Vertical lateral support of masonry walls in Seismic Design Category A, B or C shall be provided in accordance with one of the methods in Section R606.8.2.1 or Section R606.8.2.2.

R606.8.2.1 Roof structures. Masonry walls shall be anchored to roof structures with metal strap anchors spaced in accordance with the manufacturer's instructions, $^1/_2$-inch (12.7 mm) bolts spaced not more than 6 feet (1829 mm) on center, or other approved anchors. Anchors shall be embedded at least 16 inches (406 mm) into the masonry, or be hooked or welded to bond beam reinforcement placed not less than 6 inches (152 mm) from the top of the wall.

TABLE R606.4
ALLOWABLE COMPRESSIVE STRESSES FOR EMPIRICAL DESIGN OF MASONRY

TABLE R606.4
ALLOWABLE COMPRESSIVE STRESSES FOR EMPIRICAL DESIGN OF MASONRY

CONSTRUCTION; COMPRESSIVE STRENGTH OF UNIT, GROSS AREA	ALLOWABLE COMPRESSIVE STRESSES[a] GROSS CROSS-SECTIONAL AREA[b]	
	Type M or S mortar	Type N mortar
Solid masonry of brick and other solid units of clay or shale; sand-lime or concrete brick:		
8,000 + psi	350	300
4,500 psi	225	200
2,500 psi	160	140
1,500 psi	115	100
Grouted[c] masonry, of clay or shale; sand-lime or concrete:		
4,500+ psi	225	200
2,500 psi	160	140
1,500 psi	115	100
Solid masonry of solid concrete masonry units:		
3,000+ psi	225	200
2,000 psi	160	140
1,200 psi	115	100
Masonry of hollow load-bearing units:		
2,000+ psi	140	120
1,500 psi	115	100
1,000 psi	75	70
700 psi	60	55
Hollow walls (cavity or masonry bonded[d]) solid units:		
2,500+ psi	160	140
1,500 psi	115	100
Hollow units	75	70
Stone ashlar masonry:		
Granite	720	640
Limestone or marble	450	400
Sandstone or cast stone	360	320
Rubble stone masonry:		
Coarse, rough or random	120	100

For SI: 1 pound per square inch = 6.895 kPa.

a. Linear interpolation shall be used for determining allowable stresses for masonry units having compressive strengths that are intermediate between those given in the table.

b. Gross cross-sectional area shall be calculated on the actual rather than nominal dimensions.

c. See Section R607.

d. Where floor and roof loads are carried upon one wythe, the gross cross-sectional area is that of the wythe under load; if both wythes are loaded, the gross cross-sectional area is that of the wall minus the area of the cavity between the wythes. Walls bonded with metal ties shall be considered as cavity walls unless the collar joints are filled with mortar or grout.

TABLE R606.8
SPACING OF LATERAL SUPPORT FOR MASONRY WALLS

CONSTRUCTION	MAXIMUM WALL LENGTH TO THICKNESS OR WALL HEIGHT TO THICKNESS[a,b]
Bearing walls:	
Solid or solid grouted	20
All other	18
Nonbearing walls:	
Exterior	18
Interior	36

For SI: 1 foot = 304.8 mm.

a. Except for cavity walls and cantilevered walls, the thickness of a wall shall be its nominal thickness measured perpendicular to the face of the wall. For cavity walls, the thickness shall be determined as the sum of the nominal thicknesses of the individual wythes. For cantilever walls, except for parapets, the ratio of height to nominal thickness shall not exceed 6 for solid masonry, or 4 for hollow masonry. For parapets, see Section R606.2.4.

b. An additional unsupported height of 6 feet is permitted for gable end walls.

R606.8.2.2 Floor diaphragms. Masonry walls shall be anchored to floor diaphragm framing by metal strap anchors spaced in accordance with the manufacturer's instructions, $1/2$-inch-diameter (12.7 mm) bolts spaced at intervals not to exceed 6 feet (1829 mm) and installed as shown in Figure R606.10(1), or by other approved methods.

R606.9 Lintels. Masonry over openings shall be supported by steel lintels, reinforced concrete or masonry lintels or masonry arches, designed to support load imposed.

R606.10 Anchorage. Masonry walls shall be anchored to floor and roof systems in accordance with the details shown in Figure R606.10(1), R606.10(2) or R606.10(3). Footings may be considered as points of lateral support.

R606.11 Seismic requirements. The seismic requirements of this section shall apply to the design of masonry and the construction of masonry building elements located in Seismic Design Category C, D_1 or D_2. These requirements shall not apply to glass unit masonry conforming to Section R610 or masonry veneer conforming to Section R703.7.

R606.11.1 General. Masonry structures and masonry elements shall comply with the requirements of Sections R606.11.2 through R606.11.4 based on the seismic design category established in Table R301.2(1). Masonry structures and masonry elements shall comply with the requirements of Section R606.11 and Figures R606.10(1), R606.10(2) and R606.10(3) or shall be designed in accordance with ACI 530/ASCE 5/TMS 402.

R606.11.1.1 Floor and roof diaphragm construction. Floor and roof diaphragms shall be constructed of structural wood sheathing panels, attached to wood framing in accordance with Table R602.3(1) or to cold-formed steel floor framing in accordance with Table R505.3.1(2) or to cold-formed steel roof framing in accordance with Table R804.3. Additionally, sheathing panel edges perpendicular to framing members shall be backed by blocking, and sheathing shall be connected to the blocking with fasteners at the edge spacing. For Seismic Design Categories C, D_1 and D_2, where the width-to-thickness dimension of the diaphragm exceeds 2-to-1, edge spacing of fasteners shall be 4 inches (102 mm) on center.

R606.11.2 Seismic Design Category C. Structures located in Seismic Design Category C shall comply with the requirements of this section.

R606.11.2.1 Design of elements not part of the lateral force-resisting system.

R606.11.2.1.1 Load-bearing frames or columns. Elements not part of the lateral-force-resisting system shall be analyzed as to their effect on the response of the system. Such frames or columns shall be adequate for vertical load carrying capacity and induced moment due to the design story drift.

R606.11.2.1.2 Masonry partition walls. Masonry partition walls, masonry screen walls and other masonry elements that are not designed to resist vertical or lateral loads, other than those induced by their own weight, shall be isolated from the structure so that vertical and lateral forces are not imparted to these elements. Isolation joints and connectors between these elements and the structure shall be designed to accommodate the design story drift.

R606.11.2.1.3 Reinforcement requirements for masonry elements. Masonry elements listed in Section R606.11.2.1.2 shall be reinforced in either the horizontal or vertical direction as shown in Figure R606.10(2) and in accordance with the following:

1. Horizontal reinforcement. Horizontal joint reinforcement shall consist of at least two longitudinal W1.7 wires spaced not more than 16 inches (406 mm) for walls greater than 4 inches (102 mm) in width and at least one longitudinal W1.7 wire spaced not more than 16 inches (406 mm) for walls not exceeding 4 inches (102 mm) in width; or at least one No. 4 bar spaced not more than 48 inches (1219 mm). Where two longitudinal wires of joint reinforcement are used, the space between these wires shall be the widest that the mortar joint will accommodate. Horizontal reinforcement shall be provided within 16 inches (406 mm) of the top and bottom of these masonry elements.

2. Vertical reinforcement. Vertical reinforcement shall consist of at least one No. 4 bar spaced not more than 48 inches (1219 mm). Vertical reinforcement shall be located within 16 inches (406 mm) of the ends of masonry walls.

R606.11.2.2 Design of elements part of the lateral-force-resisting system.

R606.11.2.2.1 Connections to masonry shear walls. Connectors shall be provided to transfer forces between masonry walls and horizontal elements in accordance with the requirements of Section 2.1.6 of ACI 530/ASCE 5/TMS 402. Connectors shall be designed to transfer horizontal design forces acting either perpendicular or parallel to the wall, but not less than 200 pounds per linear foot (2919 N/m) of wall. The maximum spacing between connectors shall be 4 feet (1219 mm). Such anchorage mechanisms shall not induce tension stresses perpendicular to grain in ledgers or nailers.

R606.11.2.2.2 Connections to masonry columns. Connectors shall be provided to transfer forces between masonry columns and horizontal elements in accordance with the requirements of Section 2.1.6 of ACI 530/ASCE 5/TMS 402. Where anchor bolts are used to connect horizontal elements to the tops of columns, anchor bolts shall be placed within lateral ties. Lateral ties shall enclose both the vertical bars in the column and the anchor bolts. There shall be a minimum of two No. 4 lateral ties provided in the top 5 inches (127 mm) of the column.

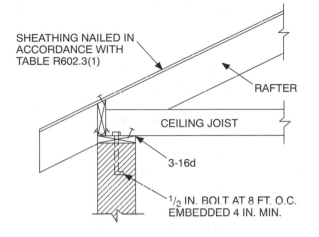

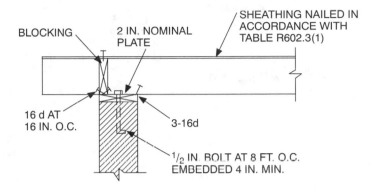

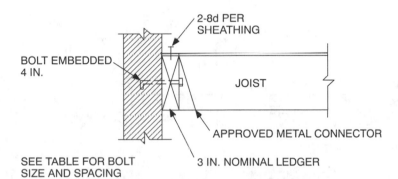

LEDGER BOLT SIZE AND SPACING

| JOIST SPAN | BOLT SIZE AND SPACING | |
	ROOF	FLOOR
10 FT.	$^1/_2$ AT 2 FT. 6 IN. $^7/_8$ AT 3 FT. 6 IN.	$^1/_2$ AT 2 FT. 0 IN. $^7/_8$ AT 2 FT. 9 IN.
10-15 FT.	$^1/_2$ AT 1 FT. 9 IN. $^7/_8$ AT 2 FT. 6 IN.	$^1/_2$ AT 1 FT. 4 IN. $^7/_8$ AT 2 FT. 0 IN.
15-20 FT.	$^1/_2$ AT 1 FT. 3 IN. $^7/_8$ AT 2 FT. 0 IN.	$^1/_2$ AT 1 FT. 0 IN. $^7/_8$ AT 1 FT. 6 IN.

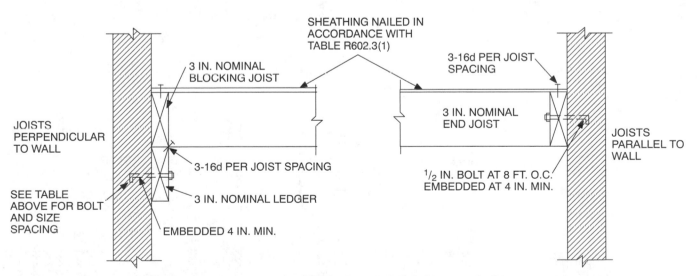

Note: Where bolts are located in hollow masonry, the cells in the courses receiving the bolt shall be grouted solid.

For SI: 1 inch = 25.4 mm, 1 foot = 304.8 mm, 1 pound per square foot = 0.0479 kN/m^2

FIGURE R606.10(1)
ANCHORAGE REQUIREMENTS FOR MASONRY WALLS LOCATED IN SEISMIC DESIGN CATEGORY
A, B OR C AND WHERE WIND LOADS ARE LESS THAN 30 PSF

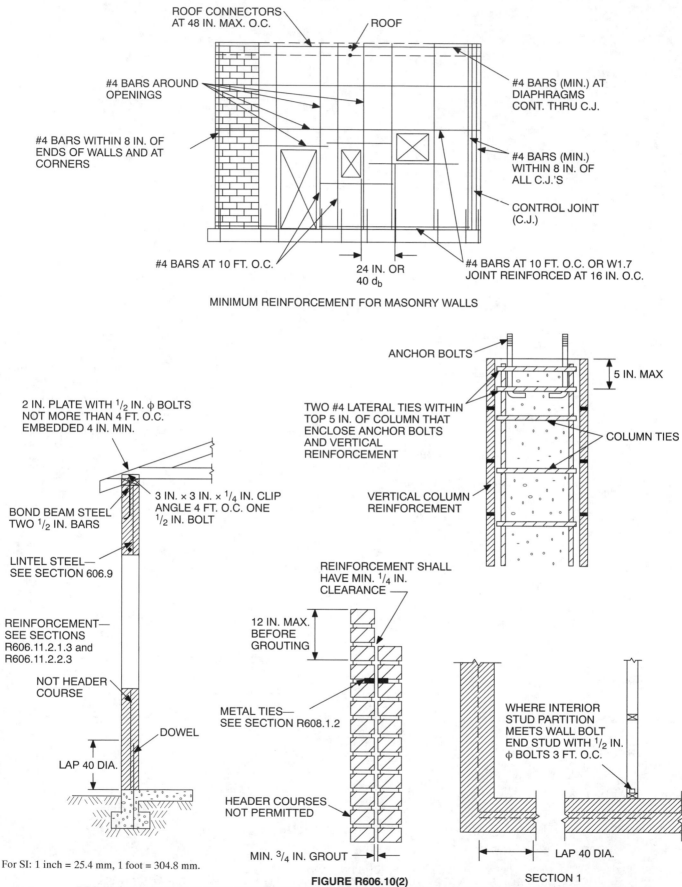

ROOF CONNECTORS AT 48 IN. MAX. O.C.

ROOF

#4 BARS AROUND OPENINGS

#4 BARS WITHIN 8 IN. OF ENDS OF WALLS AND AT CORNERS

#4 BARS (MIN.) AT DIAPHRAGMS CONT. THRU C.J.

#4 BARS (MIN.) WITHIN 8 IN. OF ALL C.J.'S

CONTROL JOINT (C.J.)

#4 BARS AT 10 FT. O.C.

24 IN. OR 40 d_b

#4 BARS AT 10 FT. O.C. OR W1.7 JOINT REINFORCED AT 16 IN. O.C.

MINIMUM REINFORCEMENT FOR MASONRY WALLS

ANCHOR BOLTS

5 IN. MAX

2 IN. PLATE WITH $1/2$ IN. φ BOLTS NOT MORE THAN 4 FT. O.C. EMBEDDED 4 IN. MIN.

TWO #4 LATERAL TIES WITHIN TOP 5 IN. OF COLUMN THAT ENCLOSE ANCHOR BOLTS AND VERTICAL REINFORCEMENT

COLUMN TIES

3 IN. × 3 IN. × $1/4$ IN. CLIP ANGLE 4 FT. O.C. ONE $1/2$ IN. BOLT

VERTICAL COLUMN REINFORCEMENT

BOND BEAM STEEL TWO $1/2$ IN. BARS

LINTEL STEEL— SEE SECTION 606.9

REINFORCEMENT SHALL HAVE MIN. $1/4$ IN. CLEARANCE

REINFORCEMENT— SEE SECTIONS R606.11.2.1.3 and R606.11.2.2.3

12 IN. MAX. BEFORE GROUTING

NOT HEADER COURSE

DOWEL

METAL TIES— SEE SECTION R608.1.2

WHERE INTERIOR STUD PARTITION MEETS WALL BOLT END STUD WITH $1/2$ IN. φ BOLTS 3 FT. O.C.

LAP 40 DIA.

HEADER COURSES NOT PERMITTED

MIN. $3/4$ IN. GROUT

LAP 40 DIA.

For SI: 1 inch = 25.4 mm, 1 foot = 304.8 mm.

SECTION 1

FIGURE R606.10(2)
REQUIREMENTS FOR REINFORCED GROUTED MASONRY CONSTRUCTION IN SEISMIC DESIGN CATEGORY C

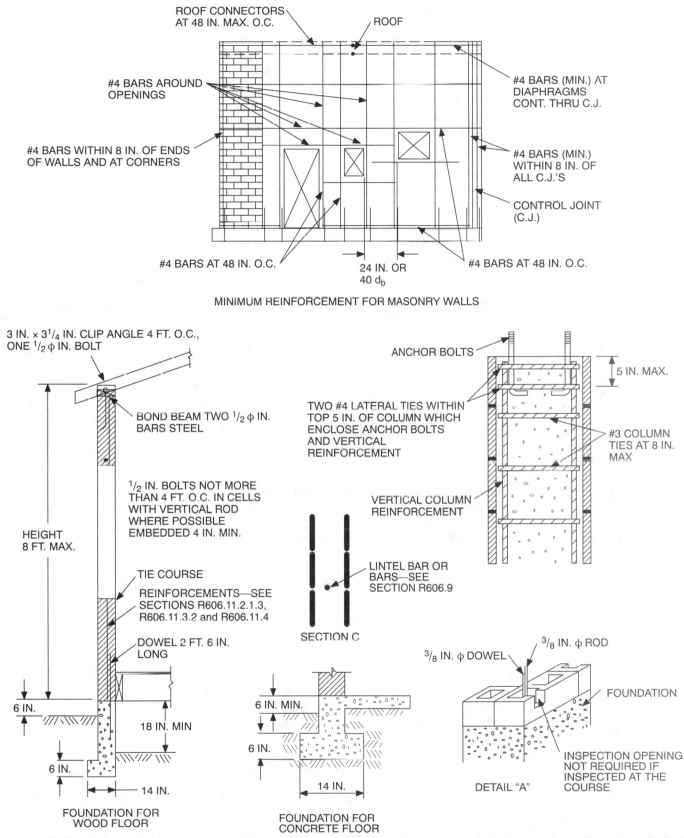

ROOF CONNECTORS AT 48 IN. MAX. O.C.

ROOF

#4 BARS AROUND OPENINGS

#4 BARS (MIN.) AT DIAPHRAGMS CONT. THRU C.J.

#4 BARS WITHIN 8 IN. OF ENDS OF WALLS AND AT CORNERS

#4 BARS (MIN.) WITHIN 8 IN. OF ALL C.J.'S

CONTROL JOINT (C.J.)

#4 BARS AT 48 IN. O.C.

24 IN. OR 40 d_b

#4 BARS AT 48 IN. O.C.

MINIMUM REINFORCEMENT FOR MASONRY WALLS

3 IN. × 3^1/$_4$ IN. CLIP ANGLE 4 FT. O.C., ONE ^{1}/$_2$ φ IN. BOLT

ANCHOR BOLTS

5 IN. MAX.

BOND BEAM TWO ^{1}/$_2$ φ IN. BARS STEEL

TWO #4 LATERAL TIES WITHIN TOP 5 IN. OF COLUMN WHICH ENCLOSE ANCHOR BOLTS AND VERTICAL REINFORCEMENT

#3 COLUMN TIES AT 8 IN. MAX

^{1}/$_2$ IN. BOLTS NOT MORE THAN 4 FT. O.C. IN CELLS WITH VERTICAL ROD WHERE POSSIBLE EMBEDDED 4 IN. MIN.

HEIGHT 8 FT. MAX.

VERTICAL COLUMN REINFORCEMENT

TIE COURSE

REINFORCEMENTS—SEE SECTIONS R606.11.2.1.3, R606.11.3.2 and R606.11.4

LINTEL BAR OR BARS—SEE SECTION R606.9

DOWEL 2 FT. 6 IN. LONG

SECTION C

^{3}/$_8$ IN. φ ROD

^{3}/$_8$ IN. φ DOWEL

6 IN.

6 IN. MIN.

FOUNDATION

18 IN. MIN

6 IN.

6 IN.

INSPECTION OPENING NOT REQUIRED IF INSPECTED AT THE COURSE

14 IN.

14 IN.

DETAIL "A"

FOUNDATION FOR WOOD FLOOR

FOUNDATION FOR CONCRETE FLOOR

Note: A full bed joint must be provided. All cells containing vertical bars are to be filled to the top of wall and provide inspection opening as shown on detail "A." Horizontal bars are to be laid as shown on detail "B." Lintel bars are to be laid as shown on Section C.

For SI: 1 inch = 25.4 mm, 1 foot = 304.8 mm.

FIGURE R606.10(3)
REQUIREMENTS FOR REINFORCED MASONRY CONSTRUCTION IN SEISMIC DESIGN CATEGORY D$_1$ OR D$_2$

R606.11.2.2.3 Minimum reinforcement requirements for masonry shear walls. Vertical reinforcement of at least one No. 4 bar shall be provided at corners, within 16 inches (406 mm) of each side of openings, within 8 inches (203 mm) of each side of movement joints, within 8 inches (203 mm) of the ends of walls, and at a maximum spacing of 10 feet (3048 mm).

Horizontal joint reinforcement shall consist of at least two wires of W1.7 spaced not more than 16 inches (406 mm); or bond beam reinforcement shall be provided of at least one No. 4 bar spaced not more than 10 feet (3048 mm). Horizontal reinforcement shall also be provided at the bottom and top of wall openings and shall extend not less than 24 inches (610 mm) nor less than 40 bar diameters past the opening; continuously at structurally connected roof and floor levels; and within 16 inches (406 mm) of the top of walls.

R606.11.3 Seismic Design Category D_1. Structures in Seismic Design Category D_1 shall comply with the requirements of Seismic Design Category C and to the additional requirements of this section. Masonry structures in Seismic Design Category D_1 shall be limited in height to one story and 9 feet (2743 mm) between lateral supports.

R606.11.3.1 Design requirements. Masonry elements other than those covered by Section R606.11.2.1.2 shall be designed in accordance with the requirements of Chapter 2 of ACI 530/ASCE 5/TMS 402.

R606.11.3.2 Minimum reinforcement requirements for masonry walls. Masonry walls other than those covered by Section R606.11.2.1.3 shall be reinforced in both the vertical and horizontal direction. The sum of the cross-sectional area of horizontal and vertical reinforcement shall be at least 0.002 times the gross cross-sectional area of the wall, and the minimum cross-sectional area in each direction shall be not less than 0.0007 times the gross cross-sectional area of the wall. Reinforcement shall be uniformly distributed. Table R606.11.3.2 provides the minimum reinforcing bar sizes required for varying thicknesses of masonry walls. The maximum spacing of reinforcement shall be 48 inches (1219 mm) provided that the walls are solid grouted and constructed of hollow open-end units, hollow units laid with full head joints or two wythe of solid units. The maximum spacing of reinforcement shall be 24 inches (610 mm) for all other masonry.

R606.11.3.2.1 Shear wall reinforcement requirements. The maximum spacing of vertical and horizontal reinforcement shall be the smaller of one-third the length of the shear wall, one-third the height of the shear wall, or 48 inches (1219 mm). The minimum cross-sectional area of vertical reinforcement shall be one-third of the required shear reinforcement. Shear reinforcement shall be anchored around vertical reinforcing bars with a standard hook.

R606.11.3.3 Minimum reinforcement for masonry columns. Lateral ties in masonry columns shall be spaced not more than 8 inches (203 mm) on center and shall be at least $^3/_8$ inch (9.5 mm) diameter. Lateral ties shall be embedded in grout.

R606.11.3.4 Material restrictions. Type N mortar or masonry cement shall not be used as part of the lateral-force-resisting system.

R606.11.3.5 Lateral tie anchorage. Standard hooks for lateral tie anchorage shall be either a 135-degree (2.4 rad) standard hook or a 180-degree (3.2 rad) standard hook.

R606.11.4 Seismic Design Category D_2. Structures in Seismic Design Category D_2 shall comply with the requirements of Seismic Design Category D_1 and to the additional requirements of this section.

TABLE R606.11.3.2
MINIMUM DISTRIBUTED WALL REINFORCEMENT FOR BUILDINGS ASSIGNED TO SEISMIC DESIGN CATEGORY D_1

NOMINAL WALL THICKNESS (inches o.c.)	MINIMUM SUM OF THE VERTICAL AND HORIZONTAL REINFORCEMENT AREAS[a] (inches per square foot)	MINIMUM REINFORCEMENT AS DISTRIBUTED IN BOTH HORIZONTAL AND VERTICAL DIRECTIONS[b] (inches per square foot)	MINIMUM BAR SIZE FOR REINFORCEMENT SPACED AT 48 INCHES
6	0.135	0.047	#4
8	0.183	0.064	#5
10	0.231	0.081	#6
12	0.279	0.098	#6

For SI: 1 inch = 25.4 mm, 1 foot = 304.8 mm, 1 square inch per foot = 2.12 mm²/mm.

a. Based on the minimum reinforcing ratio of 0.002 times the gross cross-sectional area of the wall.

b. Based on the minimum reinforcing ratio each direction of 0.0007 times the gross cross-sectional area of the wall.

R606.11.4.1 Design of elements not part of the lateral-force-resisting system. Stack bond masonry that is not part of the lateral-force-resisting system shall have a horizontal cross-sectional area of reinforcement of at least 0.0015 times the gross cross-sectional area of masonry. Table R606.11.4.1 provides minimum reinforcing bar sizes for masonry walls. The maximum spacing of horizontal reinforcement shall be 24 inches (610 mm). These elements shall be solidly grouted and shall be constructed of hollow open-end units or two wythes of solid units.

TABLE R606.11.4.1
MINIMUM REINFORCING FOR STACKED BONDED MASONRY WALLS IN SEISMIC DESIGN CATEGORY D$_2$

NOMINAL WALL THICKNESS (inches)	MINIMUM BAR SIZE SPACED AT 24 INCHES
6	#4
8	#5
10	#5
12	#6

For SI: 1 inch = 25.4 mm.

R606.11.4.2 Design of elements part of the lateral-force-resisting system. Stack bond masonry that is part of the lateral-force-resisting system shall have a horizontal cross-sectional area of reinforcement of at least 0.0025 times the gross cross-sectional area of masonry. Table R606.11.4.2 provides minimum reinforcing bar sizes for masonry walls. The maximum spacing of horizontal reinforcement shall be 16 inches (406 mm). These elements shall be solidly grouted and shall be constructed of hollow open-end units or two wythes of solid units.

TABLE R606.11.4.2
MINIMUM REINFORCING FOR STACKED BONDED MASONRY WALLS IN SEISMIC DESIGN CATEGORY D$_2$

NOMINAL WALL THICKNESS (inches)	MINIMUM BAR SIZE SPACED AT 16 INCHES
6	#4
8	#5
10	#5
12	#6

For SI: 1 inch = 25.4 mm.

R606.12 Protection for reinforcement. All bars shall be completely embedded in mortar or grout. Joint reinforcement embedded in horizontal mortar joints shall not have less than $^5/_8$-inch (15.9 mm) mortar coverage from the exposed face. All other reinforcement shall have a minimum coverage of one bar diameter over all bars, but not less than $^3/_4$ inch (19.1 mm), except where exposed to weather or soil, in which case the minimum coverage shall be 2 inches (51 mm).

R606.13 Beam supports. Beams, girders or other concentrated loads supported by a wall or column shall have a bearing of at least 3 inches (76 mm) in length measured parallel to the beam upon solid masonry not less than 4 inches (102 mm) in thickness, or upon a metal bearing plate of adequate design and dimensions to distribute the load safely, or upon a continuous

reinforced masonry member projecting not less than 4 inches (102 mm) from the face of the wall.

R606.13.1 Joist bearing. Joists shall have a bearing of not less than $1^1/_2$ inches (38 mm), except as provided in Section R606.13, and shall be supported in accordance with Figure R606.10(1).

R606.14 Metal accessories. Joint reinforcement, anchors, ties and wire fabric shall conform to the following: ASTM A 82 for wire anchors and ties; ASTM A 36 for plate, headed and bent-bar anchors; ASTM A 510 for corrugated sheet metal anchors and ties; ASTM A 951 for joint reinforcement; ASTM B 227 for copper-clad steel wire ties; or ASTM A 167 for stainless steel hardware.

R606.14.1 Corrosion protection. Minimum corrosion protection of joint reinforcement, anchor ties and wire fabric for use in masonry wall construction shall conform to Table R606.14.1.

TABLE R606.14.1
MINIMUM CORROSION PROTECTION

MASONRY METAL ACCESSORY	STANDARD
Joint reinforcement, interior walls	ASTM A 641, Class 1
Wire ties or anchors in exterior walls completely embedded in mortar or grout	ASTM A 641, Class 3
Wire ties or anchors in exterior walls not completely embedded in mortar or grout	ASTM A 153, Class B-2
Joint reinforcement in exterior walls or interior walls exposed to moist environment	ASTM A 153, Class B-2
Sheet metal ties or anchors exposed to weather	ASTM A 153, Class B-2
Sheet metal ties or anchors completely embedded in mortar or grout	ASTM A 525, Class G-60
Stainless steel hardware for any exposure	ASTM A 167, Type 304

SECTION R607
UNIT MASONRY

R607.1 Mortar. Mortar for use in masonry construction shall comply with ASTM C 270. The type of mortar shall be in accordance with Sections R607.1.1, R607.1.2 and R607.1.3 and shall meet the proportion specifications of Table R607.1 or the property specifications of ASTM C 270.

R607.1.1 Foundation walls. Masonry foundation walls constructed as set forth in Tables R404.1.1(1) through R404.1.1(4) and mortar shall be Type M or S.

R607.1.2 Masonry in Seismic Design Categories A, B and C. Mortar for masonry serving as the lateral-force-resisting system in Seismic Design Categories A, B and C shall be Type M, S or N mortar.

R607.1.3 Masonry in Seismic Design Categories D$_1$ and D$_2$. Mortar for masonry serving as the lateral-force-resisting system in Seismic Design Categories D$_1$ and D$_2$ shall be Type M or S portland cement-lime or mortar cement mortar.

R607.2 Placing mortar and masonry units.

R607.2.1 Bed and head joints. Unless otherwise required or indicated on the project drawings, head and bed joints shall be $3/8$ inch (9.5 mm) thick, except that the thickness of the bed joint of the starting course placed over foundations shall not be less than $1/4$ inch (6.4 mm) and not more than $3/4$ inch (19.1 mm).

R607.2.1.1 Mortar joint thickness tolerance. Mortar joint thickness shall be within the following tolerances from the specified dimensions:

1. Bed joint: + $1/8$ inch (3.2 mm).
2. Head joint: $1/4$ inch (6.4 mm), + $3/8$ inch (9.5 mm).
3. Collar joints: $1/4$ inch (6.4 mm), + $3/8$ inch (9.5 mm).

Exception: Nonload-bearing masonry elements and masonry veneers designed and constructed in accordance with Section R703.7 are not required to meet these tolerances.

R607.2.2 Masonry unit placement. The mortar shall be sufficiently plastic and units shall be placed with sufficient pressure to extrude mortar from the joint and produce a tight joint. Deep furrowing of bed joints that produces voids shall not be permitted. Any units disturbed to the extent that initial bond is broken after initial placement shall be removed and relaid in fresh mortar. Surfaces to be in contact with mortar shall be clean and free of deleterious materials.

R607.2.2.1 Solid masonry. All solid masonry units shall be laid with full head and bed joints and all interior vertical joints that are designed to receive mortar shall be filled.

R607.2.2.2 Hollow masonry. For hollow masonry units, all head and bed joints shall be filled solidly with mortar for a distance in from the face of the unit not less than the thickness of the face shell.

R607.3 Installation of wall ties. The installation of wall ties shall be as follows:

1. The ends of wall ties shall be embedded in mortar joints. Wall tie ends shall engage outer face shells of hollow units by at least $1/2$ inch (12.7 mm). Wire wall ties shall be embedded at least $1^1/_2$ inches (38 mm) into the mortar bed of solid masonry units or solid grouted hollow units.

2. Wall ties shall not be bent after being embedded in grout or mortar.

TABLE R607.1
MORTAR PROPORTIONS[a,b]

Mortar	Type	PROPORTIONS BY VOLUME (cementitious materials)								Aggregate ratio (measured in damp, loose conditions)
		Portland cement or blended cement	Mortar cement M	S	N	Masonry cement M	S	N	Hydrated lime or lime putty	
Cement-lime	M	1	—	—	—	—	—	—	$1/4$	
	S	1	—	—	—	—	—	—	over $1/4$ to $1/2$	
	N	1	—	—	—	—	—	—	over $1/2$ to $1^1/4$	
	O	1	—	—	—	—	—	—	over $1^1/4$ to $2^1/2$	
Mortar cement	M	1	—	—	1	—	—	—	—	Not less than $2^1/4$ and not more than 3 times the sum of separate volumes of lime, if used, and cement
	M	—	1	—	—	—	—	—		
	S	$1/2$	—	—	1	—	—	—		
	S	—	—	1	—	—	—	—		
	N	—	—	—	1	—	—	—		
	O	—	—	—	1	—	—	—		
Masonry cement	M	1				—	—	1	—	
	M	—				1	—	—		
	S	$1/2$				—	—	1		
	S	—				—	1	—		
	N	—				—	—	1		
	O	—				—	—	1		

For SI: 1 cubic foot = 0.0283 m^3, 1 pound = 0.454 kg.

a. For the purpose of these specifications, the weight of 1 cubic foot of the respective materials shall be considered to be as follows:

Portland Cement	94 pounds	Masonry Cement	Weight printed on bag
Mortar Cement	Weight printed on bag	Hydrated Lime	40 pounds
Lime Putty (Quicklime)	80 pounds	Sand, damp and loose	80 pounds of dry sand

b. Two air-entraining materials shall not be combined in mortar.

SECTION R608
MULTIPLE WYTHE MASONRY

R608.1 General. The facing and backing of multiple wythe masonry walls shall be bonded in accordance with Section R608.1.1, R608.1.2 or R608.1.3. In cavity walls, neither the facing nor the backing shall be less than 3 inches (76 mm) nominal in thickness and the cavity shall not be more than 4 inches (102 mm) nominal in width. The backing shall be at least as thick as the facing.

Exception: Cavities shall be permitted to exceed the 4-inch (102 mm) nominal dimension provided tie size and tie spacing have been established by calculation.

R608.1.1 Bonding with masonry headers. Bonding with solid or hollow masonry headers shall comply with Sections R608.1.1.1 and R608.1.1.2.

R608.1.1.1 Solid units. Where the facing and backing (adjacent wythes) of solid masonry construction are bonded by means of masonry headers, no less than 4 percent of the wall surface of each face shall be composed of headers extending not less than 3 inches (76 mm) into the backing. The distance between adjacent full-length headers shall not exceed 24 inches (610 mm) either vertically or horizontally. In walls in which a single header does not extend through the wall, headers from the opposite sides shall overlap at least 3 inches (76 mm), or headers from opposite sides shall be covered with another header course overlapping the header below at least 3 inches (76 mm).

R608.1.1.2 Hollow units. Where two or more hollow units are used to make up the thickness of a wall, the stretcher courses shall be bonded at vertical intervals not exceeding 34 inches (864 mm) by lapping at least 3 inches (76 mm) over the unit below, or by lapping at vertical intervals not exceeding 17 inches (432 mm) with units that are at least 50 percent greater in thickness than the units below.

R608.1.2 Bonding with wall ties or joint reinforcement. Bonding with wall ties or joint reinforcement shall comply with Sections R608.1.2.1 through R608.1.2.3.

R608.1.2.1 Bonding with wall ties. Bonding with wall ties, except as required by Section R610, where the facing and backing (adjacent wythes) of masonry walls are bonded with $^3/_{16}$-inch-diameter (4.8 mm) wall ties embedded in the horizontal mortar joints, there shall be at least one metal tie for each 4.5 square feet (0.418 m^2) of wall area. Ties in alternate courses shall be staggered. The maximum vertical distance between ties shall not exceed 24 inches (610 mm), and the maximum horizontal distance shall not exceed 36 inches (914 mm). Rods or ties bent to rectangular shape shall be used with hollow masonry units laid with the cells vertically. In other walls, the ends of ties shall be bent to 90-degree (0.79 rad) angles to provide hooks no less than 2 inches (51 mm) long. Additional bonding ties shall be provided at all openings, spaced not more than 3 feet (914 mm) apart around the perimeter and within 12 inches (305 mm) of the opening.

R608.1.2.2 Bonding with adjustable wall ties. Where the facing and backing (adjacent wythes) of masonry are bonded with adjustable wall ties, there shall be at least one tie for each 2.67 square feet (0.248 m^2) of wall area. Neither the vertical nor horizontal spacing of the adjustable wall ties shall exceed 24 inches (610 mm). The maximum vertical offset of bed joints from one wythe to the other shall be 1.25 inches (32 mm). The maximum clearance between connecting parts of the ties shall be $^1/_{16}$ inch (1.6 mm). When pintle legs are used, ties shall have at least two $^3/_{16}$-inch-diameter (4.8 mm) legs.

R608.1.2.3 Bonding with prefabricated joint reinforcement. Where the facing and backing (adjacent wythes) of masonry are bonded with prefabricated joint reinforcement, there shall be at least one cross wire serving as a tie for each 2.67 square feet (0.248 m^2) of wall area. The vertical spacing of the joint reinforcement shall not exceed 16 inches (406 mm). Cross wires on prefabricated joint reinforcement shall not be smaller than No. 9 gage. The longitudinal wires shall be embedded in the mortar.

R608.1.3 Bonding with natural or cast stone. Bonding with natural and cast stone shall conform to Sections R608.1.3.1 and R608.1.3.2.

R608.1.3.1 Ashlar masonry. In ashlar masonry, bonder units, uniformly distributed, shall be provided to the extent of not less than 10 percent of the wall area. Such bonder units shall extend not less than 4 inches (102 mm) into the backing wall.

R608.1.3.2 Rubble stone masonry. Rubble stone masonry 24 inches (610 mm) or less in thickness shall have bonder units with a maximum spacing of 3 feet (914 mm) vertically and 3 feet (914 mm) horizontally, and if the masonry is of greater thickness than 24 inches (610 mm), shall have one bonder unit for each 6 square feet (0.557 m^2) of wall surface on both sides.

R608.2 Masonry bonding pattern. Masonry laid in running and stack bond shall conform to Sections R608.2.1 and R608.2.2.

R608.2.1 Masonry laid in running bond. In each wythe of masonry laid in running bond, head joints in successive courses shall be offset by not less than one-fourth the unit length, or the masonry walls shall be reinforced longitudinally as required in Section R608.2.2.

R608.2.2 Masonry laid in stack bond. Where unit masonry is laid with less head joint offset than in Section R607.2.1, the minimum area of horizontal reinforcement placed in mortar bed joints or in bond beams spaced not more than 48 inches (1219 mm) apart, shall be 0.0007 times the vertical cross-sectional area of the wall.

SECTION R609
GROUTED MASONRY

R609.1 General. Grouted multiple-wythe masonry is a form of construction in which the space between the wythes is solidly filled with grout. It is not necessary for the cores of masonry units to be filled with grout. Grouted hollow unit masonry is a form of construction in which certain cells of hollow units are continuously filled with grout.

R609.1.1 Grout. Grout shall consist of cementitious material and aggregate in accordance with ASTM C 476 and the proportion specifications of Table R609.1.1. Type M or Type S mortar to which sufficient water has been added to produce pouring consistency can be used as grout.

R609.1.2 Grouting requirements. Maximum pour heights and the minimum dimensions of spaces provided for grout placement shall conform to Table R609.1.2. If the work is stopped for one hour or longer, the horizontal construction joints shall be formed by stopping all tiers at the same elevation and with the grout 1 inch (25.4 mm) below the top.

R609.1.3 Grout space (cleaning). Provision shall be made for cleaning grout space. Mortar projections that project more than 0.5 inch (12.7 mm) into grout space and any other foreign matter shall be removed from grout space prior to inspection and grouting.

R609.1.4 Grout placement. Grout shall be a plastic mix suitable for pumping without segregation of the constituents and shall be mixed thoroughly. Grout shall be placed by pumping or by an approved alternate method and shall be placed before any initial set occurs and in no case more than $1^1/_2$ hours after water has been added. Grouting shall be done in a continuous pour, in lifts not exceeding 5 feet (1524 mm). It shall be consolidated by puddling or mechanical vibrating during placing and reconsolidated after excess moisture has been absorbed but before plasticity is lost.

R609.1.4.1 Grout pumped through aluminum pipes. Grout shall not be pumped through aluminum pipes.

R609.1.5 Cleanouts. Where required by the building official, cleanouts shall be provided as specified in this section. The cleanouts shall be sealed before grouting and after inspection.

R609.1.5.1 Grouted multiple-wythe masonry. Cleanouts shall be provided at the bottom course of the exterior wythe at each pour of grout where such pour exceeds 5 feet (1524 mm) in height.

R609.1.5.2 Grouted hollow unit masonry. Cleanouts shall be provided at the bottom course of each cell to be grouted at each pour of grout, where such pour exceeds 4 feet (1219 mm) in height.

TABLE R609.1.1
GROUT PROPORTIONS BY VOLUME FOR MASONRY CONSTRUCTION

TYPE	PORTLAND CEMENT OR BLENDED CEMENT SLAG CEMENT	HYDRATED LIME OR LIME PUTTY	AGGREGATE MEASURED IN A DAMP, LOOSE CONDITION	
			Fine	Coarse
Fine	1	0 to 1/10	$2^1/_4$ to 3 times the sum of the volume of the cementitious materials	—
Coarse	1	0 to 1/10	$2^1/_4$ to 3 times the sum of the volume of the cementitious materials	1 to 2 times the sum of the volumes of the cementitious materials

TABLE R609.1.2
GROUT SPACE DIMENSIONS AND POUR HEIGHTS

GROUT TYPE	GROUT POUR MAXIMUM HEIGHT (feet)	MINIMUM WIDTH OF GROUT SPACES[a,b] (inches)	MINIMUM GROUT[b,c] SPACE DIMENSIONS FOR GROUTING CELLS OF HOLLOW UNITS (inches x inches)
Fine	1	0.75	1.5 × 2
	5	2	2 × 3
	12	2.5	2.5 × 3
	24	3	3 × 3
Coarse	1	1.5	1.5 × 3
	5	2	2.5 × 3
	12	2.5	3 × 3
	24	3	3 × 4

For SI: 1 inch = 25.4 mm, 1 foot = 304.8 mm.

a. For grouting between masonry wythes.

b. Grout space dimension is the clear dimension between any masonry protrusion and shall be increased by the horizontal projection of the diameters of the horizontal bars within the cross section of the grout space.

c. Area of vertical reinforcement shall not exceed 6 percent of the area of the grout space.

R609.2 Grouted multiple-wythe masonry. Grouted multiple-wythe masonry shall conform to all the requirements specified in Section R609.1 and the requirements of this section.

R609.2.1 Bonding of backup wythe. Where all interior vertical spaces are filled with grout in multiple-wythe construction, masonry headers shall not be permitted. Metal wall ties shall be used in accordance with Section R608.1.2 to prevent spreading of the wythes and to maintain the vertical alignment of the wall. Wall ties shall be installed in accordance with Section R608.1.2 when the backup wythe in multiple-wythe construction is fully grouted.

R609.2.2 Grout spaces. Fine grout shall be used when interior vertical space to receive grout does not exceed 2 inches (51 mm) in thickness. Interior vertical spaces exceeding 2 inches (51 mm) in thickness shall use coarse or fine grout.

R609.2.3 Grout barriers. Vertical grout barriers or dams shall be built of solid masonry across the grout space the entire height of the wall to control the flow of the grout horizontally. Grout barriers shall not be more than 25 feet (7620 mm) apart. The grouting of any section of a wall between control barriers shall be completed in one day with no interruptions greater than one hour.

R609.3 Reinforced grouted multiple-wythe masonry. Reinforced grouted multiple-wythe masonry shall conform to all the requirements specified in Sections R609.1 and R609.2 and the requirements of this section.

R609.3.1 Construction. The thickness of grout or mortar between masonry units and reinforcement shall not be less than $^1/_4$ inch (6.4 mm), except that $^1/_4$-inch (6.4 mm) bars may be laid in horizontal mortar joints at least $^1/_2$ inch (12.7 mm) thick, and steel wire reinforcement may be laid in horizontal mortar joints at least twice the thickness of the wire diameter.

R609.4 Reinforced hollow unit masonry. Reinforced hollow unit masonry shall conform to all the requirements of Section R609.1 and the requirements of this section.

R609.4.1 Construction. Requirements for construction shall be as follows:

1. All reinforced hollow-unit masonry shall be built to preserve the unobstructed vertical continuity of the cells to be filled. Walls and cross webs forming such cells to be filled shall be full-bedded in mortar to prevent leakage of grout. All head and end joints shall be solidly filled with mortar for a distance in from the face of the wall or unit not less than the thickness of the longitudinal face shells. Bond shall be provided by lapping units in successive vertical courses.

2. Cells to be filled shall have vertical alignment sufficient to maintain a clear, unobstructed continuous vertical cell of dimensions prescribed in Table R609.1.2.

3. Vertical reinforcement shall be held in position at top and bottom and at intervals not exceeding 200 diameters of the reinforcement.

4. All cells containing reinforcement shall be filled solidly with grout. Grout shall be poured in lifts of 8-foot (2438 mm) maximum height. When total grout pour exceeds 8 feet (2438 mm) in height, the grout shall be placed in lifts not exceeding 5 feet (1524 mm) and special inspection during grouting shall be required.

5. Horizontal steel shall be fully embedded by grout in an uninterrupted pour.

SECTION R610
GLASS UNIT MASONRY

R610.1 General. Panels of glass unit masonry located in load-bearing and nonload-bearing exterior and interior walls shall be constructed in accordance with this section.

R610.2 Materials. Hollow glass units shall be partially evacuated and have a minimum average glass face thickness of $^3/_{16}$ inch (4.8 mm). The surface of units in contact with mortar shall be treated with a polyvinyl butyral coating or latex-based paint. The use of reclaimed units is prohibited.

R610.3 Units. Hollow or solid glass block units shall be standard or thin units.

R610.3.1 Standard units. The specified thickness of standard units shall be at least $3^7/_8$ inches (98 mm).

R610.3.2 Thin units. The specified thickness of thin units shall be at least $3^1/_8$ inches (79 mm) for hollow units and at least 3 inches (76 mm) for solid units.

R610.4 Isolated panels. Isolated panels of glass unit masonry shall conform to the requirements of this section.

R610.4.1 Exterior standard-unit panels. The maximum area of each individual standard-unit panel shall be 144 square feet (13.4 m^2) when the design wind pressure is 20 psf (958 Pa). The maximum area of such panels subjected to design wind pressures other than 20 psf (958 Pa) shall be in accordance with Figure R610.4.1. The maximum panel dimension between structural supports shall be 25 feet (7620 mm) in width or 20 feet (6096 mm) in height.

R610.4.2 Exterior thin-unit panels. The maximum area of each individual thin-unit panel shall be 85 square feet (7.9 m^2). The maximum dimension between structural supports shall be 15 feet (4572 mm) in width or 10 feet (3048 mm) in height. Thin units shall not be used in applications where the design wind pressure as stated in Table R301.2(1) exceeds 20 psf (958 Pa).

R610.4.3 Interior panels. The maximum area of each individual standard-unit panel shall be 250 square feet (23.2 m^2). The maximum area of each thin-unit panel shall be 150 square feet (13.9 m^2). The maximum dimension between structural supports shall be 25 feet (7620 mm) in width or 20 feet (6096 mm) in height.

R610.4.4 Curved panels. The width of curved panels shall conform to the requirements of Sections R610.4.1, R610.4.2 and R610.4.3, except additional structural supports shall be provided at locations where a curved section joins a straight section, and at inflection points in multicurved walls.

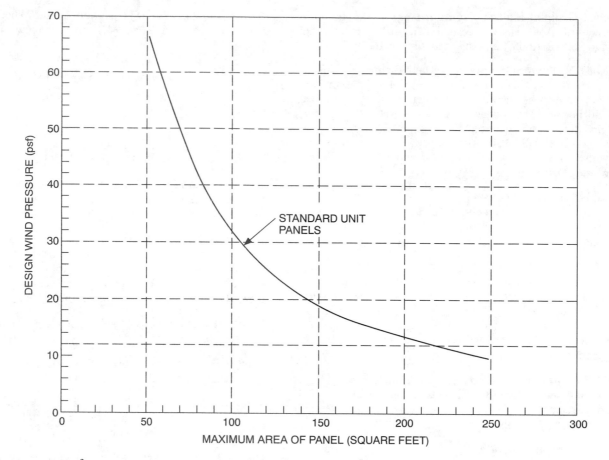

For SI: 1 square foot = 0.0929 m², 1 pound per square foot = 0.0479 kN/m².

FIGURE R610.4.1
GLASS UNIT MASONRY DESIGN WIND LOAD RESISTANCE

R610.5 Panel support. Glass unit masonry panels shall conform to the support requirements of this section.

R610.5.1 Deflection. The maximum total deflection of structural members that support glass unit masonry shall not exceed $1/600$.

R610.5.2 Lateral support. Glass unit masonry panels shall be laterally supported along the top and sides of the panel. Lateral supports for glass unit masonry panels shall be designed to resist a minimum of 200 pounds per lineal feet (2918 N/m) of panel, or the actual applied loads, whichever is greater. Except for single unit panels, lateral support shall be provided by panel anchors along the top and sides spaced a maximum of 16 inches (406 mm) on center or by channel-type restraints. Single unit panels shall be supported by channel-type restraints.

Exceptions:
1. Lateral support is not required at the top of panels that are one unit wide.
2. Lateral support is not required at the sides of panels that are one unit high.

R610.5.2.1 Panel anchor restraints. Panel anchors shall be spaced a maximum of 16 inches (406 mm) on center in both jambs and across the head. Panel anchors shall be embedded a minimum of 12 inches (305 mm) and shall be provided with two fasteners so as to resist the loads specified in Section R610.5.2.

R610.5.2.2 Channel-type restraints. Glass unit masonry panels shall be recessed at least 1 inch (25.4 mm) within channels and chases. Channel-type restraints shall be oversized to accommodate expansion material in the opening, packing and sealant between the framing restraints, and the glass unit masonry perimeter units.

R610.6 Sills. Before bedding of glass units, the sill area shall be covered with a water base asphaltic emulsion coating. The coating shall shall be a minimum of $1/8$ inch (3.2 mm) thick.

R610.7 Expansion joints. Glass unit masonry panels shall be provided with expansion joints along the top and sides at all structural supports. Expansion joints shall be a minimum of $3/8$ inch (9.5 mm) in thickness and shall have sufficient thickness to accommodate displacements of the supporting structure. Expansion joints shall be entirely free of mortar and other debris and shall be filled with resilient material.

R610.8 Mortar. Glass unit masonry shall be laid with Type S or N mortar. Mortar shall not be retempered after initial set.

Mortar unused within $1^1/_2$ hours after initial mixing shall be discarded.

R610.9 Reinforcement. Glass unit masonry panels shall have horizontal joint reinforcement spaced a maximum of 16 inches (406 mm) on center located in the mortar bed joint. Horizontal joint reinforcement shall extend the entire length of the panel but shall not extend across expansion joints. Longitudinal wires shall be lapped a minimum of 6 inches (152 mm) at splices. Joint reinforcement shall be placed in the bed joint immediately below and above openings in the panel. The reinforcement shall have not less than two parallel longitudinal wires of size W1.7 or greater, and have welded cross wires of size W1.7 or greater.

R610.10 Placement. Glass units shall be placed so head and bed joints are filled solidly. Mortar shall not be furrowed. Head and bed joints of glass unit masonry shall be $^1/_4$ inch (6.4 mm) thick, except that vertical joint thickness of radial panels shall not be less than $^1/_8$ inch (3.2 mm) or greater than $^5/_8$ inch (15.9 mm). The bed joint thickness tolerance shall be minus $^1/_{16}$ inch (1.6 mm) and plus $^1/_8$ inch (3.2 mm). The head joint thickness tolerance shall be plus or minus $^1/_8$ inch (3.2 mm).

SECTION R611
INSULATING CONCRETE FORM
WALL CONSTRUCTION

R611.1 General. Insulating Concrete Form walls shall be designed and constructed in accordance with the provisions of this section or in accordance with the provisions of ACI 318. When ACI 318 or the provisions of this section are used to design insulating concrete form walls, project drawings, typical details and specifications are not required to bear the seal of the architect or engineer responsible for design, unless otherwise required by the state law of the jurisdiction having authority.

R611.2 Applicability limits. The provisions of this section shall apply to the construction of insulating concrete form walls for buildings not greater than 60 feet (18 288 mm) in plan dimensions, and floors not greater than 32 feet (9754 mm) or roofs not greater than 40 feet (12 192 mm) in clear span. Buildings shall not exceed two stories in height above-grade with each story not greater than 10 feet (3048 mm) high. Walls constructed in accordance with the provisions of this section shall be limited to buildings subjected to a maximum design wind speed of 130 miles per hour (209 km/h), a maximum ground snow load of 70 psf (3.35 kN/m²), and Seismic Design Categories A, B and C.

R611.3 Flat insulating concrete form wall systems. Flat ICF wall systems shall comply with Figure R611.3 and shall have reinforcement in accordance with Table R611.3 and Section R611.7.

R611.4 Waffle-grid insulating concrete form wall systems. Waffle-grid wall systems shall comply with Figure R611.4 and shall have reinforcement in accordance with Table R611.4(1) and Section R611.7. The minimum core dimensions shall comply with Table R611.4(2).

R611.5 Screen-grid insulating concrete form wall systems. Screen-grid ICF wall systems shall comply with Figure R611.5 and shall have reinforcement in accordance with Table R611.5.

The minimum core dimensions shall comply with Table R611.4(2).

R611.6 Material. Insulating concrete form wall materials shall comply with this section.

R611.6.1 Concrete material. Ready-mixed concrete for insulating concrete form walls shall be in accordance with Section R402.2. Maximum slump shall not be greater than 6 inches (152 mm) as determined in accordance with ASTM C 143. Maximum aggregate size shall not be larger than $^3/_4$ inch (19.1 mm).

Exception: Concrete mixes conforming to the ICF manufacturer's recommendations.

R611.6.2 Reinforcing steel. Reinforcing steel shall meet the requirements of ASTM A 615, A 616, A 617 or A 706. The minimum yield strength of reinforcing steel shall be 40,000 psi (Grade 40) (276 MPa).

R611.6.3 Insulation materials. Insulating concrete forms material shall meet the surface burning characteristics of Section R318.1.1. A thermal barrier shall be provided on the building interior in accordance with Section R318.1.2 or Section R702.3.4.

R611.7 Wall construction. Insulating concrete form walls shall be constructed in accordance with the provisions of this section and Figure R611.7(1).

R611.7.1 Reinforcement.

R611.7.1.1 Location. Vertical and horizontal wall reinforcements shall not be placed within the middle third of the wall. Steel reinforcement shall have a minimum concrete cover in accordance with ACI 318.

Exception: Where insulated concrete forms are used and the form remains in place as cover for the concrete, the minimum concrete cover for the reinforcing steel is permitted to be reduced to $^3/_4$ inch (19.1 mm).

R611.7.1.2 Vertical steel. Above-grade concrete walls shall have reinforcement in accordance with Sections R611.3, R611.4, or R611.5 and R611.7.2. All vertical reinforcement in the top-most ICF story shall terminate with a bend or a standard hook and be provided with a minimum lap splice of 24 inches (610 mm) with the top horizontal reinforcement.

R611.7.1.3 Horizontal steel. Concrete walls with minimum thickness of 4 inches (102 mm) shall have a minimum of one continuous No. 4 horizontal reinforcing bar placed at 32 inches (812 mm) on center with one bar within 12 inches (305 mm) of the top of the wall story. Concrete walls 5.5 inches (140 mm) thick or greater shall have a minimum of one continuous No. 4 horizontal reinforcing bar placed at 48 inches (1219 mm) on center with one bar located within 12 inches (305 mm) of the top of the wall story.

Horizontal reinforcement shall be continuous around building corners using corner bars or by bending the bars. In either case, the minimum lap splice shall be 24 inches (610 mm).

TABLE R611.3
MINIMUM VERTICAL WALL REINFORCEMENT FOR FLAT ICF ABOVE-GRADE WALLS[a,b,c,d]

MAXIMUM WIND SPEED (mph)	MAXIMUM WALL HEIGHT PER STORY (feet)	MINIMUM VERTICAL REINFORCEMENT					
		Supporting light-frame roof only		Supporting light-frame second story and roof		Supporting ICF second story and light-frame roof	
		Minimum wall thickness (inches)					
		3.5[e]	5.5	3.5[e]	5.5	3.5[e]	5.5
85	8	#4@32"	N/R	#4@32"	N/R	#4@32"	N/R
	9	#4@32"	N/R	#4@32"	N/R	#3@20"; #4@24"; #5@26"	N/R
	10	#4@32"	N/R	#4@32"	N/R	#3@14"; #4@16"; #5@18"	N/R
100	8	#4@32"	N/R	#4@32"	N/R	#4@32"	N/R
	9	#4@32"	N/R	#3@24"; #4@32"; #5@34"	N/R	#3@14"; #4@18"; #5@20"	N/R
	10	#3@16"; #4@26"; #5@34"	N/R	#3@16"; #4@20"; #5@22"	N/R	Design required	N/R
110	8	#4@32"	N/R	#4@32"	N/R	#4@32"	N/R
	9	#3@16"; #4@26"; #5@34"	N/R	#3@18"; #4@20"; #5@22"	N/R	Design required	N/R
	10	Design required	N/R	#3@10"; #4@12"; #5@14"	N/R	Design required	N/R
120	8	#3@18"; #4@30"; #5@40"	#4@96"	#3@18"; #4@30"; #5@30"	#4@96"	#4@32"	#4@96"
	9	#3@12"; #4@22"; #5@30"	#4@96"	#3@12"; #4@16"; #5@16"	#4@96"	Design required	#4@96"
	10	Design required	#4@96"	Design required	#4@96"	Design required	#4@96"
130	8	#3@14"; #4@20"; #5@24"	#4@96"	#3@14"; #4@18"; #5@20"	#4@96"	Design required	#4@96"
	9	Design required	#4@96"	Design required	#4@96"	Design required	#4@96"
	10	Design required	#4@96"	Design required	#4@96"	Design required	#4@96"

For SI: 1 inch = 25.4 mm, 1 foot = 304.8 mm, 1 mile per hour = 1.6093 km/h, 1 pound per square inch = 6.895 kPa.

NOTE: This table is based on concrete with a minimum specified compressive strength of 2,500 psi, reinforcing steel with a minimum yield strength of 40,000 psi and an assumed equivalent rectangular cross-section. This table is not intended to prohibit the use of ICF manufacturer's tables based on engineering analysis in accordance with ACI 318.

a. N/R indicates no vertical wall reinforcement is required.

b. Deflection criterion is $L/240$, where L is the height of the wall story in inches.

c. Interpolation shall not be permitted.

d. See Section R611.7.1.4 for additional reinforcement requirements for dwellings in Seismic Design Category C.

e. A 3.5-inch wall is not permitted if wood ledgers are to be used to support the second floor or roof loads. See Section R611.8.

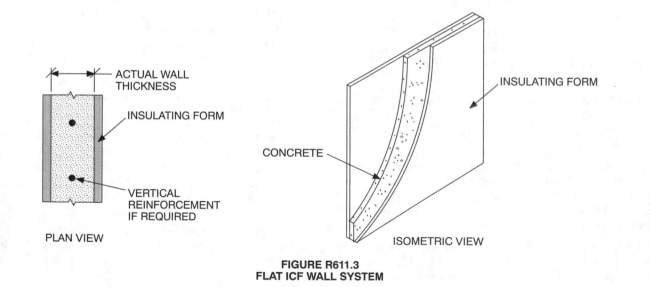

PLAN VIEW

ISOMETRIC VIEW

FIGURE R611.3
FLAT ICF WALL SYSTEM

TABLE R611.4(1)
MINIMUM VERTICAL WALL REINFORCEMENT FOR WAFFLE-GRID ICF ABOVE-GRADE WALLS[a, b, c, d, e]

MAXIMUM WIND SPEED (mph)	MAXIMUM WALL HEIGHT PER STORY (feet)	MINIMUM VERTICAL REINFORCEMENT					
		Supporting light-frame roof only		Supporting light-frame second story and roof		Supporting ICF second story and light-frame roof	
		Minimum wall thickness[d] (inches)					
		6	8	6	8	6	8
85	8	N/R	N/R	N/R	N/R	N/R	N/R
	9	N/R	N/R	N/R	N/R	N/R	N/R
	10	N/R	N/R	N/R	N/R	N/R	N/R
100	8	N/R	N/R	N/R	N/R	N/R	N/R
	9	N/R	N/R	N/R	N/R	N/R	N/R
	10	N/R	N/R	N/R	N/R	N/R	N/R
110	8	#4@96"	#4@96"	#4@96"	#4@96"	#4@96"	#4@96"
	9	#4@96"	#4@96"	#4@96"	#4@96"	#4@96"	#4@96"
	10	#3@12"; #4@24"; #5@36"	N/R	#3@12"; #4@24"; #5@24"	N/R	#3@12"; #4@24"; #5@24"	N/R
120	8	#4@96"	#4@96"	#4@96"	#4@96"	#4@96"	#4@96"
	9	#3@12"; #4@24"; #5@36"	#4@96"	#3@12"; #4@24"; #5@36"	#4@96"	#3@12"; #4@24"; #5@24"	#4@96"
	10	#3@12"; #4@24"; #5@24"	#4@96"	#3@12"; #4@24"; #5@24"	#4@96"	#3@12"; #4@12"	#4@96"
130	8	#3@12"; #4@24"; #5@36"	#4@96"	#3@12"; #4@24"; #5@36"	#4@96"	#3@12"; #4@24"; #5@24"	#4@96"
	9	#3@12"; #4@24"; #5@24"	#4@96"	#3@12"; #4@24"; #5@24"	#4@96"	#3@12"; #4@12"	#4@96"
	10	#3@12"; #4@12"; #5@24"	#4@96"	Design required	#4@96"	Design required	#4@96"

For SI: 1 inch = 25.4 mm, 1 foot = 304.8 mm, 1 pound per square inch = 6.895 kPa, 1 mile per hour = 1.6093 km/h.

NOTE: This table is based on concrete with a minimum specified compressive strength of 2,500 psi, reinforcing steel with a minimum yield strength of 40,000 psi and an assumed equivalent rectangular cross-section. This table is not intended to prohibit the use of ICF manufacturer's tables based on engineering analysis in accordance with ACI 318.

a. N/R indicates no vertical wall reinforcement is required.

b. Deflection criterion is $L/240$, where L is the height of the wall story in inches.

c. Interpolation shall not be permitted.

d. Nominal thickness is given; refer to Table R611.4(2) for actual concrete wall thickness.

e. See Section R611.7.1.4 for additional reinforcement requirements for dwellings in Seismic Design Category C.

TABLE R611.4(2)
DIMENSIONAL REQUIREMENTS FOR CORES AND WEBS IN WAFFLE-GRID AND SCREEN-GRID ICF WALLS[a,b]

WALL TYPE AND NOMINAL SIZE (inches)	MINIMUM WIDTH OF CORE (inches)	MINIMUM THICKNESS OF VERTICAL CORE (inches)	MAXIMUM SPACING OF VERTICAL CORES (inches)	MAXIMUM SPACING OF HORIZONTAL CORES (inches)	MINIMUM WEB THICKNESS (inches)
6" Waffle-Grid	6.25	5	12	16	2
8" Waffle-Grid	7	7	12	16	2
6" Screen-Grid	5.5	5.5	12	12	N/A

For SI: 1 inch = 25.4 mm.

a. For width "W," thickness "T"; spacing, and web thickness, refer to Figures R611.4 and R611.5.

b. N/A indicates not applicable.

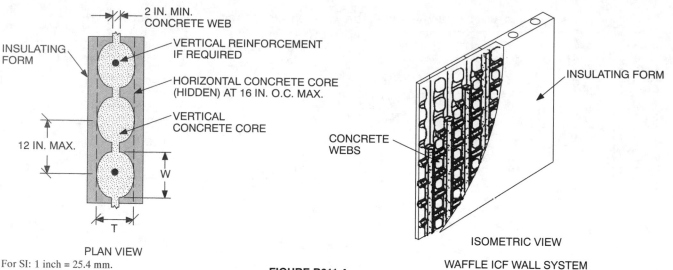

PLAN VIEW

For SI: 1 inch = 25.4 mm.

FIGURE R611.4
WAFFLE-GRID ICF WALL SYSTEM

ISOMETRIC VIEW

WAFFLE ICF WALL SYSTEM

TABLE R611.5
MINIMUM VERTICAL WALL REINFORCEMENT FOR SCREEN-GRID ICF ABOVE-GRADE WALLS[a,b,c,d,e]

MAXIMUM WIND SPEED (mph)	MAXIMUM WALL HEIGHT PER STORY (feet)	MINIMUM VERTICAL REINFORCEMENT		
		Supporting light-frame roof only	Supporting light-frame second story and roof	Supporting ICF second story and light-frame roof
		Minimum wall thickness[d] (inches)		
		6	6	6
85	8	N/R	N/R	N/R
	9	N/R	N/R	N/R
	10	N/R	N/R	N/R
100	8	N/R	N/R	N/R
	9	N/R	N/R	N/R
	10	N/R	N/R	N/R
110	8	#4@96″	#4@96″	#4@96″
	9	#4@96″	#4@96″	#4@96″
	10	#3@12″; #4@24″; #5@36″	#3@12″; #4@24″; #5@36″	N/R
120	8	#4@96″	#4@96″	#4@96″
	9	#3@24″; #4@36″	#3@24″; #4@36″; #5@36″	#4@96″
	10	#3@12″; #4@24″; #5@36″	#4@24″; #5@24″	#3@12″; #4@24″; #5@24″
130	8	#3@24″; #4@36″; #5@48″	#3@24″; #4@36″; #5@48″	#4@96″
	9	#3@12″; #4@24″; #5@36″	#3@12″; #4@24″; #5@24″	#3@12″; #4@24″; #5@24″
	10	#3@12″; #4@12″	#4@24″; #5@24″	#3@12″; #4@12″; #5@24″

For SI: 1 inch = 25.4 mm, 1 foot = 304.8 mm, 1 pound per square inch = 6.895 kPa, 1 mile per hour = 1.6093 km/h.

NOTE: This table is based on concrete with a minimum specified compressive strength of 2,500 psi, reinforcing steel with a minimum yield strength of 40,000 psi and an assumed equivalent rectangular cross-section. This table is not intended to prohibit the use of ICF manufacturer's tables based on engineering analysis in accordance with ACI 318.

a. N/R indicates no vertical wall reinforcement is required.

b. Deflection criterion is $L/240$, where L is the height of the wall story in inches.

c. Interpolation shall not be permitted.

d. Nominal thickness is given; refer to Table R611.4(2) for actual concrete wall thickness.

e. See Section R611.7.1.4 for additional requirements for dwellings in Seismic Design Category C.

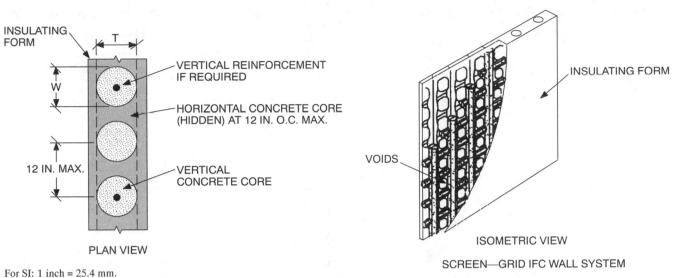

For SI: 1 inch = 25.4 mm.

FIGURE R611.5
SCREEN-GRID IFC WALL SYSTEM

TABLE R611.7(1)
MINIMUM WALL OPENING REINFORCEMENT REQUIREMENTS IN ICF WALLS

WALL TYPE AND OPENING WIDTH (L) (feet)	MINIMUM HORIZONTAL OPENING REINFORCEMENT	MINIMUM VERTICAL OPENING REINFORCEMENT
Flat, Waffle-, and Screen-Grid: L < 2 (0.61)	None required	None required
Screen-Grid: 2(0.61) ≤ L < 4 (1.2)	One No. 4 bar a minimum of 1.5 inches and a maximum of 2.5 inches above the top of the opening. One No. 4 bar within 12 inches below the bottom of the opening. Each No. 4 bar shall extend a minimum of 24 inches beyond the limits of the opening.	None required
Flat and Waffle-Grid: 2(0.61) ≤ L < 4 (1.2)	One No. 4 bar within 12 inches above the top of the opening. One No. 4 bar within 12 inches below the bottom of the opening. Each No. 4 bar shall extend a minimum of 24 inches beyond the limits of the opening.	None required
Flat, Waffle-, and Screen-Grid: L ≥ 4 (1.2)	Provide lintels in accordance with Section R611.7.3. Top and bottom lintel reinforcement shall extend a minimum of 24 inches beyond the limits of the opening.	110 mph or less - One No. 4 bar. Greater than 110 mph - Two No. 4 bars. Bars shall extend for the full height of each wall story and be within 12 inches of each side of the opening.

For SI: 1 inch = 25.4 mm, 1 foot = 304.8 mm, 1 pound per square inch = 6.895 kPa, 1 mile per hour = 1.609 km/h.

NOTE: This table is based on concrete with a minimum specified compressive strength of 2,500 psi, reinforcing steel with a minimum yield strength of 40,000 psi and an assumed equivalent rectangular cross section. This table is not intended to prohibit the use of ICF manufacturer's tables based on engineering analysis in accordance with ACI 318.

TABLE R611.7(2)
MAXIMUM ALLOWABLE CLEAR SPANS FOR ICF LINTELS FOR FLAT AND SCREEN-GRID LOAD-BEARING WALLS[a,b,c,d]
NO. 4 BOTTOM BAR SIZE

MINIMUM LINTEL THICKNESS (T) (inches)	LINTEL DEPTH (D) (inches)	MAXIMUM CLEAR SPAN (feet-inches)					
		Supporting light-framed roof		Supporting light framed second story and roof		Supporting ICF second story and light-frame roof	
		Maximum ground snow load (psf)					
		30	70	30	70	30	70
4	8	4-9	4-2	3-10	3-4	3-5	3-1
	12	6-8	5-5	5-0	4-5	4-6	4-0
	16	7-11	6-5	6-0	5-3	5-4	4-10
	20	8-11	7-4	6-9	6-0	6-1	5-6
	24	9-10	8-1	7-6	6-7	6-9	6-1
6	8	5-2	4-2	3-10	3-5	3-5	3-1
	12	6-8	5-5	5-0	4-5	4-6	4-1
	16	7-10	6-5	6-0	5-3	5-4	4-10
	20	8-10	7-3	6-9	6-0	6-1	5-6
	24	9-8	8-0	7-5	6-7	6-8	6-0
8	8	5-2	4-2	3-11	3-5	3-6	3-2
	12	6-7	5-5	5-0	4-5	4-6	4-1
	16	7-9	6-5	5-11	5-3	5-4	4-10
	20	8-8	7-2	6-8	5-11	6-0	5-5
	24	9-6	7-11	7-4	6-6	6-7	6-0
10	8	5-2	4-2	3-11	3-5	3-6	3-2
	12	6-7	5-5	5-0	4-5	4-6	4-1
	16	7-8	6-4	5-11	5-3	5-4	4-10

For SI: 1 inch = 25.4 mm, 1 foot = 304.8 mm, 1 pound per square inch = 6.895 kPa, 1 pound per square foot = 0.0479 kN/m^2.

NOTE: This table is based on concrete with a minimum specified compressive strength of 2,500 psi, reinforcing steel with a minimum yield strength of 40,000 psi and an assumed equivalent rectangular cross section. This table is not intended to prohibit the use of ICF manufacturer's tables based on engineering analysis in accordance with ACI 318.

a. Deflection criteria: L/240.

b. Design load assumptions:
   Floor dead load is 10 psf   Attic live load is 20 psf
   Floor live load is 30 psf   Roof dead load is 15 psf
   Building width is 32 feet   ICF wall dead load is 69 psf
   Light-framed wall dead load is 10 psf

c. No. 3 stirrups are required at d/2 spacing.

d. Interpolation is permitted between ground snow loads and between lintel depths.

TABLE R611.7(3)
MAXIMUM ALLOWABLE CLEAR SPANS FOR ICF LINTELS FOR FLAT AND SCREEN-GRID LOAD-BEARING WALLS[a,b,c,d]
NO. 5 BOTTOM BAR SIZE

MINIMUM LINTEL THICKNESS (T) (inches)	LINTEL DEPTH (D) (inches)	MAXIMUM CLEAR SPAN (feet-inches)					
		Supporting light-framed roof		Supporting light framed 2nd story and roof		Supporting ICF second story and light-frame roof	
		Maximum ground snow load (psf)					
		30	70	30	70	30	70
4	8	4-9	4-2	3-11	3-7	3-7	3-5
	12	7-2	6-3	5-11	5-5	5-5	5-0
	16	9-6	8-0	7-4	6-6	6-7	5-11
	20	11-1	9-1	8-4	7-5	7-6	6-9
	24	12-2	10-0	9-3	8-2	8-4	7-6
5.5	8	5-6	4-10	4-7	4-2	4-2	3-10
	12	8-3	6-9	6-3	5-6	5-7	5-0
	16	9-9	8-0	7-5	6-6	6-7	6-0
	20	10-11	9-0	8-4	7-5	7-6	6-9
	24	12-0	9-11	9-3	8-2	8-3	7-6
7.5	8	6-1	5-2	4-9	4-3	4-3	3-10
	12	8-2	6-9	6-3	5-6	5-7	5-0
	16	9-7	7-11	7-4	6-6	6-7	6-0
	20	10-10	8-11	8-4	7-4	7-6	6-9
	24	11-10	9-10	9-2	8-1	8-3	7-5
9.5	8	6-4	5-2	4-10	4-3	4-4	3-11
	12	8-2	6-8	6-2	5-6	5-7	5-0
	16	9-6	7-11	7-4	6-6	6-7	5-11
	20	10-8	8-10	8-3	7-4	7-5	6-9
	24	11-7	9-9	9-0	8-1	8-2	7-5

For SI: 1 inch = 25.4 mm, 1 foot = 304.8 mm, 1 pound per square inch = 6.895 kPa, 1 pound per square foot = 0.0479 kN/m^2.

NOTE: This table is based on concrete with a minimum specified compressive strength of 2,500 psi, reinforcing steel with a minimum yield strength of 40,000 psi and an assumed equivalent rectangular cross section. This table is not intended to prohibit the use of ICF manufacturer's tables based on engineering analysis in accordance with ACI 318.

a. Deflection criteria: $L/240$.

b. Design load assumptions:
   Floor dead load is 10 psf   Attic live load is 20 psf
   Floor live load is 30 psf   Roof dead load is 15 psf
   Building width is 32 feet   ICF wall dead load is 69 psf
   Light-framed wall dead load is 10 psf

c. No. 3 stirrups are required at $d/2$ spacing.

d. Interpolation is permitted between ground snow loads and between lintel depths.

TABLE R611.7(4)
MAXIMUM ALLOWABLE CLEAR SPANS FOR WAFFLE-GRID ICF WALL LINTELS[a,b,c,d]
NO. 4 BOTTOM BAR SIZE

MINIMUM LINTEL THICKNESS (T)[e,f] (inches)	LINTEL DEPTH (D) (inches)	MAXIMUM CLEAR SPAN (feet-inches)					
		Supporting light-framed roof		Supporting light framed 2nd story and roof		Supporting ICF second story and light-frame roof[g]	
		Maximum ground snow load (psf)					
		30	70	30	70	30	70
6	8	5-2	4-2	3-10	3-5	3-6	3-2
	12	6-8	5-5	5-0	4-5	4-7	4-2
	16	7-11	6-6	6-0	5-3	5-6	4-11
	20	8-11	7-4	6-9	6-0	6-3	5-7
	24	9-10	8-1	7-6	6-7	6-10	6-2
8	8	5-2	4-3	3-11	3-5	3-7	3-2
	12	6-8	5-5	5-1	4-5	4-8	4-2
	16	7-10	6-5	6-0	5-3	5-6	4-11
	20	8-10	7-3	6-9	6-0	6-2	5-7
	24	9-8	8-0	7-5	6-7	6-10	6-2

For SI: 1 inch = 25.4 mm, 1 foot = 304.8 mm, 1 pound per square inch = 6.895 kPa, 1 pound per square foot = 0.0479 kN/m^2.

NOTE: This table is based on concrete with a minimum specified compressive strength of 2,500 psi, reinforcing steel with a minimum yield strength of 40,000 psi and an assumed equivalent rectangular cross section. This table is not intended to prohibit the use of ICF manufacturer's tables based on engineering analysis in accordance with ACI 318.

a. Deflection criteria: $L/240$.

b. Design load assumptions:
   Floor dead load is 10 psf   Attic live load is 20 psf
   Floor live load is 30 psf   Roof dead load is 15 psf
   Building width is 32 feet   ICF wall dead load is 69 psf
   Light-framed wall dead load is 10 psf

c. No. 3 stirrups are required at $d/2$ spacing.

d. Interpolation is permitted between ground snow loads and between lintel depths.

e. For actual wall lintel width, refer to Table R611.4(2).

f. Lintel width corresponds to the nominal waffle-grid ICF wall thickness with a minimum web thickness of 2 inches.

g. ICF wall dead load used is 55 psf.

TABLE R611.7(5)
MAXIMUM ALLOWABLE CLEAR SPANS FOR WAFFLE-GRID ICF WALL LINTELS[a,b,c,d]
NO. 5 BOTTOM BAR SIZE

MINIMUM LINTEL THICKNESS (T)[e,f] (inches)	LINTEL DEPTH (D) (inches)	MAXIMUM CLEAR SPAN (feet-inches)					
		Supporting light-framed roof		Supporting light framed 2nd story and roof		Supporting ICF second story and light-frame roof[g]	
		Maximum ground snow load (psf)					
		30	70	30	70	30	70
6	8	5-4	4-8	4-5	4-1	4-5	3-10
	12	8-0	6-9	6-3	5-6	6-3	5-1
	16	9-9	8-0	7-5	6-6	7-5	6-1
	20	11-0	9-1	8-5	7-5	8-5	6-11
	24	12-2	10-0	9-3	8-2	9-3	7-8
8	8	6-0	5-2	4-9	4-3	4-9	3-11
	12	8-3	6-9	6-3	5-6	6-3	5-2
	16	9-9	8-0	7-5	6-6	7-5	6-1
	20	10-11	9-0	8-4	7-5	8-4	6-11
	24	12-0	9-11	9-2	8-2	9-2	7-8

For SI: 1 inch = 25.4 mm, 1 foot = 304.8 mm, 1 pound per square inch = 6.895 kPa, 1 pound per square foot = 0.0479 kN/m^2.

NOTE: This table is based on concrete with a minimum specified compressive strength of 2,500 psi, reinforcing steel with a minimum yield strength of 40,000 psi and an assumed equivalent rectangular cross section. This table is not intended to prohibit the use of ICF manufacturer's tables based on engineering analysis in accordance with ACI 318.

a. Deflection criteria: L/240.

b. Design load assumptions:
   Floor dead load is 10 psf   Attic live load is 20 psf
   Floor live load is 30 psf   Roof dead load is 15 psf
   Building width is 32 feet   ICF wall dead load is 69 psf
   Light-framed wall dead load is 10 psf

c. Two #3 stirrups are required.

d. Interpolation is permitted between ground snow loads and between lintel depths.

e. For actual wall lintel width, refer to Table R611.4(2).

f. Lintel width corresponds to the nominal waffle-grid ICF wall thickness with a minimum web thickness of 2 inches.

g. ICF wall dead load used is 55 psf.

TABLE R611.7(6)
MINIMUM BOTTOM BAR ICF LINTEL REINFORCEMENT FOR LARGE CLEAR SPANS IN LOAD-BEARING WALLS[a,b,c,d]

MINIMUM LINTEL THICKNESS (T[e]) (inches)	MINIMUM LINTEL DEPTH (D) (inches)	MINIMUM BOTTOM LINTEL REINFORCEMENT					
		Supporting light-frame roof only		Supporting light-frame second story and roof		Supporting ICF second story and light-frame roof[f]	
		Maximum ground snow load (psf)					
		30	70	30	70	30	70
Flat ICF lintel, 12 feet maximum clear span							
3.5	24	1-#5	1-#7	D/R	D/R	D/R	D/R
5.5	20	1-#6	1-#7	D/R	D/R	D/R	D/R
	24	1-#5	1-#7	1-#7	1-#8	1-#8	D/R
7.5	16	1-#7; 2-#5	D/R	D/R	D/R	D/R	D/R
	20	1-#6; 2-#4	1-#7; 2-#5	1-#8; 2-#6	D/R	D/R	D/R
	24	1-#6; 2-#4	1-#7; 2-#5	1-#7; 2-#5	1-#8; 2-#6	1-#8; 2-#6	1-#8; 2-#6
9.5	16	1-#7; 2-#5	D/R	D/R	D/R	D/R	D/R
	20	1-#6; 2-#4	1-#7; 2-#5	1-#8; 2-#6	1-#8; 2-#6	1-#8; 2-#6	1-#9; 2-#6
	24	1-#6; 2-#4	1-#7; 2-#5	1-#7; 2-#5	1-#8; 2-#6	1-#8; 2-#6	1-#9; 2-#6
Flat ICF lintel, 16 feet maximum clear span							
5.5	24	1-#7	D/R	D/R	D/R	D/R	D/R
7.5	24	1-#7; 2-#5	D/R	D/R	D/R	D/R	D/R
9.5	24	1-#7; 2-#5	1-#9; 2-#6	1-#9; 2-#6	D/R	D/R	D/R
Waffle-Grid ICF lintel, 12 feet maximum clear span							
6	20	1-#6	D/R	D/R	D/R	D/R	D/R
	24	1-#5	1-#7; 2-#5	1-#7; 2-#5	1-#8; 2-#6	1-#8; 2-#6	D/R
8	16	1-#7; 2-#5	D/R	D/R	D/R	D/R	D/R
	20	1-#6; 2-#4	1-#7; 2-#5	1-#8; 2-#6	D/R	D/R	D/R
	24	1-#5	1-#7; 2-#5	1-#7; 2-#5	1-#8; 2-#6	1-#8; 2-#6	1-#8; 2-#6

For SI: 1 inch = 25.4 mm, 1 foot = 304.8 mm, 1 pound per square inch = 6.895 kPa, 1 pound per square foot = 0.0479 kN/m^2.

NOTE: This table is based on concrete with a minimum specified compressive strength of 2,500 psi, reinforcing steel with a minimum yield strength of 40,000 psi and an assumed equivalent rectangular cross section. This table is not intended to prohibit the use of ICF manufacturer's tables based on engineering analysis in accordance with ACI 318.

a. D/R indicates design is required.

b. Deflection criterion is $L/240$, where L is the clear span of the lintel in inches.

c. Interpolation is permitted between ground snow loads and between lintel depths.

d. No. 3 stirrups are required at maximum $d/2$ spacing for spans greater than 4 feet.

e. Actual thickness is shown for flat lintels while nominal thickness is given for waffle-grid lintels. Lintel thickness corresponds to the nominal waffle-grid ICF wall thickness with a minimum web thickness of 2 inches. Refer to Section R611.4 for actual wall lintel width.

f. ICF wall dead load is maximum 55 psf.

TABLE R611.7(7)
MAXIMUM ALLOWABLE CLEAR SPANS FOR ICF LINTELS IN NONLOAD-BEARING WALLS[a,b,c]
NO. 4 BOTTOM BAR SIZE

MINIMUM LINTEL DEPTH (D) (inches)	MAXIMUM CLEAR SPAN	
	Supporting light-frame nonload-bearing gable end wall (feet)	Supporting ICF second story nonload-bearing wall[d] (feet)
8	12	6
12	16	8
16	16	10
20	16	12
24	16	16

For SI: 1 inch = 25.4 mm, 1 foot = 304.8 mm, 1 pound per square inch = 6.895 kPa, 1 pound per square foot = 0.0479 kN/m^2.

NOTE: This table is based on concrete with a minimum specified compressive strength of 2,500 psi, reinforcing steel with a minimum yield strength of 40,000 psi and an assumed equivalent rectangular cross-section. This table is not intended to prohibit the use of ICF manufacturer's tables based on engineering analysis in accordance with ACI 318.

a. Deflection criterion is $L/240$, where L is the clear span of the lintel in inches.

b. Linear interpolation is permitted between lintel depths.

c. No. 3 stirrups are required at maximum $d/2$ spacing for spans greater than 4 feet.

d. ICF wall dead load is maximum 69 psf.

TABLE R611.7(8)
MINIMUM PERCENTAGE OF SOLID WALL LENGTH ALONG EXTERIOR WALL LINES[a,b,c]

ICF WALL TYPE AND MINIMUM WALL THICKNESS (inches)[d]	MAXIMUM ROOF SLOPE	MINIMUM SOLID WALL LENGTH (percent)[e]									
		Wall supporting light-frame roof and ceiling					Wall supporting one ICF story and light-frame roof and ceiling				
		Maximum wind speed (mph)									
		85	100	110	120	130	85	100	110	120	130
Flat 3.5	3:12	15	15	15	15	20	30	35	40	50	55
	6:12	15	15	20	20	25	30	40	50	55	60
	9:12	20	25	30	40	45	45	60	70	85	95
	12:12	25	35	40	50	60	50	65	80	95	100
Flat 5.5	3:12	15	15	15	15	15	20	25	30	40	40
	6:12	15	15	15	15	20	20	30	35	40	45
	9:12	15	15	20	25	30	35	45	50	60	70
	12:12	20	20	25	35	40	35	50	55	70	75
Flat 7.5	3:12	15	15	15	15	15	20	20	25	30	30
	6:12	15	15	15	15	15	20	20	25	30	35
	9:12	15	15	15	20	25	25	30	40	45	50
	12:12	15	20	20	25	30	30	35	40	50	55
Waffle-Grid 6	3:12	15	15	15	15	20	25	30	35	45	50
	6:12	15	15	20	20	25	25	35	45	50	55
	9:12	20	20	25	35	40	40	55	60	75	85
	12:12	25	30	35	45	50	45	60	70	85	90
Waffle-Grid 8	3:12	15	15	15	15	15	20	25	30	35	35
	6:12	15	15	15	15	20	20	25	30	35	40
	9:12	15	15	20	25	30	30	40	45	55	60
	12:12	20	20	25	30	35	35	40	50	60	65
Screen-Grid 6	3:12	15	15	20	20	25	30	40	45	55	60
	6:12	15	20	25	30	35	30	40	50	60	70
	9:12	25	30	45	50	65	50	65	80	90	100
	12:12	35	40	55	65	80	55	70	85	100	100

For SI: 1 inch = 25.4 mm, 1 foot = 304.8 mm, 1 pound per square inch = 6.895 kPa, 1 mile per hour = 1.6093 km/h.

NOTE: This table is based on concrete with a minimum specified compressive strength of 2,500 psi, reinforcing steel with a minimum yield strength of 40,000 psi and an assumed equivalent rectangular cross section. This table is not intended to prohibit the use of ICF manufacturer's tables based on engineering analysis in accordance with ACI 318.

a. Linear interpolation between roof slopes shall be permitted.

b. Minimum percentages are applicable for maximum 10-foot wall story heights.

c. N/A indicates not applicable.

d. Actual thickness is shown for flat walls while nominal thickness is given for waffle- and screen-grid walls. Refer to Table R611.4(2) for actual waffle- and screen-grid thickness and dimensions.

e. The minimum solid wall length requirements are based on a 2:1 building aspect ratio, L/W, where L is the length parallel to the ridge of the roof and W is the length perpendicular to the ridge of the roof. For a different ration the tabular values may be adjusted by the following multipliers provided the minimum wall lengths in Section R611.7.4 are met. Interpolation is permitted.

L/W	Endwall W	Sidewall, L
2.0	1.00	0.25
1.8	0.90	0.30
1.6	0.80	0.35
1.4	0.70	0.40
1.2	0.60	0.45
1.0	0.50	0.50

TABLE R611.7(9)
MINIMUM PERCENTAGE OF SOLID WALL LENGTH FOR SEISMIC DESIGN CATEGORY C[a]

ICF WALL TYPE AND MINIMUM WALL THICKNESS (inches)[b]	MINIMUM SOLID WALL LENGTH (percent)[c]	
	Wall supporting light-frame roof and ceiling	Wall supporting one ICF story and light-frame roof and ceiling
Flat, 3.5	20	35
Flat, 5.5	15	30
Flat 7.5	15	25
Waffle-grid, 6	20	35
Waffle-grid, 8	20	30
Screen-grid	25	45

For SI: 1 inch – 25.4 mm, 1 foot = 304.8 mm, 1 pound per square foot = 0.0479 kN/m^2.

a. Minimum percentages are for maximum 10-foot wall story height.

b. Actual thickness is shown for flat walls while nominal thickness is given for waffle-grid and screen-grid walls. Refer to Table R611.4(2) for actual waffle-grid and screen-grid thickness and dimension.

c. The minimum solid wall length requirements are based on a 2:1 building aspect ratio, L/W, where L is the length parallel to the ridge of the roof and W is the length perpendicular to the ridge of the roof. For a different ratio, the tabular values may be adjusted by the following multipliers provided the minimum wall lengths in Section R611.7.4 are met. Interpolation is permitted.

L/W	Endwall W	Sidewall, L
2.0	1.00	0.25
1.8	0.90	0.30
1.6	0.80	0.35
1.4	0.70	0.40
1.2	0.60	0.45
1.0	0.50	0.50

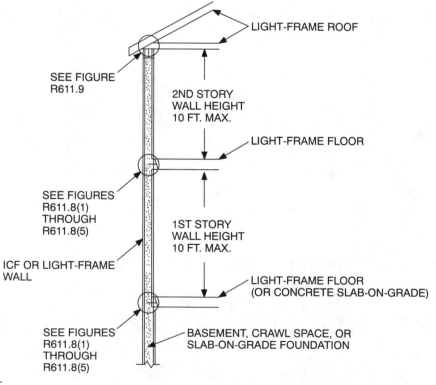

LIGHT-FRAME ROOF

SEE FIGURE R611.9

2ND STORY WALL HEIGHT 10 FT. MAX.

LIGHT-FRAME FLOOR

SEE FIGURES R611.8(1) THROUGH R611.8(5)

1ST STORY WALL HEIGHT 10 FT. MAX.

ICF OR LIGHT-FRAME WALL

LIGHT-FRAME FLOOR (OR CONCRETE SLAB-ON-GRADE)

SEE FIGURES R611.8(1) THROUGH R611.8(5)

BASEMENT, CRAWL SPACE, OR SLAB-ON-GRADE FOUNDATION

For SI: 1 foot = 304.8 mm.

Note: Section cut through flat wall or vertical core of waffle- or screen-grid wall.

FIGURE R611.7(1)
ICF WALL CONSTRUCTION

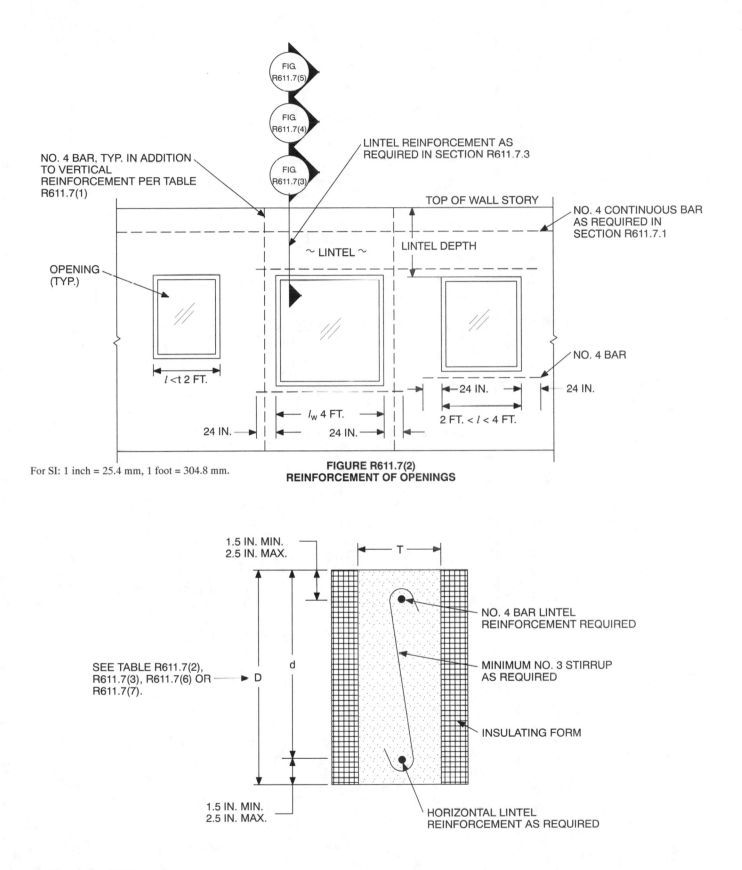

For SI: 1 inch = 25.4 mm, 1 foot = 304.8 mm.

FIGURE R611.7(2)
REINFORCEMENT OF OPENINGS

For SI: 1 inch = 25.4 mm.

Note: Section cut through flat wall.

FIGURE R611.7(3)
ICF LINTELS FOR FLAT AND SCREEN-GRID WALLS

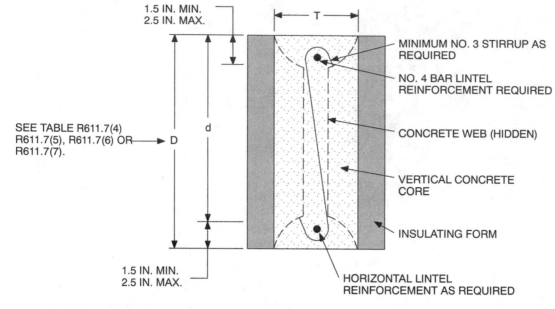

For SI: 1 inch = 25.4 mm.

Note: Section cut through vertical core of a waffle-grid lintel.

**FIGURE R611.7(4)
SINGLE FORM HEIGHT WAFFLE-GRID LINTEL**

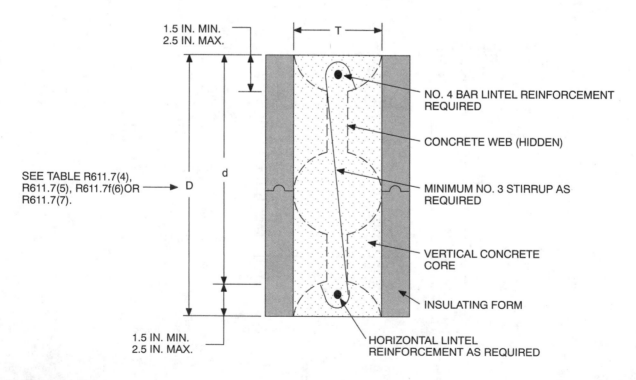

For SI: 1 inch = 25.4 mm.

Note: Section cut through vertical core of a waffle-grid lintel.

**FIGURE R611.7(5)
DOUBLE FORM HEIGHT WAFFLE-GRID LINTEL**

R611.7.1.4 Dwellings in Seismic Design Category C.
Dwellings in Seismic Design Category C shall have horizontal and vertical reinforcement in accordance with the following:

1. Vertical reinforcement consisting of at least one No. 4 reinforcing bar, extending continuously from support to support, shall be provided at each corner, at each side of each opening, and at the ends of walls.

2. Horizontal reinforcement consisting of at least one No. 4 reinforcing bar, continuously at structurally connected roof and floor levels and at the top of the wall, at the bottom of load-bearing walls or in the top of foundations where doweled to the wall and at a maximum spacing of 10 feet (3048 mm).

Vertical reinforcement provided in accordance with Sections R611.7.1.2 and R611.7.2, and horizontal reinforcement provided in accordance with Sections R611.7.1.3 and R611.7.3, shall be permitted to be used to meet the requirements of this section.

R611.7.1.5 Lap splices. Where lap splicing of reinforcing steel is necessary, the lap splice shall be a minimum of $40d_b$, where d_b is the diameter of the smaller bar. The maximum distance between noncontact bars at a lap splice shall not exceed $8d_b$.

R611.7.2 Wall openings. Wall openings shall have a minimum of 8 inches (203 mm) of depth of concrete for flat and waffle-grid ICF walls and 12 inches (305 mm) for screen-grid walls over the length of the opening. Reinforcement around openings shall be provided in accordance with Table R611.7(1) and Figure R611.7(2). All reinforcement placed horizontally above or below an opening shall extend a minimum of 24 inches (610 mm) beyond the limits of the opening. Wall opening reinforcement shall be provided in addition to the reinforcement required by Sections R611.3, R611.4, R611.5 and R611.7.1. The perimeter of all wall openings shall be framed with a minimum 2-by-4 plate, anchored to the wall with $^1/_2$-inch (12.7 mm) diameter anchor bolts spaced a maximum of 24 inches (610 mm) on center. The bolts shall be embedded into the concrete a minimum of 4 inches (102 mm) and have a minimum of $1^1/_2$ (38 mm) inches of concrete cover to the face of the wall.

Exception: The 2-by-4 plate is not required where the wall is formed to provide solid concrete around the perimeter of the opening with a minimum depth of 4 inches (102 mm) for the full thickness of the wall.

R611.7.3 Lintels.

R611.7.3.1 General requirements. Lintels shall be provided over all openings greater than or equal to 4 feet (1219 mm) in width for flat or waffle-grid ICF walls, and greater than 2 feet (610 mm) for screen-grid ICF walls. Lintels for flat ICF walls and screen-grid ICF walls shall be constructed in accordance with Figure R611.7(3). Lintels for waffle-grid ICF walls shall be constructed in accordance with Figure R611.7(4) or Figure R611.7(5). Lintel depths are permitted to be increased by the height of ICF wall located directly above the lintels, provided that the lintel depth spans the entire length of the opening.

R611.7.3.2 Stirrups. A minimum of No. 3 stirrups shall be installed for all flat and screen-grid wall lintels at a maximum spacing of $d/2$ where d equals the depth of the lintel (D) minus the bottom cover of concrete as shown in Figure R611.7(3), R611.7(4) or R611.7(5). A minimum of two No. 3 stirrups shall be placed in each vertical core of waffle-grid lintels.

R611.7.3.3 Horizontal reinforcement. One No. 4 horizontal bar shall be provided in the top of the lintel. Horizontal reinforcement placed within 12 inches (305 mm) of the top of the wall in accordance with Section R611.7.1.3 shall be permitted to serve as the top or bottom reinforcement in the lintel provided the reinforcement meets the location requirements in Figure R611.7(2), R611.7(3), R611.7(4) or R611.7(5), and the size requirements in Table R611.7(2), R611.7(3), R611.7(4), R611.7(5), R611.7(6) or R611.7(7).

R611.7.3.4 Load-bearing walls. Lintels for flat and screen-grid ICF walls supporting roof or floor loads shall comply with Table R611.7(2) or Table R611.7(3). Lintels for waffle-grid ICF walls supporting roof or floor loads shall comply with Table R611.7(4) or Table R611.7(5).

Exception: Where spans larger than those permitted in Table R611.7(2), R611.7(3), R611.7(4) or R611.7(5) are required, the lintels shall comply with Table R611.7(6).

R611.7.3.5 Nonload-bearing walls. Lintels for nonload-bearing flat, waffle-grid and screen-grid ICF walls shall comply with Table R611.7(7).

R611.7.4 Minimum length of wall without openings. Exterior ICF walls shall have a minimum of solid wall length to total wall length in accordance with Table R611.7(8), but not less than 15 percent for ICF walls supporting a light framed roof or 20 percent for ICF walls supporting an ICF or light framed second story and light framed roof. For attached dwellings in Seismic Design Category C, the minimum percentage of solid wall length shall be greater than or equal to the requirements in Table R611.7(9). The minimum percentage of solid wall length shall include only those solid wall segments that are a minimum of 24 inches (610 mm) in length. The maximum distance between wall segments included in determining solid wall length shall not exceed 18 feet (5486 mm). A minimum length of 24 inches (610 mm) of solid wall segment, extending the full height of each wall story, shall occur at all corners of exterior walls.

R611.8 ICF wall-to-floor connections.

R611.8.1 Top bearing. Floors bearing on the top of ICF foundation walls in accordance with Figure R611.8(1) shall have the wood sill plate anchored to the ICF wall with minimum $^1/_2$-inch (12.7 mm) diameter bolts embedded a minimum of 7 inches (178 mm) and placed at a maximum spacing of 6 feet (1829 mm) on center and not more than 12 inches (305 mm) from corners. Anchor bolts for waffle-grid and screen-grid walls shall be located in the cores. In conditions where wind speeds are in excess of 90 miles per hour (144 km/h), the $^1/_2$-inch (12.7 mm) diameter anchor bolts shall be placed at a maximum spacing of 4 feet (1219 mm) on center. Bolts shall extend a minimum of 7 inches (178 mm) into concrete. Sill plates shall be protected against decay where required by Section R323. Cold-formed steel framing systems shall be anchored to the concrete in accordance with Section R505.3.1 or Section R603.3.1.

R611.8.2 Ledger bearing. Wood ledger boards supporting bearing ends of joists or trusses shall be anchored to flat ICF walls with minimum thickness of 5.5 inches (140 mm) and to waffle- or screen-grid ICF walls with minimum nominal thickness of 6 inches (152 mm) in accordance with Figure R611.8(2), R611.8(3), R611.8(4) or R611.8(5) and Table R611.8. The ledger shall be a minimum 2 by 8, No. 2 Southern Pine or No. 2 Douglas Fir. Ledgers anchored to nonload-bearing walls to support floor or roof sheathing shall be attached with $1/2$-inch (12.7 mm) diameter or headed anchor bolts spaced a maximum of 6 feet (1829 mm) on center. Anchor bolts shall be embedded a minimum of 4 inches (102 mm) into the concrete.

R611.8.2.1 Seismic Design Category C. In Seismic Design Category C, additional anchorage mechanisms shall be installed at a maximum spacing of 6 feet (1829 mm) on center. Such anchorage mechanisms shall not induce tension stresses perpendicular to grain in ledgers or nailers. The capacity of such anchors shall result in connections capable of resisting 200 pounds per linear foot (2.9 kN/m). Such anchorage mechanisms shall not induce tension stresses perpendicular to grain in ledgers or nailers.

R611.8.3 Floor and roof diaphragm construction. Floor and roof diaphragms shall be constructed of structural wood sheathing panels, attached to wood framing in accordance with Table R602.3(1) or to cold-formed steel floor framing in accordance with Table R505.3.1(2) or to cold-formed steel roof framing in accordance with Table R804.3. Additionally, sheathing panel edges perpendicular to framing members shall be backed by blocking and sheathing shall be connected to the blocking with fasteners at the edge spacing. For Seismic Design Category C, where the width-to-thickness dimension of the diaphragm exceeds 2-to-1, edge spacing of fasteners shall be 4 inches (102 mm) on center.

TABLE R611.8
FLOOR LEDGER-ICF WALL CONNECTION (SIDE-BEARING CONNECTION) REQUIREMENTS[a,b,c]

MAXIMUM FLOOR CLEAR SPAN[d] (feet)	MAXIMUM ANCHOR BOLT SPACING[e] (inches)			
	Staggered $1/2$-inch-diameter anchor bolts	Staggered $5/8$-inch-diameter anchor bolts	Two $1/2$-inch-diameter anchor bolts[f]	Two $5/8$-inch-diameter anchor bolts[f]
8	18	20	36	40
10	16	18	32	36
12	14	18	28	36
14	12	16	24	32
16	10	14	20	28
18	9	13	18	26
20	8	11	16	22
22	7	10	14	20
24	7	9	14	18
26	6	9	12	18
28	6	8	12	16
30	5	8	10	16
32	5	7	10	14

For SI: 1 inch = 25.4 mm, 1 foot = 304.8 mm.

a. Minimum ledger board nominal depth shall be 8 inches. The thickness of the ledger board shall be a minimum of 2 inches. Thickness of ledger board is in nominal lumber dimensions. Ledger board shall be minimum No. 2 Grade.

b. Minimum edge distance shall be 2 inches for $1/2$-inch-diameter anchor bolts and 2.5 inches for $5/8$-inch-diameter anchor bolts.

c. Interpolation is permitted between floor spans.

d. Floor span corresponds to the clear span of the floor structure (i.e., joists or trusses) spanning between load-bearing walls or beams.

e. Anchor bolts shall extend through the ledger to the center of the flat ICF wall thickness or the center of the horizontal or vertical core thickness of the waffle-grid or screen-grid ICF wall system.

f. Minimum vertical distance between bolts shall be 1.5 inches for $1/2$-inch-diameter anchor bolts and 2 inches for $5/8$-inch-diameter anchor bolts.

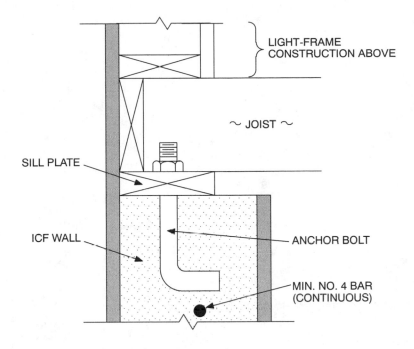

FIGURE R611.8(1)
SECTION CUT THROUGH FLAT WALL OR VERTICAL CORE
OF WAFFLE- OR SCREEN-GRID WALL

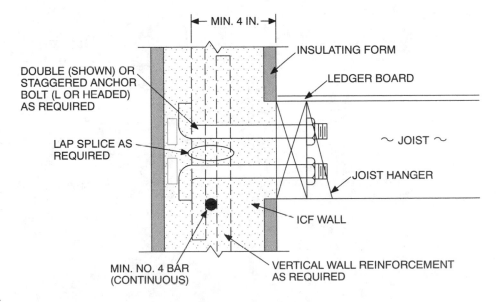

For SI: 1 inch = 25.4 mm.

Note: Section cut through flat wall or vertical core of a waffle- or screen-grid wall.

FIGURE R611.8(2)
FLOOR LEDGER—ICF WALL CONNECTION (SIDE-BEARING CONNECTION)

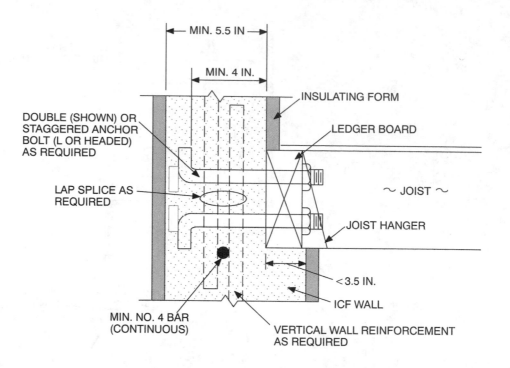

For SI: 1 inch = 25.4 mm.

Note: Section cut through flat wall or vertical core of a waffle- or screen-grid wall.

FIGURE R611.8(3)
FLOOR LEDGER—ICF WALL CONNECTION (SIDE-BEARING CONNECTION)

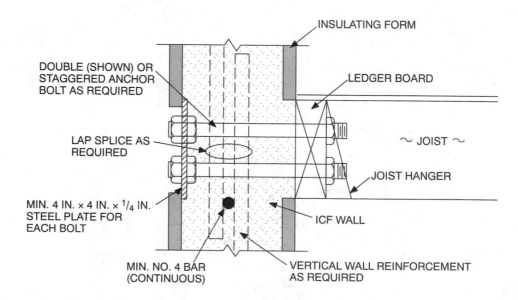

For SI: 1 inch = 25.4 mm.

Note: Section cut through flat wall.

FIGURE R611.8(4)
WOOD FLOOR LEDGER—ICF WALL SYSTEM CONNECTION
(THROUGH-BOLT CONNECTION)

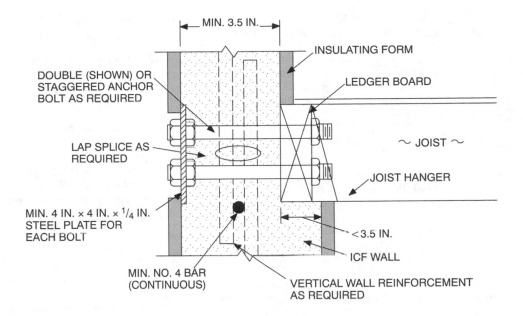

For SI: 1 inch = 25.4 mm.

Note: Section cut through flat wall.

FIGURE R611.8(5)
WOOD FLOOR LEDGER TO ICF WALL SYSTEM CONNECTION DETAIL

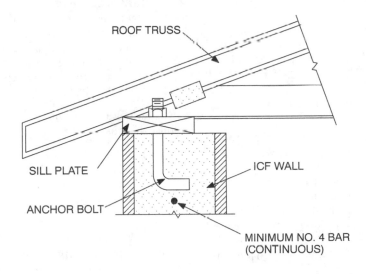

Note: Section cut through flat wall or vertical cove of waffle- or screen-grid wall.

FIGURE R611.9
ICF WALL TO TOP SILL PLATE (ROOF) CONNECTION

R611.9 ICF wall to top sill plate (roof) connections. Wood sill plates attaching roof framing to ICF walls shall be anchored with minimum $1/2$ inch (12.7 mm) diameter anchor bolt embedded a minimum of 7 inches (178 mm) and placed at 6 feet (1829 mm) on center in accordance with Figure R611.9. Anchor bolts shall be located in the cores of waffle-grid and screen-grid ICF walls. Roof assemblies subject to wind uplift pressure of 20 pounds per square foot (1.44 kN/m^2) or greater as established in Table R301.2(2) shall have rafter or truss ties provided in accordance with Table R802.11.

SECTION R612
CONVENTIONALLY FORMED CONCRETE WALL CONSTRUCTION

R612.1 General. Conventionally formed concrete walls with flat surfaces shall be designed and constructed in accordance with the provisions of Section R611 for Flat ICF walls or in accordance with the provisions of ACI 318.

SECTION R613
EXTERIOR WINDOWS AND GLASS DOORS

R613.1 General. This section prescribes performance and construction requirements for exterior window systems installed in wall systems. Waterproofing, sealing and flashing systems are not included in the scope of this section.

R613.2 Performance. Exterior windows and doors shall be designed to resist the design wind loads specified in Table R301.2(2) adjusted for height and exposure per Table R301.2(3).

R613.3 Testing and labeling. Exterior windows and glass doors shall be tested by an approved independent laboratory, and bear a label identifying manufacturer, performance characteristics and approved inspection agency to indicate compliance with the requirements of the following specification:

AAMA/NWWDA 101/ I.S.2

Exceptions:

1. Decorative glazed openings.
2. Exterior window and door assemblies not included within the scope of AAMA/NWWDA 101/I.S.2 shall be tested in accordance with ASTM E 330. Assemblies covered by this exception containing glass shall comply with Section R308.5.
3. Structural wind load design pressures for window units smaller than the size tested in accordance with this section shall be permitted to be higher than the design value of the tested unit provided such higher pressures are determined by accepted engineering analysis. All components of the small unit shall be the same as the tested unit. Where such calculated design pressures are used they shall be validated by an additional test of the window unit having the highest allowable design pressure.

R613.4 Windborne debris protection. Protection of exterior windows and glass doors in buildings located in hurricane-prone regions from windborne debris shall be in accordance with Section R301.2.1.2.

R613.5 Anchorage methods. The methods cited in this section apply only to anchorage of window and glass door assemblies to the main force-resisting system.

R613.5.1 Anchoring requirements. Window and glass door assemblies shall be anchored in accordance with the published manufacturer's recommendations to achieve the design pressure specified. Substitute anchoring systems used for substrates not specified by the fenestration manufacturer shall provide equal or greater anchoring performance as demonstrated by accepted engineering practice.

R613.5.2 Anchorage details. Products shall be anchored in accordance with the minimum requirements illustrated in Figures R613.5(1), R613.5(2), R613.5(3), R613.5(4), R613.5(5), R613.5(6), R613.5(7) and R613.5(8).

R613.5.2.1 Masonry, concrete or other structural substrate. Where the wood shim or buck thickness is less than $1^1/_2$ inches (38 mm), window and glass door assemblies shall be anchored through the jamb, or by jamb clip and anchors shall be embedded directly into the masonry, concrete or other substantial substrate material. Anchors shall adequately transfer load from the window or door frame into the rough opening substrate [see Figures R613.5(1) and R613.5(2).]

Where the wood shim or buck thickness is 1.5 inches (38 mm) or greater, the buck is securely fastened to the masonry, concrete or other substantial substrate and the buck extends beyond the interior face of the window or door frame, window and glass door assemblies shall be anchored through the jamb, or by jamb clip, or through the flange to the secured wood buck. Anchors shall be embedded into the secured wood buck to adequately transfer load from the window or door frame assembly [see Figures R613.5(3), R613.5(4) and R613.5(5)].

R613.5.2.2 Wood or other approved framing material. Where the framing material is wood or other approved framing material, window and glass door assemblies shall be anchored through the frame, or by frame clip, or through the flange. Anchors shall be embedded into the frame construction to adequately transfer load [Figures R613.5(6), R613.5(7) and R613.5(8)].

R613.6 Mullions occurring between individual window and glass door assemblies.

R613.6.1 Mullions. Mullions shall be tested by an approved testing laboratory or be engineered in accordance with accepted engineering practice. Both methods shall use performance criteria cited in Sections R613.6.2, R613.6.3 and R613.6.4.

R613.6.2 Load transfer. Mullions shall be designed to transfer the design pressure loads applied by the window and door assemblies to the rough opening substrate.

R613.6.3 Deflection. Mullions shall be capable of resisting the design pressure loads applied by the window and door assemblies to be supported without deflecting more than $L/175$, where L = the span of mullion in inches.

R613.6.4 Structural safety factor. Mullions shall be capable of resisting a load of 1.5 times the design pressure loads applied by the window and door assemblies to be supported without exceeding the appropriate material stress levels. If tested by an approved laboratory, the 1.5 times the design pressure load shall be sustained for 10 seconds, and the permanent deformation shall not exceed 0.4 percent of the mullion span after the 1.5 times design pressure load is removed.

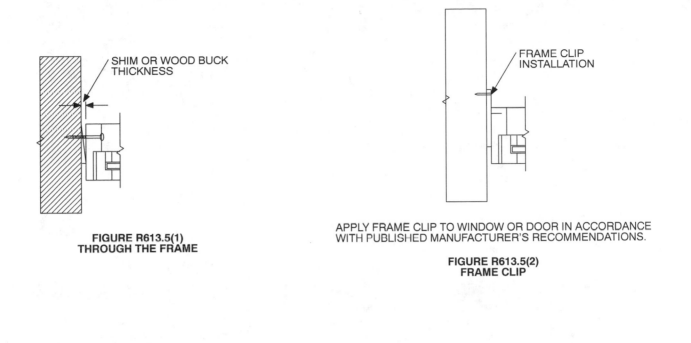

FIGURE R613.5(1)
THROUGH THE FRAME

APPLY FRAME CLIP TO WINDOW OR DOOR IN ACCORDANCE
WITH PUBLISHED MANUFACTURER'S RECOMMENDATIONS.

FIGURE R613.5(2)
FRAME CLIP

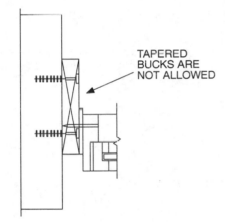

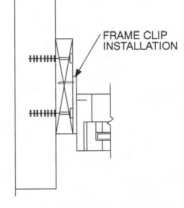

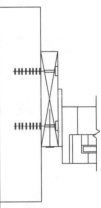

THROUGH THE FRAME ANCHORING
METHOD. ANCHORS SHALL BE
PROVIDED TO TRANSFER LOAD FROM
THE WINDOW OR DOOR FRAME INTO
THE ROUGH OPENING SUBSTRATE.

FIGURE R613.5(3)
THROUGH THE FRAME

APPLY FRAME CLIP TO WINDOW OR DOOR
FRAME IN ACCORDANCE WITH PUBLISHED
MANUFACTURER'S RECOMMENDATIONS.
ANCHORS SHALL BE PROVIDED TO
TRANSFER LOAD FROM THE FRAME CLIP
INTO THE ROUGH OPENING SUBSTRATE

FIGURE R613.5(4)
FRAME CLIP

APPLY ANCHORS THROUGH FLANGE
IN ACCORDANCE WITH PUBLISHED
MANUFACTURER'S
RECOMMENDATIONS.

FIGURE R613.5(5)
THROUGH THE FLANGE

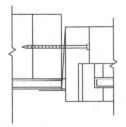

FIGURE R613.5(6)
THROUGH THE FRAME

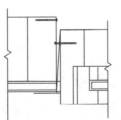

FIGURE R613.5(7)
FRAME CLIP

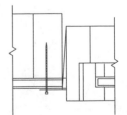

FIGURE R613.5(8)
THROUGH THE FLANGE

CHAPTER 7
WALL COVERING

SECTION R701
GENERAL

R701.1 Application. The provisions of this chapter shall control the design and construction of the interior and exterior wall covering for all buildings.

R701.2 Installation. Products sensitive to adverse weather shall not be installed until adequate weather protection for the installation is provided. Exterior sheathing shall be dry before applying exterior cover.

SECTION R702
INTERIOR COVERING

R702.1 General. Interior coverings shall be installed in accordance with this chapter and Tables R702.1(1), R702.1(2), R702.1(3) and R702.3.5. Interior finishes and materials shall conform to the flame spread and smoke-density requirements of Section R319.

TABLE R702.1(1)
THICKNESS OF PLASTER

PLASTER BASE	FINISHED THICKNESS OF PLASTER FROM FACE OF LATH, MASONRY, CONCRETE (inches)	
	Gypsum plaster	Portland cement mortar
Expanded metal lath	$5/8$, minimum[a]	$5/8$, minimum[a]
Wire lath	$5/8$, minimum[a]	$3/4$, minimum (interior)[b] $7/8$, minimum (exterior)[b]
Gypsum lath[g]	$1/2$, minimum	$3/4$, minimum (interior)[b]
Masonry walls[c]	$1/2$, minimum	$1/2$, minimum
Monolithic concrete walls[c,d]	$5/8$, maximum	$7/8$, maximum
Monolithic concrete ceilings[c,d]	$3/8$, maximum[e]	$1/2$, maximum
Gypsum veneer base[f,g]	$1/16$, minimum	$3/4$, minimum (interior)[b]
Gypsum sheathing[g]	—	$3/4$, minimum (interior)[b] $7/8$, minimum (exterior)[b]

For SI: 1 inch = 25.4 mm.

a. When measured from back plane of expanded metal lath, exclusive of ribs, or self-furring lath, plaster thickness shall be $3/4$ inch minimum.

b. When measured from face of support or backing.

c. Because masonry and concrete surfaces may vary in plane, thickness of plaster need not be uniform.

d. When applied over a liquid bonding agent, finish coat may be applied directly to concrete surface.

e. Approved acoustical plaster may be applied directly to concrete or over base coat plaster, beyond the maximum plaster thickness shown.

f. Attachment shall be in accordance with Table R702.3.5.

g. Where gypsum board is used as a base for portland cement plaster, weather-resistant sheathing paper complying with Section R703.2 shall be provided.

TABLE R702.1(2)
GYPSUM PLASTER PROPORTIONS[a]

NUMBER	COAT	PLASTER BASE OR LATH	MAXIMUM VOLUME AGGREGATE PER 100 POUNDS NEAT PLASTER[b] (cubic feet)	
			Damp loose sand[a]	Perlite or vermiculite[c]
Two-coat work	Base coat	Gypsum lath	2.5	2
	Base coat	Masonry	3	3
Three-coat work.	First coat	Lath	2[d]	2
	Second coat	Lath	3[d]	2[e]
	First and second coats	Masonry	3	3

For SI: 1 inch = 25.4 mm, 1 cubic foot = 0.0283 m^3, 1 pound = 0.454 kg.

a. Wood-fibered gypsum plaster may be mixed in the proportions of 100 pounds of gypsum to not more than 1 cubic foot of sand where applied on masonry or concrete.

b. When determining the amount of aggregate in set plaster, a tolerance of 10 percent shall be allowed.

c. Combinations of sand and lightweight aggregate may be used, provided the volume and weight relationship of the combined aggregate to gypsum plaster is maintained.

d. If used for both first and second coats, the volume of aggregate may be 2.5 cubic feet.

e. Where plaster is 1 inch or more in total thickness, the proportions for the second coat may be increased to 3 cubic feet.

TABLE R702.1(3)
PORTLAND CEMENT PLASTER

Coat	MAXIMUM VOLUME AGGREGATE PER VOLUME CEMENTITIOUS MATERIAL[a]				MINIMUM PERIOD MOIST COATS	MINIMUM INTERVAL BETWEEN
	Portland cement plaster[b] maximum volume aggregate per volume cement	Portland cement-lime plaster[c]				
		Maximum volume lime per volume cement	Maximum volume sand per volume cement and lime	Approximate minimum thickness[d] curing (inches)		
First	4	$^3/_4$	4	$^3/_8$[e]	48[f] Hours	48[g] Hours
Second	5	$^3/_4$	5	First and second coats	48 Hours	7 Days[h]
Finished	3[i]	—	3[i]	$^1/_8$	—	Note[h]

For SI: 1 inch = 25.4 mm, 1 pound = 0.454 kg.

a. When determining the amount of aggregate in set plaster, a tolerance of 10 percent may be allowed.

b. From 10 to 20 pounds of dry hydrated lime (or an equivalent amount of lime putty) may be added as a plasticizing agent to each sack of Type I and Type II standard portland cement in base coat plaster.

c. No additions of plasticizing agents shall be made.

d. See Table R702.1(1).

e. Measured from face of support or backing to crest of scored plaster.

f. Twenty-four-hour minimum period for moist curing of interior portland cement plaster.

g. Twenty-four hour minimum interval between coats of interior portland cement plaster.

h. Finish coat plaster may be applied to interior portland cement base coats after a 48-hour period.

i. For finish coat, plaster up to an equal part of dry hydrated lime by weight (or an equivalent volume of lime putty) may be added to Type I, Type II and Type III standard portland cement.

R702.2 Interior plaster. Gypsum plaster or portland cement plastering materials shall conform to ASTM C 5, C 28, C 35, C 37, C 59, C 61, C 587, C 588, C 631, C 847, C 897, C 933, C 1032 and C 1047, and shall be installed or applied in conformance with ASTM C 843, C 844 and C 1063. Plaster shall not be less than three coats when applied over metal lath and not less than two coats when applied over other bases permitted by this section, except that veneer plaster may be applied in one coat not to exceed $^3/_{16}$ inch (4.76 mm) thickness, provided the total thickness is as set forth in Table R702.1(1).

R702.2.1 Support. Support spacing for gypsum or metal lath on walls or ceilings shall not exceed 16 inches (406 mm) for $^3/_8$ inch thick (9.5 mm) or 24 inches (610 mm) for $^1/_2$-inch-thick (12.7 mm) plain gypsum lath. Gypsum lath shall be installed at right angles to support framing with end joints in adjacent courses staggered by at least one framing space.

R702.3 Gypsum board.

R702.3.1 Materials. All gypsum board materials and accessories shall conform to ASTM C 36, C 79, C 475, C 514, C 630, C 960, C 1002, C 1047, C 1177, C1178, C1278 and C 1395 and shall be installed in accordance with the provisions of this section. Adhesives for the installation of gypsum board shall conform to ASTM C 557.

R702.3.2 Wood framing. Wood framing supporting gypsum board shall not be less than 2 inches (51 mm) nominal thickness in the least dimension except that wood furring strips not less than 1-inch-by-2 inch (25.4 mm by 51 mm) nominal dimension may be used over solid backing or framing spaced not more than 24 inches (610 mm) on center.

R702.3.3 Steel framing. Steel framing supporting gypsum board shall not be less than 1.25 inches (32 mm) wide in the least dimension. Light-gage nonload-bearing steel framing shall comply with ASTM C 645. Load-bearing steel framing and steel framing from 0.033 inch to 0.112 inch (0.838 mm to 2.84 mm) thick shall comply with ASTM C 955.

R702.3.4 Insulating concrete form walls. Foam plastics for insulating concrete form walls constructed in accordance with Sections R404.4 and R611 on the interior of habitable spaces shall be covered in accordance with Section R318.1.2. Adhesives are permitted to be used in conjunction with mechanical fasteners. Adhesives used for interior and exterior finishes shall be compatible with the insulating form materials.

R702.3.5 Application. Maximum spacing of supports and the size and spacing of fasteners used to attach gypsum board shall comply with Table R702.3.5. Gypsum sheathing shall be attached to exterior walls in accordance with Table R602.3(1). Gypsum board shall be applied at right angles or parallel to framing members. All edges and ends of gypsum board shall occur on the framing members, except those edges and ends that are perpendicular to the framing members. Interior gypsum board shall not be installed where it is exposed to the weather.

R702.3.6 Fastening. Screws for attaching gypsum board to wood framing shall be Type W or Type S in accordance with ASTM C 1002 and shall penetrate the wood not less than $^5/_8$ inch (15.9 mm). Screws for attaching gypsum board to light-gage steel framing shall be Type S in accordance with ASTM C 1002 and shall penetrate the steel not less than $^3/_8$ inch (9.5 mm). Screws for attaching gypsum board to steel framing 0.033 inch to 0.112 inch (0.838 mm to 2.84 mm) thick shall comply with ASTM C 954.

TABLE R702.3.5
MINIMUM THICKNESS AND APPLICATION OF GYPSUM BOARD

THICKNESS OF GYPSUM BOARD (inches)	APPLICATION	ORIENTATION OF GYPSUM BOARD TO FRAMING	MAXIMUM SPACING OF FRAMING MEMBERS (inches o.c.)	MAXIMUM SPACING OF FASTENERS (inches)		SIZE OF NAILS FOR APPLICATION TO WOOD FRAMING[c]
				Nails[a]	Screws[b]	
Application without adhesive						
$3/8$	Ceiling[d]	Perpendicular	16	7	12	13 gage, $1^1/4''$ long, $^{19}/64''$ head; 0.098 diameter, $1^1/4''$ long, annular-ringed; or 4d cooler nail, 0.080″ diameter, $1^3/8''$ long, $^7/32''$ head.
	Wall	Either direction	16	8	16	
$1/2$	Ceiling	Either direction	16	7	12	13 gage, $1^3/8''$ long, $^{19}/64''$ head; 0.098 diameter, $1^1/4''$ long, annular-ringed; 5d cooler nail, 0.086 diameter, $1^5/8''$ long, $^{15}/64''$ head; or gypsum board nail, 0.086 diameter, $1^5/8''$ long, $^9/32''$ head.
	Ceiling[d]	Perpendicular	24	7	12	
	Wall	Either direction	24	8	12	
	Wall	Either direction	16	8	16	
$5/8$	Ceiling	Either direction	16	7	12	13 gage, $1^5/8''$ long, $^{19}/64''$ head; 0.098 diameter, $1^3/8''$ long, annular-ringed; 6d cooler nail, 0.092 diameter, $1^7/8''$ long, $1/4''$ head; or gypsum board nail, 0.0915 diameter, $1^7/8''$ long, $^{19}/64''$ head.
	Ceiling	Perpendicular	24	7	12	
	Wall	Either direction	24	8	12	
	Wall	Either direction	16	8	16	
Application with adhesive						
$3/8$	Ceiling[d]	Perpendicular	16	16	16	Same as above for $3/8''$ gypsum board
	Wall	Either direction	16	16	24	
$1/2$ or $5/8$	Ceiling	Either direction	16	16	16	Same as above for $1/2''$ and $5/8''$ gypsum board, respectively
	Ceiling[d]	Perpendicular	24	12	16	
	Wall	Either direction	24	16	24	
two $3/8$ layers	Ceiling	Perpendicular	16	16	16	Base ply nailed as above for $1/2''$ gypsum board; face ply installed with adhesive
	Wall	Either direction	24	24	24	

For SI: 1 inch = 25.4 mm.

a. For application without adhesive, a pair of nails spaced not less than 2 inches apart or more than $2^1/2$ inches apart may be used with the pair of nails spaced 12 inches on center.

b. Screws shall be Type S or W per ASTM C 1002 and shall be sufficiently long to penetrate wood framing not less than $5/8$ inch and metal framing not less than $3/8$ inch.

c. Where metal framing is used with a clinching design to receive nails by two edges of metal, the nails shall be not less than $5/8$ inch longer than the gypsum board thickness and shall have ringed shanks. Where the metal framing has a nailing groove formed to receive the nails, the nails shall have barbed shanks or be 5d, $13^1/2$ gage, $1^5/8$ inches long, $^{15}/64$-inch head for $1/2$-inch gypsum board; and 6d, 13 gage, $1^7/8$ inches long, $^{15}/64$-inch head for $5/8$-inch gypsum board.

d. Three-eighths-inch-thick single-ply gypsum board shall not be used on a ceiling where a water-based textured finish is to be applied, or where it will be required to support insulation above a ceiling. On ceiling applications to receive a water-based texture material, either hand or spray applied, the gypsum board shall be applied perpendicular to framing. When applying a water-based texture material, the minimum gypsum board thickness shall be increased from $3/8$ inch to $1/2$ inch for 16-inch on center framing, and from $1/2$ inch to $5/8$ inch for 24-inch on center framing or $1/2$-inch sag-resistant gypsum ceiling board shall be used.

R702.4 Ceramic tile.

R702.4.1 General. Ceramic tile surfaces shall be installed in accordance with ANSI A108.1, A108.4, A108.5, A108.6, A108.11, A118.1, A118.3, A136.1 and A137.1.

R702.4.2 Gypsum backer. Gypsum board utilized as the base or backer board for adhesive application of ceramic tile or other nonabsorbent finish material shall conform with ASTM C 630 or C 1178. Water-resistant gypsum backing board shall be permitted to be used on ceilings where framing spacing does not exceed 12 inches (305 mm) on center for $1/2$ inch thick (12.7 mm) or 16 inches (406 mm) for $5/8$-inch-thick (15.9 mm) gypsum board. All cut or exposed edges, including those at wall intersections, shall be sealed as recommended by the manufacturer.

R702.5 Other finishes. Wood veneer paneling and hardboard paneling shall be placed on wood or cold-formed steel framing spaced not more than 16 inches (406 mm) on center. Wood veneer and hard board paneling less than $1/4$ inch (6.4 mm) nominal thickness shall not have less than a $3/8$-inch (9.5 mm) gypsum board backer. Wood veneer paneling not less than $1/4$-inch (6.4 mm) nominal thickness shall conform to ANSI/HPVA HP-1. Hardboard paneling shall conform to ANSI/AHA A135.5.

R702.6 Wood shakes and shingles. Wood shakes and shingles shall conform to CSSB *Grading Rules for Wood Shakes and Shingles* and shall be permitted to be installed directly to the studs with maximum 24 inches (610 mm) on center spacing.

R702.6.1 Attachment. Nails, staples or glue are permitted for use in attaching shakes or shingles to the wall, and the shakes or shingles shall be permitted to be attached directly to the surface provided the fasteners are appropriate for the type of wall surface material. When nails or staples are used, two fasteners shall be provided and shall be placed so that they are covered by the course above.

R702.6.2 Furring strips. Where furring strips are used, they shall be 1 inch by 2 inches or 1 inch by 3 inches (25 mm by 51 mm or 25 mm by 76 mm), spaced a distance on center equal to the desired exposure, and shall be attached to the wall by nailing through other wall material into the studs.

SECTION R703
EXTERIOR COVERING

R703.1 General. Exterior walls shall provide the building with a weather-resistant exterior wall envelope. The exterior wall envelope shall include flashing as described in Section R703.8. The exterior wall envelope shall be designed and constructed in such a manner as to prevent the accumulation of water within the wall assembly by providing a water-resistive barrier behind the exterior veneer as required by Section R703.2.

R703.2 Weather-resistive sheathing paper. A minimum of one layer of No. 15 ashphalt felt complying with ASTM D 226 for Type 1 felt or other approved weather-resistive material shall be applied over sheathing of all exterior walls. See Table R703.4. Such felt or material shall be applied horizontally, with the upper layer lapped over the lower layer not less than 2 inches (51 mm). Where joints occur, felt shall be lapped not less than 6 inches (152 mm). Where joints occur, felt shall be lapped not less than 6 inches (152 mm). Building paper or other approved material shall be continuous up to the underside of the rafter or truss top chord and terminated at penetrations and building appendages in such a manner to meet the requirements of the exterior wall envelope as described in Section R703.1.

Exception: Such felt or material is permitted to be omitted in the following situations:

1. In detached accessory buildings.

2. Where specifically prohibited by a sheathing and/or siding manufacturer.

R703.3 Wood, hardboard and wood structural panel siding.

R703.3.1 Panel siding. Joints in wood, hardboard or wood structural panel siding shall be made as follows unless otherwise approved. Vertical joints in panel siding shall occur over framing members, unless wood or wood structural panel sheathing is used, and shall be shiplapped or covered with a batten. Horizontal joints in panel siding shall be lapped a minimum of 1 inch (25.4 mm) or shall be shiplapped or shall be flashed with Z-flashing and occur over solid blocking, wood or wood structural panel sheathing.

R703.3.2 Horizontal siding. Horizontal lap siding shall be lapped a minimum of 1 inch (25.4 mm), or 0.5 inch (12.7 mm) if rabbeted, and shall have the ends caulked, covered with a batten, or sealed and installed over a strip of flashing.

R703.4 Attachments. Unless specified otherwise, all wall coverings shall be securely fastened in accordance with Table R703.4 or with other approved aluminum, stainless steel, zinc-coated or other approved corrosion-resistive fasteners.

R703.5 Wood shakes and shingles. Wood shakes and shingles shall conform to CSSB "Grading Rules for Wood Shakes and Shingles."

R703.5.1 Application. Wood shakes or shingles shall be applied either single-course or double-course over nominal $^1/_2$-inch (12.7 mm) wood-based sheathing or to furring strips over $^1/_2$-inch (12.7 mm) nominal nonwood sheathing. A weather-resistant permeable membrane shall be provided over all sheathing, with horizontal overlaps in the membrane of not less than 2 inches (51 mm) and vertical overlaps of not less than 6 inches (152 mm). Where furring strips are used, they shall be 1 inch by 3 inches or 1 inch by 4 inches (25 mm by 76 mm or 25 mm by 102 mm) and shall be fastened horizontally to the studs with 7d or 8d box nails and shall be spaced a distance on center equal to the actual weather exposure of the shakes or shingles, not to exceed the maximum exposure specified in Table R703.5.2. The spacing between adjacent shingles to allow for expansion shall not exceed $^1/_4$ inch (6.4 mm), and between adjacent shakes, it shall not exceed $^1/_2$ inch (12.7 mm). The offset spacing between joints in adjacent courses shall be a minimum of $1^1/_2$ inches (38 mm).

R703.5.2 Weather exposure. The maximum weather exposure for shakes and shingles shall not exceed that specified in Table R703.5.2.

R703.5.3 Attachment. Each shake or shingle shall be held in place by two hot-dipped zinc-coated, stainless steel, or aluminum nails or staples. The fasteners shall be long enough to penetrate the sheathing or furring strips by a minimum of $^1/_2$ inch (12.7 mm) and shall not be overdriven.

R703.5.3.1 Staple attachment. Staples shall not be less than 16 gage and shall have a crown width of not less than $^7/_{16}$ inch (11.1 mm), and the crown of the staples shall be parallel with the butt of the shake or shingle. In single-course application, the fasteners shall be concealed by the course above and shall be driven approximately 1 inch (25 mm) above the butt line of the succeeding course and $^3/_4$ inch (19.1 mm) from the edge. In double-course applications, the exposed shake or shingle shall be face-nailed with two casing nails, driven approximately 2 inches (51 mm) above the butt line and $^3/_4$ inch (19.1 mm) from each edge. In all applications, staples shall be concealed by the course above. With shingles wider than 8 inches (203 mm) two additional nails shall be required and shall be nailed approximately 1 inch (25.4 mm) apart near the center of the shingle.

R703.5.4 Bottom courses. The bottom courses shall be doubled.

TABLE R703.4
WEATHER-RESISTANT SIDING ATTACHMENT AND MINIMUM THICKNESS[a,b,c,d,e,f,g,h,i,j,k,l,m,n,o,p,q]

SIDING MATERIAL		NOMINAL THICKNESS[a] (inches)	JOINT TREATMENT	SHEATHING PAPER REQUIRED
Horizontal aluminum[e]	Without insulation	0.019[f]	Lap	Yes
		0.024	Lap	Yes
	With insulation	0.019	Lap	Yes
Brick veneer Concrete masonry veneer		2 2	Section R703	Yes
Hardboard[l] Panel siding-vertical		$^7/_{16}$	Note q	Yes Note q
Siding vertical Hardboard[l] Lap-siding-horizontal		$^7/_{16}$	Note q	Yes Note q
Steel[i]		29 ga.	Lap	Yes
Stone veneer		2	Section R703	Yes
Particleboard panels		$^3/_8$ - $^1/_2$	Note g	Yes Note g
		$^5/_8$	Note g	Yes Note g
Plywood panel[j] (exterior grade)		$^3/_8$	Note g	Yes Note g
Vinyl Siding[n]		0.035	Lap	Yes
Wood[k] Rustic, drop		$^3/_8$ Min	Lap	Yes
Shiplap		$^{19}/_{32}$ Average	Lap	Yes
Bevel		$^7/_{16}$	Lap	Yes
Butt tip		$^3/_{16}$	Lap	Yes

SIDING MATERIAL		Wood or wood structural panel sheathing	Fiberboard sheathing into stud	Gypsum sheathing into stud
Horizontal aluminum[e]	Without insulation	0.120 nail $1^1/_2''$ long	0.120 nail 2″ long	0.120 nail 2″ long
		0.120 nail $1^1/_2''$ long	0.120 nail 2″ long	0.120 nail 2″ long
	With insulation	0.120 nail $1^1/_2''$ long	0.120 nail $2^1/_2''$ long	0.120 nail $2^1/_2''$ long
Brick veneer Concrete masonry veneer		See Section R703 and Figure R703.7[h]		
Hardboard[l] Panel siding-vertical		Note n	Note n	Note n
Siding vertical Hardboard[l] Lap-siding-horizontal		Note p	Note p	Note p
Steel[i]		0.113 nail $1^3/_4''$ Staple $1^3/_4''$	0.113 nail $2^3/_4''$ Staple $2^1/_2''$	0.113 nail $2^1/_2''$ Staple $2^1/_4''$
Stone veneer		See Section R703 and Figure R703.7		
Particleboard panels		6d box nail	6d box nail	6d box nail
		6d box nail	8d box nail	8d box nail
Plywood panel[j] (exterior grade)		0.099 nail 2″	0.113 nail $2^1/_2''$	0.099 nail 2″
Vinyl Siding[n]		0.113 nail $1^1/_2''$ Staple $1^3/_4''$	0.113 nail 2″ Staple $2^1/_2''$	0.113 nail 2″ Staple $2^1/_2''$
Wood[k] Rustic, drop		Fastener penetration into stud 1″		
Shiplap				
Bevel				
Butt tip				

(continued)

TABLE R703.4—continued
WEATHER-RESISTANT SIDING ATTACHMENT AND MINIMUM THICKNESS[a,b,c,d,e,f,g,h,i,j,k,l,m,n,o,p,q]

SIDING MATERIAL		Direct to studs	Number or spacing of fasteners
Horizontal aluminum[e]	Without insulation	Not allowed	Same as stud spacing
		Not allowed	
	With insulation	0.120 nail $1^1/_2''$ long	
Brick veneer Concrete masonry veneer		See Section R703 and Figure R703.7[h]	
Hardboard[l] Panel siding-vertical		Note n	6″ panel edges 12″ inter. sup.[o]
Siding vertical Hardboard[l] Lap-siding-horizontal		Note p	Same as stud spacing 2 per bearing
Steel[i]		Not allowed	Same as stud spacing
Stone veneer		See Section R703 and Figure R703.7	
Particleboard panels		6d box nail, $3/_8$ not allowed	6″ panel edges 12″ inter. sup.
		6d box nail	
Plywood panel[j] (exterior grade)		0.099 nail 2″	6″ on edges
Vinyl Siding[n]		Not allowed	Same as stud spacing
Wood[k] Rustic, drop Shiplap Bevel Butt tip		0.113 nail $2^1/_2''$ Staple 2″	Face nailing up to 6″ widths, 1 nail per bearing; 8″ widths and over, 2 nails per bearing

For SI: 1 inch = 25.4 mm.

a. Based on stud spacing of 16 inches on center Where studs are spaced 24 inches, siding shall be applied to sheathing approved for that spacing.

b. Nail is a general description and shall be T-head, modified round head, or round head with smooth or deformed shanks.

c. Staples shall have a minimum crown width of $7/_{16}$-inch outside diameter and be manufactured of minimum No. 16 gage wire.

d. Nails or staples shall be aluminum, galvanized, or rust-preventive coated and shall be driven into the studs for fiberboard or gypsum backing.

e. Aluminum nails shall be used to attach aluminum siding.

f. Aluminum (0.019 inch) shall be unbacked only when the maximum panel width is 10 inches and the maximum flat area is 8 inches. The tolerance for aluminum siding shall be +0.002 inch of the nominal dimension.

g. If boards or panels are applied over sheathing or a weather-resistant membrane, joints need not be treated. Otherwise, vertical joints shall occur at studs and be covered with battens or be lapped.

h. All attachments shall be coated with a corrosion-resistive coating.

i. Shall be of approved type.

j. Three-eighths-inch plywood shall not be applied directly to studs spaced greater than 16 inches on center when long dimension is parallel to studs. One-half-inch plywood shall not may be applied directly to studs spaced greater than 24 inches on center. The stud spacing shall not exceed the panel span rating provided by the manufacturer unless the panels are installed with the face grain perpendicular to studs or over sheathing approved for that stud spacing.

k. Woodboard sidings applied vertically shall be nailed to horizontal nailing strips or blocking set 24 inches on center. Nails shall penetrate 1.5 inches into studs, studs and wood sheathing combined, or blocking. A weather-resistant membrane shall be installed weatherboard fashion under the vertical siding unless the siding boards are lapped or battens are used.

l. Hardboard siding shall comply with AHA A135.6.

m. Vinyl siding shall comply with ASTM D 3679.

n. Minimum shank diameter of 0.092 inch, minimum head diameter of 0.225 inch, and nail length must accommodate sheathing and penetrate framing 1.5 inches.

o. When used to resist shear forces, the spacing must be 4 inches at panel edges and 8 inches on interior supports.

p. Minimum shank diameter of 0.099 inch, minimum head diameter of 0.240 inch, and nail length must accommodate sheathing and penetrate framing 1.5 inches.

q. Vertical end joints shall occur at studs and shall be covered with a joint cover or shall be caulked.

TABLE R703.5.2
MAXIMUM WEATHER EXPOSURE FOR WOOD SHAKES AND SHINGLES ON EXTERIOR WALLS[a,b,c]
(Dimensions are in inches)

LENGTH	EXPOSURE FOR SINGLE COURSE	EXPOSURE FOR DOUBLE COURSE
Shingles[a]		
16	$7^1/_2$	12^b
18	$8^1/_2$	14^c
24	$11^1/_2$	16
Shakes[a]		
18	$8^1/_2$	14
24	$11^1/_2$	18

For SI: 1 inch = 25.4 mm.

a. Dimensions given are for No. 1 grade.

b. A maximum 10-inch exposure is permitted for No. 2 grade.

c. A maximum 11-inch exposure is permitted for No. 2 grade.

R703.6 Exterior plaster. Installation of these materials shall be in compliance with ASTM C 926 and ASTM C 1063.

R703.6.1 Lath. All lath and lath attachments shall be of corrosion-resistant materials. Expanded metal or woven wire lath shall be attached with $1^1/_2$-inch-long (38 mm), 11 gage nails having a $^7/_{16}$-inch (11.1 mm) head, or $^7/_8$-inch-long (22.2 mm), 16 gage staples, spaced at no more than 6 inches (152 mm) at supports.

R703.6.2 Plaster. Plastering with portland cement plaster shall be not less than three coats when applied over metal lath or wire lath and shall be not less than two coats when applied over masonry, concrete or gypsum backing. If the plaster surface is completely covered by veneer or other facing material or is completely concealed, plaster application need be only two coats, provided the total thickness is as set forth in Table R702.1(1).

On wood-frame construction with an on-grade floor slab system, exterior plaster shall be applied in such a manner as to cover, but not extend below, lath, paper and screed.

The proportion of aggregate to cementitious materials shall be as set forth in Table R702.1(3).

R703.6.3 Weather-resistant barriers. Weather-resistant barriers shall be installed as required in Section R703.2 and, where applied over wood-based sheathing, shall include a weather-resistive vapor permeable barrier with a performance at least equivalent to two layers of Grade D paper.

R703.6.4 Weep screeds. A minimum 0.019-inch (No. 26 galvanized sheet gage), corrosion-resistant weep screed with a minimum vertical attachment flange of $3^1/_2$ inches shall be provided at or below the foundation plate line on exterior stud walls in accordance with ASTM C 926. The weep screed shall be placed a minimum of 4 inches above the earth or 2 inches above paved areas and shall be of a type that will allow trapped water to drain to the exterior of the building. The weather-resistant barrier shall lap the attachment flange. The exterior lath shall cover and terminate on the attachment flange of the weep screed.

R703.7 Stone and masonry veneer, general. All stone and masonry veneer shall be installed in accordance with this chapter, Table R703.4 and Figure R703.7. Such veneers installed over a backing of wood or cold-formed steel shall be limited to the first story above grade and shall not exceed 5 inches (127 mm) in thickness.

Exceptions:

1. In Seismic Design Categories A and B, exterior masonry veneer with a backing of wood or cold-formed steel framing shall not exceed 30 feet (9144 mm) in height above the noncombustible foundation, with an additional 8 feet (2348 mm) permitted for ends.

2. In Seismic Design Category C, exterior masonry veneer with a backing of wood or cold-formed steel framing shall not exceed 30 feet (9144 mm) in height above the noncombustible foundation, with an additional 8 feet (2348 mm) permitted for gabled ends. In other than the topmost story, the length of bracing shall be 1.5 times the length otherwise required in Chapter 6.

R703.7.1 Interior veneer support. Masonry veneers to a maximum height of 12 feet 8 inches (38,608 mm) used as interior wall finishes shall be permitted to be supported on wood or cold-formed steel floors that are designed to support the loads imposed.

R703.7.2 Exterior veneer support. Exterior masonry veneers having an installed weight of 40 pounds per square foot (195 kg/m^2) or less shall be permitted to be supported by cold-formed steel wall construction. When masonry veneer supported by cold-formed steel wall construction adjoins masonry veneer supported by the foundation, there shall be a movement joint between the veneer supported by the cold-formed steel wall construction and the veneer supported by the foundation. The cold-formed steel wall construction providing lateral support to the masonry veneer shall be designed to limit the lateral deflection to $^1/_{600}$ of the span. The design of the cold-formed steel wall construction shall consider the weight of the veneer and any other loads such as wind loads.

R703.7.3 Lintels. Masonry veneer shall not support any vertical load other than the dead load of the veneer above. Veneer above openings shall be supported on lintels of noncombustible materials and the allowable span shall not exceed the values set forth in Table R703.7.3. The lintels shall have a length of bearing of not less than 4 inches (102 mm).

TABLE R703.7.3
ALLOWABLE SPANS FOR LINTELS SUPPORTING MASONRY VENEER[a,b,c]

TABLE R703.7.3
ALLOWABLE SPANS FOR LINTELS SUPPORTING MASONRY VENEER[a,b,c]

SIZE OF STEEL ANGLE[a,c] (inches)	NO STORY ABOVE	ONE STORY ABOVE	TWO STORIES ABOVE	NO. OF $1/2$" OR EQUIVALENT REINFORCING BARS[c]
$3 \times 3 \times 1/4$	6'-0"	3'-6"	3'-0"	1
$4 \times 3 \times 1/4$	8'-0"	5'-0"	3'-0"	1
$6 \times 3^{1}/_{2} \times 1/4$	14'-0"	8'-0"	3'-6"	2
$2\text{-}6 \times 3^{1}/_{2} \times 1/4$	20'-0"	11'-0"	5'-0"	4

For SI: 1 inch = 25.4 mm, 1 foot =304.8 mm.

a. Long leg of the angle shall be placed in a vertical position.

b. Depth of reinforced lintels shall not be less than 8 inches and all cells of hollow masonry lintels shall be grouted solid. Reinforcing bars shall extend not less than 8 inches into the support.

c. Steel members indicated are adequate typical examples; other steel members meeting structural design requirements may be used.

R703.7.4 Anchorage. Masonry veneer shall be anchored to the supporting wall with corrosion-resistant metal ties. Where veneer is anchored to wood backings through the use of corrugated sheet metal ties, the distance separating the veneer from the sheathing material shall be a maximum of 1 inch (25 mm). Where the veneer is anchored to wood backings through the use of metal strand wire ties, the distance separating the veneer from the sheathing material shall be a maximum of $4^{1}/_{2}$ inches (114 mm). Where the veneer is anchored to cold-formed steel backings, adjustable metal strand wire ties shall be used. Where veneer is anchored to cold-formed steel backings, the distance separating the veneer from the sheathing material shall be a maximum of 4.5 inches (114 mm).

R703.7.4.1 Size and spacing. Veneer ties, if strand wire, shall not be less in thickness than No. 9 U.S. gage wire and shall have a hood embedded in the mortar joint, or if sheet metal, shall be not less than No. 22 U.S. gage by $7/8$ inch (22.3 mm) corrugated. Each tie shall be spaced not more than 24 inches (610 mm) on center horizontally and shall support not more than $3^{1}/_{4}$ square feet (0.302 m^2) of wall area.

Exception: In Seismic Design Category D$_1$ or D$_2$ and in wind areas of more than 30 pounds per square foot (1.44 kN/m^2), each tie shall support not more than 2 square feet (0.186 m^2) of wall area.

R703.7.4.1.1 Veneer ties around wall openings. Additional metal ties shall be provided around all wall openings greater than 16 inches (406 mm) in either dimension. Metal ties around the perimeter of openings shall be spaced not more than 3 feet (9144 mm) on center and placed within 12 inches (305 mm) of the wall opening.

R703.7.4.1.2 Seismic Design Categories D$_1$ and D$_2$. In Seismic Design Categories D$_1$ and D$_2$, veneer ties shall be mechanically attached to horizontal joint reinforcement wire a minimum of No. 9 gage. The horizontal joint reinforcement shall be continuous in the veneer bed joint, with lap splices permitted between the veneer tie spacing.

R703.7.4.2 Air space. The veneer shall be separated from the sheathing by an air space of a minimum of 1 inch (25.4 mm) but not more than 4.5 inches (114 mm). The weather-resistant membrane or asphalt-saturated felt required by Section R703.2 is not required over water-repellent sheathing materials.

R703.7.4.3 Mortar or grout fill. As an alternate to the air space required by Section R703.7.4.2, mortar or grout shall be permitted to fill the air space. When the 1-inch (25.4 mm) space is filled with mortar, a weather-resistant membrane or building paper is required over studs or sheathing. When filling the air space, it is permitted to replace the sheathing and weather-resistant membrane or asphalt-saturated felt paper with a wire mesh and approved paper or an approved paper-backed reinforcement attached directly to the studs.

R703.7.5 Flashing. Flashing shall be located beneath the first course of masonry above finished ground level above the foundation wall or slab and at other points of support, including structural floors, shelf angles and lintels when masonry veneers are designed in accordance with Section R703.7. See Section R703.8 for additional requirements.

R703.7.6 Weepholes. Weepholes shall be provided in the outside wythe of masonry walls at a maximum spacing of 33 inches (838 mm) on center. Weepholes shall not be less than $3/16$ inch (4.8 mm) in diameter. Weepholes shall be located immediately above the flashing.

R703.8 Flashing. Approved corrosion-resistive flashing shall be provided in the exterior wall envelope in such a manner as to prevent entry of water into the wall cavity or penetration of water to the building structural framing components. The flashing shall extend to the surface of the exterior wall finish and shall be installed to prevent water from reentering the exterior wall envelope. Approved corrosion-resistant flashings shall be installed at all of the following locations:

1. At top of all exterior window and door openings in such a manner as to be leakproof.
2. At the intersection of chimneys or other masonry construction with frame or stucco walls, with projecting lips on both sides under stucco copings.
3. Under and at the ends of masonry, wood or metal copings and sills.
4. Continuously above all projecting wood trim.
5. Where exterior porches, decks or stairs attach to a wall or floor assembly of wood-frame construction.
6. At wall and roof intersections.
7. At built-in gutters.

M
N
M

8. Where exterior material meets in other than a vertical line.

R703.9 Exterior insulation finish systems, general. All Exterior Insulation Finish Systems (EIFS) shall be installed in accordance with the manufacturer's installation instructions and the requirements of this section. Decorative trim shall not be face nailed through the EIFS. The EIFS shall terminate not less than 6 inches (152 mm) above the finished ground level.

R703.9.1 Weather-resistive barrier. All EIFS shall have a weather-resistive barrier applied between the underlying water-sensitive building components and the exterior insulation, and a means of draining water to the exterior of the veneer. A weather-resistive barrier shall be compliant with ASTM D 226 Type I asphalt saturated felt or equivalent, shall be applied horizontally with the upper layer lapped over the lower layer not less than 2 inches (51 mm), and shall have all vertical joints lapped not less than 6 inches (152 mm).

R703.9.2 Flashing, general. Flashing of EIFS shall be provided in accordance with the requirements of Section R703.8.

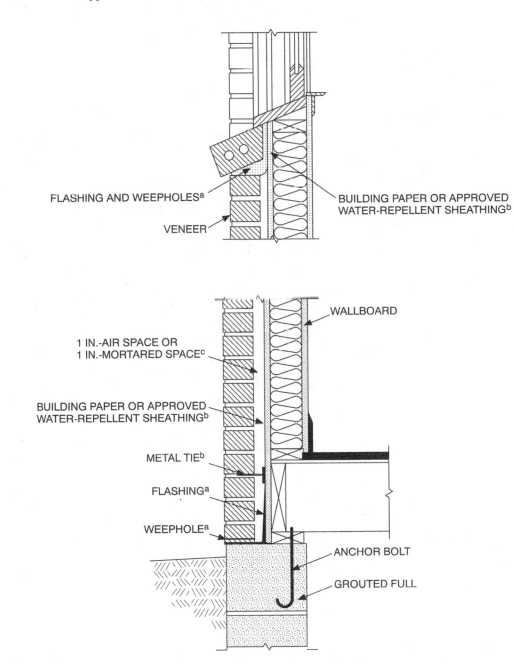

FLASHING AND WEEPHOLES[a]

VENEER

BUILDING PAPER OR APPROVED WATER-REPELLENT SHEATHING[b]

WALLBOARD

1 IN.-AIR SPACE OR 1 IN.-MORTARED SPACE[c]

BUILDING PAPER OR APPROVED WATER-REPELLENT SHEATHING[b]

METAL TIE[b]

FLASHING[a]

WEEPHOLE[a]

ANCHOR BOLT

GROUTED FULL

For SI: 1 inch = 25.4 mm.

FIGURE R703.7
MASONRY VENEER WALL DETAILS
(continued)

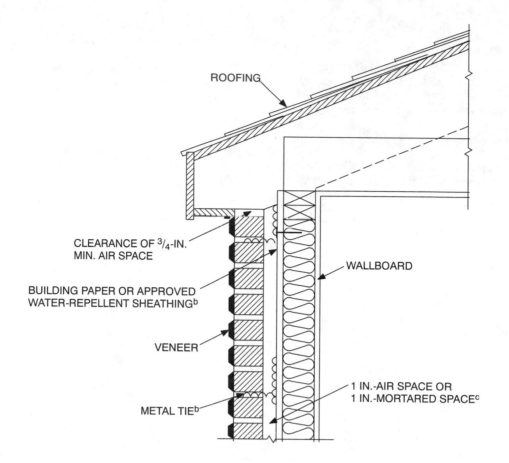

ROOFING

CLEARANCE OF $^3/_4$-IN. MIN. AIR SPACE

BUILDING PAPER OR APPROVED WATER-REPELLENT SHEATHING[b]

VENEER

METAL TIE[b]

WALLBOARD

1 IN.-AIR SPACE OR 1 IN.-MORTARED SPACE[c]

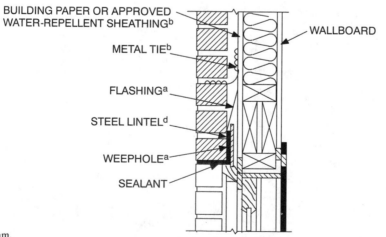

BUILDING PAPER OR APPROVED WATER-REPELLENT SHEATHING[b]

METAL TIE[b]

FLASHING[a]

STEEL LINTEL[d]

WEEPHOLE[a]

SEALANT

WALLBOARD

For SI: 1 inch = 25.4 mm.

a. See Sections R703.7.5 and R703.7.6.
b. See Sections R703.2 and R703.7.4.
c. See Section R703.7.4.2 and R703.7.4.3.

FIGURE R703.7—continued
MASONRY VENEER WALL DETAILS

FIGURE R703.7.1
EXTERIOR MASONRY VENEER SUPPORT BY WOOD CONSTRUCTION

Not adopted by the State of Minnesota.

CHAPTER 8
ROOF-CEILING CONSTRUCTION

SECTION R801
GENERAL

R801.1 Application. The provisions of this chapter shall control the design and construction of the roof-ceiling system for all buildings.

R801.2 Requirements. Roof and ceiling construction shall be capable of accommodating all loads imposed according to Section R301 and of transmitting the resulting loads to the supporting structural elements.

R801.3 Roof drainage. In areas where expansive or collapsible soils are known to exist, all dwellings shall have a controlled method of water disposal from roofs that will collect and discharge all roof drainage to the ground surface at least 5 feet (1524 mm) from foundation walls or to an approved drainage system.

SECTION R802
WOOD ROOF FRAMING

R802.1 Identification and grade. Load-bearing dimension lumber for rafters, trusses and ceiling joists shall be identified by a grade mark of a lumber grading or inspection agency that has been approved by an accreditation body that complies with DOC PS 20. In lieu of a grade mark, a certificate of inspection issued by a lumber grading or inspection agency meeting the requirements of this section shall be accepted.

R802.1.1 Blocking. Blocking shall be a minimum of utility grade lumber.

R802.1.2 End-jointed lumber. Approved end-jointed lumber identified by a grade mark conforming to Section R802.1 may be used interchangeably with solid-sawn members of the same species and grade.

R802.1.3 Fire-retardant-treated lumber. The allowable unit stresses for fire-retardant-treated lumber, including fastener values, shall be developed from an approved method of investigation that considers the effects of anticipated temperature and humidity to which the fire-retardant lumber will be subjected, the type of treatment and redrying process.

R802.1.3.1 Labeling and grade marking. Fire-retardant-treated lumber and wood structural panels shall bear the identification mark of an approved agency. Such identification marks shall indicate conformance with appropriate standards. Additionally, fire-retardant-treated lumber and wood structural panels shall be identified in accordance with Section R802.1 and Section R803.2.1 respectively.

R802.1.3.2 Moisture content. Fire-retardant-treated wood shall be dried in accordance with AWPA C20 to a moisture content of 19 percent or less for lumber and 15 percent or less in accordance with AWPA C27 for wood structural panels before use.

R802.2 Design and construction. Roof-ceilings shall be designed and constructed in accordance with the provisions of this chapter and Figures R606.10(1), R606.10(2) and R606.10(3) or in accordance with AFPA/NDS. Components of roof-ceilings shall be fastened in accordance with Table R602.3(1).

R802.3 Framing details. Rafters shall be framed to ridge board or to each other with a gusset plate as a tie. Ridge board shall be at least 1-inch (25.4 mm) nominal thickness and not less in depth than the cut end of the rafter. At all valleys and hips there shall be a valley or hip rafter not less than 2-inch (51 mm) nominal thickness and not less in depth than the cut end of the rafter. Hip and valley rafters shall be supported at the ridge by a brace to a bearing partition or be designed to carry and distribute the specific load at that point. Where the roof pitch is less than three units vertical in 12 units horizontal (25-percent slope), structural members that support rafters and ceiling joists, such as ridge beams, hips and valleys, shall be designed as beams.

R802.3.1 Ceiling joist and rafter connections. Ceiling joists and rafters shall be nailed to each other in accordance with Tables R602.3(1) and R802.5.1(9), and the assembly shall be nailed to the top wall plate in accordance with Table R602.3(1). Ceiling joists shall be continuous or securely joined where they meet over interior partitions and nailed to adjacent rafters to provide a continuous tie across the building when such joists are parallel to the rafters.

Where ceiling joists are not parallel to rafters, subflooring or metal straps attached to the ends of the rafters shall be installed in a manner to provide a continuous tie across the building, or rafters shall be tied to 1-inch by 4-inch (25.4 mm by 102 mm) (nominal) minimum-size crossties. The connections shall be in accordance with Table R602.3(1) or connections of equivalent capacities shall be provided. Where ceiling joists or rafter ties are not provided at the top plate, the ridge formed by these rafters shall also be supported by a girder designed in accordance with accepted engineering practice.

Rafter ties shall be spaced not more than 4 feet (1219 mm) on center.

R802.3.2 Ceiling joists lapped. Ends of ceiling joists shall be lapped a minimum of 3 inches (76 mm) or butted over bearing partitions or beams and toenailed to the bearing member. When ceiling joists are used to provide resistance to rafter thrust, lapped joists shall be nailed together in accordance with Table R602.3(1) and butted joists shall be tied together in a manner to resist such thrust.

R802.4 Allowable ceiling joist spans. Spans for ceiling joists shall be in accordance with Tables R802.4(1) and R802.4(2). For other grades and species and for other loading conditions, refer to the AF&PA Span Tables for Joists and Rafters.

**TABLE R802.4(1)
CEILING JOIST SPANS FOR COMMON LUMBER SPECIES
(Uninhabitable attics without storage, live load = 20 psf, L/Δ = 240)**

CEILING JOIST SPACING (inches)	SPECIES AND GRADE	DEAD LOAD = 5 psf			
		2x4	2x6	2x8	2x10
		Maximum ceiling joist spans			
		(feet - inches)	(feet - inches)	(feet - inches)	(feet - inches)
12	Douglas fir-larch SS	13-2	20-8	Note a	Note a
	Douglas fir-larch #1	12-8	19-11	Note a	Note a
	Douglas fir-larch #2	12-5	19-6	25-8	Note a
	Douglas fir-larch #3	10-10	15-10	20-1	24-6
	Hem-fir SS	12-5	19-6	25-8	Note a
	Hem-fir #1	12-2	19-1	25-2	Note a
	Hem-fir #2	11-7	18-2	24-0	Note a
	Hem-fir #3	10-10	15-10	20-1	24-6
	Southern pine SS	12-11	20-3	Note a	Note a
	Southern pine #1	12-8	19-11	Note a	Note a
	Southern pine #2	12-5	19-6	25-8	Note a
	Southern pine #3	11-6	17-0	21-8	25-7
	Spruce-pine-fir SS	12-2	19-1	25-2	Note a
	Spruce-pine-fir #1	11-10	18-8	24-7	Note a
	Spruce-pine-fir #2	11-10	18-8	24-7	Note a
	Spruce-pine-fir #3	10-10	15-10	20-1	24-6
16	Douglas fir-larch SS	11-11	18-9	24-8	Note a
	Douglas fir-larch #1	11-6	18-1	23-10	Note a
	Douglas fir-larch #2	11-3	17-8	23-0	Note a
	Douglas fir-larch #3	9-5	13-9	17-5	21-3
	Hem-fir SS	11-3	17-8	23-4	Note a
	Hem-fir #1	11-0	17-4	22-10	Note a
	Hem-fir #2	10-6	16-6	21-9	Note a
	Hem-fir #3	9-5	13-9	17-5	21-3
	Southern pine SS	11-9	18-5	24-3	Note a
	Southern pine #1	11-6	18-1	23-1	Note a
	Southern pine #2	11-3	17-8	23-4	Note a
	Southern pine #3	10-0	14-9	18-9	22-2
	Spruce-pine-fir SS	11-0	17-4	22-10	Note a
	Spruce-pine-fir #1	10-9	16-11	22-4	Note a
	Spruce-pine-fir #2	10-9	16-11	22-4	Note a
	Spruce-pine-fir #3	9-5	13-9	17-5	21-3
19.2	Douglas fir-larch SS	11-3	17-8	23-3	Note a
	Douglas fir-larch #1	10-10	17-0	22-5	Note a
	Douglas fir-larch #2	10-7	16-7	21-0	25-8
	Douglas fir-larch #3	8-7	12-6	15-10	19-5
	Hem-fir SS	10-7	16-8	21-11	Note a
	Hem-fir #1	10-4	16-4	21-6	Note a
	Hem-fir #2	9-11	15-7	20-6	25-3
	Hem-fir #3	8-7	12-6	15-10	19-5
	Southern -pine SS	11-0	17-4	22-10	Note a
	Southern pine #1	10-10	17-0	22-5	Note a
	Southern pine #2	10-7	16-8	21-11	Note a
	Southern pine #3	9-1	13-6	17-2	20-3
	Spruce-pine-fir SS	10-4	16-4	21-6	Note a
	Spruce-pine-fir #1	10-2	15-11	21-0	25-8
	Spruce-pine-fir #2	10-2	15-11	21-0	25-8
	Spruce-pine-fir #3	8-7	12-6	15-10	19-5

(continued)

CEILING JOIST SPANS FOR COMMON LUMBER SPECIES
(Uninhabitable attics without storage, live load = 20 psf, L/Δ = 240)

CEILING JOIST SPACING (inches)	SPECIES AND GRADE		DEAD LOAD = 5 psf			
			2x4	2x6	2x8	2x10
			Maximum ceiling joist spans			
			(feet - inches)	(feet - inches)	(feet - inches)	(feet - inches)
24	Douglas fir-larch	SS	10-5	16-4	21-7	Note a
	Douglas fir-larch	#1	10-0	15-9	20-1	24-6
	Douglas fir-larch	#2	9-10	14-10	18-9	22-11
	Douglas fir-larch	#3	7-8	11-2	14-2	17-4
	Hem-fir	SS	9-10	15-6	20-5	Note a
	Hem-fir	#1	9-8	15-2	19-7	23-11
	Hem-fir	#2	9-2	14-5	18-6	22-7
	Hem-fir	#3	7-8	11-2	14-2	17-4
	Southern pine	SS	10-3	16-1	21-2	Note a
	Southern pine	#1	10-0	15-9	20-10	Note a
	Southern pine	#2	9-10	15-6	20-1	23-11
	Southern pine	#3	8-2	12-0	15-4	18-1
	Spruce-pine-fir	SS	9-8	15-2	19-11	25-5
	Spruce-pine-fir	#1	9-5	14-9	18-9	22-11
	Spruce-pine-fir	#2	9-5	14-9	18-9	22-11
	Spruce-pine-fir	#3	7-8	11-2	14-2	17-4

Check sources for availability of lumber in lengths greater than 20 feet.

For SI: 1 inch = 25.4 mm, 1 foot = 304.8 mm, 1 pound per square foot = 0.0479 kN/m^2.

a. Span exceeds 26 feet in length

TABLE R802.4(2)
CEILING JOIST SPANS FOR COMMON LUMBER SPECIES
(Uninhabitable attics with limited storage, live load = 20 psf, L/Δ = 240)

CEILING JOIST SPACING (inches)	SPECIES AND GRADE	DEAD LOAD = 10 psf			
		2x4	2x6	2x8	2x10
		Maximum ceiling joist spans			
		(feet - inches)	(feet - inches)	(feet - inches)	(feet - inches)
12	Douglas fir-larch SS	10-5	16-4	21-7	Note a
	Douglas fir-larch #1	10-0	15-9	20-1	24-6
	Douglas fir-larch #2	9-10	14-10	18-9	22-11
	Douglas fir-larch #3	7-8	11-2	14-2	17-4
	Hem-fir SS	9-10	15-6	20-5	Note a
	Hem-fir #1	9-8	15-2	19-7	23-11
	Hem-fir #2	9-2	14-5	18-6	22-7
	Hem-fir #3	7-8	11-2	14-2	17-4
	Southern pine SS	10-3	16-1	21-2	Note a
	Southern pine #1	10-0	15-9	20-10	Note a
	Southern pine #2	9-10	15-6	20-1	23-11
	Southern pine #3	8-2	12-0	15-4	18-1
	Spruce-pine-fir SS	9-8	15-2	19-11	25-5
	Spruce-pine-fir #1	9-5	14-9	18-9	22-11
	Spruce-pine-fir #2	9-5	14-9	18-9	22-11
	Spruce-pine-fir #3	7-8	11-2	14-2	17-4
16	Douglas fir-larch SS	9-6	14-11	19-7	25-0
	Douglas fir-larch #1	9-1	13-9	17-5	21-3
	Douglas fir-larch #2	8-9	12-10	16-3	19-10
	Douglas fir-larch #3	6-8	9-8	12-4	15-0
	Hem-fir SS	8-11	14-1	18-6	23-8
	Hem-fir #1	8-9	13-5	16-10	20-8
	Hem-fir #2	8-4	12-8	16-0	19-7
	Hem-fir #3	6-8	9-8	12-4	15-0
	Southern pine SS	9-4	14-7	19-3	24-7
	Southern pine #1	9-1	14-4	18-11	23-1
	Southern pine #2	8-11	13-6	17-5	20-9
	Southern pine #3	7-1	10-5	13-3	15-8
	Spruce-pine-fir SS	8-9	13-9	18-1	23-1
	Spruce-pine-fir #1	8-7	12-10	16-3	19-10
	Spruce-pine-fir #2	8-7	12-10	16-3	19-10
	Spruce-pine-fir #3	6-8	9-8	12-4	15-0
19.2	Douglas fir-larch SS	8-11	14-0	18-5	23-4
	Douglas fir-larch #1	8-7	12-6	15-10	19-5
	Douglas fir-larch #2	8-0	11-9	14-10	18-2
	Douglas fir-larch #3	6-1	8-10	11-3	13-8
	Hem-fir SS	8-5	13-3	17-5	22-3
	Hem-fir #1	8-3	12-3	15-6	18-11
	Hem-fir #2	7-10	11-7	14-8	17-10
	Hem-fir #3	6-1	8-10	11-3	13-8
	Southern pine SS	8-9	13-9	18-1	23-1
	Southern pine #1	8-7	13-6	17-9	21-1
	Southern pine #2	8-5	12-3	15-10	18-11
	Southern pine #3	6-5	9-6	12-1	14-4
	Spruce-pine-fir SS	8-3	12-11	17-1	21-8
	Spruce-pine-fir #1	8-0	11-9	14-10	18-2
	Spruce-pine-fir #2	8-0	11-9	14-10	18-2
	Spruce-pine-fir #3	6-1	8-10	11-3	13-8

(continued)

TABLE R802.4(2)—continued
CEILING JOIST SPANS FOR COMMON LUMBER SPECIES
(Uninhabitable attics with limited storage, live load = 20 psf, L/Δ = 240)

CEILING JOIST SPACING (inches)	SPECIES AND GRADE		DEAD LOAD = 10 psf			
			2x4	2x6	2x8	2x10
			Maximum Ceiling Joist Spans			
			(feet - inches)	(feet - inches)	(feet - inches)	(feet - inches)
24	Douglas fir-larch	SS	8-3	13-0	17-1	20-11
	Douglas fir-larch	#1	7-8	11-2	14-2	17-4
	Douglas fir-larch	#2	7-2	10-6	13-3	16-3
	Douglas fir-larch	#3	5-5	7-11	10-0	12-3
	Hem-fir	SS	7-10	12-3	16-2	20-6
	Hem-fir	#1	7-6	10-11	13-10	16-11
	Hem-fir	#2	7-1	10-4	13-1	16-0
	Hem-fir	#3	5-5	7-11	10-0	12-3
	Southern pine	SS	8-1	12-9	16-10	21-6
	Southern pine	#1	8-0	12-6	15-10	18-10
	Southern pine	#2	7-8	11-0	14-2	16-11
	Southern pine	#3	5-9	8-6	10-10	12-10
	Spruce-pine-fir	SS	7-8	12-0	15-10	19-5
	Spruce-pine-fir	#1	7-2	10-6	13-3	16-3
	Spruce-pine-fir	#2	7-2	10-6	13-3	16-3
	Spruce-pine-fir	#3	5-5	7-11	10-0	12-3

For SI: 1 inch = 25.4 mm, 1 foot = 304.8 mm, 1 pound per square foot = 0.0479 kN/m².

a. Check sources for availability of lumber in lengths greater than 20 feet.

R802.5 Allowable rafter spans. Spans for rafters shall be in accordance with Tables R802.5.1(1) through R802.5.1(8). For other grades and species and for other loading conditions, refer to the AF&PA Span Tables for Joists and Rafters. The span of each rafter shall be measured along the horizontal projection of the rafter.

R802.5.1 Purlins. Purlins are permitted to be installed to reduce the span of rafters as shown in Figure R802.5.1. Purlins shall be sized no less than the required size of the rafters that they support. Purlins shall be continuous and shall be supported by 2-inch by 4-inch (51 mm by 102 mm) braces installed to bearing walls at a slope not less than 45 degrees from the horizontal. The braces shall be spaced not more than 4 feet (1219 mm) on center and the unbraced length of braces shall not exceed 8 feet (2438 mm).

R802.6 Bearing. The ends of each rafter or ceiling joist shall have not less than 1¹/₂ inches (38 mm) of bearing on wood or metal and not less than 3 inches (76 mm) on masonry or concrete.

R802.6.1 Finished ceiling material. If the finished ceiling material is installed on the ceiling prior to the attachment of the ceiling to the walls, such as in construction at a factory, a compression strip of the same thickness as the finish ceiling material shall be installed directly above the top plate of bearing walls if the compressive strength of the finish ceiling material is less than the loads it will be required to withstand. The compression strip shall cover the entire length of such top plate and shall be at least one-half the width of the top plate. It shall be of material capable of transmitting the loads transferred through it.

R802.7 Cutting and notching. Structural roof members shall not be cut, bored or notched in excess of the limitations specified in this section.

R802.7.1 Sawn lumber. Notches in solid lumber joists, rafters and beams shall not exceed one-sixth of the depth of the member, shall not be longer than one-third of the depth of the member and shall not be located in the middle one-third of the span. Notches at the ends of the member shall not exceed one-fourth the depth of the member. The tension side of members 4 inches (102 mm) or greater in nominal thickness shall not be notched except at the ends of the members. The diameter of the holes bored or cut into members shall not exceed one-third the depth of the member. Holes shall not be closer than 2 inches (51 mm) to the top or bottom of the member, or to any other hole located in the member. Where the member is also notched, the hole shall not be closer than 2 inches (51 mm) to the notch.

Exception: Notches on cantilevered portions of rafters are permitted provided the dimension of the remaining portion of the rafter is not less than 4-inch nominal (102 mm) and the length of the cantilever does not exceed 24 inches (610 mm).

R802.7.2 Engineered wood products. Cuts, notches and holes bored in laminated veneer lumber, glue-laminated members or I-joists are not permitted unless the effect of such penetrations are specifically considered in the design of the member.

TABLE R802.5.1(1)
RAFTER SPANS FOR COMMON LUMBER SPECIES
(Roof live load=20 psf, ceiling not attached to rafters, L/Δ=180)

RAFTER SPACING (inches)	SPECIES AND GRADE		DEAD LOAD = 10 psf					DEAD LOAD = 20 psf				
			2x4	2x6	2x8	2x10	2x12	2x4	2x6	2x8	2x10	2x12
			Maximum rafter spans[a]									
			(feet - inches)	(feet - inches)	(feet - inches)	(feet - inches)	(feet - inches)	(feet - inches)	(feet - inches)	(feet - inches)	(feet - inches)	(feet - inches)
12	Douglas fir-larch	SS	11-6	18-0	23-9	Note b	Note b	11-6	18-0	23-5	Note b	Note b
	Douglas fir-larch	#1	11-1	17-4	22-5	Note b	Note b	10-6	15-4	19-5	23-9	Note b
	Douglas fir-larch	#2	10-10	16-7	21-0	25-8	Note b	9-10	14-4	18-2	22-3	25-9
	Douglas fir-larch	#3	8-7	12-6	15-10	19-5	22-6	7-5	10-10	13-9	16-9	19-6
	Hem-fir	SS	10-10	17-0	22-5	Note b	Note b	10-10	17-0	22-5	Note b	Note b
	Hem-fir	#1	10-7	16-8	21-10	Note b	Note b	10-3	14-11	18-11	23-2	Note b
	Hem-fir	#2	10-1	15-11	20-8	25-3	Note b	9-8	14-2	17-11	21-11	25-5
	Hem-fir	#3	8-7	12-6	15-10	19-5	22-6	7-5	10-10	13-9	16-9	19-6
	Southern pine	SS	11-3	17-8	23-4	Note b	Note b	11-3	17-8	23-4	Note b	Note b
	Southern pine	#1	11-1	17-4	22-11	Note b	Note b	11-1	17-3	21-9	25-10	Note b
	Southern pine	#2	10-10	17-0	22-5	Note b	Note b	10-6	15-1	19-5	23-2	Note b
	Southern pine	#3	9-1	13-6	17-2	20-3	24-1	7-11	11-8	14-10	17-6	20-11
	Spruce-pine-fir	SS	10-7	16-8	21-11	Note b	Note b	10-7	16-8	21-9	Note b	Note b
	Spruce-pine-fir	#1	10-4	16-3	21-0	25-8	Note b	9-10	14-4	18-2	22-3	25-9
	Spruce-pine-fir	#2	10-4	16-3	21-0	25-8	Note b	9-10	14-4	18-2	22-3	25-9
	Spruce-pine-fir	#3	8-7	12-6	15-10	19-5	22-6	7-5	10-10	13-9	16-9	19-6
16	Douglas fir-larch	SS	10-5	16-4	21-7	Note b	Note b	10-5	16-0	20-3	24-9	Note b
	Douglas fir-larch	#1	10-0	15-4	19-5	23-9	Note b	9-1	13-3	16-10	20-7	23-10
	Douglas fir-larch	#2	9-10	14-4	18-2	22-3	25-9	8-6	12-5	15-9	19-3	22-4
	Douglas fir-larch	#3	7-5	10-10	13-9	16-9	19-6	6-5	9-5	11-11	14-6	16-10
	Hem-fir	SS	9-10	15-6	20-5	Note b	Note b	9-10	15-6	19-11	24-4	Note b
	Hem-fir	#1	9-8	14-11	18-11	23-2	Note b	8-10	12-11	16-5	20-0	23-3
	Hem-fir	#2	9-2	14-2	17-11	21-11	25-5	8-5	12-3	15-6	18-11	22-0
	Hem-fir	#3	7-5	10-10	13-9	16-9	19-6	6-5	9-5	11-11	14-6	16-10
	Southern pine	SS	10-3	16-1	21-2	Note b	Note b	10-3	16-1	21-2	Note b	Note b
	Southern pine	#1	10-0	15-9	20-10	25-10	Note b	10-0	15-0	18-10	22-4	Note b
	Southern pine	#2	9-10	15-1	19-5	23-2	Note b	9-1	13-0	16-10	20-1	23-7
	Southern pine	#3	7-11	11-8	14-10	17-6	20-11	6-10	10-1	12-10	15-2	18-1
	Spruce-pine-fir	SS	9-8	15-2	19-11	25-5	Note b	9-8	14-10	18-10	23-0	Note b
	Spruce-pine-fir	#1	9-5	14-4	18-2	22-3	25-9	8-6	12-5	15-9	19-3	22-4
	Spruce-pine-fir	#2	9-5	14-4	18-2	22-3	25-9	8-6	12-5	15-9	19-3	22-4
	Spruce-pine-fir	#3	7-5	10-10	13-9	16-9	19-6	6-5	9-5	11-11	14-6	16-10
19.2	Douglas fir-larch	SS	9-10	15-5	20-4	25-11	Note b	9-10	14-7	18-6	22-7	Note b
	Douglas fir-larch	#1	9-5	14-0	17-9	21-8	25-2	8-4	12-2	15-4	18-9	21-9
	Douglas fir-larch	#2	8-11	13-1	16-7	20-3	23-6	7-9	11-4	14-4	17-7	20-4
	Douglas fir-larch	#3	6-9	9-11	12-7	15-4	17-9	5-10	8-7	10-10	13-3	15-5
	Hem-fir	SS	9-3	14-7	19-2	24-6	Note b	9-3	14-4	18-2	22-3	25-9
	Hem-fir	#1	9-1	13-8	17-4	21-1	24-6	8-1	11-10	15-0	18-4	21-3
	Hem-fir	#2	8-8	12-11	16-4	20-0	23-2	7-8	11-2	14-2	17-4	20-1
	Hem-fir	#3	6-9	9-11	12-7	15-4	17-9	5-10	8-7	10-10	13-3	15-5
	Southern pine	SS	9-8	15-2	19-11	25-5	Note b	9-8	15-2	19-11	25-5	Note b
	Southern pine	#1	9-5	14-10	19-7	23-7	Note b	9-3	13-8	17-2	20-5	24-4
	Southern pine	#2	9-3	13-9	17-9	21-2	24-10	8-4	11-11	15-4	18-4	21-6
	Southern pine	#3	7-3	10-8	13-7	16-0	19-1	6-3	9-3	11-9	13-10	16-6
	Spruce-pine-fir	SS	9-1	14-3	18-9	23-11	Note b	9-1	13-7	17-2	21-0	24-4
	Spruce-pine-fir	#1	8-10	13-1	16-7	20-3	23-6	7-9	11-4	14-4	17-7	20-4
	Spruce-pine-fir	#2	8-10	13-1	16-7	20-3	23-6	7-9	11-4	14-4	17-7	20-4
	Spruce-pine-fir	#3	6-9	9-11	12-7	15-4	17-9	5-10	8-7	10-10	13-3	15-5

(continued)

TABLE R802.5.1(1)—continued
RAFTER SPANS FOR COMMON LUMBER SPECIES
(Roof live load=20 psf, ceiling not attached to rafters, L/Δ=180)

RAFTER SPACING (inches)	SPECIES AND GRADE		DEAD LOAD = 10 psf					DEAD LOAD = 20 psf				
			2x4	2x6	2x8	2x10	2x12	2x4	2x6	2x8	2x10	2x12
			Maximum rafter spans[a]									
			(feet - inches)	(feet - inches)	(feet - inches)	(feet - inches)	(feet - inches)	(feet - inches)	(feet - inches)	(feet - inches)	(feet - inches)	(feet - inches)
24	Douglas fir-larch	SS	9-1	14-4	18-10	23-4	23-4	8-11	13-1	16-7	20-3	23-5
	Douglas fir-larch	#1	8-7	12-6	15-10	19-5	19-5	7-5	10-10	13-9	16-9	19-6
	Douglas fir-larch	#2	8-0	11-9	14-10	18-2	18-2	6-11	10-2	12-10	15-8	18-3
	Douglas fir-larch	#3	6-1	8-10	11-3	13-8	13-8	5-3	7-8	9-9	11-10	13-9
	Hem-fir	SS	8-7	13-6	17-10	22-9	22-9	8-7	12-10	16-3	19-10	23-0
	Hem-fir	#1	8-4	12-3	15-6	18-11	18-11	7-3	10-7	13-5	16-4	19-0
	Hem-fir	#2	7-11	11-7	14-8	17-10	17-10	6-10	10-0	12-8	15-6	17-11
	Hem-fir	#3	6-1	8-10	11-3	13-8	13-8	5-3	7-8	9-9	11-10	13-9
	Southern pine	SS	8-11	14-1	18-6	23-8	23-8	8-11	14-1	18-6	22-11	Note b
	Southern pine	#1	8-9	13-9	17-9	21-1	21-1	8-3	12-3	15-4	18-3	21-9
	Southern pine	#2	8-7	12-3	15-10	18-11	18-11	7-5	10-8	13-9	16-5	19-3
	Southern pine	#3	6-5	9-6	12-1	14-4	14-4	5-7	8-3	10-6	12-5	14-9
	Spruce-pine-fir	SS	8-5	13-3	17-5	21-8	21-8	8-4	12-2	15-4	18-9	21-9
	Spruce-pine-fir	#1	8-0	11-9	14-10	18-2	18-2	6-11	10-2	12-10	15-8	18-3
	Spruce-pine-fir	#2	8-0	11-9	14-10	18-2	18-2	6-11	10-2	12-10	15-8	18-3
	Spruce-pine-fir	#3	6-1	8-10	11-3	13-8	13-8	5-3	7-8	9-9	11-10	13-9

Check sources for availability of lumber in lengths greater than 20 feet.

For SI: 1 inch = 25.4 mm, 1 foot = 304.8 mm, 1 pound per square foot = 0.0479 kN/m^2.

a. The tabulated rafter spans assume that ceiling joists are located at the bottom of the attic space or that some other method of resisting the outward push of the rafters on the bearing walls, such as rafter ties, is provided at that location. When ceiling joists or rafter ties are located higher in the attic space, the rafter spans shall be multiplied by the factors given below:

H_C/H_R	Rafter Span Adjustment Factor
2/3 or greater	0.50
1/2	0.58
1/3	0.67
1/4	0.76
1/5	0.83
1/6	0.90
1/7.5 and less	1.00

where: H_C = Height of ceiling joists or rafter ties measured vertically above the top of the rafter support walls.

H_R = Height of roof ridge measured vertically above the top of the rafter support walls.

b. Span exceeds 26 feet in length.

TABLE R802.5.1(2)
RAFTER SPANS FOR COMMON LUMBER SPECIES
(Roof live load=20 psf, ceiling attached to rafters, L/Δ=240)

RAFTER SPACING (inches)	SPECIES AND GRADE		DEAD LOAD = 10 psf					DEAD LOAD = 20 psf				
			2x4	2x6	2x8	2x10	2x12	2x4	2x6	2x8	2x10	2x12
			(feet-inches)	(feet-inches)	(feet-inches)	(feet-inches)	(feet-inches)	(feet-inches)	(feet-inches)	(feet-inches)	(feet-inches)	(feet-inches)
12	Douglas fir-larch	SS	10-5	16-4	21-7	Note b	Note b	10-5	16-4	21-7	Note b	Note b
	Douglas fir-larch	#1	10-0	15-9	20-10	Note b	Note b	10-0	15-4	19-5	23-9	Note b
	Douglas fir-larch	#2	9-10	15-6	20-5	25-8	Note b	9-10	14-4	18-2	22-3	25-9
	Douglas fir-larch	#3	8-7	12-6	15-10	19-5	22-6	7-5	10-10	13-9	16-9	19-6
	Hem-fir	SS	9-10	15-6	20 5	Note b	Note b	9-10	15-6	20-5	Note b	Note b
	Hem-fir	#1	9-8	15-2	19-11	25-5	Note b	9-8	14-11	18-11	23-2	Note b
	Hem-fir	#2	9-2	14-5	19-0	24-3	Note b	9-2	14-2	17-11	21-11	25-5
	Hem-fir	#3	8-7	12-6	15-10	19-5	22-6	7-5	10-10	13-9	16-9	19-6
	Southern pine	SS	10-3	16-1	21-2	Note b	Note b	10-3	16-1	21-2	Note b	Note b
	Southern pine	#1	10-0	15-9	20-10	Note b	Note b	10-0	15-9	20-10	25-10	Note b
	Southern pine	#2	9-10	15-6	20-5	Note b	Note b	9-10	15-1	19-5	23-2	Note b
	Southern pine	#3	9-1	13-6	17-2	20-3	24-1	7-11	11-8	14-10	17-6	20-11
	Spruce-pine-fir	SS	9-8	15-2	19-11	25-5	Note b	9-8	15-2	19-11	25-5	Note b
	Spruce-pine-fir	#1	9-5	14-9	19-6	24-10	Note b	9-5	14-4	18-2	22-3	25-9
	Spruce-pine-fir	#2	9-5	14-9	19-6	24-10	Note b	9-5	14-4	18-2	22-3	25-9
	Spruce-pine-fir	#3	8-7	12-6	15-10	19-5	22-6	7-5	10-10	13-9	16-9	19-6
16	Douglas fir-larch	SS	9-6	14-11	19-7	25-0	Note b	9-6	14-11	19-7	24-9	Note b
	Douglas fir-larch	#1	9-1	14-4	18-11	23-9	Note b	9-1	13-3	16-10	20-7	23-10
	Douglas fir-larch	#2	8-11	14-1	18-2	22-3	25-9	8-6	12-5	15-9	19-3	22-4
	Douglas fir-larch	#3	7-5	10-10	13-9	16-9	19-6	6-5	9-5	11-11	14-6	16-10
	Hem-fir	SS	8-11	14-1	18-6	23-8	Note b	8-11	14-1	18-6	23-8	Note b
	Hem-fir	#1	8-9	13-9	18-1	23-1	Note b	8-9	12-11	16-5	20-0	23-3
	Hem-fir	#2	8-4	13-1	17-3	21-11	25-5	8-4	12-3	15-6	18-11	22-0
	Hem-fir	#3	7-5	10-10	13-9	16-9	19-6	6-5	9-5	11-11	14-6	16-10
	Southern pine	SS	9-4	14-7	19-3	24-7	Note b	9-4	14-7	19-3	24-7	Note b
	Southern pine	#1	9-1	14-4	18-11	24-1	Note b	9-1	14-4	18-10	22-4	Note b
	Southern pine	#2	8-11	14-1	18-6	23-2	Note b	8-11	13-0	16-10	20-1	23-7
	Southern pine	#3	7-11	11-8	14-10	17-6	20-11	6-10	10-1	12-10	15-2	18-1
	Spruce-pine-fir	SS	8-9	13-9	18-1	23-1	Note b	8-9	13-9	18-1	23-0	Note b
	Spruce-pine-fir	#1	8-7	13-5	17-9	22-3	25-9	8-6	12-5	15-9	19-3	22-4
	Spruce-pine-fir	#2	8-7	13-5	17-9	22-3	25-9	8-6	12-5	15-9	19-3	22-4
	Spruce-pine-fir	#3	7-5	10-10	13-9	16-9	19-6	6-5	9-5	11-11	14-6	16-10
19.2	Douglas fir-larch	SS	8-11	14-0	18-5	23-7	Note b	8-11	14-0	18-5	22-7	Note b
	Douglas fir-larch	#1	8-7	13-6	17-9	21-8	25-2	8-4	12-2	15-4	18-9	21-9
	Douglas fir-larch	#2	8-5	13-1	16-7	20-3	23-6	7-9	11-4	14-4	17-7	20-4
	Douglas fir-larch	#3	6-9	9-11	12-7	15-4	17-9	5-10	8-7	10-10	13-3	15-5
	Hem-fir	SS	8-5	13-3	17-5	22-3	Note b	8-5	13-3	17-5	22-3	25-9
	Hem-fir	#1	8-3	12-11	17-1	21-1	24-6	8-1	11-10	15-0	18-4	21-3
	Hem-fir	#2	7-10	12-4	16-3	20-0	23-2	7-8	11-2	14-2	17-4	20-1
	Hem-fir	#3	6-9	9-11	12-7	15-4	17-9	5-10	8-7	10-10	13-3	15-5
	Southern pine	SS	8-9	13-9	18-1	23-1	Note b	8-9	13-9	18-1	23-1	Note b
	Southern pine	#1	8-7	13-6	17-9	22-8	Note b	8-7	13-6	17-2	20-5	24-4
	Southern pine	#2	8-5	13-3	17-5	21-2	24-10	8-4	11-11	15-4	18-4	21-6
	Southern pine	#3	7-3	10-8	13-7	16-0	19-1	6-3	9-3	11-9	13-10	16-6
	Spruce-pine-fir	SS	8-3	12-11	17-1	21-9	Note b	8-3	12-11	17-1	21-0	24-4
	Spruce-pine-fir	#1	8-1	12-8	16-7	20-3	23-6	7-9	11-4	14-4	17-7	20-4
	Spruce-pine-fir	#2	8-1	12-8	16-7	20-3	23-6	7-9	11-4	14-4	17-7	20-4
	Spruce-pine-fir	#3	6-9	9-11	12-7	15-4	17-9	5-10	8-7	10-10	13-3	15-5

(continued)

TABLE R802.5.1(2)—continued
RAFTER SPANS FOR COMMON LUMBER SPECIES
(Roof live load=20 psf, ceiling attached to rafters, L/Δ=240)

RAFTER SPACING (inches)	SPECIES AND GRADE		DEAD LOAD = 10 psf					DEAD LOAD = 20 psf				
			2x4	2x6	2x8	2x10	2x12	2x4	2x6	2x8	2x10	2x12
			Maximum rafter spans[a]									
			(feet - inches)	(feet - inches)	(feet - inches)	(feet - inches)	(feet - inches)	(feet - inches)	(feet - inches)	(feet - inches)	(feet - inches)	(feet - inches)
24	Douglas fir-larch	SS	8-3	13-0	17-2	21-10	Note b	8-3	13-0	16-7	20-3	23-5
	Douglas fir-larch	#1	8-0	12-6	15-10	19-5	22-6	7-5	10-10	13-9	16-9	19-6
	Douglas fir-larch	#2	7-10	11-9	14-10	18-2	21-0	6-11	10-2	12-10	15-8	18-3
	Douglas fir-larch	#3	6-1	8-10	11-3	13-8	15-11	5-3	7-8	9-9	11-10	13-9
	Hem-fir	SS	7-10	12-3	16-2	20-8	25-1	7-10	12-3	16-2	19-10	23-0
	Hem-fir	#1	7-8	12-0	15-6	18-11	21-11	7-3	10-7	13-5	16-4	19-0
	Hem-fir	#2	7-3	11-5	14-8	17-10	20-9	6-10	10-0	12-8	15-6	17-11
	Hem-fir	#3	6-1	8-10	11-3	13-8	15-11	5-3	7-8	9-9	11-10	13-9
	Southern pine	SS	8-1	12-9	16-10	21-6	Note b	8-1	12-9	16-10	21-6	Note b
	Southern pine	#1	8-0	12-6	16-6	21-1	25-2	8-0	12-3	15-4	18-3	21-9
	Southern pine	#2	7-10	12-3	15-10	18-11	22-2	7-5	10-8	13-9	16-5	19-3
	Southern pine	#3	6-5	9-6	12-1	14-4	17-1	5-7	8-3	10-6	12-5	14-9
	Spruce-pine-fir	SS	7-8	12-0	15-10	20-2	24-7	7-8	12-0	15-4	18-9	21-9
	Spruce-pine-fir	#1	7-6	11-9	14-10	18-2	21-0	6-11	10-2	12-10	15-8	18-3
	Spruce-pine-fir	#2	7-6	11-9	14-10	18-2	21-0	6-11	10-2	12-10	15-8	18-3
	Spruce-pine-fir	#3	6-1	8-10	11-3	13-8	15-11	5-3	7-8	9-9	11-10	13-9

Check sources for availability of lumber in lengths greater than 20 feet.

For SI: 1 inch = 25.4 mm, 1 foot = 304.8 mm, 1 pound per square foot = 0.0479 kN/m².

a. The tabulated rafter spans assume that ceiling joists are located at the bottom of the attic space or that some other method of resisting the outward push of the rafters on the bearing walls, such as rafter ties, is provided at that location. When ceiling joists or rafter ties are located higher in the attic space, the rafter spans shall be multiplied by the factors given below:

H_C/H_R	Rafter Span Adjustment Factor
2/3 or greater	0.50
1/2	0.58
1/3	0.67
1/4	0.76
1/5	0.83
1/6	0.90
1/7.5 and less	1.00

where: H_C = Height of ceiling joists or rafter ties measured vertically above the top of the rafter support walls.

H_R = Height of roof ridge measured vertically above the top of the rafter support walls.

b. Span exceeds 26 feet in length.

TABLE R802.5.1(3)
RAFTER SPANS FOR COMMON LUMBER SPECIES
(Ground snow load=30 psf, ceiling not attached to rafters, L/Δ=180)

RAFTER SPACING (inches)	SPECIES AND GRADE		DEAD LOAD = 10 psf					DEAD LOAD = 20 psf				
			2x4	2x6	2x8	2x10	2x12	2x4	2x6	2x8	2x10	2x12
			Maximum rafter spans[a]									
			(feet-inches)	(feet-inches)	(feet-inches)	(feet-inches)	(feet-inches)	(feet-inches)	(feet-inches)	(feet-inches)	(feet-inches)	(feet-inches)
12	Douglas fir-larch	SS	10-0	15-9	20-9	Note b	Note b	10-0	15-9	20-1	24-6	Note b
	Douglas fir-larch	#1	9-8	14-9	18-8	22-9	Note b	9-0	13-2	16-8	20-4	23-7
	Douglas fir-larch	#2	9-5	13-9	17-5	21-4	24-8	8-5	12-4	15-7	19-1	22-1
	Douglas fir-larch	#3	7-1	10-5	13-2	16-1	18-8	6-4	9-4	11-9	14-5	16-8
	Hem-fir	SS	9-6	14-10	19-7	25-0	Note b	9-6	14-10	19-7	24-1	Note b
	Hem-fir	#1	9-3	14-4	18-2	22-2	25-9	8-9	12-10	16-3	19-10	23-0
	Hem-fir	#2	8-10	13-7	17-2	21-0	24-4	8-4	12-2	15-4	18-9	21-9
	Hem-fir	#3	7-1	10-5	13-2	16-1	18-8	6-4	9-4	11-9	14-5	16-8
	Southern pine	SS	9-10	15-6	20-5	Note b	Note b	9-10	15-6	20-5	Note b	Note b
	Southern pine	#1	9-8	15-2	20-0	24-9	Note b	9-8	14-10	18-8	22-2	Note b
	Southern pine	#2	9-6	14-5	18-8	22-3	Note b	9-0	12-11	16-8	19-11	23-4
	Southern pine	#3	7-7	11-2	14-3	16-10	20-0	6-9	10-0	12-9	15-1	17-11
	Spruce-pine-fir	SS	9-3	14-7	19-2	24-6	Note b	9-3	14-7	18-8	22-9	Note b
	Spruce-pine-fir	#1	9-1	13-9	17-5	21-4	24-8	8-5	12-4	15-7	19-1	22-1
	Spruce-pine-fir	#2	9-1	13-9	17-5	21-4	24-8	8-5	12-4	15-7	19-1	22-1
	Spruce-pine-fir	#3	7-1	10-5	13-2	16-1	18-8	6-4	9-4	11-9	14-5	16-8
16	Douglas fir-larch	SS	9-1	14-4	18-10	23-9	Note b	9-1	13-9	17-5	21-3	24-8
	Douglas fir-larch	#1	8-9	12-9	16-2	19-9	22-10	7-10	11-5	14-5	17-8	20-5
	Douglas fir-larch	#2	8-2	11-11	15-1	18-5	21-5	7-3	10-8	13-6	16-6	19-2
	Douglas fir-larch	#3	6-2	9-0	11-5	13-11	16-2	5-6	8-1	10-3	12-6	14-6
	Hem-fir	SS	8-7	13-6	17-10	22-9	Note b	8-7	13-6	17-1	20-10	24-2
	Hem-fir	#1	8-5	12-5	15-9	19-3	22-3	7-7	11-1	14-1	17-2	19-11
	Hem-fir	#2	8-0	11-9	14-11	18-2	21-1	7-2	10-6	13-4	16-3	18-10
	Hem-fir	#3	6-2	9-0	11-5	13-11	16-2	5-6	8-1	10-3	12-6	14-6
	Southern pine	SS	8-11	14-1	18-6	23-8	Note b	8-11	14-1	18-6	23-8	Note b
	Southern pine	#1	8-9	13-9	18-1	21-5	25-7	8-8	12-10	16-2	19-2	22-10
	Southern pine	#2	8-7	12-6	16-2	19-3	22-7	7-10	11-2	14-5	17-3	20-2
	Southern pine	#3	6-7	9-8	12-4	14-7	17-4	5-10	8-8	11-0	13-0	15-6
	Spruce-pine-fir	SS	8-5	13-3	17-5	22-1	25-7	8-5	12-9	16-2	19-9	22-10
	Spruce-pine-fir	#1	8-2	11-11	15-1	18-5	21-5	7-3	10-8	13-6	16-6	19-2
	Spruce-pine-fir	#2	8-2	11-11	15-1	18-5	21-5	7-3	10-8	13-6	16-6	19-2
	Spruce-pine-fir	#3	6-2	9-0	11-5	13-11	16-2	5-6	8-1	10-3	12-6	14-6
19.2	Douglas fir-larch	SS	8-7	13-6	17-9	21-8	25-2	8-7	12-6	15-10	19-5	22-6
	Douglas fir-larch	#1	7-11	11-8	14-9	18-0	20-11	7-1	10-5	13-2	16-1	18-8
	Douglas fir-larch	#2	7-5	10-11	13-9	16-10	19-6	6-8	9-9	12-4	15-1	17-6
	Douglas fir-larch	#3	5-7	8-3	10-5	12-9	14-9	5-0	7-4	9-4	11-5	13-2
	Hem-fir	SS	8-1	12-9	16-9	21-4	24-8	8-1	12-4	15-7	19-1	22-1
	Hem-fir	#1	7-9	11-4	14-4	17-7	20-4	6-11	10-2	12-10	15-8	18-2
	Hem-fir	#2	7-4	10-9	13-7	16-7	19-3	6-7	9-7	12-2	14-10	17-3
	Hem-fir	#3	5-7	8-3	10-5	12-9	14-9	5-0	7-4	9-4	11-5	13-2
	Southern pine	SS	8-5	13-3	17-5	22-3	Note b	8-5	13-3	17-5	22-0	25-9
	Southern pine	#1	8-3	13-0	16-6	19-7	23-4	7-11	11-9	14-9	17-6	20-11
	Southern pine	#2	7-11	11-5	14-9	17-7	20-7	7-1	10-2	13-2	15-9	18-5
	Southern pine	#3	6-0	8-10	11-3	13-4	15-10	5-4	7-11	10-1	11-11	14-2
	Spruce-pine-fir	SS	7-11	12-5	16-5	20-2	23-4	7-11	11-8	14-9	18-0	20-11
	Spruce-pine-fir	#1	7-5	10-11	13-9	16-10	19-6	6-8	9-9	12-4	15-1	17-6
	Spruce-pine-fir	#2	7-5	10-11	13-9	16-10	19-6	6-8	9-9	12-4	15-1	17-6
	Spruce-pine-fir	#3	5-7	8-3	10-5	12-9	14-9	5-0	7-4	9-4	11-5	13-2

(continued)

TABLE R802.5.1(3)—continued
RAFTER SPANS FOR COMMON LUMBER SPECIES
(Ground snow load=30 psf, ceiling not attached to rafters, L/Δ=180)

RAFTER SPACING (inches)	SPECIES AND GRADE		DEAD LOAD = 10 psf					DEAD LOAD = 20 psf				
			2x4	2x6	2x8	2x10	2x12	2x4	2x6	2x8	2x10	2x12
			Maximum rafter spans[a]									
			(feet - inches)	(feet - inches)	(feet - inches)	(feet - inches)	(feet - inches)	(feet - inches)	(feet - inches)	(feet - inches)	(feet - inches)	(feet - inches)
24	Douglas fir-larch	SS	7-11	12-6	15-10	19-5	22-6	7-8	11-3	14-2	17-4	20-1
	Douglas fir-larch	#1	7-1	10-5	13-2	16-1	18-8	6-4	9-4	11-9	14-5	16-8
	Douglas fir-larch	#2	6-8	9-9	12-4	15-1	17-6	5-11	8-8	11-0	13-6	15-7
	Douglas fir-larch	#3	5-0	7-4	9-4	11-5	13-2	4-6	6-7	8-4	10-2	11-10
	Hem-fir	SS	7-6	11-10	15-7	19-1	22-1	7-6	11-0	13-11	17-0	19-9
	Hem-fir	#1	6-11	10-2	12-10	15-8	18-2	6-2	9-1	11-6	14-0	16-3
	Hem-fir	#2	6-7	9-7	12-2	14-10	17-3	5-10	8-7	10-10	13-3	15-5
	Hem-fir	#3	5-0	7-4	9-4	11-5	13-2	4-6	6-7	8-4	10-2	11-10
	Southern pine	SS	7-10	12-3	16-2	20-8	25-1	7-10	12-3	16-2	19-8	23-0
	Southern pine	#1	7-8	11-9	14-9	17-6	20-11	7-1	10-6	13-2	15-8	18-8
	Southern pine	#2	7-1	10-2	13-2	15-9	18-5	6-4	9-2	11-9	14-1	16-6
	Southern pine	#3	5-4	7-11	10-1	11-11	14-2	4-9	7-1	9-0	10-8	12-8
	Spruce-pine-fir	SS	7-4	11-7	14-9	18-0	20-11	7-1	10-5	13-2	16-1	18-8
	Spruce-pine-fir	#1	6-8	9-9	12-4	15-1	17-6	5-11	8-8	11-0	13-6	15-7
	Spruce-pine-fir	#2	6-8	9-9	12-4	15-1	17-6	5-11	8-8	11-0	13-6	15-7
	Spruce-pine-fir	#3	5-0	7-4	9-4	11-5	13-2	4-6	6-7	8-4	10-2	11-10

Check sources for availability of lumber in lengths greater than 20 feet.

For SI: 1 inch = 25.4 mm, 1 foot = 304.8 mm, 1 pound per square foot = 0.0479 kN/m^2.

a. The tabulated rafter spans assume that ceiling joists are located at the bottom of the attic space or that some other method of resisting the outward push of the rafters on the bearing walls, such as rafter ties, is provided at that location. When ceiling joists or rafter ties are located higher in the attic space, the rafter spans shall be multiplied by the factors given below:

H_C/H_R	Rafter Span Adjustment Factor
2/3 or greater	0.50
1/2	0.58
1/3	0.67
1/4	0.76
1/5	0.83
1/6	0.90
1/7.5 and less	1.00

where: H_C = Height of ceiling joists or rafter ties measured vertically above the top of the rafter support walls.

   H_R = Height of roof ridge measured vertically above the top of the rafter support walls.

b. Span exceeds 26 feet in length.

TABLE R802.5.1(4)
RAFTER SPANS FOR COMMON LUMBER SPECIES
(Ground snow load=50 psf, ceiling not attached to rafters, L/Δ=180)

RAFTER SPACING (inches)	SPECIES AND GRADE		DEAD LOAD = 10 psf					DEAD LOAD = 20 psf				
			2x4	2x6	2x8	2x10	2x12	2x4	2x6	2x8	2x10	2x12
			Maximum rafter spans[a]									
			(feet - inches)	(feet - inches)	(feet - inches)	(feet - inches)	(feet - inches)	(feet - inches)	(feet - inches)	(feet - inches)	(feet - inches)	(feet - inches)
12	Douglas fir-larch	SS	8-5	13-3	17-6	22-4	26-0	8-5	13-3	17-0	20-9	24-0
	Douglas fir-larch	#1	8-2	12-0	15-3	18-7	21-7	7-7	11-2	14-1	17-3	20-0
	Douglas fir-larch	#2	7-8	11-3	14-3	17-5	20-2	7-1	10-5	13-2	16-1	18-8
	Douglas fir-larch	#3	5-10	8-6	10-9	13-2	15-3	5-5	7-10	10-0	12-2	14-1
	Hem-fir	SS	8-0	12-6	16-6	21-1	25-6	8-0	12-6	16-6	20-4	23-7
	Hem-fir	#1	7-10	11-9	14-10	18-1	21-0	7-5	10-10	13-9	16-9	19-5
	Hem-fir	#2	7-5	11-1	14-0	17-2	19-11	7-0	10-3	13-0	15-10	18-5
	Hem-fir	#3	5-10	8-6	10-9	13-2	15-3	5-5	7-10	10-0	12-2	14-1
	Southern pine	SS	8-4	13-0	17-2	21-11	Note b	8-4	13-0	17-2	21-11	Note b
	Southern pine	#1	8-2	12-10	16-10	20-3	24-1	8-2	12-6	15-9	18-9	22-4
	Southern pine	#2	8-0	11-9	15-3	18-2	21-3	7-7	10-11	14-1	16-10	19-9
	Southern pine	#3	6-2	9-2	11-8	13-9	16-4	5-9	8-5	10-9	12-9	15-2
	Spruce-pine-fir	SS	7-10	12-3	16-2	20-8	24-1	7-10	12-3	15-9	19-3	22-4
	Spruce-pine-fir	#1	7-8	11-3	14-3	17-5	20-2	7-1	10-5	13-2	16-1	18-8
	Spruce-pine-fir	#2	7-8	11-3	14-3	17-5	20-2	7-1	10-5	13-2	16-1	18-8
	Spruce-pine-fir	#3	5-10	8-6	10-9	13-2	15-3	5-5	7-10	10-0	12-2	14-1
16	Douglas fir-larch	SS	7-8	12-1	15-10	19-5	22-6	7-8	11-7	14-8	17-11	20-10
	Douglas fir-larch	#1	7-1	10-5	13-2	16-1	18-8	6-7	9-8	12-2	14-11	17-3
	Douglas fir-larch	#2	6-8	9-9	12-4	15-1	17-6	6-2	9-0	11-5	13-11	16-2
	Douglas fir-larch	#3	5-0	7-4	9-4	11-5	13-2	4-8	6-10	8-8	10-6	12-3
	Hem-fir	SS	7-3	11-5	15-0	19-1	22-1	7-3	11-5	14-5	17-8	20-5
	Hem-fir	#1	6-11	10-2	12-10	15-8	18-2	6-5	9-5	11-11	14-6	16-10
	Hem-fir	#2	6-7	9-7	12-2	14-10	17-3	6-1	8-11	11-3	13-9	15-11
	Hem-fir	#3	5-0	7-4	9-4	11-5	13-2	4-8	6-10	8-8	10-6	12-3
	Southern pine	SS	7-6	11-10	15-7	19-11	24-3	7-6	11-10	15-7	19-11	23-10
	Southern pine	#1	7-5	11-7	14-9	17-6	20-11	7-4	10-10	13-8	16-2	19-4
	Southern pine	#2	7-1	10-2	13-2	15-9	18-5	6-7	9-5	12-2	14-7	17-1
	Southern pine	#3	5-4	7-11	10-1	11-11	14-2	4-11	7-4	9-4	11-0	13-1
	Spruce-pine-fir	SS	7-1	11-2	14-8	18-0	20-11	7-1	10-9	13-8	15-11	19-4
	Spruce-pine-fir	#1	6-8	9-9	12-4	15-1	17-6	6-2	9-0	11-5	13-11	16-2
	Spruce-pine-fir	#2	6-8	9-9	12-4	15-1	17-6	6-2	9-0	11-5	13-11	16-2
	Spruce-pine-fir	#3	5-0	7-4	9-4	11-5	13-2	4-8	6-10	8-8	10-6	12-3
19.2	Douglas fir-larch	SS	7-3	11-4	14-6	17-8	20-6	7-3	10-7	13-5	16-5	19-0
	Douglas fir-larch	#1	6-6	9-6	12-0	14-8	17-1	6-0	8-10	11-2	13-7	15-9
	Douglas fir-larch	#2	6-1	8-11	11-3	13-9	15-11	5-7	8-3	10-5	12-9	14-9
	Douglas fir-larch	#3	4-7	6-9	8-6	10-5	12-1	4-3	6-3	7-11	9-7	11-2
	Hem-fir	SS	6-10	10-9	14-2	17-5	20-2	6-10	10-5	13-2	16-1	18-8
	Hem-fir	#1	6-4	9-3	11-9	14-4	16-7	5-10	8-7	10-10	13-3	15-5
	Hem-fir	#2	6-0	8-9	11-1	13-7	15-9	5-7	8-1	10-3	12-7	14-7
	Hem-fir	#3	4-7	6-9	8-6	10-5	12-1	4-3	6-3	7-11	9-7	11-2
	Southern pine	SS	7-1	11-2	14-8	18-9	22-10	7-1	11-2	14-8	18-7	21-9
	Southern pine	#1	7-0	10-8	13-5	16-0	19-1	6-8	9-11	12-5	14-10	17-8
	Southern pine	#2	6-6	9-4	12-0	14-4	16-10	6-0	8-8	11-2	13-4	15-7
	Southern pine	#3	4-11	7-3	9-2	10-10	12-11	4-6	6-8	8-6	10-1	12-0
	Spruce-pine-fir	SS	6-8	10-6	13-5	16-5	19-1	6-8	9-10	12-5	15-3	17-8
	Spruce-pine-fir	#1	6-1	8-11	11-3	13-9	15-11	5-7	8-3	10-5	12-9	14-9
	Spruce-pine-fir	#2	6-1	8-11	11-3	13-9	15-11	5-7	8-3	10-5	12-9	14-9
	Spruce-pine-fir	#3	4-7	6-9	8-6	10-5	12-1	4-3	6-3	7-11	9-7	11-2

(continued)

TABLE R802.5.1(4)—continued
RAFTER SPANS FOR COMMON LUMBER SPECIES
(Ground snow load=50 psf, ceiling not attached to rafters, L/Δ=180)

RAFTER SPACING (inches)	SPECIES AND GRADE		DEAD LOAD = 10 psf					DEAD LOAD = 20 psf				
			2x4	2x6	2x8	2x10	2x12	2x4	2x6	2x8	2x10	2x12
			Maximum rafter spans[a]									
			(feet - inches)	(feet - inches)	(feet - inches)	(feet - inches)	(feet - inches)	(feet - inches)	(feet - inches)	(feet - inches)	(feet - inches)	(feet - Inches)
24	Douglas fir-larch	SS	6- 8	10- 3	13- 0	15-10	18- 4	6- 6	9- 6	12- 0	14- 8	17- 0
	Douglas fir-larch	#1	5-10	8- 6	10- 9	13- 2	15- 3	5- 5	7-10	10- 0	12- 2	14- 1
	Douglas fir-larch	#2	5- 5	7-11	10- 1	12- 4	14- 3	5- 0	7- 4	9- 4	11- 5	13- 2
	Douglas fir-larch	#3	4- 1	6- 0	7- 7	9- 4	10- 9	3-10	5- 7	7- 1	8- 7	10- 0
	Hem-fir	SS	6- 4	9-11	12- 9	15- 7	18- 0	6- 4	9- 4	11- 9	14- 5	16- 8
	Hem-fir	#1	5- 8	8- 3	10- 6	12-10	14-10	5- 3	7- 8	9- 9	11-10	13- 9
	Hem-fir	#2	5- 4	7-10	9-11	12- 1	14- 1	4-11	7- 3	9- 2	11- 3	13- 0
	Hem-fir	#3	4- 1	6- 0	7- 7	9- 4	10- 9	3-10	5- 7	7- 1	8- 7	10- 0
	Southern pine	SS	6- 7	10- 4	13- 8	17- 5	21- 0	6- 7	10- 4	13- 8	16- 7	19- 5
	Southern pine	#1	6- 5	9- 7	12- 0	14- 4	17- 1	6- 0	8-10	11- 2	13- 3	15- 9
	Southern pine	#2	5-10	8- 4	10- 9	12-10	15- 1	5- 5	7- 9	10- 0	11-11	13-11
	Southern pine	#3	4- 4	6- 5	8- 3	9- 9	11- 7	4- 1	6- 0	7- 7	9- 0	10- 8
	Spruce-pine-fir	SS	6- 2	9- 6	12- 0	14- 8	17- 1	6- 0	8-10	11- 2	13- 7	15- 9
	Spruce-pine-fir	#1	5- 5	7-11	10- 1	12- 4	14- 3	5- 0	7- 4	9- 4	11- 5	13- 2
	Spruce-pine-fir	#2	5- 5	7-11	10- 1	12- 4	14- 3	5- 0	7- 4	9- 4	11- 5	13- 2
	Spruce-pine-fir	#3	4- 1	6- 0	7- 7	9- 4	10- 9	3-10	5- 7	7- 1	8- 7	10- 0

Check sources for availability of lumber in lengths greater than 20 feet.

For SI: 1 inch = 25.4 mm, 1 foot = 304.8 mm, 1 pound per square foot = 0.0479 kN/m^2.

a. The tabulated rafter spans assume that ceiling joists are located at the bottom of the attic space or that some other method of resisting the outward push of the rafters on the bearing walls, such as rafter ties, is provided at that location. When ceiling joists or rafter ties are located higher in the attic space, the rafter spans shall be multiplied by the factors given below:

H_C/H_R	Rafter Span Adjustment Factor
2/3 or greater	0.50
1/2	0.58
1/3	0.67
1/4	0.76
1/5	0.83
1/6	0.90
1/7.5 and less	1.00

where: H_C = Height of ceiling joists or rafter ties measured vertically above the top of the rafter support walls.

H_R = Height of roof ridge measured vertically above the top of the rafter support walls.

b. Span exceeds 26 feet in length.

TABLE R802.5.1(5)
RAFTER SPANS FOR COMMON LUMBER SPECIES
(Ground snow load=30 psf, ceiling attached to rafters, L/Δ=240)

RAFTER SPACING (inches)	SPECIES AND GRADE		DEAD LOAD = 10 psf					DEAD LOAD = 20 psf				
			2x4	2x6	2x8	2x10	2x12	2x4	2x6	2x8	2x10	2x12
			Maximum rafter spans[a]									
			(feet-inches)	(feet-inches)	(feet-inches)	(feet-inches)	(feet-inches)	(feet-inches)	(feet-inches)	(feet-inches)	(feet-inches)	(feet-inches)
12	Douglas fir-larch	SS	9-1	14-4	18-10	24-1	Note b	9-1	14-4	18-10	24-1	Note b
	Douglas fir-larch	#1	8-9	13-9	18-2	22-9	Note b	8-9	13-2	16-8	20-4	23-7
	Douglas fir-larch	#2	8-7	13-6	17-5	21-4	24-8	8-5	12-4	15-7	19-1	22-1
	Douglas fir-larch	#3	7-1	10-5	13-2	16-1	18-8	6-4	9-4	11-9	14-5	16-8
	Hem-fir	SS	8-7	13-6	17-10	22-9	Note b	8-7	13-6	17-10	22-9	Note b
	Hem-fir	#1	8-5	13-3	17-5	22-2	25-9	8-5	12-10	16-3	19-10	23-0
	Hem-fir	#2	8-0	12-7	16-7	21-0	24-4	8-0	12-2	15-4	18-9	21-9
	Hem-fir	#3	7-1	10-5	13-2	16-1	18-8	6-4	9-4	11-9	14-5	16-8
	Southern pine	SS	8-11	14-1	18-6	23-8	Note b	8-11	14-1	18-6	23-8	Note b
	Southern pine	#1	8-9	13-9	18-2	23-2	Note b	8-9	13-9	18-2	22-2	Note b
	Southern pine	#2	8-7	13-6	17-10	22-3	Note b	8-7	12-11	16-8	19-11	23-4
	Southern pine	#3	7-7	11-2	14-3	16-10	20-0	6-9	10-0	12-9	15-1	17-11
	Spruce-pine-fir	SS	8-5	13-3	17-5	22-3	Note b	8-5	13-3	17-5	22-3	Note b
	Spruce-pine-fir	#1	8-3	12-11	17-0	21-4	24-8	8-3	12-4	15-7	19-1	22-1
	Spruce-pine-fir	#2	8-3	12-11	17-0	21-4	24-8	8-3	12-4	15-7	19-1	22-1
	Spruce-pine-fir	#3	7-1	10-5	13-2	16-1	18-8	6-4	9-4	11-9	14-5	16-8
16	Douglas fir-larch	SS	8-3	13-0	17-2	21-10	Note b	8-3	13-0	17-2	21-3	24-8
	Douglas fir-larch	#1	8-0	12-6	16-2	19-9	22-10	7-10	11-5	14-5	17-8	20-5
	Douglas fir-larch	#2	7-10	11-11	15-1	18-5	21-5	7-3	10-8	13-6	16-6	19-2
	Douglas fir-larch	#3	6-2	9-0	11-5	13-11	16-2	5-6	8-1	10-3	12-6	14-6
	Hem-fir	SS	7-10	12-3	16-2	20-8	25-1	7-10	12-3	16-2	20-8	24-2
	Hem-fir	#1	7-8	12-0	15-9	19-3	22-3	7-7	11-1	14-1	17-2	19-11
	Hem-fir	#2	7-3	11-5	14-11	18-2	21-1	7-2	10-6	13-4	16-3	18-10
	Hem-fir	#3	6-2	9-0	11-5	13-11	16-2	5-6	8-1	10-3	12-6	14-6
	Southern pine	SS	8-1	12-9	16-10	21-6	Note b	8-1	12-9	16-10	21-6	Note b
	Southern pine	#1	8-0	12-6	16-6	21-1	25-7	8-0	12-6	16-2	19-2	22-10
	Southern pine	#2	7-10	12-3	16-2	19-3	22-7	7-10	11-2	14-5	17-3	20-2
	Southern pine	#3	6-7	9-8	12-4	14-7	17-4	5-10	8-8	11-0	13-0	15-6
	Spruce-pine-fir	SS	7-8	12-0	15-10	20-2	24-7	7-8	12-0	15-10	19-9	22-10
	Spruce-pine-fir	#1	7-6	11-9	15-1	18-5	21-5	7-3	10-8	13-6	16-6	19-2
	Spruce-pine-fir	#2	7-6	11-9	15-1	18-5	21-5	7-3	10-8	13-6	16-6	19-2
	Spruce-pine-fir	#3	6-2	9-0	11-5	13-11	16-2	5-6	8-1	10-3	12-6	14-6
19.2	Douglas fir-larch	SS	7-9	12-3	16-1	20-7	25-0	7-9	12-3	15-10	19-5	22-6
	Douglas fir-larch	#1	7-6	11-8	14-9	18-0	20-11	7-1	10-5	13-2	16-1	18-8
	Douglas fir-larch	#2	7-4	10-11	13-9	16-10	19-6	6-8	9-9	12-4	15-1	17-6
	Douglas fir-larch	#3	5-7	8-3	10-5	12-9	14-9	5-0	7-4	9-4	11-5	13-2
	Hem-fir	SS	7-4	11-7	15-3	19-5	23-7	7-4	11-7	15-3	19-1	22-1
	Hem-fir	#1	7-2	11-4	14-4	17-7	20-4	6-11	10-2	12-10	15-8	18-2
	Hem-fir	#2	6-10	10-9	13-7	16-7	19-3	6-7	9-7	12-2	14-10	17-3
	Hem-fir	#3	5-7	8-3	10-5	12-9	14-9	5-0	7-4	9-4	11-5	13-2
	Southern pine	SS	7-8	12-0	15-10	20-2	24-7	7-8	12-0	15-10	20-2	24-7
	Southern pine	#1	7-6	11-9	15-6	19-7	23-4	7-6	11-9	14-9	17-6	20-11
	Southern pine	#2	7-4	11-5	14-9	17-7	20-7	7-1	10-2	13-2	15-9	18-5
	Southern pine	#3	6-0	8-10	11-3	13-4	15-10	5-4	7-11	10-1	11-11	14-2
	Spruce-pine-fir	SS	7-2	11-4	14-11	19-0	23-1	7-2	11-4	14-9	18-0	20-11
	Spruce-pine-fir	#1	7-0	10-11	13-9	16-10	19-6	6-8	9-9	12-4	15-1	17-6
	Spruce-pine-fir	#2	7-0	10-11	13-9	16-10	19-6	6-8	9-9	12-4	15-1	17-6
	Spruce-pine-fir	#3	5-7	8-3	10-5	12-9	14-9	5-0	7-4	9-4	11-5	13-2

(continued)

TABLE R802.5.1(5)—continued
RAFTER SPANS FOR COMMON LUMBER SPECIES
(Ground snow load=30 psf, ceiling attached to rafters, L/Δ=240)

RAFTER SPACING (inches)	SPECIES AND GRADE		DEAD LOAD = 10 psf					DEAD LOAD = 20 psf				
			2x4	2x6	2x8	2x10	2x12	2x4	2x6	2x8	2x10	2x12
			Maximum rafter spans[a]									
			(feet - inches)	(feet - inches)	(feet - inches)	(feet - inches)	(feet - inches)	(feet - inches)	(feet - inches)	(feet - inches)	(feet - inches)	(feet - inches)
24	Douglas fir-larch	SS	7- 3	11- 4	15- 0	19- 1	22- 6	7- 3	11- 3	14- 2	17- 4	20- 1
	Douglas fir-larch	#1	7- 0	10- 5	13- 2	16- 1	18- 8	6- 4	9- 4	11- 9	14- 5	16- 8
	Douglas fir-larch	#2	6- 8	9- 9	12- 4	15- 1	17- 6	5- 11	8- 8	11- 0	13- 6	15- 7
	Douglas fir-larch	#3	5- 0	7- 4	9- 4	11- 5	13- 2	4- 6	6- 7	8- 4	10- 2	11-10
	Hem-fir	SS	6-10	10- 9	14- 2	18- 0	21-11	6-10	10- 9	13-11	17- 0	19- 9
	Hem-fir	#1	6- 8	10- 2	12-10	15- 8	18- 2	6- 2	9- 1	11- 6	14- 0	16- 3
	Hem-fir	#2	6- 4	9- 7	12- 2	14-10	17- 3	5-10	8- 7	10-10	13- 3	15- 5
	Hem-fir	#3	5- 0	7- 4	9- 4	11- 5	13- 2	4- 6	6- 7	8- 4	10- 2	11-10
	Southern pine	SS	7- 1	11- 2	14- 8	18- 9	22-10	7- 1	11- 2	14- 8	18- 9	22-10
	Southern pine	#1	7- 0	10-11	14- 5	17- 6	20-11	7- 0	10- 6	13- 2	15- 8	18- 8
	Southern pine	#2	6-10	10- 2	13- 2	15- 9	18- 5	6- 4	9- 2	11- 9	14- 1	16- 6
	Southern pine	#3	5- 4	7-11	10- 1	11-11	14- 2	4- 9	7- 1	9- 0	10- 8	12- 8
	Spruce-pine-fir	SS	6- 8	10- 6	13-10	17- 8	20-11	6- 8	10- 5	13- 2	16- 1	18- 8
	Spruce-pine-fir	#1	6- 6	9- 9	12- 4	15- 1	17- 6	5-11	8- 8	11- 0	13- 6	15- 7
	Spruce-pine-fir	#2	6- 6	9- 9	12- 4	15- 1	17- 6	5-11	8- 8	11- 0	13- 6	15- 7
	Spruce-pine-fir	#3	5- 0	7- 4	9- 4	11- 5	13- 2	4- 6	6- 7	8- 4	10- 2	11-10

Check sources for availability of lumber in lengths greater than 20 feet.

For SI: 1 inch = 25.4 mm, 1 foot = 304.8 mm, 1 pound per square foot = 0.0479 kN/m².

a. The tabulated rafter spans assume that ceiling joists are located at the bottom of the attic space or that some other method of resisting the outward push of the rafters on the bearing walls, such as rafter ties, is provided at that location. When ceiling joists or rafter ties are located higher in the attic space, the rafter spans shall be multiplied by the factors given below:

H_C/H_R	Rafter Span Adjustment Factor
2/3 or greater	0.50
1/2	0.58
1/3	0.67
1/4	0.76
1/5	0.83
1/6	0.90
1/7.5 and less	1.00

where: H_C = Height of ceiling joists or rafter ties measured vertically above the top of the rafter support walls.

H_R = Height of roof ridge measured vertically above the top of the rafter support walls.

b. Span exceeds 26 feet in length.

TABLE R802.5.1(6)
RAFTER SPANS FOR COMMON LUMBER SPECIES
(Ground snow load=50 psf, ceiling attached to rafters, L/Δ=240)

RAFTER SPACING (inches)	SPECIES AND GRADE		DEAD LOAD = 10 psf					DEAD LOAD = 20 psf				
			2x4	2x6	2x8	2x10	2x12	2x4	2x6	2x8	2x10	2x12
			Maximum rafter spans[a]									
			(feet - inches)	(feet - inches)	(feet - inches)	(feet - inches)	(feet - inches)	(feet - inches)	(feet - inches)	(feet - inches)	(feet - inches)	(feet - inches)
12	Douglas fir-larch	SS	7- 8	12- 1	15-11	20- 3	24- 8	7- 8	12- 1	15-11	20- 3	24- 0
	Douglas fir-larch	#1	7- 5	11- 7	15- 3	18- 7	21- 7	7- 5	11- 2	14- 1	17- 3	20- 0
	Douglas fir-larch	#2	7- 3	11- 3	14- 3	17- 5	20- 2	7- 1	10- 5	13- 2	16- 1	18- 8
	Douglas fir-larch	#3	5-10	8- 6	10- 9	13- 2	15- 3	5- 5	7-10	10- 0	12- 2	14- 1
	Hem-fir	SS	7- 3	11- 5	15- 0	19- 2	23- 4	7- 3	11- 5	15- 0	19- 2	23- 4
	Hem-fir	#1	7- 1	11- 2	14- 8	18- 1	21- 0	7- 1	10-10	13- 9	16- 9	19- 5
	Hem-fir	#2	6- 9	10- 8	14- 0	17- 2	19-11	6- 9	10- 3	13- 0	15-10	18- 5
	Hem-fir	#3	5-10	8- 6	10- 9	13- 2	15- 3	5- 5	7-10	10- 0	12- 2	14- 1
	Southern pine	SS	7- 6	11-10	15- 7	19-11	24- 3	7- 6	11-10	15- 7	19-11	24- 3
	Southern pine	#1	7- 5	11- 7	15- 4	19- 7	23- 9	7- 5	11- 7	15- 4	18- 9	22- 4
	Southern pine	#2	7- 3	11- 5	15- 0	18- 2	21- 3	7- 3	10-11	14- 1	16-10	19- 9
	Southern pine	#3	6- 2	9- 2	11- 8	13- 9	16- 4	5- 9	8- 5	10- 9	12- 9	15- 2
	Spruce-pine-fir	SS	7- 1	11- 2	14- 8	18- 9	22-10	7- 1	11- 2	14- 8	18- 9	22- 4
	Spruce-pine-fir	#1	6-11	10-11	14- 3	17- 5	20- 2	6-11	10- 5	13- 2	16- 1	18- 8
	Spruce-pine-fir	#2	6-11	10-11	14- 3	17- 5	20- 2	6-11	10- 5	13- 2	16- 1	18- 8
	Spruce-pine-fir	#3	5-10	8- 6	10- 9	13- 2	15- 3	5- 5	7-10	10- 0	12- 2	14- 1
16	Douglas fir-larch	SS	7- 0	11- 0	14- 5	18- 5	22- 5	7- 0	11- 0	14- 5	17-11	20-10
	Douglas fir-larch	#1	6- 9	10- 5	13- 2	16- 1	18- 8	6- 7	9- 8	12- 2	14-11	17- 3
	Douglas fir-larch	#2	6- 7	9- 9	12- 4	15- 1	17- 6	6- 2	9- 0	11- 5	13-11	16- 2
	Douglas fir-larch	#3	5- 0	7- 4	9- 4	11- 5	13- 2	4- 8	6-10	8- 8	10- 6	12- 3
	Hem-fir	SS	6- 7	10- 4	13- 8	17- 5	21- 2	6- 7	10- 4	13- 8	17- 5	20- 5
	Hem-fir	#1	6- 5	10- 2	12-10	15- 8	18- 2	6- 5	9- 5	11-11	14- 6	16-10
	Hem-fir	#2	6- 2	9- 7	12- 2	14-10	17- 3	6- 1	8-11	11- 3	13- 9	15-11
	Hem-fir	#3	5- 0	7- 4	9- 4	11- 5	13- 2	4- 8	6-10	8- 8	10- 6	12- 3
	Southern pine	SS	6-10	10- 9	14- 2	18- 1	22- 0	6-10	10- 9	14- 2	18- 1	22- 0
	Southern pine	#1	6- 9	10- 7	13-11	17- 6	20-11	6- 9	10- 7	13- 8	16- 2	19- 4
	Southern pine	#2	6- 7	10- 2	13- 2	15- 9	18- 5	6- 7	9- 5	12- 2	14- 7	17- 1
	Southern pine	#3	5- 4	7-11	10- 1	11-11	14- 2	4-11	7- 4	9- 4	11- 0	13- 1
	Spruce-pine-fir	SS	6- 5	10- 2	13- 4	17- 0	20- 9	6- 5	10- 2	13- 4	16- 8	19- 4
	Spruce-pine-fir	#1	6- 4	9- 9	12- 4	15- 1	17- 6	6- 2	9- 0	11- 5	13-11	16- 2
	Spruce-pine-fir	#2	6- 4	9- 9	12- 4	15- 1	17- 6	6- 2	9- 0	11- 5	13-11	16- 2
	Spruce-pine-fir	#3	5- 0	7- 4	9- 4	11- 5	13- 2	4- 8	6-10	8- 8	10- 6	12- 3
19.2	Douglas fir-larch	SS	6- 7	10- 4	13- 7	17- 4	20- 6	6- 7	10- 4	13- 5	16- 5	19- 0
	Douglas fir-larch	#1	6- 4	9- 6	12- 0	14- 8	17- 1	6- 0	8-10	11- 2	13- 7	15- 9
	Douglas fir-larch	#2	6- 1	8-11	11- 3	13- 9	15-11	5- 7	8- 3	10- 5	12- 9	14- 9
	Douglas fir-larch	#3	4- 7	6- 9	8- 6	10- 5	12- 1	4- 3	6- 3	7-11	9- 7	11- 2
	Hem-fir	SS	6- 2	9- 9	12-10	16- 5	19-11	6- 2	9- 9	12-10	16- 1	18- 8
	Hem-fir	#1	6- 1	9- 3	11- 9	14- 4	16- 7	5-10	8- 7	10-10	13- 3	15- 5
	Hem-fir	#2	5- 9	8- 9	11- 1	13- 7	15- 9	5- 7	8- 1	10- 3	12- 7	14- 7
	Hem-fir	#3	4- 7	6- 9	8- 6	10- 5	12- 1	4- 3	6- 3	7-11	9- 7	11- 2
	Southern pine	SS	6- 5	10- 2	13- 4	17- 0	20- 9	6- 5	10- 2	13- 4	17- 0	20- 9
	Southern pine	#1	6- 4	9-11	13- 1	16- 0	19- 1	6- 4	9-11	12- 5	14-10	17- 8
	Southern pine	#2	6- 2	9- 4	12- 0	14- 4	16-10	6- 0	8- 8	11- 2	13- 4	15- 7
	Southern pine	#3	4-11	7- 3	9- 2	10-10	12-11	4- 6	6- 8	8- 6	10- 1	12- 0
	Spruce-pine-fir	SS	6- 1	9- 6	12- 7	16- 0	19- 1	6- 1	9- 6	12- 5	15- 3	17- 8
	Spruce-pine-fir	#1	5-11	8-11	11- 3	13- 9	15-11	5- 7	8- 3	10- 5	12- 9	14- 9
	Spruce-pine-fir	#2	5-11	8-11	11-3	13- 9	15-11	5- 7	8- 3	10-5	12-9	14-9
	Spruce-pine-fir	#3	4- 7	6- 9	8- 6	10- 5	12- 1	4-3	6-3	7-11	9- 7	11- 2

(continued)

TABLE R802.5.1(6)—continued
RAFTER SPANS FOR COMMON LUMBER SPECIES
(Ground snow load=50 psf, ceiling attached to rafters, L/Δ=240)

RAFTER SPACING (inches)	SPECIE AND GRADE		DEAD LOAD = 10 psf					DEAD LOAD = 20 psf				
			2x4	2x6	2x8	2x10	2x12	2x4	2x6	2x8	2x10	2x12
			Maximum rafter spans[a]									
			(feet - inches)	(feet - inches)	(feet - inches)	(feet - inches)	(feet - inches)	(feet - inches)	(feet - inches)	(feet - inches)	(feet - inches)	(feet - inches)
24	Douglas fir-larch	SS	6- 1	9- 7	12- 7	15-10	18- 4	6- 1	9- 6	12- 0	14- 8	17- 0
	Douglas fir-larch	#1	5-10	8- 6	10- 9	13- 2	15- 3	5- 5	7-10	10- 0	12- 2	14- 1
	Douglas fir-larch	#2	5- 5	7-11	10- 1	12- 4	14- 3	5- 0	7- 4	9- 4	11- 5	13- 2
	Douglas fir-larch	#3	4- 1	6- 0	7- 7	9- 4	10- 9	3-10	5- 7	7- 1	8- 7	10- 0
	Hem-fir	SS	5- 9	9- 1	11-11	15- 2	18- 0	5- 9	9- 1	11- 9	14- 5	15-11
	Hem-fir	#1	5- 8	8- 3	10- 6	12-10	14-10	5- 3	7- 8	9- 9	11-10	13- 9
	Hem-fir	#2	5- 4	7-10	9-11	12- 1	14- 1	4-11	7- 3	9- 2	11- 3	13- 0
	Hem-fir	#3	4- 1	6- 0	7- 7	9- 4	10- 9	3-10	5- 7	7- 1	8- 7	10- 0
	Southern pine	SS	6- 0	9- 5	12- 5	15-10	19- 3	6- 0	9- 5	12- 5	15-10	19- 3
	Southern pine	#1	5-10	9- 3	12- 0	14- 4	17- 1	5-10	8-10	11- 2	13- 3	15- 9
	Southern pine	#2	5- 9	8- 4	10- 9	12-10	15- 1	5- 5	7- 9	10- 0	11-11	13-11
	Southern pine	#3	4- 4	6- 5	8- 3	9- 9	11- 7	4- 1	6- 0	7- 7	9- 0	10- 8
	Spruce-pine-fir	SS	5- 8	8-10	11- 8	14- 8	17- 1	5- 8	8-10	11- 2	13- 7	15- 9
	Spruce-pine-fir	#1	5- 5	7-11	10- 1	12- 4	14- 3	5- 0	7- 4	9- 4	11- 5	13- 2
	Spruce-pine-fir	#2	5- 5	7-11	10- 1	12- 4	14- 3	5- 0	7- 4	9- 4	11- 5	13- 2
	Spruce-pine-fir	#3	4- 1	6- 0	7- 7	9- 4	10- 9	3-10	5- 7	7- 1	8- 7	10- 0

Check sources for availability of lumber in lengths greater than 20 feet.

For SI: 1 inch = 25.4 mm, 1 foot = 304.8 mm, 1 pound per square foot = 0.0479 kN/m².

a. The tabulated rafter spans assume that ceiling joists are located at the bottom of the attic space or that some other method of resisting the outward push of the rafters on the bearing walls, such as rafter ties, is provided at that location. When ceiling joists or rafter ties are located higher in the attic space, the rafter spans shall be multiplied by the factors given below:

H_C/H_R	Rafter Span Adjustment Factor
2/3 or greater	0.50
1/2	0.58
1/3	0.67
1/4	0.76
1/5	0.83
1/6	0.90
1/7.5 and less	1.00

where: H_C = Height of ceiling joists or rafter ties measured vertically above the top of the rafter support walls.

         H_R = Height of roof ridge measured vertically above the top of the rafter support walls.

b. Span exceeds 26 feet in length.

TABLE R802.5.1(7)
RAFTER SPANS FOR 70 PSF GROUND SNOW LOAD
(Ceiling not attached to rafters, L/Δ=180)

RAFTER SPACING (inches)	SPECIES AND GRADE		DEAD LOAD = 10 psf					DEAD LOAD = 20 psf				
			2x4	2x6	2x8	2x10	2x12	2x4	2x6	2x8	2x10	2x12
			Maximum Rafter Spans[a]									
			(feet - inches)	(feet - inches)	(feet - inches)	(feet - inches)	(feet - inches)	(feet - inches)	(feet - inches)	(feet - inches)	(feet - inches)	(feet - inches)
12	Douglas fir-larch	SS	7- 7	11-10	15- 8	19- 5	22- 6	7- 7	11-10	15- 0	18- 3	21- 2
	Douglas fir-larch	#1	7- 1	10- 5	13- 2	16- 1	18- 8	6- 8	9-10	12- 5	15- 2	17- 7
	Douglas fir-larch	#2	6- 8	9- 9	12- 4	15- 1	17- 6	6- 3	9- 2	11- 8	14- 2	16- 6
	Douglas fir-larch	#3	5- 0	7- 4	9- 4	11- 5	13- 2	4- 9	6-11	8- 9	10- 9	12- 5
	Hem-fir	SS	7- 2	11- 3	14- 9	18-10	22- 1	7- 2	11- 3	14- 8	18- 0	20-10
	Hem-fir	#1	6-11	10- 2	12-10	15- 8	18- 2	6- 6	9- 7	12- 1	14-10	17- 2
	Hem-fir	#2	6- 7	9- 7	12- 2	14-10	17- 3	6- 2	9- 1	11- 5	14- 0	16- 3
	Hem-fir	#3	5- 0	7- 4	9- 4	11- 5	13- 2	4- 9	6-11	8- 9	10- 9	12- 5
	Southern pine	SS	7- 5	11- 8	15- 4	19- 7	23-10	7- 5	11- 8	15- 4	19- 7	23-10
	Southern pine	#1	7- 3	11- 5	14- 9	17- 6	20-11	7- 3	11- 1	13-11	16- 6	19- 8
	Southern pine	#2	7- 1	10- 2	13- 2	15- 9	18- 5	6- 8	9- 7	12- 5	14-10	17- 5
	Southern pine	#3	5- 4	7-11	10- 1	11-11	14- 2	5- 1	7- 5	9- 6	11- 3	13- 4
	Spruce-pine-fir	SS	7- 0	11- 0	14- 6	18- 0	20-11	7- 0	11- 0	13-11	17- 0	19- 8
	Spruce-pine-fir	#1	6- 8	9- 9	12- 4	15- 1	17- 6	6- 3	9- 2	11- 8	14- 2	16- 6
	Spruce-pine-fir	#2	6- 8	9- 9	12- 4	15- 1	17- 6	6- 3	9- 2	11- 8	14- 2	16- 6
	Spruce-pine-fir	#3	5- 0	7- 4	9- 4	11- 5	13- 2	4- 9	6-11	8- 9	10- 9	12- 5
16	Douglas fir-larch	SS	6-10	10- 9	13- 9	16-10	19- 6	6-10	10- 3	13- 0	15-10	18- 4
	Douglas fir-larch	#1	6- 2	9- 0	11- 5	13-11	16- 2	5-10	8- 6	10- 9	13- 2	15- 3
	Douglas fir-larch	#2	5- 9	8- 5	10- 8	13- 1	15- 2	5- 5	7-11	10- 1	12- 4	14- 3
	Douglas fir-larch	#3	4- 4	6- 4	8- 1	9-10	11- 5	4- 1	6- 0	7- 7	9- 4	10- 9
	Hem-fir	SS	6- 6	10- 2	13- 5	16- 6	19- 2	6- 6	10- 1	12- 9	15- 7	18- 0
	Hem-fir	#1	6- 0	8- 9	11- 2	13- 7	15- 9	5- 8	8- 3	10- 6	12-10	14-10
	Hem-fir	#2	5- 8	8- 4	10- 6	12-10	14-11	5- 4	7-10	9-11	12- 1	14- 1
	Hem-fir	#3	4- 4	6- 4	8- 1	9-10	11- 5	4- 1	6- 0	7- 7	9- 4	10- 9
	Southern pine	SS	6- 9	10- 7	14- 0	17-10	21- 8	6- 9	10- 7	14- 0	17-10	21- 0
	Southern pine	#1	6- 7	10- 2	12- 9	15- 2	18- 1	6- 5	9- 7	12- 0	14- 4	17- 1
	Southern pine	#2	6- 2	8-10	11- 5	13- 7	16- 0	5-10	8- 4	10- 9	12-10	15- 1
	Southern pine	#3	4- 8	6-10	8- 9	10- 4	12- 3	4- 4	6- 5	8- 3	9- 9	11- 7
	Spruce-pine-fir	SS	6- 4	10- 0	12- 9	15- 7	18- 1	6- 4	9- 6	12- 0	14- 8	17- 1
	Spruce-pine-fir	#1	5- 9	8- 5	10- 8	13- 1	15- 2	5- 5	7-11	10- 1	12- 4	14- 3
	Spruce-pine-fir	#2	5- 9	8- 5	10- 8	13- 1	15- 2	5- 5	7-11	10- 1	12- 4	14- 3
	Spruce-pine-fir	#3	4- 4	6- 4	8- 1	9-10	11- 5	4- 1	6- 0	7- 7	9- 4	10- 9
19.2	Douglas fir-larch	SS	6- 5	9-11	12- 7	15- 4	17- 9	6- 5	9- 4	11-10	14- 5	16- 9
	Douglas fir-larch	#1	5- 7	8- 3	10- 5	12- 9	14- 9	5- 4	7- 9	9-10	12- 0	13-11
	Douglas fir-larch	#2	5- 3	7- 8	9- 9	11-11	13-10	5- 0	7- 3	9- 2	11- 3	13- 0
	Douglas fir-larch	#3	4- 0	5-10	7- 4	9- 0	10- 5	3- 9	5- 6	6-11	8- 6	9-10
	Hem-fir	SS	6- 1	9- 7	12- 4	15- 1	17- 4	6- 1	9- 2	11- 8	14- 2	15-5
	Hem-fir	#1	5- 6	8- 0	10- 2	12- 5	14- 5	5- 2	7- 7	9- 7	11- 8	13- 7
	Hem-fir	#2	5- 2	7- 7	9- 7	11- 9	13- 7	4-11	7- 2	9- 1	11- 1	12-10
	Hem-fir	#3	4- 0	5-10	7- 4	9- 0	10- 5	3- 9	5- 6	6-11	8- 6	9-10
	Southern pine	SS	6- 4	10- 0	13- 2	16- 9	20- 4	6- 4	10- 0	13- 2	16- 5	19- 2
	Southern pine	#1	6- 3	9- 3	11- 8	13-10	16- 6	5-11	8- 9	11- 0	13- 1	15- 7
	Southern pine	#2	5- 7	8- 1	10- 5	12- 5	14- 7	5- 4	7- 7	9-10	11- 9	13- 9
	Southern pine	#3	4- 3	6- 3	8- 0	9- 5	11- 2	4- 0	5-11	7- 6	8-10	10- 7
	Spruce-pine-fir	SS	6- 0	9- 2	11- 8	14- 3	16- 6	5-11	8- 8	11- 0	13- 5	15- 7
	Spruce-pine-fir	#1	5- 3	7- 8	9- 9	11-11	13-10	5- 0	7- 3	9- 2	11- 3	13- 0
	Spruce-pine-fir	#2	5- 3	7- 8	9- 9	11-11	13-10	5- 0	7- 3	9- 2	11- 3	13- 0
	Spruce-pine-fir	#3	4- 0	5-10	7- 4	9- 0	10- 5	3- 9	5- 6	6-11	8- 6	9-10

(continued)

TABLE R802.5.1(7)—continued
RAFTER SPANS FOR 70 PSF GROUND SNOW LOAD
(Ceiling not attached to rafters, L/Δ=180)

RAFTER SPACING (inches)	SPECIES AND GRADE		DEAD LOAD = 10 psf					DEAD LOAD = 20 psf				
			2x4	2x6	2x8	2x10	2x12	2x4	2x6	2x8	2x10	2x12
			Maximum rafter spans[a]									
			(feet - inches)	(feet - inches)	(feet - inches)	(feet - inches)	(feet - inches)	(feet - inches)	(feet - inches)	(feet - inches)	(feet - inches)	(feet - inches)
24	Douglas fir-larch	SS	6- 0	8-10	11- 3	13- 9	15-11	5- 9	8- 4	10- 7	12-11	15- 0
	Douglas fir-larch	#1	5- 0	7- 4	9- 4	11- 5	13- 2	4- 9	6-11	8- 9	10- 9	12- 5
	Douglas fir-larch	#2	4- 8	6-11	8- 9	10- 8	12- 4	4- 5	6- 6	8- 3	10- 0	11- 8
	Douglas fir-larch	#3	3- 7	5- 2	6- 7	8- 1	9- 4	3- 4	4-11	6- 3	7- 7	8-10
	Hem-fir	SS	5- 8	8- 8	11- 0	13- 6	13-11	5- 7	8- 3	10- 5	12- 4	12-4
	Hem-fir	#1	4-11	7- 2	9- 1	11- 1	12-10	4- 7	6- 9	8- 7	10- 6	12- 2
	Hem-fir	#2	4- 8	6- 9	8- 7	10- 6	12- 2	4- 4	6- 5	8- 1	9-11	11- 6
	Hem-fir	#3	3- 7	5- 2	6- 7	8- 1	9- 4	3- 4	4-11	6- 3	7- 7	8-10
	Southern pine	SS	5-11	9- 3	12- 2	15- 7	18- 2	5-11	9- 3	12- 2	14- 8	17- 2
	Southern pine	#1	5- 7	8- 3	10- 5	12- 5	14- 9	5- 3	7-10	9-10	11- 8	13-11
	Southern pine	#2	5- 0	7- 3	9- 4	11- 1	13- 0	4- 9	6-10	8- 9	10- 6	12- 4
	Southern pine	#3	3- 9	5- 7	7- 1	8- 5	10- 0	3- 7	5- 3	6- 9	7-11	9- 5
	Spruce-pine-fir	SS	5- 6	8- 3	10- 5	12- 9	14- 9	5- 4	7- 9	9-10	12- 0	12-11
	Spruce-pine-fir	#1	4- 8	6-11	8- 9	10- 8	12- 4	4- 5	6- 6	8- 3	10- 0	11- 8
	Spruce-pine-fir	#2	4- 8	6-11	8- 9	10- 8	12- 4	4- 5	6- 6	8- 3	10- 0	11- 8
	Spruce-pine-fir	#3	3- 7	5- 2	6- 7	8- 1	9- 4	3- 4	4-11	6- 3	7- 7	8-10

Check sources for availability of lumber in lengths greater than 20 feet.

For SI: 1 inch = 25.4 mm, 1 foot = 304.8 mm, 1 pound per square foot = 0.0479 kN/m^2.

a. The tabulated rafter spans assume that ceiling joists are located at the bottom of the attic space or that some other method of resisting the outward push of the rafters on the bearing walls, such as rafter ties, is provided at that location. When ceiling joists or rafter ties are located higher in the attic space, the rafter spans shall be multiplied by the factors given below:

H_C/H_R	Rafter Span Adjustment Factor
2/3 or greater	0.50
1/2	0.58
1/3	0.67
1/4	0.76
1/5	0.83
1/6	0.90
1/7.5 and less	1.00

where: H_C = Height of ceiling joists or rafter ties measured vertically above the top of the rafter support walls.

H_R = Height of roof ridge measured vertically above the top of the rafter support walls.

TABLE R802.5.1(8)
RAFTER SPANS FOR 70 PSF GROUND SNOW LOAD
(Ceiling attached to rafters, L/Δ=240)

RAFTER SPACING (inches)	SPECIES AND GRADE		DEAD LOAD = 10 psf					DEAD LOAD = 20 psf				
			2x4	2x6	2x8	2x10	2x12	2x4	2x6	2x8	2x10	2x12
			Maximum rafter spans[a]									
			(feet - inches)	(feet - inches)	(feet - inches)	(feet - inches)	(feet - inches)	(feet - inches)	(feet - inches)	(feet - inches)	(feet - inches)	(feet - inches)
12	Douglas fir-larch	SS	6-10	10-9	14-3	18-2	22-1	6-10	10-9	14-3	18-2	21-2
	Douglas fir-larch	#1	6-7	10-5	13-2	16-1	18-8	6-7	9-10	12-5	15-2	17-7
	Douglas fir-larch	#2	6-6	9-9	12-4	15-1	17-6	6-3	9-2	11-8	14-2	16-6
	Douglas fir-larch	#3	5-0	7-4	9-4	11-5	13-2	4-9	6-11	8-9	10-9	12-5
	Hem-fir	SS	6-6	10-2	13-5	17-2	20-10	6-6	10-2	13-5	17-2	20-10
	Hem-fir	#1	6-4	10-0	12-10	15-8	18-2	6-4	9-7	12-1	14-10	17-2
	Hem-fir	#2	6-1	9-6	12-2	14-10	17-3	6-1	9-1	11-5	14-0	16-3
	Hem-fir	#3	5-0	7-4	9-4	11-5	13-2	4-9	6-11	8-9	10-9	12-5
	Southern pine	SS	6-9	10-7	14-0	17-10	21-8	6-9	10-7	14-0	17-10	21-8
	Southern pine	#1	6-7	10-5	13-8	17-6	20-11	6-7	10-5	13-8	16-6	19-8
	Southern pine	#2	6-6	10-2	13-2	15-9	18-5	6-6	9-7	12-5	14-10	17-5
	Southern pine	#3	5-4	7-11	10-1	11-11	14-2	5-1	7-5	9-6	11-3	13-4
	Spruce-pine-fir	SS	6-4	10-0	13-2	16-9	20-5	6-4	10-0	13-2	16-9	19-8
	Spruce-pine-fir	#1	6-2	9-9	12-4	15-1	17-6	6-2	9-2	11-8	14-2	16-6
	Spruce-pine-fir	#2	6-2	9-9	12-4	15-1	17-6	6-2	9-2	11-8	14-2	16-6
	Spruce-pine-fir	#3	5-0	7-4	9-4	11-5	13-2	4-9	6-11	8-9	10-9	12-5
16	Douglas fir-larch	SS	6-3	9-10	12-11	16-6	19-6	6-3	9-10	12-11	15-10	18-4
	Douglas fir-larch	#1	6-0	9-0	11-5	13-11	16-2	5-10	8-6	10-9	13-2	15-3
	Douglas fir-larch	#2	5-9	8-5	10-8	13-1	15-2	5-5	7-11	10-1	12-4	14-3
	Douglas fir-larch	#3	4-4	6-4	8-1	9-10	11-5	4-1	6-0	7-7	9-4	10-9
	Hem-fir	SS	5-11	9-3	12-2	15-7	18-11	5-11	9-3	12-2	15-7	18-0
	Hem-fir	#1	5-9	8-9	11-2	13-7	15-9	5-8	8-3	10-6	12-10	14-10
	Hem-fir	#2	5-6	8-4	10-6	12-10	14-11	5-4	7-10	9-11	12-1	14-1
	Hem-fir	#3	4-4	6-4	8-1	9-10	11-5	4-1	6-0	7-7	9-4	10-9
	Southern pine	SS	6-1	9-7	12-8	16-2	19-8	6-1	9-7	12-8	16-2	19-8
	Southern pine	#1	6-0	9-5	12-5	15-2	18-1	6-0	9-5	12-0	14-4	17-1
	Southern pine	#2	5-11	8-10	11-5	13-7	16-0	5-10	8-4	10-9	12-10	15-1
	Southern pine	#3	4-8	6-10	8-9	10-4	12-3	4-4	6-5	8-3	9-9	11-7
	Spruce-pine-fir	SS	5-9	9-1	11-11	15-3	18-1	5-9	9-1	11-11	14-8	17-1
	Spruce-pine-fir	#1	5-8	8-5	10-8	13-1	15-2	5-5	7-11	10-1	12-4	14-3
	Spruce-pine-fir	#2	5-8	8-5	10-8	13-1	15-2	5-5	7-11	10-1	12-4	14-3
	Spruce-pine-fir	#3	4-4	6-4	8-1	9-10	11-5	4-1	6-0	7-7	9-4	10-9
19.2	Douglas fir-larch	SS	5-10	9-3	12-2	15-4	17-9	5-10	9-3	11-10	14-5	16-9
	Douglas fir-larch	#1	5-7	8-3	10-5	12-9	14-9	5-4	7-9	9-10	12-0	13-11
	Douglas fir-larch	#2	5-3	7-8	9-9	11-11	13-10	5-0	7-3	9-2	11-3	13-0
	Douglas fir-larch	#3	4-0	5-10	7-4	9-0	10-5	3-9	5-6	6-11	8-6	9-10
	Hem-fir	SS	5-6	8-8	11-6	14-8	17-4	5-6	8-8	11-6	14-2	15-5
	Hem-fir	#1	5-5	8-0	10-2	12-5	14-5	5-2	7-7	9-7	11-8	13-7
	Hem-fir	#2	5-2	7-7	9-7	11-9	13-7	4-11	7-2	9-1	11-1	12-10
	Hem-fir	#3	4-0	5-10	7-4	9-0	10-5	3-9	5-6	6-11	8-6	9-10
	Southern pine	SS	5-9	9-1	11-11	15-3	18-6	5-9	9-1	11-11	15-3	18-6
	Southern pine	#1	5-8	8-11	11-8	13-10	16-6	5-8	8-9	11-0	13-1	15-7
	Southern pine	#2	5-6	8-1	10-5	12-5	14-7	5-4	7-7	9-10	11-9	13-9
	Southern pine	#3	4-3	6-3	8-0	9-5	11-2	4-0	5-11	7-6	8-10	10-7
	Spruce-pine-fir	SS	5-5	8-6	11-3	14-3	16-6	5-5	8-6	11-0	13-5	15-7
	Spruce-pine-fir	#1	5-3	7-8	9-9	11-11	13-10	5-0	7-3	9-2	11-3	13-0
	Spruce-pine-fir	#2	5-3	7-8	9-9	11-11	13-10	5-0	7-3	9-2	11-3	13-0
	Spruce-pine-fir	#3	4-0	5-10	7-4	9-0	10-5	3-9	5-6	6-11	8-6	9-10

(continued)

TABLE R802.5.1(8)—continued
RAFTER SPANS FOR 70 PSF GROUND SNOW LOAD[a]
(Ceiling attached to rafters, L/Δ=240)

RAFTER SPACING (inches)	SPECIES AND GRADE		DEAD LOAD = 10 psf					DEAD LOAD = 20 psf				
			2x4	2x6	2x8	2x10	2x12	2x4	2x6	2x8	2x10	2x12
			Maximum rafter spans[a]									
			(feet - inches)	(feet - inches)	(feet - inches)	(feet - inches)	(feet - inches)	(feet - inches)	(feet - inches)	(feet - inches)	(feet - inches)	(feet - inches)
24	Douglas fir-larch	SS	5- 5	8- 7	11- 3	13- 9	15-11	5- 5	8- 4	10- 7	12-11	15- 0
	Douglas fir-larch	#1	5- 0	7- 4	9- 4	11- 5	13- 2	4- 9	6-11	8- 9	10- 9	12- 5
	Douglas fir-larch	#2	4- 8	6-11	8- 9	10- 8	12- 4	4- 5	6- 6	8- 3	10- 0	11- 8
	Douglas fir-larch	#3	3- 7	5- 2	6- 7	8- 1	9- 4	3- 4	4-11	6- 3	7- 7	8-10
	Hem-fir	SS	5- 2	8- 1	10- 8	13- 6	13-11	5- 2	8- 1	10- 5	12- 4	12-4
	Hem-fir	#1	4-11	7- 2	9- 1	11- 1	12-10	4- 7	6- 9	8- 7	10- 6	12- 2
	Hem-fir	#2	4- 8	6- 9	8- 7	10- 6	12- 2	4- 4	6- 5	8- 1	9-11	11- 6
	Hem-fir	#3	3- 7	5- 2	6- 7	8- 1	9- 4	3- 4	4-11	6- 3	7- 7	8-10
	Southern pine	SS	5- 4	8- 5	11- 1	14- 2	17- 2	5- 4	8- 5	11- 1	14- 2	17- 2
	Southern pine	#1	5- 3	8- 3	10- 5	12- 5	14- 9	5- 3	7-10	9-10	11- 8	13-11
	Southern pine	#2	5- 0	7- 3	9- 4	11- 1	13- 0	4- 9	6-10	8- 9	10- 6	12- 4
	Southern pine	#3	3- 9	5- 7	7- 1	8- 5	10- 0	3- 7	5- 3	6- 9	7-11	9- 5
	Spruce-pine-fir	SS	5- 0	7-11	10- 5	12- 9	14- 9	5- 0	7- 9	9-10	12- 0	12-11
	Spruce-pine-fir	#1	4- 8	6-11	8- 9	10- 8	12- 4	4- 5	6- 6	8- 3	10- 0	11- 8
	Spruce-pine-fir	#2	4- 8	6-11	8- 9	10- 8	12- 4	4- 5	6- 6	8- 3	10- 0	11- 8
	Spruce-pine-fir	#3	3- 7	5- 2	6- 7	8- 1	9- 4	3- 4	4-11	6- 3	7- 7	8-10

Check sources for availability of lumber in lengths greater than 20 feet.

For SI: 1 inch = 25.4 mm, 1 foot = 304.8 mm, 1 pound per square foot = 0.0479 kN/m².

a. The tabulated rafter spans assume that ceiling joists are located at the bottom of the attic space or that some other method of resisting the outward push of the rafters on the bearing walls, such as rafter ties, is provided at that location. When ceiling joists or rafter ties are located higher in the attic space, the rafter spans shall be multiplied by the factors given below:

H_C/H_R	Rafter Span Adjustment Factor
2/3 or greater	0.50
1/2	0.58
1/3	0.67
1/4	0.76
1/5	0.83
1/6	0.90
1/7.5 and less	1.00

where: H_C = Height of ceiling joists or rafter ties measured vertically above the top of the rafter support walls.

H_R = Height of roof ridge measured vertically above the top of the rafter support walls.

TABLE R802.5.1(9)
RAFTER/CEILING JOIST HEEL JOINT CONNECTIONS[a,b,c,d,e,f]

RAFTER SLOPE	RAFTER SPACING (inches)	GROUND SNOW LOAD (psf)											
		30 psf				50 psf				70 psf			
		Roof span (feet)											
		12	20	28	36	12	20	28	36	12	20	28	36
		Required number of 16d common nails[a,b] per heel joint splices[c,d,e,f]											
3:12	12	4	6	8	11	5	8	12	15	6	11	15	20
	16	5	8	11	14	6	11	15	20	8	14	20	26
	24	7	11	16	21	9	16	23	30	12	21	30	39
4:12	12	3	5	6	8	4	6	9	11	5	8	12	15
	16	4	6	8	11	5	8	12	15	6	11	15	20
	24	5	9	12	16	7	12	17	22	9	16	23	29
5:12	12	3	4	5	7	3	5	7	9	4	7	9	12
	16	3	5	7	9	4	7	9	12	5	9	12	16
	24	4	7	10	13	6	10	14	18	7	13	18	23
7:12	12	3	3	4	5	3	4	5	7	3	5	7	9
	16	3	4	5	6	3	5	7	9	4	6	9	11
	24	3	5	7	9	4	7	10	13	5	9	13	17
9:12	12	3	3	3	4	3	3	4	5	3	4	5	7
	16	3	3	4	5	3	4	5	7	3	5	7	9
	24	3	4	6	7	3	6	8	10	4	7	10	13
12:12	12	3	3	3	3	3	3	3	4	3	3	4	5
	16	3	3	3	4	3	3	4	5	3	4	5	7
	24	3	3	4	6	3	4	6	8	3	6	8	10

For SI: 1 inch = 25.4 mm, 1 foot = 304.8 mm, 1 pound per square foot = 0.0479 kN/m^2.

a. 40d box nails shall be permitted to be substituted for 16d common nails.

b. Nailing requirements shall be permitted to be reduced 25 percent if nails are clinched.

c. Heel joint connections are not required when the ridge is supported by a load-bearing wall, header or ridge beam.

d. When intermediate support of the rafter is provided by vertical struts or purlins to a loadbearing wall, the tabulated heel joint connection requirements shall be permitted to be reduced proportionally to the reduction in span.

e. Equivalent nailing patterns are required for ceiling joist to ceiling joist lap splices.

f. When rafter ties are substituted for ceiling joists, the heel joint connection requirement shall be taken as the tabulated heel joint connection requirement for two-thirds of the actual rafter-slope.

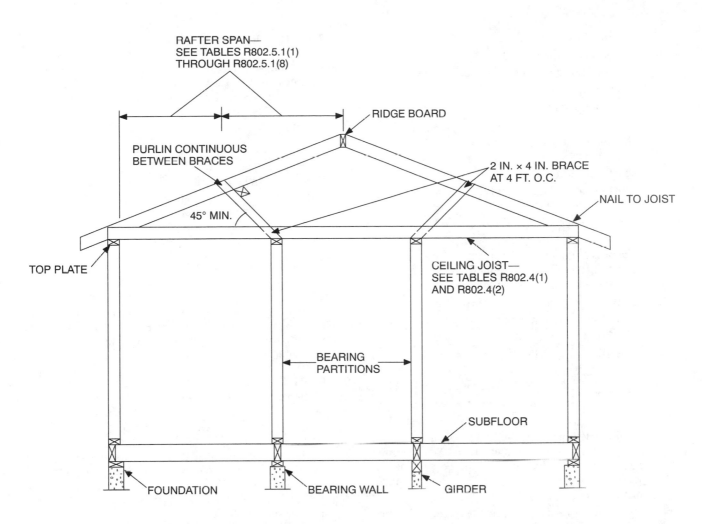

For SI: 1 inch = 25.4 mm, 1 foot = 304.8 mm, 1 degree = 0.018 rad.

Note: Where ceiling joists run perpendicular to the rafters, rafter ties shall be nailed to the rafter near the plate line and spaced not more than 4 feet on center.

FIGURE R802.5.1
BRACED RAFTER CONSTRUCTION

R802.8 Lateral support. Rafters and ceiling joists having a depth-to-thickness ratio exceeding 5 to 1 based on nominal dimensions shall be provided with lateral support at points of bearing to prevent rotation.

R802.8.1 Bridging. Rafters and ceiling joists having a depth-to-thickness ratio exceeding 6 to 1 based on nominal dimensions shall be supported laterally by solid blocking, diagonal bridging (wood or metal) or a continuous 1-inch by 3-inch (25.4 mm by 76 mm) wood strip nailed across the rafters or ceiling joists at intervals not exceeding 8 feet (2438 mm).

R802.9 Framing of openings. Openings in roof and ceiling framing shall be framed with header and trimmer joists. When the header joist span does not exceed 4 feet (1219 mm), the header joist may be a single member the same size as the ceiling joist or rafter. Single trimmer joists may be used to carry a single header joist that is located within 3 feet (914 mm) of the trimmer joist bearing. When the header joist span exceeds 4 feet (1219 mm), the trimmer joists and the header joist shall be doubled and of sufficient cross section to support the ceiling joists or rafter framing into the header. Approved hangers shall be used for the header joist to trimmer joist connections when the header joist span exceeds 6 feet (1829 mm). Tail joists over 12 feet (3658 mm) long shall be supported at the header by framing anchors or on ledger strips not less than 2 inches by 2 inches (51 mm by 51 mm).

R802.10 Wood trusses.

R802.10.1 Truss design drawings. Truss design drawings, prepared in conformance with Section R802.10.1, shall be provided to the building official and approved prior to installation. Truss design drawings shall include, at a minimum, the information specified below. Truss design drawing shall be provided with the shipment of trusses delivered to the jobsite.

1. Slope or depth, span and spacing.
2. Location of all joints.

3. Required bearing widths.
4. Design loads as applicable.
   4.1. Top chord live load (including snow loads).
   4.2. Top chord dead load.
   4.3. Bottom chord live load.
   4.4. Bottom chord dead load.
   4.5. Concentrated loads and their points of application.
   4.6. Controlling wind and earthquake loads.
5. Adjustments to lumber and joint connector design values for conditions of use.
6. Each reaction force and direction.
7. Joint connector type and description (e.g., size, thickness or gauge) and the dimensioned location of each joint connector except where symmetrically located relative to the joint interface.
8. Lumber size, species and grade for each member.
9. Connection requirements for:
   9.1. Truss to truss girder.
   9.2. Truss ply to ply.
   9.3. Field splices.
10. Calculated deflection ratio and/or maximum description for live and total load.
11. Maximum axial compression forces in the truss members to enable the building designer to design the size, connections and anchorage of the permanent continuous lateral bracing. Forces shall be shown on the truss design drawing or on supplemental documents.
12. Required permanent truss member bracing location.

R802.10.2 Design. Wood trusses shall be designed in accordance with accepted engineering practice. The design and manufacture of metal plate connected wood trusses shall comply with ANSI/TPI 1. The truss design drawings shall be prepared by a registered professional where required by the statutes of the jurisdiction in which the project is to be constructed in accordance with Minnesota Rules, Chapter 1300.

R802.10.3 Bracing. Trusses shall be braced to prevent rotation and provide lateral stability in accordance with the requirements specified in the construction documents for the building and on the individual truss design drawings. In the absence of specific bracing requirements, trusses shall be braced in accordance with TPI/HIB.

R802.10.4 Alterations to trusses. Truss members shall not be cut, notched, drilled, spliced or otherwise altered in any way without the approval of a registered design professional. Alterations resulting in the addition of load (e.g., HVAC equipment, water heater) that exceeds the design load for the truss shall not be permitted without verification that the truss is capable of supporting such additional loading.

R802.11 Roof tie-down. Roof assemblies subject to wind uplift pressures of 20 pounds per square foot (0.958 kN/m^2) or greater, as established in Table R301.2(2), adjusted for height and exposure per Table R301.2(3), shall have rafter or truss ties provided at bearing locations in accordance with Table R802.11. A continuous load path shall be provided to transmit the uplift forces from the rafter or truss ties to the foundation. Wind uplift pressure on roof assemblies shall be determined using an effective wind area of 100 square feet (9.3 m^2) and Zone 1 in Table R301.2(2).

TABLE R802.11
REQUIRED STRENGTH OF TRUSS OR RAFTER TIE-DOWN CONNECTIONS TO RESIST WIND UPLIFT FORCES[a,b,c,d]
(Pounds per tie-down connection)

DESIGN WIND LOAD (psf)[d]	TOTAL ROOF WIDTH INCLUDING OVERHANG (feet)				
	24	28	32	36	40
20	192	224	256	288	320
30	432	504	576	648	720
40	672	784	895	1,008	1,120
50	912	1,064	1,216	1,368	1,520
60	1,152	1,344	1,536	1,728	1,920

For SI: 1 inch = 25.4 mm, 1 foot = 304.8 mm, 1 pound per square foot = 0.0479 kN/m^2, 1 pound = 0.454 kg.

a. Wind uplift forces are based on 24-inch spacing of roof trusses or rafters. For spacing other than 24 inches, forces shall be adjusted accordingly.
b. Interpolation is permitted for intermediate values of wind uplift pressures and roof widths.
c. The rated capacity of approved tie-down devices is permitted to include up to a 60-percent increase for wind effects where allowed by material specifications.
d. Figure R301.2(4) and Table R301.2(2) shall be used in determining the design wind load.

SECTION R803
ROOF SHEATHING

R803.1 Lumber sheathing. Allowable spans for lumber used as roof sheathing shall conform to Table R803.1. Spaced lumber sheathing for wood shingle and shake roofing shall conform to the requirements of Sections R905.7 and R905.8. Spaced lumber sheathing is not allowed in Seismic Design Category D_2.

TABLE R803.1
MINIMUM THICKNESS OF LUMBER ROOF SHEATHING

RAFTER OR BEAM SPACING (inches)	MINIMUM NET THICKNESS (inches)
24	$^5/_8$
48[a]	
60[b]	$1^1/_2$ T & G
72[c]	

For SI: 1 inch = 25.4 mm.

a. Minimum 270 F_b, 340,000 E.
b. Minimum 420 F_b, 660,000 E.
c. Minimum 600 F_b, 1,150,000 E.

R803.2 Wood structural panel sheathing.

R803.2.1 Identification and grade. Wood structural panels shall conform to DOC PS 1, DOC PS 2 or, when manufactured in Canada, CSA 0437, and shall be identified by grade mark or certificate of inspection issued by an approved agency. Wood structural panels shall comply with the grades specified in Table R503.2.1.1(1).

R803.2.1.1 Exposure durability. All wood structural panels, when designed to be permanently exposed in outdoor applications, shall be of an exterior exposure durability. Wood structural panel roof sheathing exposed to the underside may be of interior type bonded with exterior glue, identified as Exposure 1.

R803.2.1.2 Fire-retardant-treated plywood. The allowable unit stresses for fire-retardant-treated plywood, including fastener values, shall be developed from an approved method of investigation that considers the effects of anticipated temperature and humidity to which the fire-retardant-treated plywood will be subjected, the type of treatment and redrying process. The fire-retardant-treated plywood shall be graded by an approved agency.

R803.2.2 Allowable spans. The maximum allowable spans for wood structural panel roof sheathing shall not exceed the values set forth in Table R503.2.1.1(1).

R803.2.3 Installation. Wood structural panel used as roof sheathing shall be installed with joints staggered or nonstaggered in accordance with Table R602.3(1), or APA E30 for wood roof framing or with Table R804.3 for steel roof framing.

SECTION R804
STEEL ROOF FRAMING

R804.1 General. Elements shall be straight and free of any defects that would significantly affect their structural performance. Cold-formed steel roof framing members shall comply with the requirements of this section.

R804.1.1 Applicability limits. The provisions of this section shall control the construction of steel roof framing for buildings not greater than 60 feet (18 288 mm) in length perpendicular to the joist, rafter or truss span, not greater than 36 feet (10 973 mm) in width parallel to the joist span or truss, not greater than two stories in height with each story not greater than 10 feet (3048 mm) high, and roof slopes not smaller than 3:12 (25-percent slope) or greater than 12:12 (100-percent slope). Steel roof framing constructed in accordance with the provisions of this section shall be limited to sites subjected to a maximum design wind speed of 130 miles per hour (209 km/h) Exposure A, B or C and a maximum ground snow load of 70 psf (3.35 kN/m²).

R804.1.2 In-line framing. Steel roof framing constructed in accordance with Section R804 shall be located directly in-line with load-bearing studs below with a maximum tolerance of $^3/_4$ inch (19.1 mm) between the centerline of the stud and roof joist/rafter.

R804.2 Structural framing. Load-bearing steel roof framing members shall comply with Figure R804.2(1) and the dimensional and minimum thickness requirements specified in Tables R804.2(1) and R804.2(2). Tracks shall comply with Figure R804.2(2) and shall have a minimum flange width of $1^1/_4$ inches (32 mm). The maximum inside bend radius for load-bearing members shall be the greater of $^3/_{32}$ inch (2.4 mm) or twice the uncoated steel thickness. Holes in roof framing members shall not exceed 1.5 inches (38 mm) in width or 4 inches (102 mm) in length as shown in Figure R804.2(3). Holes shall be permitted only along the centerline of the web of the framing member. Holes shall not be less than 24 inches (610 mm) center-to-center and shall not be located less than 10 inches (254 mm) from the edge of the hole to the edge of the bearing surface or support unless patched in accordance with Section R804.3.6.

R804.2.1 Material. Load-bearing steel framing members shall be cold-formed to shape from structural quality sheet steel complying with the requirements of one of the following:

1. ASTM A 653; Grades 33, 37, 40 and 50 (Classes 1 and 3).

2. ASTM A 792; Grades 33, 37, 40 and 50A.

3. ASTM A 875; Grades 33, 37, 40 and 50 (Classes 1 and 3).

4. Steels that comply with ASTM A 653, except for tensile and elongation, shall be permitted provided the ratio of tensile strength to yield point is at least 1.08 and the total elongation is at least 10 percent for a 2-inch (51 mm) gage length or 7 percent for an 8-inch (203 mm) gage length.

R804.2.2 Identification. Load-bearing steel framing members shall have a legible label, stencil, stamp or embossment with the following information as a minimum:

1. Manufacturer's identification.

2. Minimum uncoated steel thickness in inches (mm).

3. Minimum coating designation.

4. Minimum yield strength, in kips per square inch (ksi).

TABLE R804.2(1)
LOAD-BEARING COLD-FORMED STEEL MEMBER SIZES

NOMINAL MEMBER SIZE MEMBER DESIGNATION[a]	WEB DEPTH (inches)	MINIMUM FLANGE WIDTH (inches)	MAXIMUM FLANGE WIDTH (inches)	MINIMUM LIP SIZE (inches)
350S162-t	3.5	1.625	2	0.5
550S162-t	5.5	1.625	2	0.5
800S162-t	8	1.625	2	0.5
1000S162-t	10	1.625	2	0.5
1200S162-t	12	1.625	2	0.5

For SI: 1 inch = 25.4 mm.

a. The member designation is defined by the first number representing the member depth in $^1/_{100}$ inch, the letter "s" representing a stud or joist member, the second number representing the flange width in $^1/_{100}$ inch, and the letter "t" shall be a number representing the minimum base metal thickness in mils [see Table R804.2(2)].

TABLE R804.2(2)
MINIMUM THICKNESS OF COLD-FORMED STEEL ROOF FRAMING MEMBERS

DESIGNATION (mils)	MINIMUM UNCOATED THICKNESS (inches)	REFERENCED GAGE NUMBER
33	0.033	20
43	0.043	18
54	0.054	16
68	0.068	14

For SI: 1 inch = 25.4 mm, 1 mil = 0.0254 mm.

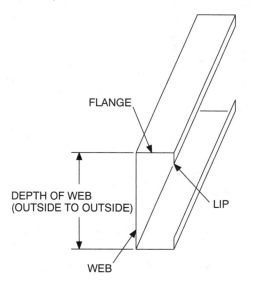

FLANGE

DEPTH OF WEB
(OUTSIDE TO OUTSIDE)

LIP

WEB

FIGURE R804.2(1)
C-SECTION

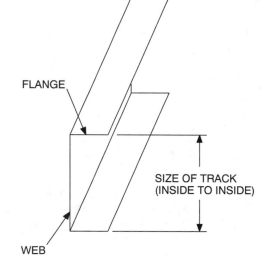

FLANGE

SIZE OF TRACK
(INSIDE TO INSIDE)

WEB

FIGURE R804.2(2)
TRACK SECTION

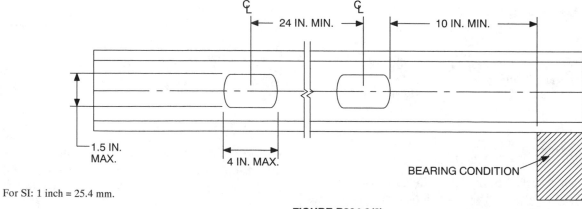

24 IN. MIN.

10 IN. MIN.

1.5 IN. MAX.

4 IN. MAX.

BEARING CONDITION

For SI: 1 inch = 25.4 mm.

FIGURE R804.2(3)
WEB HOLES

R804.2.3 Corrosion protection. Load-bearing steel framing shall have a metallic coating complying with one of the following:

1. A minimum of G 60 in accordance with ASTM A 653.

2. A minimum of AZ 50 in accordance with ASTM A 792.

3. A minimum of GF 60 in accordance with ASTM A 875.

R804.2.4 Fastening requirements. Screws for steel-to-steel connections shall be installed with a minimum edge distance and center-to-center spacing of $^1/_2$ inch (12.7 mm), shall be self-drilling tapping, and shall conform to SAE J78. Structural sheathing shall be attached to roof rafters with minimum No. 8 self-drilling tapping screws that conform to SAE J78. Screws for attaching structural sheathing to steel roof framing shall have a minimum head diameter of 0.292 inch (7.4 mm) with countersunk heads and shall be installed with a minimum edge distance of $^3/_8$ inch (9.5 mm). Gypsum board ceilings shall be attached to steel joists with minimum No. 6 screws conforming to ASTM C 954 and shall be installed in accordance with Section R805. For all connections, screws shall extend through the steel a minimum of three exposed threads. All self-drilling tapping screws conforming to SAE J78 shall have a minimum Type II coating in accordance with ASTM B 633.

Where No. 8 screws are specified in a steel-to-steel connection, the required number of screws in the connection is permitted to be reduced in accordance with the reduction factors in Table R804.2.4 when larger screws are used or when one of the sheets of steel being connected is thicker that 33 mils (0.83 mm). When applying the reduction factor, the resulting number of screws shall be rounded up.

TABLE R804.2.4
SCREW SUBSTITUTION FACTOR

SCREW SIZE	THINNEST CONNECTED STEEL SHEET (mils)	
	33	43
#8	1.0	0.67
#10	0.93	0.62
#12	0.86	0.56

For SI: 1 mil = 0.0254 mm.

R804.3 Roof construction. Steel roof systems constructed in accordance with the provisions of this section shall consist of both ceiling joists and rafters in accordance with Figure R804.3 and fastened in accordance with Table R804.3.

R804.3.1 Allowable ceiling joist spans. The clear span of cold-formed steel ceiling joists shall not exceed the limits set forth in Table R804.3.1(1) or R804.3.1(2). Ceiling joists shall have a minimum bearing length of 1.5 inches (38 mm) and shall be connected to rafters (heel joint) in accordance with Figure R804.3.1(1) and Table R804.3.1(3). When continuous joists are framed across interior bearing supports, the interior bearing supports shall be located within 24 inches (610 mm) of midspan of the ceiling joist, and the individual spans shall not exceed the applicable spans in Table R804.3.1(1) or R804.3.1(2). Where required in Table R804.3.1(1) or R804.3.1(2), bearing stiffeners shall be installed at each bearing location in accordance with Section R804.3.8 and Figure R804.3.8. When the attic is to be used as an occupied space, the ceiling joists shall be designed in accordance with Section R505.

TABLE R804.3
ROOF FRAMING FASTENING SCHEDULE[a,b]

DESCRIPTION OF BUILDING ELEMENTS	NUMBER AND SIZE OF FASTENERS	SPACING OF FASTENERS
Ceiling joist to top track of load-bearing wall	2 No. 10 screws	Each joist
Roof sheathing (oriented strand board or plywood) to rafters	No. 8 screws	6″ o.c. on edges and 12″ o.c. at interior supports. 6″ o.c. at gable end truss
Truss to bearing wall[a]	2 No. 10 screws	Each truss
Gable end truss to endwall top track	No. 10 screws	12″ o.c.
Rafter to ceiling joist	Minimum No. 10 screws, per Table R804.3.1(3)	Evenly spaced, less than ½″ from all edges.

For SI: 1 inch = 25.4 mm, 1 foot = 304.8 mm, 1 pound per square foot = 0.0479 kN/m², 1 mil = 0.0254 mm.

a. Screws shall be applied through the flanges of the truss or ceiling joist or a 54 mil clip angle shall be used with two No. 10 screws in each leg. See Section R804.4 for additional requirements to resist uplift forces.

b. Spacing of fasteners on roof sheathing panel edges applies to panel edges supported by framing members and at all roof plane perimeters. Blocking of roof sheathing panel edges perpendicular to the framing members shall not be required except at the intersection of adjacent roof planes. Roof perimeter shall be supported by framing members or cold-formed blocking of the same depth and gauge as the floor members.

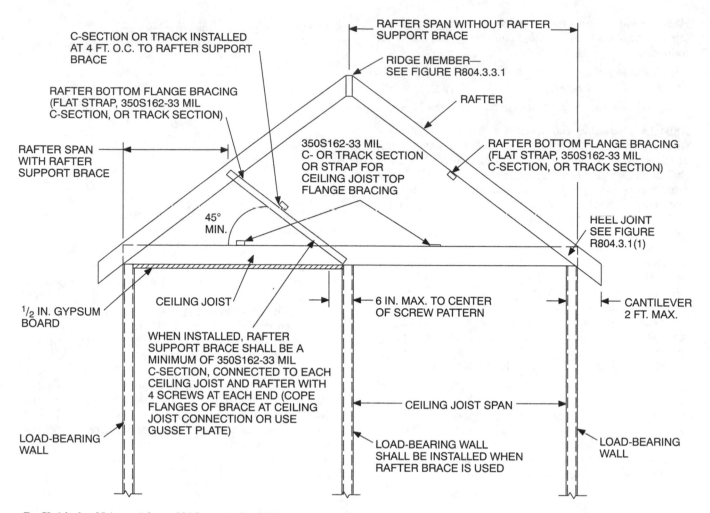

For SI: 1 inch = 25.4 mm, 1 foot = 304.8 mm, 1 mil = 0.0254 mm.

**FIGURE R804.3
STEEL ROOF CONSTRUCTION**

TABLE R804.3.1(1)
ALLOWABLE SPANS FOR COLD-FORMED STEEL CEILING JOISTS[a,b,c] 10 psf live load (no attic storage)

NOMINAL JOIST SIZE	LATERAL SUPPORT OF TOP (COMPRESSION) FLANGE					
	Unbraced		Mid-span bracing		Third-point bracing	
	Spacing (inches)		Spacing (inches)		Spacing (inches)	
	16	24	16	24	16	24
350S162-33	9'-2"	8'-3"	11'-9"	10'-1"	11'-9"	10'-4"
350S162-43	9'-11"	8'-10"	12'-10"	11'-2"	12'-10"	11'-2"
350S162-54	10'-8"	9'-6"	13'-9"	12'-0"	13'-9"	12'-0"
350S162-68	11'-7"	10'-4"	14'-8"	12'-10"	14'-8"	12'-10"
550S162-33	10'-5"	9'-5"	14'-5"	12'-8"c	16'-4"	13'-10"c
550S162-43	11'-2"	10'-1"	15'-7"	13'-10"	18'-0"	15'-5"
550S162-54	12'-0"	10'-9"	16'-7"	14'-9"	19'-5"	16'-8"
550S162-68	12'-11"	11'-7"	17'-8"	15'-10"	20'-11"	18'-1"
800S162-33	11'-8"c	10'-6"c	16'-5"c	14'-9"c	19'-5"c	16'-7"c
800S162-43	12'-6"	11'-3"	17'-6"	15'-10"	21'-2"	18'-7"
800S162-54	13'-4"	11'-11"	18'-7"	16'-9"	22'-7"	20'-0"
800S162-68	14'-3"	12'-9"	19'-8"	17'-8"	23'-11"	21'-4"
1000S162-43	13'-4"c	12'-1"c	18'-9"c	16'-11"c	22'-11"c	20'-6"c
1000S162-54	14'-2"	12'-9"	19'-10"	17'-10"	24'-2"	21'-9"
1000S162-68	15'-2"	13'-7"	21'-0"	18'-11"	25'-6"	23'-0"
1200S162-43	14'-1"c	12'-8"c	19'-10"c	17'-11"c	24'-3"c	21'-6"c
1200S162-54	15'-0"c	13'-5"c	20'-11"c	18'-11"c	25'-7"c	23'-1"c
1200S162-68	15'-11"	14'-4"	22'-2"	19'-11"	27'-0"	24'-4"

For SI: 1 inch = 25.4 mm, 1 foot = 304.8 mm, 1 pound per square foot = 0.0479 kN/m².
a. Deflection criteria: L/240 for total loads.
b. Ceiling dead load = 5 psf.
c. Bearing stiffeners are required at all bearing points and concentrated load locations.

TABLE R804.3.1(2)
ALLOWABLE SPANS FOR COLD-FORMED STEEL CEILING JOISTS[a,b,c]
20 psf live load (Limited attic storage where development of future rooms is not possible)

NOMINAL JOIST SIZE	LATERAL SUPPORT OF TOP FLANGE					
	Unbraced		Mid-span bracing		Third-point bracing	
	Spacing (inches)		Spacing (inches)		Spacing (inches)	
	16	24	16	24	16	24
350S162-33	8'-0"	6'-0"	9'-8"	6'-0"	9'-0"	6'-0"
350S162-43	8'-8"	7'-8"	10'-9"	9'-1"	10'-10"	9'-5"
350S162-54	9'-3"	8'-3"	11'-7"	9'-11"	11'-7"	10'-1"
350S162-68	10'-0"	8'-11"	12'-5"	10'-10"	12'-5"	10'-10"
550S162-33	9'-2"	6'-0"	12'-2"c	10'-5"c	13'-3"	11'-0"c
550S162-43	9'-10"	8'-10"	13'-4"	11'-6"	14'-9"	12'-5"
550S162-54	10'-5"	9'-5"	14'-4"	12'-6"	16'-1"	13'-7"
550S162-68	11'-3"	10'-0"	15'-4"	13'-5"	17'-5"	14'-10"
800S162-33	10'-3"c	9'-3"c	14'-4"c	12'-5"c	15'-11"c	13'-4"c
800S162-43	10'-11"	9'-10"	15'-5"	13'-8"c	17'-11"c	15'-5"c
800S162-54	11'-8"	10'-6"	16'-3"	14'-7"	19'-3"	16'-8"
800S162-68	12'-5"	11'-2"	17'-3"	15'-6"	20'-7"	18'-0"
1000S162-43	11'-9"	10'-7"c	16'-6"c	14'-10"c	19'-10"c	17'-1"c
1000S162-54	12'-5"	11'-2"	17'-5"	15'-8"	21'-1"	18'-7"
1000S162-68	13'-3"	11'-10"	18'-5"	16'-7"	22'-4"	19'-11"
1200S162-43	12'-5"c	11'-2"c	17'-5"c	15'-8"c	20'-9"c	18'-0"c
1200S162-54	13'-1"c	11'-9"c	18'-5"c	16'-7"c	22'-5"c	20'-1"c
1200S162-68	13'-11"	12'-6"	19'-5"	17'-6"	23'-8"	21'-3"

For SI: 1 inch = 25.4 mm, 1 foot = 304.8 mm, 1 pound per square foot = 0.0479 kN/m².
a. Deflection criteria: L/240 for total loads.
b. Ceiling dead load = 5 psf.
c. Bearing stiffeners are required at all bearing points and concentrated load locations.

TABLE R804.3.1(3)
NUMBER OF SCREWS REQUIRED FOR CEILING JOIST TO RAFTER CONNECTION[a]

ROOF SLOPE	BUILDING WIDTH (feet)															
	24				28				32				36			
	Ground snow load (psf)				Ground snow load (psf)				Ground snow load (psf)				Ground snow load (psf)			
	20	30	50	70	20	30	50	70	20	30	50	70	20	30	50	70
3/12	5	6	9	12	6	7	10	13	7	8	12	15	8	9	13	17
4/12	4	5	7	9	5	6	8	10	6	6	9	12	6	7	10	13
5/12	4	4	6	7	4	5	7	9	5	5	8	10	5	6	9	11
6/12	3	4	5	7	4	4	6	8	4	5	7	9	4	5	7	10
7/12	3	3	5	6	3	4	5	7	4	4	6	8	4	5	7	9
8/12	3	3	4	5	3	3	5	6	3	4	5	7	4	4	6	8
9/12	2	3	4	5	3	3	4	6	3	4	5	6	3	4	6	7
10/12	2	3	4	5	3	3	4	5	3	3	5	6	3	4	5	7
11/12	2	3	4	4	3	3	4	5	3	3	5	6	3	4	5	6
12/12	2	3	3	4	2	3	4	5	3	3	4	6	3	4	5	6

For SI: 1 foot = 304.8 mm, 1 pound per square fot = 0.0479 kN/m².

a. Screws shall be No. 10 minimum.

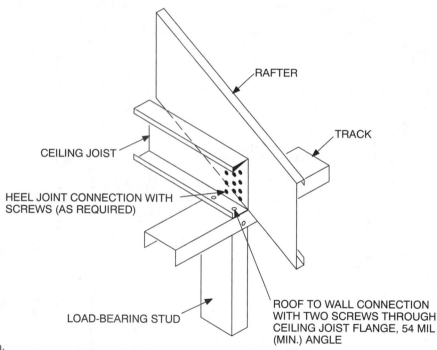

For SI: 1 mil = 0.0254 mm.

FIGURE R804.3.1(1)
JOIST TO RAFTER CONNECTION

R804.3.2 Ceiling joist bracing. The bottom flanges of steel ceiling joists shall be laterally braced in accordance with Section R702. The top flanges of steel ceiling joists shall be laterally braced with a minimum of 33 mil (0.84 mm) C-section, 33 mil (0.84 mm) track section, or 1¹/₂ inch by 33 mil (38 mm by 0.84 mm) continuous steel strapping as required in Table R804.3.1(1) or R804.3.1(2). Lateral bracing shall be installed in accordance with Figure R804.3. C-section, tracks or straps shall be fastened to the top flange at each joist with at least one No. 8 screw and shall be fastened to blocking with at least two No. 8 screws. Blocking or bridging (X-bracing) shall be installed between joists in-line

with strap bracing at a maximum spacing of 12 feet (3658 mm) measured perpendicular to the joists, and at the termination of all straps. The third point bracing span values from Table R804.3.1(1) or R804.3.1(2) shall be used for straps installed at closer spacings than third point bracing, or when sheathing is applied to the top of the ceiling joists.

R804.3.3 Allowable rafter spans. The horizontal projection of the rafter span, as shown in Figure R804.3, shall not exceed the limits set forth in Table R804.3.3(1). Wind speeds shall be converted to equivalent ground snow loads in accordance with Table R804.3.3(2). Rafter spans shall be selected based on the higher of the ground snow load or the equivalent snow load converted from the wind speed. When required, a rafter support brace shall be a minimum of 350S162-33 C-section with maximum length of 8 feet (2438 mm) and shall be connected to a ceiling joist and rafter with four No. 10 screws at each end.

R804.3.3.1 Rafter framing. Rafters shall be connected to a parallel ceiling joist to form a continuous tie between exterior walls in accordance with Figures R804.3 and R804.3.1(1) and Table R804.3.1(3). Rafters shall be connected to a ridge member with a minimum 2-inch by 2-inch (51 mm by 51 mm) clip angle fastened with minimum No. 10 screws to the ridge member in accordance with Figure R804.3.3.1 and Table R804.3.3.1. The clip angle shall have a minimum steel thickness as the rafter member and shall extend the full depth of the rafter member. The ridge member shall be fabricated from a C-section and a track section, which shall be of a minimum size and steel thickness as the adjacent rafters and shall be installed in accordance with Figure R804.3.3.1.

TABLE R804.3.3(1)
ALLOWABLE HORIZONTAL RAFTER SPANS[a,b]

NOMINAL RAFTER SIZE	GROUND SNOW LOAD							
	20 psf		30 psf		50 psf		70 psf	
	Spacing (inches-feet)		Spacing (inches-feet)		Spacing (inches-feet)		Spacing (inches-feet)	
	16	24	16	24	16	24	16	24
550S162-33	12'-8"	10'-4"	11'-9"	9'-7"	9'-11"	8'-1"	8'-10"	7'-2"
550S162-43	15'-5"	12'-7"	14'-3"	11'-8"	12'-1"	9'-10"	10'-8"	8'-9"
550S162-54	13'-0"	14'-2"	16'-1"	13'-1"	13'-8"	11'-2"	12'-1"	9'-10"
550S162-68	18'-1"	15'-10"	17'-3"	14'-9"	15'-4"	12'-6"	13'-6"	11'-1"
800S162-33	15'-5"	11'-5"	14'-4"	9'-10"	10'-7"	7'-1"	8'-3"	5'-6"
800S162-43	19'-1"	15'-7"	17'-9"	14'-6"	15'-1"	12'-3"	13'-3"	10'-9"
800S162-54	22'-7"	18'-5"	21'-0"	17'-1"	17'-9"	14'-6"	15'-9"	12'-10"
800S162-68	24'-7"	20'-9"	23'-4"	19'-3"	20'-0"	16'-4"	17'-8"	14'-5"
1000S162-43	21'-2"	17'-3"	19'-8"	16'-0"	16'-8"	13'-1"	14'-9"	10'-3"
1000S162 54	25'-1"	20'-6"	23'-3"	19'-0"	19'-9"	16'-1"	17'-5"	14'-3"
1000S162-68	29'-6"	24'-6"	27'-9"	22'-9"	23'-8"	19'-3"	21'-0"	17'-1"
1200S162-43	23'-0"	18'-2"	21'-4"	15'-7"	16'-9"	11'-3"	13'-2"	8'-9"
1200S162-54	27'-3"	22'-3"	25'-3"	20'-7"	21'-5"	17'-6"	18'-11"	15'-5"
1200S162-68	32'-1"	26'-2"	29'-9"	24'-3"	25'-3"	20'-7"	22'-4"	18'-2"

For SI: 1 inch = 25.4 mm, 1 foot = 304.8 mm, 1 pound per square foot – 0.0479 kN/m².

a. Deflection criteria: *L*/240 for live loads and *L*/180 for total loads.

b. Roof dead load = 12 pounds per square foot.

TABLE R804.3.3(2)
BASIC WIND SPEED TO EQUIVALENT SNOW LOAD CONVERSION[a]

BASIC WIND SPEED AND EXPOSURE		EQUIVALENT GROUND SNOW LOAD (psf)									
		Roof slope									
Exp. A/B	Exp. C	3:12	4:12	5:12	6:12	7:12	8:12	9:12	10:12	11:12	12:12
85 mph	—	20	20	20	20	20	20	30	30	30	30
100 mph	85 mph	20	20	20	20	30	30	30	30	50	50
110 mph	100 mph	20	20	20	20	30	50	50	50	50	50
120 mph	110 mph	30	30	30	50	50	50	70	70	70	—
130 mph	120 mph	30	50	50	50	70	70	70	—	—	—
—	130 mph	50	50	50	70	70	—	—	—	—	—

For SI: 1 mile per hour = 0.447 m/s, 1 pound per square foot = 0.0479 kN/m²

a. In areas where the basic wind speed equals or exceeds 110 miles per hour the equivalent snow load shall be used only to determine the size of members. Connections of rafters to the ridge and the roof members to walls shall comply with Sections R804.3.3.1.1 and R804.4.1.

R804.3.3.1.1 High wind ridge tension connections. In areas where the basic wind speed is 110 miles per hour (177 km/h) or greater, roof rafters shall be provided with a connection at the ridge line to transfer tension loads. The ridge connection shall be capable of resisting the unit loads listed in Table R804.3.3.1.1(1) multiplied by the appropriate spacing multiplier. Alternatively, a steel ridge strap shall be provided with minimum No. 8 screws on each end of the strap as required in Table R804.3.3.1.1(1). The number of screws shall be increased to account for the spacing multipliers shown in the table. The width and thickness of the steel ridge strap shall be as shown in Table R804.3.3.1.1(2), based upon the required number of screws on one side of the strap.

TABLE R804.3.3.1
NUMBER OF SCREWS REQUIRED AT EACH LEG OF CLIP ANGLE FOR RAFTER TO RIDGE MEMBER CONNECTION[a]

BUILDING WIDTH (feet)	GROUND SNOW LOAD (psf)			
	0 to 20	21 to 30	31 to 50	51 to 70
24	2	3	4	4
28	2	3	4	5
32	3	3	4	5
36	3	4	5	6

For SI: 1 foot = 304.8 mm, 1 pound per square foot = 0.0479 kN/m^2.

a. Screws shall be No. 10 minimum.

TABLE R804.3.3.1.1(1)
RIDGE TENSION STRAP CONNECTION REQUIREMENTS PER FOOT OF RIDGE SPAN[c]

Roof pitch	Roof span (feet)	BASIC WIND SPEED (mph)			BASIC WIND SPEED (mph)		
		110	120	130	110	120	130
		Number of #8 screws in each end of a steel ridge strap [Table R804.3.3.1.1(2)]			Required ridge construction capacity[a,b] (plf)		
3:12	24	2	2	3	475	624	788
	28	2	3	3	554	727	919
	32	2	3	3	633	831	1051
	36	3	3	4	712	935	1182
4:12	24	2	2	3	378	495	765
	28	2	2	3	441	577	727
	32	2	2	3	504	659	831
	36	2	4	3	567	742	935
5:12	24	1	2	2	289	380	480
	28	1	2	2	338	443	560
	32	2	2	2	386	507	640
	36	2	2	3	434	570	720
6:12	24	1	1	2	262	342	431
	28	1	2	2	306	399	503
	32	2	2	2	350	457	575
	36	2	2	2	393	514	647
7:12-12:12	24	1	2	2	246	320	401
	28	1	2	2	287	373	468
	32	1	2	2	328	426	535
	36	2	3	2	369	480	602
Framing spacing		12 in.	16 in.	24 in.	19.2 in.	—	—
Multiplier		1.0	1.33	2.0	1.6	—	—

For SI: 1 inch = 25.4 mm, 1 foot = 304.8 mm, 1 pound force = 4.45 N, 1 mile per hour = 0.447 m/s, 1 pound per square foot = 0.0479 kN/m^2, 1 pound per linear foot = 14.60 N/m.

a. Connection requirements are based on a foot assembly dead load of 10 pounds per square foot.

b. Connection capacities shown in the table are based on a 12-inch ridge strap spacing. For spacing greater than 12 inches, capacity values shall be increased using the multipliers in the table above.

c. The required number of screws shown in the table are based on a 12-inch strap spacing. For spacing other than 12 inches, the appropriate connection capacity in the table shall be increased using the multipliers above and dividing by the screw shear value of 263 pounds = 350 pounds/screw.

TABLE R804.3.3.1.1(2)
MINIMUM SIZE OF RIDGE STRAP

STRAP WIDTH (inches)	MINIMUM THICKNESS OF RIDGE STRAP (inches) REQUIRED NUMBER OF RIDGE STRAP SCREWS[a]					
	4 or less	5	6	7	8	9
1.25	0.043	0.054	0.054	—	—	—
1.5	0.043	0.043	0.054	0.054	—	—
1.75	0.043	0.043	0.043	0.054	0.054	—
2	0.043	0.043	0.043	0.043	0.054	0.054

For SI: 1 inch = 25.4 mm.

a. Required number of screws per Table R804.3.3.1.1(1) on each end of the ridge strap.

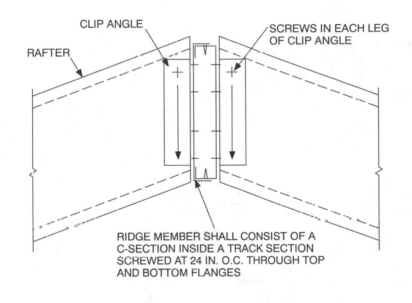

CLIP ANGLE

SCREWS IN EACH LEG OF CLIP ANGLE

RAFTER

RIDGE MEMBER SHALL CONSIST OF A C-SECTION INSIDE A TRACK SECTION SCREWED AT 24 IN. O.C. THROUGH TOP AND BOTTOM FLANGES

For SI: 1 inch = 25.4 mm.

FIGURE R804.3.3.1
RIDGE BOARD CONNECTION

R804.3.3.2 Roof cantilevers. Roof cantilevers shall not exceed 24 inches (610 mm) in accordance with Figure R804.3. Roof cantilevers shall be supported by a header in accordance with Section R603.6 or shall be supported by the floor framing in accordance with Section R505.3.7.

R804.3.4 Rafter bottom flange bracing. The bottom flanges of steel rafters shall be continuously braced with a minimum 33-mil (0.84 mm) C-section, 33-mil (0.84 mm) track section, or a $1^1/_2$-inch by 33-mil (38 mm by 0.84 mm) steel strapping at a maximum spacing of 8 feet (2438 mm) as measured parallel to the rafters. Bracing shall be installed in accordance with Figure R804.3. The C-section, track section, or straps shall be fastened to blocking with at least two No. 8 screws. Blocking or bridging (X-bracing) shall be installed between rafters in-line with the continuous bracing at a maximum spacing of 12 feet (3658 mm) measured perpendicular to the rafters and at the termination of all straps. The ends of continuous bracing shall be fastened to blocking with at least two No. 8 screws.

R804.3.5 Cutting and notching. Flanges and lips of load-bearing steel roof framing members shall not be cut or notched. Holes in webs shall be in accordance with Section R804.2.

R804.3.6 Hole patching. Holes in ceiling joist and rafters with dimensions conforming to Section R804.2 that are closer than 10 inches (254 mm) from the edge of the hole to the edge of bearing surface shall be patched with a solid steel plate, C-section or track section in accordance with Figure R804.3.6. The steel patch shall be of a minimum thickness as the receiving member and shall extend at least 1 inch (25.4 mm) beyond all edges of the hole. The steel patch shall be fastened to the web with No. 8 screws (minimum) spaced no greater than 1 inch (25.4 mm) center-to-center along the edges of the patch, with a minimum edge distance of $^1/_2$ inch (12.7 mm).

R804.3.7 Splicing. Rafters and other structural members, except ceiling joists, shall not be spliced. Splices in ceiling joists shall only be permitted at interior bearing points and shall be constructed in accordance with Figure R804.3.7(1). Spliced ceiling joists shall be connected with the same number and size of screws on connection. Splicing of tracks shall conform with Figure R804.3.7(2).

R804.3.8 Bearing stiffener. A bearing stiffener shall be fabricated from a minimum 33-mil (0.84 mm) C-section or track section. Each stiffener shall be fastened to the web of the ceiling joist with a minimum of four No. 8 screws equally spaced as shown in Figure R804.3.8. Stiffeners shall extend across the full depth of the web and shall be installed on either side of the web.

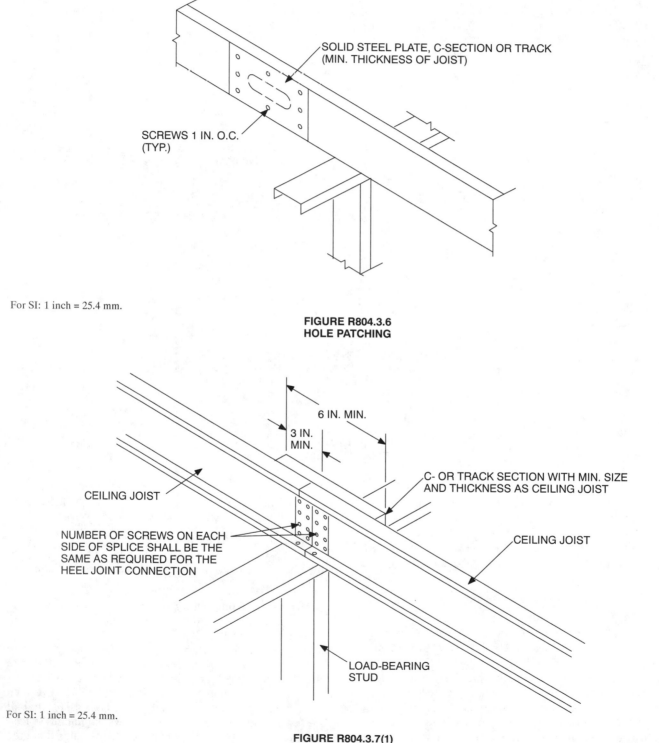

SOLID STEEL PLATE, C-SECTION OR TRACK
(MIN. THICKNESS OF JOIST)

SCREWS 1 IN. O.C.
(TYP.)

For SI: 1 inch = 25.4 mm.

FIGURE R804.3.6
HOLE PATCHING

6 IN. MIN.

3 IN.
MIN.

CEILING JOIST

C- OR TRACK SECTION WITH MIN. SIZE
AND THICKNESS AS CEILING JOIST

NUMBER OF SCREWS ON EACH
SIDE OF SPLICE SHALL BE THE
SAME AS REQUIRED FOR THE
HEEL JOINT CONNECTION

CEILING JOIST

LOAD-BEARING
STUD

For SI: 1 inch = 25.4 mm.

FIGURE R804.3.7(1)
SPLICED CEILING JOISTS

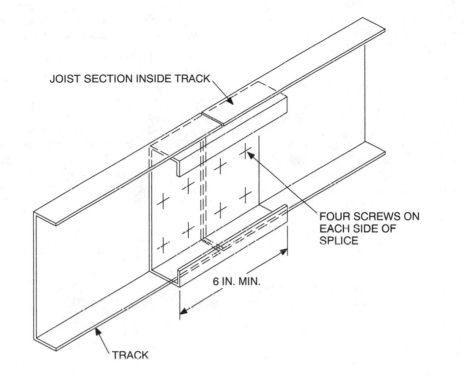

JOIST SECTION INSIDE TRACK

FOUR SCREWS ON
EACH SIDE OF
SPLICE

6 IN. MIN.

TRACK

For SI: 1 inch = 25.4 mm.

**FIGURE R804.3.7(2)
TRACK SPLICE**

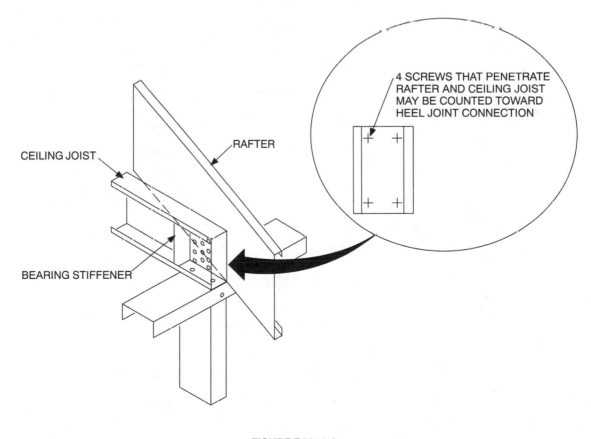

RAFTER

CEILING JOIST

BEARING STIFFENER

4 SCREWS THAT PENETRATE
RAFTER AND CEILING JOIST
MAY BE COUNTED TOWARD
HEEL JOINT CONNECTION

**FIGURE R804.3.8
BEARING STIFFENER**

R804.3.9 Headers. Roof-ceiling framing above wall openings shall be supported on headers. The allowable spans for headers in bearing walls shall not exceed the values set forth in Table R603.6(1).

R804.3.10 Framing of opening. Openings in roof and ceiling framing shall be framed with headers and trimmers between ceiling joists or rafters. Header joist spans shall not exceed 4 feet (1219 mm). Header and trimmer joists shall be fabricated from joist and track sections, which shall be of a minimum size and thickness in accordance with Figures R804.3.10(1) and R804.3.10(2). Each header joist shall be connected to trimmer joist with a minimum of four 2-inch by 2-inch (51 by 51 mm) clip angles. Each clip angle shall be fastened to both the header and trimmer joists with four No. 8 screws, evenly spaced, through each leg of the clip angle. The clip angles shall have a steel thickness not less than that of the floor joist.

R804.4 Roof tie-down. Roof assemblies subject to wind uplift pressures of 20 pounds per square foot (0.96 kN/m^2) or greater,

as established in Table R301.2(2), shall have rafter-to-bearing wall ties provided in accordance with Table R802.11.

R804.4.1 High wind roof tie-down. In areas where the basic wind speed is 110 miles per hour (177 km/h) or greater, roof rafters or trusses shall be attached to their supporting wall assemblies by connections capable of resisting the uplift loads listed in Table R603.8.3.2.1(1). Alternatively, a 1^1/$_4$-inch (32 mm) by minimum 33-mil (0.84 mm) steel uplift strap connecting the rafter or truss to the in-line framing stud below shall be permitted. Each end of the uplift strap shall be fastened with minimum No. 8 screws as required by Table R603.8.3.2.1(2).

SECTION R805
CEILING FINISHES

R805.1 Ceiling installation. Ceilings shall be installed in accordance with the requirements for interior wall finishes as provided in Section R702.

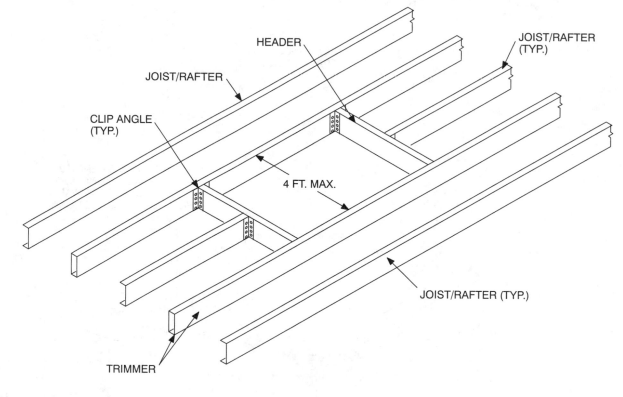

For SI: 1 foot = 304.8 mm.

**FIGURE R804.3.10(1)
ROOF OPENING**

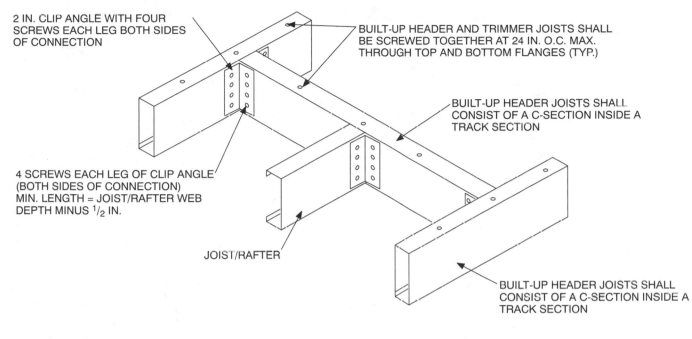

2 IN. CLIP ANGLE WITH FOUR SCREWS EACH LEG BOTH SIDES OF CONNECTION

BUILT-UP HEADER AND TRIMMER JOISTS SHALL BE SCREWED TOGETHER AT 24 IN. O.C. MAX. THROUGH TOP AND BOTTOM FLANGES (TYP.)

BUILT-UP HEADER JOISTS SHALL CONSIST OF A C-SECTION INSIDE A TRACK SECTION

4 SCREWS EACH LEG OF CLIP ANGLE (BOTH SIDES OF CONNECTION) MIN. LENGTH = JOIST/RAFTER WEB DEPTH MINUS 1/2 IN.

JOIST/RAFTER

BUILT-UP HEADER JOISTS SHALL CONSIST OF A C-SECTION INSIDE A TRACK SECTION

For SI: 1 inch = 25.4 mm.

FIGURE R804.3.10(2)
HEADER TO TRIMMER CONNECTION

SECTION R806
ROOF VENTILATION

R806.1 Ventilation required. Enclosed attics and enclosed rafter spaces formed where ceilings are applied directly to the underside of roof rafters shall have cross ventilation for each separate space by ventilating openings protected against the entrance of rain or snow. Ventilating openings shall be provided with corrosion-resistant wire mesh, with $1/8$ inch (3.2 mm) minimum to $1/4$ inch (6.35 mm) maximum openings.

R806.2 Minimum area. The total net free ventilating area shall not be less than 1 to 150 of the area of the space ventilated except that the total area is permitted to be reduced to 1 to 300, provided at least 50 percent and not more than 80 percent of the required ventilating area is provided by ventilators located in the upper portion of the space to be ventilated at least 3 feet (914 mm) above eave or cornice vents with the balance of the required ventilation provided by eave or cornice vents. As an alternative, the net free cross-ventilation area may be reduced to 1 to 300 when a vapor barrier having a transmission rate not exceeding 1 perm (57.4 mg/s · m² · Pa) is installed on the warm side of the ceiling.

R806.3 Vent clearance. Where eave or cornice vents are installed, insulation shall not block the free flow of air. A minimum of a 1-inch (25.4 mm) space shall be provided between the insulation and the roof sheathing at the location of the vent.

SECTION R807
ATTIC ACCESS

R807.1 Attic access. In buildings with combustible ceiling or roof construction, an attic access opening shall be provided to attic areas that exceed 30 square feet (2.8 m²) and have a vertical height of 30 inches (762 mm) or greater.

The rough-framed opening shall not be less than 22 inches by 30 inches (559 mm by 762 mm) and shall be located in a hallway or other readily accessible location. A 30-inch (762 mm) minimum unobstructed headroom in the attic space shall be provided at some point above the access opening. See Minnesota Rules, Chapter 1346 for access requirements where mechanical equipment is located in attics.

SECTION R808
INSULATION CLEARANCE

R808.1 Combustible insulation. Combustible insulation shall be separated a minimum of 3 inches (76 mm) from recessed lighting fixtures, fan motors and other heat-producing devices.

Exception: When heat-producing devices are listed for lesser clearances, combustible insulation complying with the listing requirements shall be separated in accordance with the conditions stipulated in the listing.

Recessed lighting fixtures installed in the building thermal envelope shall meet the requirements of Minnesota Statutes Section 16B.617, Minnesota Energy Code.

CHAPTER 9
ROOF ASSEMBLIES

SECTION R901
GENERAL

R901.1 Scope. The provisions of this chapter shall govern the design, materials, construction and quality of roof assemblies.

SECTION R902
ROOF CLASSIFICATION

R902.1 Roofing covering materials. Roofs shall be covered with materials as set forth in Sections R904 and R905. Class A, B or C roofing shall be installed in areas designated by law as requiring their use or when the edge of the roof is less than 3 feet (914 mm) from a property line. Classes A, B and C roofing required to be listed by this section shall be tested in accordance with UL 790 or ASTM E 108. Roof assemblies with coverings of brick, masonry, slate, clay or concrete roof tile, exposed concrete roof deck, ferrous or copper shingles or sheets, and metal sheets and shingles, shall be considered Class A roof coverings.

R902.2 Wood shingles and shakes. When testing wood shingles and shakes in accordance with ASTM E 108 (including the rain test) and ASTM D 2898, the fire tests shall include the intermittent flame test, spread of flame test, burning brand test and flying brand test; additionally, at the conclusion of the rain test, test panels shall be subjected to the intermittent flame test, burning brand test and flying brand test.

R902.2.1 Fire-retardant-treated shingles and shakes.
Fire-retardant-treated wood shakes and shingles shall be treated by impregnation with chemicals by the full-cell vacuum-pressure process, in accordance with AWPA C1. Each bundle shall be marked to identify the manufactured unit and the manufacturer, and shall also be labeled to identify the classification of the material in accordance with the testing required in Section R902.2, the treating company and the quality control agency.

SECTION R903
WEATHER PROTECTION

R903.1 General. Roof decks shall be covered with approved roof coverings secured to the building or structure in accordance with the provisions of this chapter. Roof assemblies shall be designed and installed in accordance with this code and the approved manufacturer's installation instructions such that the roof assembly shall serve to protect the building or structure.

R903.2 Flashing. Flashings shall be installed in such a manner as to prevent moisture entering the wall through the joints in the coping, through moisture permeable material, at intersections with the roof plane or at parapet wall penetrations.

R903.2.1 Locations.
Flashings shall be installed at wall and roof intersections; wherever there is a change in roof slope or

direction; and around roof openings. Where flashing is of metal, the metal shall be corrosion-resistant with a thickness of not less than 0.019 inch (No. 26 galvanized sheet).

R903.3 Coping. Parapet walls shall be properly coped with noncombustible, weatherproof materials of a width no less than the thickness of the parapet wall.

R903.4 Roof drainage. Unless roofs are sloped to drain over roof edges, roof drains shall be installed at each low point of the roof. Where required for roof drainage, scuppers shall be placed level with the roof surface in a wall or parapet. The scupper shall be located as determined by the roof slope and contributing roof area.

R903.4.1 Overflow drains and scuppers.
Where roof drains are required, overflow drains having the same size as the roof drains shall be installed with the inlet flow line located 2 inches (51 mm) above the low point of the roof, or overflow scuppers having three times the size of the roof drains and having a minimum opening height of 4 inches (102 mm) may be installed in the adjacent parapet walls with the inlet flow located 2 inches (51 mm) above the low point of the adjacent roof. The installation and sizing of overflow drains, leaders and conductors shall comply with the *International Plumbing Code*.

Overflow drains shall discharge to an approved location and shall not be connected to roof drain lines.

SECTION R904
MATERIALS

R904.1 Scope. The requirements set forth in this section shall apply to the application of roof covering materials specified herein. Roof assemblies shall be applied in accordance with this chapter and the manufacturer's installation instructions. Installation of roof assmblies shall comply with the applicable provisions of Section R905.

R904.2 Compatibility of materials. Roof assemblies shall be of materials that are compatible with each other and with the building or structure to which the materials are applied.

R904.3 Material specifications and physical characteristics. Roof covering materials shall conform to the applicable standards listed in this chapter. In the absence of applicable standards or where materials are of questionable suitability, testing by an approved testing agency shall be required by the building offical to determine the character, quality and limitations of application of the materials.

R904.4 Product identification. Roof covering materials shall be delivered in packages bearing the manufacturer's identifying marks and approved testing agency labels when required. Bulk shipments of materials shall be accompanied with the same information issued in the form of a certificate or on a bill of lading by the manufacturer.

SECTION R905
REQUIREMENTS FOR ROOF COVERINGS

R905.1 Roof covering application. Roof coverings shall be applied in accordance with the applicable provisions of this section and the manufacturer's installation instructions.

R905.2 Asphalt shingles. The installation of asphalt shingles shall comply with the provisions of this section.

R905.2.1 Sheathing requirements. Asphalt shingles shall be fastened to solidly sheathed decks.

R905.2.2 Slope. Asphalt shingles shall only be used on roof slopes of two units vertical in 12 units horizontal (2:12) or greater. For roof slopes from two units vertical in 12 units horizontal (2:12) up to four units vertical in 12 units horizontal (4:12), double underlayment application is required in accordance with Section R905.2.7.

R905.2.3 Underlayment. Unless otherwise noted, required underlayment shall conform with ASTM D 226, Type I, or ASTM D 4869, Type I.

Self-adhering polymer modified bitumen sheet shall comply with ASTM D 1970.

R905.2.4 Asphalt shingles. Asphalt shingles shall have self-seal strips or be interlocking, and comply with ASTM D 225 or D 3462.

R905.2.5 Fasteners. Fasteners for asphalt shingles shall be galvanized steel, stainless steel, aluminum or copper roofing nails, minimum 12 gage [0.105 inch (2.67 mm)] shank with a minimum $^3/_8$-inch (9.5 mm) diameter head, ASTM F 1667, of a length to penetrate through the roofing materials and a minimum of $^3/_4$ inch (19.1 mm) into the roof sheathing. Where the roof sheathing is less than $^3/_4$ inch (19.1 mm) thick, the fasteners shall penetrate through the sheathing. Fasteners shall comply with ASTM F 1667.

R905.2.6 Attachment. Asphalt shingles shall have the minimum number of fasteners required by the manufacturer. For normal application, asphalt shingles shall be secured to the roof with not less than four fasteners per strip shingle or two fasteners per individual shingle. Where the roof slope exceeds 20 units vertical in 12 units horizontal (20:12), special methods of fastening are required.

Exception: Asphalt strip shingles shall have a minimum of six fasteners per shingle where the roof is in one of the following categories:

1. The basic wind speed per Figure R301.2(4) is 110 miles per hour (177 km/h) or greater and the eave is 20 feet (6096 mm) or higher above grade.
2. The basic wind speed per Figure R301.2(4) is 120 miles per hour (193 km/h) or greater.
3. Special wind zones per Figure R301.2(4).

R905.2.7 Underlayment application. For roof slopes from two units vertical in 12 units horizontal (17-percent slope), up to four units vertical in 12 units horizontal (33-percent slope), underlayment shall be two layers applied in the following manner. Apply a 19-inch (483 mm) strip of underlayment felt parallel with and starting at the eaves, fastened sufficiently to hold in place. Starting at the eave, apply 36-inch-wide (914 mm) sheets of underlayment, overlapping successive sheets 19 inches (483 mm), and fastened sufficiently to hold in place. For roof slopes of four units vertical in 12 units horizontal (33-percent slope) or greater, underlayment shall be one layer applied in the following manner. Underlayment shall be applied shingle fashion, parallel to and starting from the eave and lapped 2 inches (51 mm), fastened sufficiently to hold in place. End laps shall be offset by 6 feet (1829 mm).

R905.2.7.1 Ice protection. In areas where the average daily temperature in January is 25°F (-4°C) or less, an ice barrier that consists of a least two layers of underlayment cemented together or of a self-adhering polymer modified bitumen sheet, shall be used in lieu of normal underlayment and extend from the eave's edge to a point at least 24 inches (610 mm) inside the exterior wall line of the building.

R905.2.7.2 Underlayment and high wind. Underlayment applied in areas subject to high winds [greater than 110 mph (177km/h) per Figure R301.2(4)] shall be applied with corrosion-resistant fasteners in accordance with manufacturer's installation instructions. Fasteners are to be applied along the overlap not farther apart than 36 inches (914 mm) on center.

R905.2.8 Flashing. Flashing for asphalt shingles shall comply with this section.

R905.2.8.1 Base and cap flashing. Base and cap flashing shall be installed in accordance with manufacturer's installation instructions. Base flashing shall be of either corrosion-resistant metal of minimum nominal 0.019-inch (0.483 mm) thickness or mineral surface roll roofing weighing a minimum of 77 pounds per 100 square feet (3.76 kg/m^2). Cap flashing shall be corrosion-resistant metal of minimum nominal 0.019-inch (0.483 mm) thickness.

R905.2.8.2 Valleys. Valley linings shall be installed in accordance with manufacturer's installation instructions before applying shingles. Valley linings of the following types shall be permitted:

1. For open valley (valley lining exposed) lined with metal, the valley lining shall be at least 24 inches (610 mm) wide and of any of the corrosion-resistant metals in Table R905.2.8.2.
2. For open valleys, valley lining of two plies of mineral surface roll roofing, complying with ASTM D 249, shall be permitted. The bottom layer shall be 18 inches (457 mm) and the top layer a minimum of 36 inches (914 mm) wide.
3. For closed valleys (valley covered with shingles), valley lining of one ply of smooth roll roofing complying with ASTM D 224 Type II or Type III and at least 36 inches (914 mm) wide or valley lining as described in Items 1 and 2 above shall be permitted. Specialty underlayment complying with ASTM D 1970 may be used in lieu of the lining material.

TABLE R905.2.8.2
VALLEY LINING MATERIAL

MATERIAL	MINIMUM THICKNESS (inches)	GAGE	WEIGHT (pounds)
Copper	—	—	1
Aluminum	0.024	—	—
Stainless steel	—	28	—
Galvanized steel	0.0179	26 (zinc coated G90)	—
Zinc alloy	0.027	—	—
Lead	—	—	$2^1/_2$
Painted terne	—	—	20

For SI: 1 inch = 25.4 mm, 1 pound = 0.454 kg.

R905.2.8.3 Crickets and saddles. A cricket or saddle shall be installed on the ridge side of any chimney greater than 30 inches (762 mm) wide. Cricket or saddle coverings shall be sheet metal or of the same material as the roof covering.

R905.2.8.4 Sidewall flashing. Flashing against a vertical sidewall shall be by the step-flashing method.

R905.2.8.5 Other flashing. Flashing against a vertical front wall, as well as soil stack, vent pipe and chimney flashing, shall be applied according to asphalt shingle manufacturer's printed instructions.

R905.3 Clay and concrete tile. The installation of clay and concrete shall comply with the provisions of this section. Clay roof tile shall comply with ASTM C1167.

R905.3.1 Deck requirements. Concrete and clay tile shall be installed only over solid sheathing or spaced structural sheathing boards.

R905.3.2 Deck slope. Clay and concrete roof tile shall be installed on roof slopes of two and one-half units vertical in 12 units horizontal ($2^1/_2$:12) or greater. For roof slopes from two and one-half units vertical in 12 units horizontal ($2^1/_2$:12) to four units vertical in 12 units horizontal (4:12), double underlayment application is required in accordance with Section R905.3.3.

R905.3.3 Underlayment. Unless otherwise noted, required underlayment shall conform with ASTM D 226, Type II; ASTM D 2626, Type I; or ASTM D 249 mineral surfaced roll roofing.

R905.3.3.1 Low slope roofs. For roof slopes from two and one half units vertical in 12 units horizontal ($2^1/_2$:12), up to four units vertical in 12 units horizontal (4:12), underlayment shall be a minimum of two layers underlayment applies as follows:

1. Starting at the eave, a 19-inch (483 mm) strip of underlayment shall be applied parallel with the eave and fastened sufficiently in place.

2. Starting at the eave, 36-inch-wide (914 mm) strips of underlayment felt shall be applied, overlapping successive sheets 19 inches (483 mm), and fastened sufficiently in place.

R905.3.3.2 High slope roofs. For roof slopes of four units vertical in 12 units horizontal (4:12) or greater, underlayment shall be a minimum of one layer of underlayment felt applied shingle fashion, parallel to and starting from the eaves and lapped 2 inches (51 mm), fastened sufficiently in place.

R905.3.3.3 Underlayment and high wind. Underlayment applied in areas subject to high wind [greater than 110 miles per hour (177 km/h) per Figure R301.2(4)] shall be applied with corrosion-resistant fasteners in accordance with manufacturer's installation instructions. Fasteners are to be applied along the overlap not farther apart than 36 inches (914 mm) on center.

R905.3.4 Tile. Clay roof tile shall comply with ASTM C 1167.

R905.3.5 Concrete tile. Concrete roof tiles shall be in accordance with the physical test requirements as follows:

1. The transverse strength of tiles shall be determined according to Section 5.3 of ASTM C 1167 and in accordance with Table R905.3.5

2. The absorption of concrete roof tiles shall be according to Section 8 of ASTM C 140. Roof tiles shall absorb not more than 15 percent of the dry weight of the tile during a 24-hour immersion test.

3. Roof tiles shall be tested for freeze/thaw resistance according to Section 8 of ASTM C 67. Roof tiles shall show no breakage and not have more than 1-percent loss in dry weight of any individual concrete roof tile.

TABLE R905.3.5
TRANSVERSE BREAKING STRENGTH OF CONCRETE ROOF TILE

TILE PROFILE	DRY (pounds)	
	AVERAGE OF 5 TILES	INDIVIDUAL TILE
High profile	400	350
Medium profile	300	250
Flat profile	300	250

For SI: 1 pound – 4.45 N.

R905.3.6 Fasteners. Nails shall be corrosion-resistant and not less than 11 gage, $^5/_{16}$-inch (10.6 mm) head, and of sufficient length to penetrate the deck a minimum of $^3/_4$ inch (19.1 mm) or through the thickness of the deck, whichever is less. Attaching wire for clay or concrete tile shall not be smaller than 0.083 inch (2.1 mm). Perimeter fastening areas include three tile courses but not less than 36 inches (914 mm) from either side of hips or ridges and edges of eaves and gable rakes.

R905.3.7 Application. Tile shall be applied in accordance with this chapter and the manufacturer's installation instructions, based on the following:

1. Climatic conditions.
2. Roof slope.
3. Underlayment system.
4. Type of tile being installed.

Clay and concrete roof tiles shall be fastened in accordance with this section and the manufacturer's installation instructions. Perimeter tiles shall be fastened with a minimum of one fastener per tile. Tiles with installed weight less than 9 pounds per square foot (0.43 kN/m^2) require a minimum of one fastener per tile regardless of roof slope. Clay and concrete roof tile attachment shall be in accordance with the manufacturer's installation instructions where applied in areas where the wind speed exceeds 100 miles per hour (161 km/h) and on buildings where the roof is located more than 40 feet (12 192 mm) above grade. In areas subject to snow, a minimum of two fasteners per tile is required. In all other areas, clay and concrete roof tiles shall be attached in accordance with Table R905.3.7.

TABLE R905.3.7
CLAY AND CONCRETE TILE ATTACHMENT

SHEATHING	ROOF SLOPE	NUMBER OF FASTENERS
Solid without battens	All	One per tile
Spaced or solid with battens and slope < 5:12	Fasteners not required	—
Spaced sheathing without battens	5:12 ≤ slope < 12:12	One per tile/every other row
	12:12 ≤ slope < 24:12	One per tile

R905.3.8 Flashing. At the juncture of roof vertical surfaces, flashing and counter flashing shall be provided in accordance with this chapter and the manufacturer's installation instructions and, where of metal, shall not be less than 0.019 inch (0.48 mm) (No. 26 galvanized sheet gage) corrosion-resistant metal. The valley flashing shall extend at least 11 inches (279 mm) from the center line each way and have a splash diverter rib not less than 1 inch (25.4 mm) high at the flow line formed as part of the flashing. Sections of flashing shall have an end lap of not less than 4 inches (102 mm). For roof slopes of 3:12 and over, valley flashing shall have a 36-inch-wide (914 mm) underlayment of one layer of Type I underlayment running the full length of the valley, in addition to other required underlayment. In areas where the average daily temperature in January is 25°F (-4°C) or less, metal valley flashing underlayment shall be solid cemented to the roofing underlayment for slopes under 7:12.

R905.4 Metal roof shingles. The installation of metal roof shingles shall comply with the provisions of this section.

R905.4.1 Deck requirements. Metal roof shingles shall be applied to a solid or closely fitted deck, except where the roof covering is specifically designed to be applied to spaced sheathing.

R905.4.2 Deck slope. Metal roof shingles shall not be installed on roof slopes below three units vertical in 12 units horizontal (25-percent slope).

R905.4.3 Underlayment. In areas where the average daily temperature in January is 25°F (-4°C) or less, an ice barrier that consists of at least two layers of underlayment cemented together or of a self-adhering polymer modified bitumen sheet shall be used in lieu of normal underlayment and extend from the eave's edge to a point at least 24 inches (610 mm) inside the exterior wall line of the building. Underlayment shall comply with ASTM D 226, Type I.

R905.4.4 Material standards. Metal roof shingle roof coverings of galvanized steel shall be 0.013 inch (0.378 mm) minimum thickness. Metal roof shingle roof coverings of aluminum shall be of 0.024 inch (0.610 mm) minimum thickness.

R905.4.5 Application. Metal roof shingles shall be secured to the roof in accordance with this chapter and the approved manufacturer's installation instructions.

R905.4.6 Flashing. Roof valley flashing shall be provided of corrosion-resistant metal of the same material as the roof covering or shall comply with the standards in Table R905.10.3. The valley flashing shall extend at least 8 inches (203 mm) from the center line each way and shall have a splash diverter rib not less than $^3/_4$ inch (19.1 mm) high at the flow line formed as part of the flashing. Sections of flashing shall have an end lap of not less than 4 inches (102 mm). The metal valley flashing shall have a 36-inch-wide (914 mm) underlayment directly under it consisting of one layer of underlayment running the full length of the valley, in addition to underlayment required for metal roof shingles. In areas where the average daily temperature in January is 25°F (-4°C) or less , the metal valley flashing underlayment shall be solid cemented to the roofing underlayment for roof slopes under seven units vertical in 12 units horizontal (58.3-percent slope) or self-adhering polymer modified bitumen sheet.

R905.5 Mineral-surfaced roll roofing. The installation of mineral-surfaced rolling roofing shall comply with this section.

R905.5.1 Deck requirements. Mineral-surfaced roll roofing shall be fastened to solidly sheathed roofs.

R905.5.2 Deck slope. Mineral-surfaced roll roofing shall not be applied on roof slopes below one unit vertical in 12 units horizontal (8-percent slope).

R905.5.3 Underlayment. In areas where the average daily temperature in January is 25°F (-4°C) or less, an ice barrier that consists of at least two layers of underlayment cemented together or of a self-adhering polymer modified bitumen sheet shall extend from the eave's edge to a point at least 24 inches (610 mm) inside the exterior wall line of the building. Underlayment shall conform with ASTM D 226, Type I.

R905.5.4 Material standards. Mineral-surfaced roll roofing shall conform to ASTM D 224, D 249, D 371 or D 3909.

R905.5.5 Application. Mineral-surfaced roll roofing shall be installed in accordance with this chapter and the manufacturer's installation instructions.

R905.6 Slate and slate-type shingles. The installation of slate and slate-type shingles shall comply with the provisions of this section.

R905.6.1 Deck requirements. Slate shingles shall be fastened to solidly sheathed roofs.

R905.6.2 Deck slope. Slate shingles shall only be used on slopes of four units vertical in 12 units horizontal (33-percent slope) or greater.

R905.6.3 Underlayment. In areas where the average daily temperature in January is 25°F (-4°C) or less, an ice barrier that consists of at least two layers of underlayment cemented together or of a self-adhering polymer modified bitumen sheet shall extend from the eave's edge to a point at least 24 inches (610 mm) inside the exterior wall line of the building. Underlayment shall comply with ASTM D 226, Type II.

R905.6.4 Material standards. Slate shingles shall comply with ASTM C 406.

R905.6.5 Application. Minimum headlap for slate shingles shall be in accordance with Table R905.6.5. Slate shingles shall be secured to the roof with two fasteners per slate. Slate shingles shall be installed in accordance with this chapter and the manufacturer's installation instructions.

TABLE R905.6.5
SLATE SHINGLE HEADLAP

SLOPE	HEADLAP (inches)
4:12 ≤ slope < 8:12	4
8:12 ≤ slope < 20:12	3
slope ≥ 20:12	2

For SI: 1 inch = 25.4 mm.

R905.6.6 Flashing. Flashing and counterflashing shall be made with sheet metal. Valley flashing shall be a minimum of 15 inches (381 mm) wide. Valley and flashing metal shall be a minimum uncoated thickness of 0.0179-inch (0.455 mm) zinc coated G90. Chimneys, stucco or brick walls shall have a minimum of two plies of felt for a cap flashing consisting of a 4-inch-wide (102 mm) strip of felt set in plastic cement and extending 1 inch (25.4 mm) above the first felt and a top coating of plastic cement. The felt shall extend over the base flashing 2 inches (51 mm).

R905.7 Wood shingles. The installation of wood shingles shall comply with the provisions of this section.

R905.7.1 Deck requirements. Wood shingles shall be installed on solid or spaced sheathing. Where spaced sheathing is used, sheathing boards shall not be less than 1-inch by 4-inch (25.4 mm by 102 mm) nominal dimensions and shall be spaced on centers equal to the weather exposure to coincide with the placement of fasteners.

R905.7.1.1 Solid sheathing required. In areas where the average daily temperature in January is 25°F (-4°C) or less, solid sheathing is required on that portion of the roof requiring the application of an ice shield.

R905.7.2 Deck slope. Wood shingles shall be installed on slopes of three units vertical in 12 units horizontal (25-percent slope) or greater.

R905.7.3 Underlayment. In areas where the average daily temperature in January is 25°F (-4°C) or less, an ice barrier that consists of at least two layers of underlayment cemented together or of a self-adhering polymer modified bitumen sheet shall extend from the eave's edge to a point at least 24 inches (610 mm) inside the exterior wall line of the building. Underlayment shall comply with ASTM D 226, Type I.

R905.7.4 Material standards. Wood shingles shall be of naturally durable wood and comply with the requirements of Table R905.7.4.

TABLE R905.7.4
WOOD SHINGLE MATERIAL REQUIREMENTS

MATERIAL	MINIMUM GRADES	APPLICABLE GRADING RULES
Wood shingles of naturally durable wood	1, 2 or 3	Cedar Shake and Shingle Bureau

R905.7.5 Application. Wood shingles shall be installed according to this chapter and the manufacturer's installation instructions. Wood shingles shall be laid with a side lap not less than 1½ inches (38 mm) between joints in courses, and no two joints in any three adjacent courses shall be in direct alignment. Spacing between shingles shall not be less than ¼ inch to ⅜ inch (6.4 mm to 9.5 mm). Weather exposure for wood shingles shall not exceed those set in Table R905.7.5. Fasteners for wood shingles shall be corrosion-resistant with a minimum penetration of ½ inch (12.7 mm) into the sheathing. For sheathing less than ½ inch (12.7 mm) in thickness, the fasteners shall extend through the sheathing. Wood shingles shall be attached to the roof with two fasteners per shingle, positioned no more than ¾ inch (19.1 mm) from each edge and no more than 1 inch (25.4 mm) above the exposure line.

TABLE R905.7.5
WOOD SHINGLE WEATHER EXPOSURE AND ROOF SLOPE

ROOFING MATERIAL	LENGTH (inches)	GRADE	EXPOSURE (inches) 3:12 pitch to < 4:12	4:12 pitch or steeper
Shingles of naturally durable wood	16	No. 1	3¾	5
		No. 2	3½	4
		No. 3	3	3½
	18	No. 1	4¼	5½
		No. 2	4	4½
		No. 3	3½	4
	24	No. 1	5¾	7½
		No. 2	5½	6½
		No. 3	5	5½

For SI: 1 inch = 25.4 mm.

R905.7.6 Valley flashing. Roof flashing shall be not less than No. 26 gage [0.019 inches (0.48 mm)] corrosion-resistant sheet metal and shall extend 10 inches (254 mm) from the centerline each way for roofs having slopes less than 12 units vertical in 12 units horizontal (100-percent slope), and 7 inches (178 mm) from the centerline each way for slopes of 12 units vertical in 12 units horizontal and greater. Sections of flashing shall have an end lap of not less than 4 inches (102 mm).

R905.7.7 Label required. Each bundle of shingles shall be identified by a label of an approved grading or inspection bureau or agency.

R905.8 Wood shakes. The installation of wood shakes shall comply with the provisions of this section.

R905.8.1 Deck requirements. Wood shakes shall only be used on solid or spaced sheathing. Where spaced sheathing is used, sheathing boards shall not be less than 1-inch by 4-inch (25 mm by 102 mm) nominal dimensions and shall be spaced on centers equal to the weather exposure to coincide with the placement of fasteners. Where 1-inch by 4-inch (25 mm by 102 mm) spaced sheathing is installed at 10 inches (254 mm) on center, additional 1-inch by 4-inch (25 mm by 102 mm) boards shall be installed between the sheathing boards.

R905.8.1.1 Solid sheathing required. In areas where the average daily temperature in January is 25°F (-4°C) or less, solid sheathing is required on that portion of the roof requiring an ice barrier.

R905.8.2 Deck slope. Wood shakes shall only be used on slopes of three units vertical in 12 units horizontal (25-percent slope) or greater.

R905.8.3 Underlayment. In areas where the average daily temperature in January is 25°F (-4°C) or less, an ice barrier that consists of at least two layers of underlayment cemented together or a self-adhering polymer modified bitumen sheet shall extend from the edge of the eave to a point at least 24 inches (610 mm) inside the exterior wall line of the building. Underlayment shall comply with ASTM D 226, Type I.

R905.8.4 Interlayment. Interlayment shall comply with ASTM D 226, Type I.

R905.8.5 Material standards. Wood shakes shall comply with the requirements of Table R905.8.5.

TABLE R905.8.5
WOOD SHAKE MATERIAL REQUIREMENTS

MATERIAL	MINIMUM GRADES	APPLICABLE GRADING RULES
Wood shakes of naturally durable wood	1	Cedar Shake and Shingle Bureau
Taper sawn shakes of naturally durable wood	1 or 2	Cedar Shake and Shingle Bureau
Preservative-treated shakes and shingles of naturally durable wood	1	Cedar Shake and Shingle Bureau
Fire-retardant-treated shakes and shingles of naturally durable wood	1	Cedar Shake and Shingle Bureau
Preservative-treated tapersawn shakes of southern yellow pine treated in accordance with AWPA Standard C2	1 or 2	Forest Products Laboratory of the Texas Forest Services

R905.8.6 Application. Wood shakes shall be installed according to this chapter and the manufacturer's installation instructions. Wood shakes shall be laid with a side lap not less than 1$^1/_2$ inches (38 mm) between joints in adjacent courses. Spacing between shakes in the same course shall be $^1/_8$ inch to $^5/_8$ inch (3.2 mm to 15.9 mm) for shakes and taper-sawn shakes of naturally durable wood and shall be $^1/_4$ inch to $^3/_8$ inch (6.4 mm to 9.5 mm) for preservative tapersawn shakes. Weather exposure for wood shakes shall not exceed those set forth in Table R905.8.6. Fasteners for wood shakes shall be corrosion-resistant, with a minimum penetration of $^1/_2$ inch (12.7 mm) into the sheathing. For sheathing less than $^1/_2$ inch (12.7 mm) in thickness, the fasteners shall extend through the sheathing. Wood shakes shall be attached to the roof with two fasteners per shake, positioned no more than 1 inch (25.4 mm) from each edge and no more than 2 inches (51 mm) above the exposure line.

TABLE R905.8.6
WOOD SHAKE WEATHER EXPOSURE AND ROOF SLOPE

ROOFING MATERIAL	LENGTH (inches)	GRADE	EXPOSURE (inches) 4:12 pitch or steeper
Shakes of naturally durable wood	18	No. 1	7$^1/_2$
	24	No. 1	10[a]
Preservative-treated taper sawn shakes of southern yellow pine	18	No. 1	7$^1/_2$
	24	No. 1	10
	18	No. 2	5$^1/_2$
	24	No. 2	7$^1/_2$
Taper-sawn shakes of naturally durable wood	18	No. 1	7$^1/_2$
	24	No. 1	10
	18	No. 2	5$^1/_2$
	24	No. 2	7$^1/_2$

For SI: 1 inch = 25.4 mm.

a. For 24-inch by $^3/_8$-inch handsplit shakes, the maximum exposure is 7$^1/_2$ inches.

R905.8.7 Shake placement. The starter course at the eaves shall be doubled and the bottom layer shall be either 15-inch (381 mm), 18-inch (457 mm) or 24-inch (610 mm) wood shakes or wood shingles. Fifteen-inch (381 mm) or 18-inch (457 mm) wood shakes may be used for the final course at the ridge. Shakes shall be interlaid with 18-inch-wide (457 mm) strips of not less than No. 30 felt shingled between each course in such a manner that no felt is exposed to the weather by positioning the lower edge of each felt strip above the butt end of the shake it covers a distance equal to twice the weather exposure.

R905.8.8 Valley flashing. Roof valley flashing shall not be less than No. 26 gage [0.019 inches (0.48 mm)] corrosion-resistant sheet metal and shall extend at least 11 inches (279 mm) from the centerline each way. Sections of flashing shall have an end lap of not less than 4 inches (102 mm).

R905.8.9 Label required. Each bundle of shakes shall be identified by a label of an approved grading or inspection bureau or agency.

R905.9 Built-up roofs. The installation of built-up roofs shall comply with the provisions of this section.

R905.9.1 Slope. Built-up roofs shall have a design slope of a minimum of one-fourth unit vertical in 12 units horizontal (2-percent slope) for drainage, except for coal-tar built-up roofs, which shall have a design slope of a minimum one-eighth unit vertical in 12 units horizontal (1-percent slope).

R905.9.2 Material standards. Built-up roof covering materials shall comply with the standards in Table R905.9.2.

R905.9.3 Application. Built-up roofs shall be installed according to this chapter and the manufacturer's installation instructions.

R905.10 Metal roof panels. The installation of metal roof panels shall comply with the provisions of this section.

R905.10.1 Deck requirements. Metal roof panel roof coverings shall be applied to a solid or spaced sheathing, except where the roof covering is specifically designed to be applied to spaced supports.

R905.10.2 Slope. The minimum slope for lapped, nonsoldered seam metal roofs without applied lap sealant shall be three units vertical in 12 units horizontal (25-percent slope). The minimum slope for lapped, nonsoldered seam metal roofs with applied lap sealant shall be one-half vertical unit in 12 units horizontal (4-percent slope). The minimum slope for standing seam roof systems shall be one-fourth unit vertical in 12 units horizontal (2-percent slope).

R905.10.3 Material standards. Metal-sheet roof covering systems that incorporate supporting structural members shall be designed in accordance with the *International Building Code*. Metal-sheet roof coverings installed over structural decking shall comply with Table R905.10.3.

TABLE R905.9.2
BUILT-UP ROOFING MATERIAL STANDARDS

MATERIAL STANDARD	STANDARD
Acrylic coatings used in roofing	ASTM D 6083
Aggregate surfacing	ASTM D 1863
Asphalt adhesive used in roofing	ASTM D 3747
Asphalt cements used in roofing	ASTM D 3019; D 2822; D 4586
Asphalt-coated glass fiber base sheet	ASTM D 4601
Asphalt coatings used in roofing	ASTM D 1227; D 2823; D 2824; D 4479
Asphalt glass felt	ASTM D 2178
Asphalt primer used in roofing	ASTM D 41
Asphalt-saturated and asphalt-coated organic felt base sheet	ASTM D 2626
Asphalt-saturated organic felt (perforated)	ASTM D 226
Asphalt used in roofing	ASTM D 312
Coal tar cements used in roofing	ASTM D 4022; D 5643
Coal-tar saturated organic felt	ASTM D 227
Coal-tar used in roofing	ASTM D 450, Types I or II
Glass mat, coal tar	ASTM D 4990
Glass mat, venting type	ASTM D 4897
Mineral-surfaced inorganic cap sheet	ASTM D 3909
Thermoplastic fabrics used in roofing	ASTM D 5665; D 5726

TABLE R905.10.3
METAL ROOF COVERINGS STANDARDS AND INSTALLATION

ROOF COVERING TYPE	STANDARD APPLICATION RATE/THICKNESS
Galvanized steel	ASTM A 653 G-90 zinc coated, 0.013 inch thick minimum
Prepainted steel	ASTM A 755
Aluminum zinc alloy coated steel	ASTM A 792 AZ 50
Lead-coated copper	ASTM B 101
Copper	ASTM B 370, 16 oz. per sq. ft. for metal sheet roof covering systems; 12 oz. per sq. ft. for preformed metal shingle systems.CDA 4115
Hard lead	2 lbs. per sq. ft.
Soft lead	3 lbs. per sq. ft.
Aluminum	0.024 inch minimum thickness
Terne (tin) and terne coated stainless	Terne coating of 40 lb. per double base box, field painted where applicable in accordance with manufacturer's installation instructions.

For SI: 1 inch = 25.4 mm, 1 square foot = 0.0929 m², 1 pound = 0.454 kg, 1 ounce per square foot = 305 g/m², 1 pound per square foot = 0.0479 kN/m².

R905.10.4 Attachment. Metal roofing shall be installed in accordance with this chapter and the manufacturer's installation instructions. Metal roofing fastened directly to steel framing shall be attached by approved fasteners. The following fasteners shall be used:

1. Galvanized fasteners shall be used for galvanized roofs.
2. Hard copper or copper alloy shall be used for copper roofs.
3. Stainless steel fasteners are acceptable for metal roofs.

R905.11 Modified bitumen roofing. The installation of modified bitumen roofing shall comply with the provisions of this section.

R905.11.1 Slope. Modified bitumen membrane roofs shall have a design slope of a minimum of one-fourth unit vertical in 12 units horizontal (2-percent slope) for drainage.

R905.11.2 Material standards. Modified bitumen roof coverings shall comply with the standards in Table R905.11.2.

TABLE R905.11.2
MODIFIED BITUMEN ROOFING MATERIAL STANDARDS

MATERIAL	STANDARD
Modified bitumen roof membrane	ASTM D 6162; D 6163; D 6164; D 6222; D 6223; CGSB 37-56M
Asphalt primer	ASTM D 41
Asphalt cement	ASTM D 3019
Asphalt adhesive	ASTM D 3747
Asphalt coating	ASTM D 1227; D 2824
Acrylic coating	ASTM D 6083

R905.11.3 Application. Modified bitumen roofs shall be installed according to this chapter and the manufacturer's installation instructions.

R905.12 Thermoset single-ply roofing. The installation of thermoset single-ply roofing shall comply with the provisions of this section.

R905.12.1 Slope. Thermoset single-ply membrane roofs shall have a design slope of a minimum of one-fourth unit vertical in 12 units horizontal (2-percent slope) for drainage.

R905.12.2 Materials standards. Thermoset single-ply roof coverings shall comply with RMA RP-1, RP-2 or RP-3, or ASTM D 4637 or CGSB 37-52M.

R905.12.3 Application. Thermoset single-ply roofs shall be installed according to this chapter and the manufacturer's installation instructions.

R905.13 Thermoplastic single-ply roofing. The installation of thermoplastic single-ply roofing shall comply with the provisions of this section.

R905.13.1 Slope. Thermoplastic single-ply membrane roofs shall have a design slope of a minimum of one-fourth unit vertical in 12 units horizontal (2-percent slope).

R905.13.2 Material standards. Thermoplastic single-ply roof coverings shall comply with ASTM D 4434 or CGSB 37-54M.

R905.13.3 Application. Thermoplastic single-ply roofs shall be installed according to this chapter and the manufacturer's installation instructions.

R905.14 Sprayed polyurethane foam roofing. The installation of sprayed polyurethane foam roofing shall comply with the provisions of this section.

R905.14.1 Slope. Sprayed polyurethane foam roofs shall have a design slope of a minimum of one-fourth unit vertical in 12 units horizontal (2-percent slope) for drainage.

R905.14.2 Material standards. Spray-applied polyurethane-foam insulation shall comply with ASTM C 1029.

R905.14.3 Application. Foamed in place roof insulation shall be installed in accordance with this chapter and the manufacturer's installation instructions. A liquid-applied protective coating that complies with Section R905.15 shall be applied no less than 2 hours nor more than 72 hours following the application of the foam.

R905.14.4 Foam plastics. Foam plastic materials and installation shall comply with Section R318.

R905.15 Liquid-applied coatings. The installation of liquid-applied coatings shall comply with the provisions of this section.

R905.15.1 Slope. Liquid-applied roofs shall have a design slope of a minimum of one-fourth unit vertical in 12 units horizontal (2-percent slope).

R905.15.2 Material standards. Liquid-applied roof coatings shall comply with ASTM C 836, C 957, D 1227, D 3468 or D 6083.

R905.15.3 Application. Liquid-applied roof coatings shall be installed according to this chapter and the manufacturer's installation instructions.

SECTION R906
ROOF INSULATION

R906.1 General. The use of above deck thermal insulation shall be permitted provided such insulation is covered with an approved roof covering and passes FM 4450 or UL 1256.

SECTION R907
REROOFING

R907.1 General. Materials and methods of application used for recovering or replacing an existing roof covering shall comply with the requirements of this chapter. Roof repairs to existing roofs and roof coverings shall comply with the provisions of Chapter 34 of the *International Building Code*, but more than 25 percent of the roof covering of any building shall not be removed and replaced within a 12-month period unless the entire roof covering is made to conform to the requirements for new roofing.

Exception: Reroofing shall not be required to meet the minimum design slope requirement of one-fourth vertical in 12 units horizontal (2-percent slope) in Section R905 for roofs that provide positive roof drainage.

R907.2 Structural and construction loads. The structural roof components shall be capable of supporting the roof covering system and the material and equipment loads that will be encountered during installation of the roof covering system.

R907.3 Recovering versus replacement. New roof coverings shall not be installed without first removing existing roof coverings where any of the following conditions occur:

1. Where the existing roof or roof covering is water-soaked or has deteriorated to the point that the existing roof or roof covering is not adequate as a base for additional roofing.
2. Where the existing roof covering is wood shake, slate, clay, cement or asbestos-cement tile.
3. Where the existing roof has two or more applications of any type of roof covering.
4. For asphalt shingles, when the building is located in an area subject to severe hail damage according to Figure R907.3.

Exceptions:
1. Complete and separate roofing systems, such as standing-seam metal roof systems, that are designed to transmit the roof loads directly to the building's structural system and that do not rely on existing roofs and roof coverings for support shall not require the removal of existing roof coverings.
2. Metal panel, metal shingle, and concrete and clay tile roof coverings shall be permitted to be installed over existing wood shake roofs when applied in accordance with Section R907.4.

R907.4 Roof recovering. Where the application of a new roof covering over wood shingle or shake roofs creates a combustible concealed space, the entire existing surface shall be covered with gypsum board, mineral fiber, glass fiber or other approved materials securely fastened in place.

R907.5 Reinstallation of materials. Existing slate, clay or cement tile shall be permitted for reinstallation, except that damaged, cracked or broken slate or tile shall not be reinstalled. Existing vent flashing, metal edgings, drain outlets, collars and metal counterflashings shall not be reinstalled where rusted, damaged or deteriorated. Aggregate surfacing materials shall not be reinstalled.

R907.6 Flashings. Flashings shall be reconstructed in accordance with approved manufacturer's installation instructions. Metal flashing to which bituminous materials are to be adhered shall be primed prior to installation.

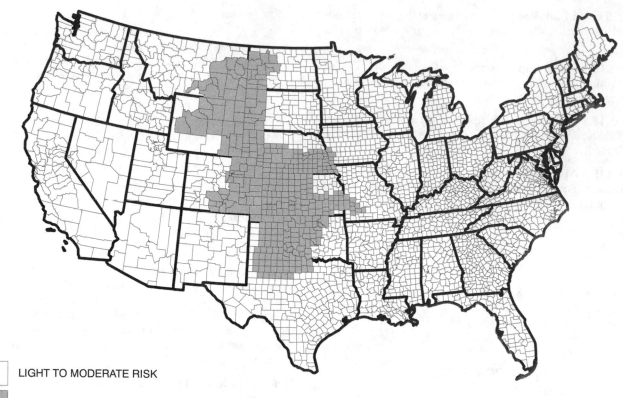

LIGHT TO MODERATE RISK

SEVERE RISK

For SI: 1 inch = 25.4 mm.

a. Shaded portion of map denotes locations with a high probability of severe hail. A severe classification is where weather conditions frequently produce damaging hailstorms.

b. Areas with greater than a 50/50 chance of a 1-inch or larger diameter hailstone occurring at a point at least once in a 5-year period.

**FIGURE R907.3
HAIL RISK MAP[a,b]**

CHAPTER 10

CHIMNEYS AND FIREPLACES

SECTION R1001
MASONRY CHIMNEYS

R1001.1 General. Masonry chimneys shall be constructed, anchored, supported and reinforced as required in this chapter and the applicable provisions of Chapters 3, 4 and 6. In Seismic Design Categories D_1 and D_2, masonry and concrete chimneys shall be reinforced and anchored as detailed in Section R1003 for chimneys serving fireplaces. In Seismic Design Category A, B or C, reinforcement and seismic anchorage is not required. Chimneys shall be structurally sound, durable, smoke-tight and capable of conveying flue gases to the exterior safely.

R1001.1.1 Support. Masonry chimneys shall be supported on foundations of solid masonry or concrete at least 12 inches (305 mm) thick and at least 6 inches (152 mm) beyond each side of the exterior dimensions of the chimney. Footings shall be founded on natural, undisturbed earth below the frostline. In areas not subject to freezing, footings shall be located a minimum of 12 inches (305 mm) below finished grade.

R1001.2 Corbeling. Masonry chimneys shall not be corbeled more than one-half of the chimney's wall thickness from a wall or foundation, nor shall a chimney be corbeled from a wall or foundation that is less than 12 inches (305 mm) in thickness unless it projects equally on each side of the wall, except that on the second story of a two-story dwelling, corbeling of chimneys on the exterior of the enclosing walls may equal the wall thickness. The projection of a single course shall not exceed one-half the unit height or one-third of the unit bed depth, whichever is less.

R1001.3 Changes in dimension. The chimney wall or chimney flue lining shall not change in size or shape within 6 inches (152 mm) above or below where the chimney passes through floor components, ceiling components or roof components.

R1001.4 Offsets. Where a masonry chimney is constructed with a fireclay flue liner surrounded by one wythe of masonry, the maximum offset shall be such that the centerline of the flue above the offset does not extend beyond the center of the chimney wall below the offset. Where the chimney offset is supported by masonry below the offset in an approved manner, the maximum offset limitations shall not apply. Each individual corbeled masonry course of the offset shall not exceed the projection limitations specified in Section R1001.2.

R1001.5 Additional load. Chimneys shall not support loads other than their own weight unless they are designed and constructed to support the additional load. Masonry chimneys shall be permitted to be constructed as part of the masonry walls or reinforced concrete walls of the building.

R1001.6 Termination. Chimneys shall extend at least 2 feet (610 mm) higher than any portion of a building within 10 feet (3048 mm), but shall not be less than 3 feet (914 mm) above the point where the chimney passes through the roof.

R1001.7 Wall thickness. Masonry chimney walls shall be constructed of solid masonry units or hollow masonry units grouted solid with not less than a 4-inch (102 mm) nominal thickness.

R1001.8 Flue lining (material). Masonry chimneys shall be lined. The lining material shall be appropriate for the type of appliance connected, according to the terms of the appliance listing and manufacturer's instructions.

R1001.8.1 Residential-type appliances (general). Flue lining systems shall comply with one of the following:

1. Clay flue lining complying with the requirements of ASTM C 315 or equivalent.
2. Listed chimney lining systems complying with UL 1777.
3. Factory-built chimneys or chimney units listed for installation within masonry chimneys.
4. Other approved materials that will resist, without cracking, softening or corrosion, and flue gases and condensate at temperatures up to 1,800°F (982°C).

R1001.8.2 Flue linings for specific appliances. Flue linings other than these covered in Section R1001.8.1, intended for use with specific types of appliances, shall comply with Sections R1001.8.3 through R1001.8.6.

R1001.8.3 Gas appliances. Flue lining systems for gas appliances shall be in accordance with Minnesota Rules, Chapter 1346.

R1001.8.4 Pellet fuel-burning appliances. Flue lining and vent systems for use in masonry chimneys with pellet fuel burning appliances shall be limited to the following:

1. Flue lining systems complying with Section R1001.8.1.
2. Pellet vents listed for installation within masonry chimneys. (See Section R1001.8.6 for marking.)

R1001.8.5 Oil-fired appliances approved for use with Type L vent. Flue lining and vent systems for use in masonry chimneys with oil-fired appliances approved for use with Type L vent shall be limited to the following:

1. Flue lining systems complying with Section R1001.8.1.
2. Listed chimney liners complying with UL 641. (See Section R1001.8.6 for marking.)

R1001.8.6 Notice of usage. When a flue is relined with a material not complying with Section R1001.8.1, the chimney shall be plainly and permanently identified by a label attached to a wall, ceiling or other conspicuous location adjacent to where the connector enters the chimney. The label shall include the following message or equivalent language:

THIS CHIMNEY FLUE IS FOR USE ONLY WITH [TYPE OR CATEGORY OF APPLIANCE] APPLIANCES THAT BURN [TYPE OF FUEL]. DO NOT CONNECT OTHER TYPES OF APPLIANCES.

R1001.9 Flue lining (installation). Flue liners shall be installed in accordance with ASTM C 1283 and extend from a point not less than 8 inches (203 mm) below the lowest inlet or, in the case of fireplaces, from the top of the smoke chamber to a point above the enclosing walls. The lining shall be carried up vertically, with a maximum slope no greater than 30 degrees from the vertical.

Fireclay flue liners shall be laid in medium-duty refractory mortar conforming to ASTM C 199 with tight mortar joints left smooth on the inside and installed to maintain an air space or insulation not to exceed the thickness of the flue liner separating the flue liners from the interior face of the chimney masonry walls. Flue lining shall be supported on all sides. Only enough mortar shall be placed to make the joint and hold the liners in position.

R1001.9.1 Listed materials. Listed materials used as flue linings shall be installed in accordance with the terms of their listings and manufacturer's instructions.

R1001.9.2 Space around lining. The space surrounding a chimney lining system or vent installed within a masonry chimney shall not be used to vent any other appliance.

Exception: This shall not prevent the installation of a separate flue lining in accordance with the manufacturer's installation instructions.

R1001.10 Multiple flues. When two or more flues are located in the same chimney, masonry wythes shall be built between adjacent flue linings. The masonry wythes shall be at least 4 inches (102 mm) thick and bonded into the walls of the chimney.

Exception: When venting only one appliance, two flues may adjoin each other in the same chimney with only the flue lining separation between them. The joints of the adjacent flue linings shall be staggered at least 4 inches (102 mm).

R1001.11 Flue area (appliance). Chimney flues shall not be smaller in area than that of the area of the connector from the appliance [see Tables R1001.11(1) and R1001.11(2)]. The sizing of a chimney flue to which multiple-appliance venting systems are connected shall be in accordance with Minnesota Rules, Chapter 1346.

MNM

TABLE R1001.11(1)
NET CROSS-SECTIONAL AREA OF ROUND FLUE SIZES[a]

FLUE SIZE, INSIDE DIAMETER (inches)	CROSS-SECTIONAL AREA (square inches)
6	28
7	38
8	50
10	78
10³/₄	90
12	113
15	176
18	254

For SI: 1 inch = 25.4 mm, 1 square inch = 645.16 mm².

a. Flue sizes are based on ASTM C 315.

TABLE R1001.11(2)
NET CROSS-SECTIONAL AREA OF SQUARE AND RECTANGULAR FLUE SIZES[a]

FLUE SIZE, OUTSIDE DIMENSIONS (inches)	CROSS-SECTIONAL AREA (square inches)
4¹/₂ × 13	34
7¹/₂ × 7¹/₂	37
8¹/₂ × 8¹/₂	47
7¹/₂ × 11¹/₂	58
8¹/₂ × 13	74
7¹/₂ × 15¹/₂	82
11¹/₂ × 11¹/₂	91
8¹/₂ × 17¹/₂	101
13 × 13	122
11¹/₂ × 15¹/₂	124
13 × 17¹/₂	165
15¹/₂ × 15¹/₂	168
15¹/₂ × 19¹/₂	214
17¹/₂ × 17¹/₂	226
19¹/₂ × 19¹/₂	269
20 × 20	286

For SI: 1 inch = 25.4 mm, 1 square inch = 645.16 mm².

a. Flue sizes are based on ASTM C 315.

R1001.12 Flue area (masonry fireplace). Flue sizing for chimneys serving fireplaces shall be in accordance with Section R1001.12.1 or Section R1001.12.2.

R1001.12.1 Option 1. Round chimney flues shall have a minimum net cross-sectional area of at ¹/₁₂ of the fireplace opening. Square chimney flues shall have a minimum net cross-sectional area of ¹/₁₀ of the fireplace opening. Rectangular chimney flues with an aspect ratio less than 2 to 1 shall have a minimum net cross-sectional area of ¹/₁₀ of the fireplace opening. Rectangular chimney flues with an aspect ratio of 2 to 1 or more shall have a minimum net cross-sectional area of ¹/₈ of the fireplace opening.

R1001.12.2 Option 2. The minimum net cross-sectional area of the chimney flue shall be determined in accordance with Figure R1001.12.2. A flue size providing at least the equivalent net cross-sectional area shall be used. Cross-sectional areas of clay flue linings are provided in Tables R1001.11(1) and R1001.11(2) or as provided by the manufacturer or as measured in the field. The height of the chimney shall be measured from the firebox floor to the top of the chimney flue.

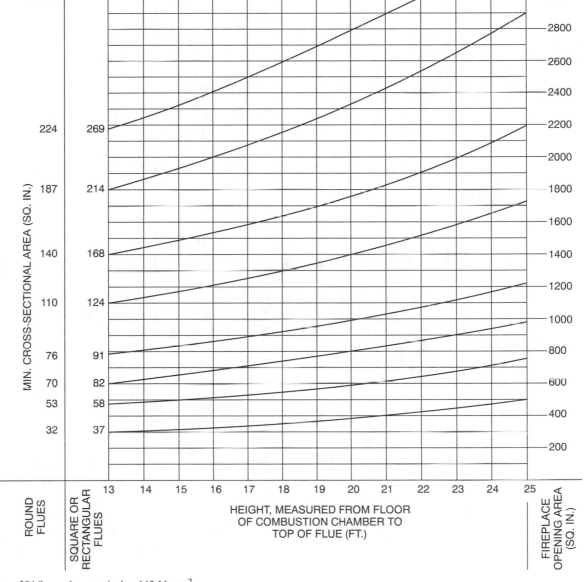

For SI: 1 foot = 304.8 mm, 1 square inch = 645.16 mm².

FIGURE R1001.12.2
FLUE SIZES FOR MASONRY CHIMNEYS

R1001.13 Inlet. Inlets to masonry chimneys shall enter from the side. Inlets shall have a thimble of fireclay, rigid refractory material or metal that will prevent the connector from pulling out of the inlet or from extending beyond the wall of the liner.

R1001.14 Masonry chimney cleanout openings. Cleanout openings shall be provided within 6 inches (152 mm) of the base of each flue within every masonry chimney. The upper edge of the cleanout shall be located at least 6 inches (152 mm) below the lowest chimney inlet opening. The height of the opening shall be at least 6 inches (152 mm). The cleanout shall be provided with a noncombustible cover.

Exception: Chimney flues serving masonry fireplaces where cleaning is possible through the fireplace opening.

R1001.15 Chimney clearances. Any portion of a masonry chimney located in the interior of the building or within the exterior wall of the building shall have a minimum air space clearance to combustibles of 2 inches (51 mm). Chimneys located entirely outside the exterior walls of the building, including chimneys that pass through the soffit or cornice, shall have a minimum air space clearance of 1 inch (25.4 mm). The air space shall not be filled, except to provide fire blocking in accordance with Section R1001.16.

Exceptions:

1. Masonry chimneys equipped with a chimney lining system listed and labeled for use in chimneys in contact with combustibles in accordance with UL 1777 and installed in accordance with the manufacturer's installation instructions are permitted to have combustible material in contact with their exterior surfaces.

2. When masonry chimneys are constructed as part of masonry or concrete walls, combustible materials shall

not be in contact with the masonry or concrete wall less than 12 inches (306 mm) from the inside surface of the nearest flue lining.

3. Exposed combustible trim and the edges of sheathing materials, such as wood siding and flooring, shall be permitted to abut the masonry chimney side walls, in accordance with Figure R1001.15 provided such combustible trim or sheathing is a minimum of 12 inches (306 mm) from the inside surface of the nearest flue lining. Combustible material and trim shall not overlap the corners of the chimney by more than 1 inch (25 mm).

R1001.16 Chimney fireblocking. All spaces between chimneys and floors and ceilings through which chimneys pass shall be fireblocked with noncombustible material securely fastened in place. The fireblocking of spaces between chimneys and

wood joists, beams or headers shall be to a depth of 1 inch (25 mm) and shall only be placed on strips of metal or metal lath laid across the spaces between combustible material and the chimney.

TABLE R1001.17
CRICKET DIMENSIONS

ROOF SLOPE	H
12 - 12	$^{1}/_{2}$ of W
8 - 12	$^{1}/_{3}$ of W
6 - 12	$^{1}/_{4}$ of W
4 - 12	$^{1}/_{6}$ of W
3 - 12	$^{1}/_{8}$ of W

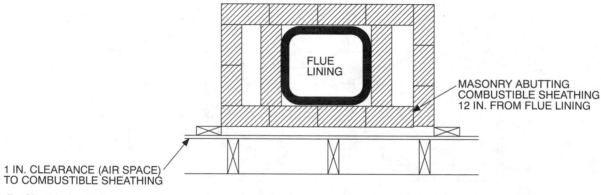

For SI:　1 inch = 25.4 mm.

FIGURE R1001.15
CLEARANCE FROM COMBUSTIBLES

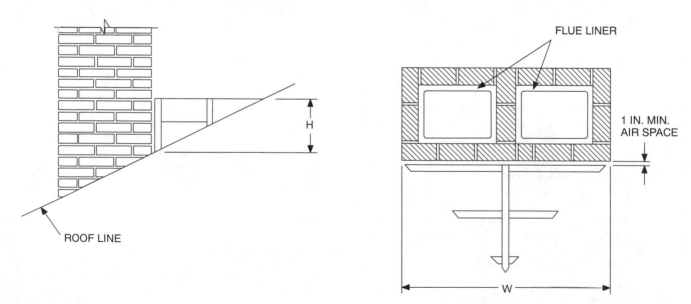

For SI:　1 inch = 25.4 mm.

FIGURE R1001.17
CHIMNEY CRICKET

R1001.17 Chimney crickets. Chimneys shall be provided with crickets when the dimension parallel to the ridgeline is greater than 30 inches (762 mm) and does not intersect the ridgeline. The intersection of the cricket and the chimney shall be flashed and counterflashed in the same manner as normal roof-chimney intersections. Crickets shall be constructed in compliance with Figure R1001.17 and Table R1001.17.

SECTION R1002
FACTORY-BUILT CHIMNEYS

R1002.1 Listing. Factory-built chimneys shall be listed and labeled and shall be installed and terminated in accordance with the manufacturer's installation instructions.

R1002.2 Decorative shrouds. Decorative shrouds shall not be installed at the termination of factory-built chimneys except where such shrouds are listed and labeled for use with the specific factory-built chimney system and installed in accordance with the manufacturer's installation instructions.

R1002.3 Solid fuel appliances. Factory-built chimneys for use with solid fuel-burning appliances shall comply with the Type HT requirements of UL 103.

> **Exception:** Chimneys for use with fireplace stoves listed only to UL 737 shall comply with the requirements of UL 103.

R1002.4 Factory-built fireplaces. Chimneys for use with factory-built fireplaces shall comply with the requirements of UL 127.

R1002.5 Support. Where factory-built chimneys are supported by structural members, such as joists and rafters, such members shall be designed to support the additional load.

R1002.6 Medium-heat appliances. Factory-built chimneys for medium-heat appliances producing flue gases having a temperature above 1,000°F (538°C), measured at the entrance to the chimney shall comply with UL 959.

SECTION R1003
MASONRY FIREPLACES

R1003.1 General. Masonry fireplaces shall be constructed in accordance with this section and the applicable provisions of Chapters 3 and 4.

R1003.2 Footings and foundations. Foundations for masonry fireplaces and their chimneys shall be constructed of concrete or solid masonry at least 12 inches (305 mm) thick and shall extend at least 6 inches (152 mm) beyond the face of the fireplace or support wall on all sides. Footings shall be founded on natural, undisturbed earth or engineered fill below frost depth. In areas not subjected to freezing, footings shall be at least 12 inches (305 mm) below finished grade.

R1003.3 Seismic reinforcing. Masonry or concrete chimneys in Seismic Design Categories D_1 and D_2 shall be reinforced. Reinforcing shall conform to the requirements set forth in Table R1003.1 and Section R609, Grouted Masonry.

R1003.3.1 Vertical reinforcing. For chimneys up to 40 inches (1016 mm) wide, four No. 4 continuous vertical bars shall be placed between wythes of solid masonry or within the cells of hollow unit masonry and grouted in accordance with Section R609. Grout shall be prevented from bonding with the flue liner so that the flue liner is free to move with thermal expansion. For chimneys greater than 40 inches (1016 mm) wide, two additional No. 4 vertical bars shall be provided for each additional flue incorporated in the chimney or for each additional 40 inches (1016 mm) in width or fraction thereof.

R1003.3.2 Horizontal reinforcing. Vertical reinforcement shall be placed within $1/4$-inch (6.4 mm) ties, or other reinforcing of equivalent net cross-sectional area, placed in the bed joints according to Section R607 at a minimum of every 18 inches (457 mm) of vertical height. Two such ties shall be provided at each bend in the vertical bars.

R1003.4 Seismic anchorage. Masonry and concrete chimneys in Seismic Design Categories D_1 and D_2 shall be anchored at each floor, ceiling or roof line more than 6 feet (1829 mm) above grade, except where constructed completely within the exterior walls. Anchorage shall conform to the requirements of Section R1003.4.1.

R1003.4.1 Anchorage. Two $3/16$-inch by 1-inch (4.8 mm by 25.4 mm) straps shall be embedded a minimum of 12 inches (305 mm) into the chimney. Straps shall be hooked around the outer bars and extend 6 inches (152 mm) beyond the bend. Each strap shall be fastened to a minimum of four floor ceiling or floor joists or rafters with two $1/2$-inch (12.7 mm) bolts.

R1003.5 Fireplace walls. Masonry fireplaces shall be constructed of solid masonry units, hollow masonry units grouted solid, stone or reinforced concrete. When a lining of firebrick at least 2 inches (51 mm) in thickness or other approved lining is provided, the total minimum thickness of back and side walls shall be 8 inches (203 mm) of solid masonry, including the lining. The width of joints between firebricks shall not be greater than $1/4$ inch (6.4 mm). When no lining is provided, the total minimum thickness of back and side walls shall be 10 inches (254 mm) of solid masonry. Firebrick shall conform to ASTM C 27 or C 1261 and shall be laid with medium-duty refractory mortar conforming to ASTM C 199.

R1003.6 Steel fireplace units. Steel fireplace units incorporating a firebox liner of not less than $1/4$ inch (6.4 mm) in thickness and an air chamber may be installed with masonry to provide a total thickness at the back and sides of not less than 8 inches (203 mm), of which not less than 4 inches (102 mm) shall be of solid masonry. Warm-air ducts employed with steel fireplace units of the circulating air type shall be constructed of metal or masonry.

R1003.7 Lintel and throat. Masonry over a fireplace opening shall be supported by a lintel of noncombustible material. The minimum required bearing length on each end of the fireplace opening shall be 4 inches (102 mm). The fireplace throat or damper shall be located a minimum of 8 inches (203 mm) above the lintel.

TABLE R1003.1
SUMMARY OF REQUIREMENTS FOR MASONRY FIREPLACES AND CHIMNEYS

ITEM	LETTER[a]	REQUIREMENTS
Hearth slab thickness	A	4″
Hearth extension (each side of opening)	B	8″ fireplace opening < 6 sq. ft. 12″ fireplace opening ≥ 6 sq. ft.
Hearth extension (front of opening)	C	16″ fireplace opening < 6 sq. ft. 20″ fireplace opening ≥ 6 sq. ft.
Hearth slab reinforcing	D	Reinforced to carry its own weight and all imposed loads.
Thickness of wall of firebox	E	10″ solid brick or 8″ where a firebrick lining is used. Joints in firebrick $1/4$″ max.
Distance from top of opening to throat	F	8″
Smoke chamber wall thickness unlined walls	G	6″ 8″
Chimney Vertical reinforcing[b]	H	Four No. 4 full-length bars for chimney up to 40″ wide. Add two No. 4 bars for each additional 40″ or fraction of width or each additional flue.
Horizontal reinforcing	J	$1/4$″ ties at 18″ and two ties at each bend in vertical steel.
Bond beams	K	No specified requirement
Fireplace lintel	L	Noncombustible material.
Chimney walls with flue lining	M	Solid masonry units or hollow masonry units grouted solid with at least 4 inch nominal thickness.
Distances between adjacent flues	N	See Section R1001.10.
Effective flue area (based on area of fireplace opening)	P	See Section R1001.12.
Clearances: Combustible material Mantel and trim Above roof	R	See Sections R1001.15 and R1003.12. See Section R1001.13. 3′ at roofline and 2′ at 10′.
Anchorage[b] Strap Number Embedment into chimney Fasten to Bolts	S	$3/16$″ × 1″ Two 12″ hooked around outer bar with 6″ extension 4 joists Two $1/2$″ diameter.
Footing Thickness Width	T	12″ min. 6″ each side of fireplace wall.

For SI: 1 inch = 25.4 mm, 1 foot = 304.8 mm, 1 square foot = 0.0929 m^2.

NOTE: This table provides a summary of major requirements for the construction of masonry chimneys and fireplaces. Letter references are to Figure R1003.1, which shows examples of typical construction. This table does not cover all requirements, nor does it cover all aspects of the indicated requirements. For the actual mandatory requirements of the code, see the indicated section of text.

a. The letters refer to Figure R1003.1.

b. Not required in Seismic Design Category A, B or C.

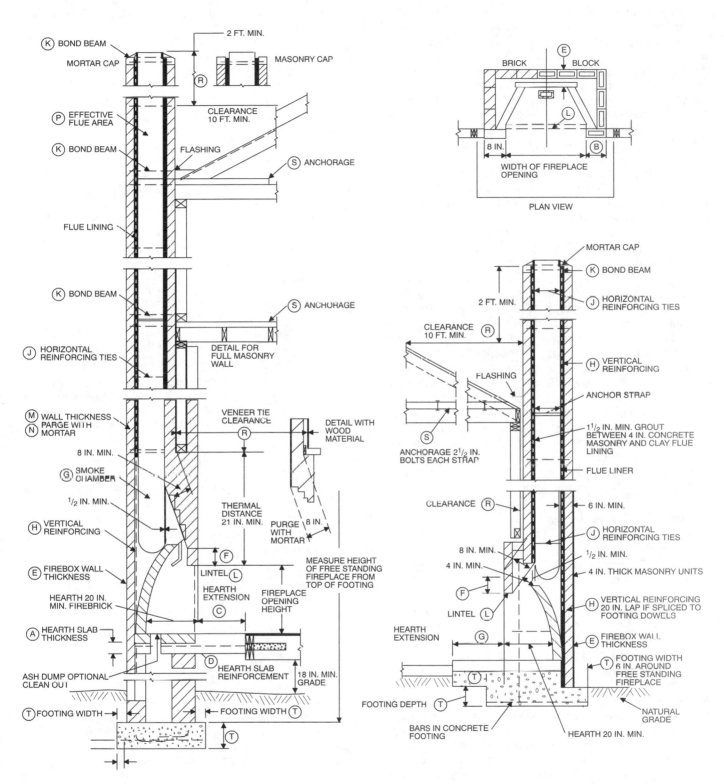

BRICK FIREBOX AND CHIMNEY—
SECTIONAL SIDE VIEW ON WOOD FLOOR

BRICK FIREBOX AND BLOCK CHIMNEY—
SECTIONAL SIDE VIEW ON CONCRETE SLAB

For SI: 1 inch = 25.4 mm, 1 foot = 304.8 mm.

FIGURE R1003.1
FIREPLACE AND CHIMNEY DETAILS

R1003.8 Smoke chamber. Smoke chamber walls shall be constructed of solid masonry units, hollow masonry units grouted solid, stone or reinforced concrete. Corbelling of masonry units shall not leave unit cores exposed to the inside of the smoke chamber. When a lining of firebrick at least 2 inches (51 mm) thick, or a lining of vitrified clay at least $5/8$ inch (15.9 mm) thick, is provided, the total minimum thickness of front, back and side walls shall be 6 inches (152 mm) of solid masonry, including the lining. Firebrick shall conform to ASTM C 27 or C 1261 and shall be laid with medium-duty refractory mortar conforming to ASTM C 199. Where no lining is provided, the total minimum thickness of front, back and side walls shall be 8 inches (203 mm) of solid masonry. When the inside surface of the smoke chamber is formed by corbeled masonry, the inside surface shall be parged smooth.

R1003.8.1 Smoke chamber dimensions. The inside height of the smoke chamber from the fireplace throat to the beginning of the flue shall not be greater than the inside width of the fireplace opening. The inside surface of the smoke chamber shall not be inclined more than 45 degrees (0.39 rad) from vertical when prefabricated smoke chamber linings are used or when the smoke chamber walls are rolled or sloped rather than corbeled. When the inside surface of the smoke chamber is formed by corbeled masonry, the walls shall not be corbeled more than 30 degrees (0.26 rad) from vertical.

R1003.9 Hearth and hearth extension. Masonry fireplace hearths and hearth extensions shall be constructed of concrete or masonry, supported by noncombustible materials, and reinforced to carry their own weight and all imposed loads. No combustible material shall remain against the underside of hearths and hearth extensions after construction.

R1003.9.1 Hearth thickness. The minimum thickness of fireplace hearths shall be 4 inches (102 mm).

R1003.9.2 Hearth extension thickness. The minimum thickness of hearth extensions shall be 2 inches (51 mm).

Exception: When the bottom of the firebox opening is raised at least 8 inches (203 mm) above the top of the hearth extension, a hearth extension of not less than $3/8$-inch-thick (9.5 mm) brick, concrete, stone, tile or other approved noncombustible material is permitted.

R1003.10 Hearth extension dimensions. Hearth extensions shall extend at least 16 inches (406 mm) in front of and at least 8 inches (203 mm) beyond each side of the fireplace opening. Where the fireplace opening is 6 square feet (0.557 m^2) or larger, the hearth extension shall extend at least 20 inches (508 mm) in front of and at least 12 inches (305 mm) beyond each side of the fireplace opening.

R1003.11 Firebox dimensions. The firebox of a concrete or masonry fireplace shall have a minimum depth of 20 inches (508 mm). The throat shall not be less than 8 inches (203 mm) above the fireplace opening. The throat opening shall not be less than 4 inches (102 mm) in depth. The cross-sectional area of the passageway above the firebox, including the throat,

damper and smoke chamber, shall not be less than the cross-sectional area of the flue.

Exception: Rumford fireplaces shall be permitted provided that the depth of the fireplace is at least 12 inches (305 mm) and at least one-third of the width of the fireplace opening, that the throat is at least 12 inches (305 mm) above the lintel and is at least $1/20$ the cross-sectional area of the fireplace opening.

R1003.12 Fireplace clearance. All wood beams, joists, studs and other combustible material shall have a clearance of not less than 2 inches (51 mm) from the front faces and sides of masonry fireplaces and not less than 4 inches (102 mm) from the back faces of masonry fireplaces. The air space shall not be filled, except to provide fire blocking in accordance with Section R1003.14.

Exceptions:

1. Masonry fireplaces listed and labeled for use in contact with combustibles in accordance with UL 127 and installed in accordance with the manufacturer's installation instructions are permitted to have combustible material in contact with their exterior surfaces.

2. When masonry fireplaces are part of masonry or concrete walls, combustible materials shall not be in contact with the masonry or concrete walls less than 12 inches (305 mm) from the inside surface of the nearest firebox lining.

3. Exposed combustible trim and the edges of sheathing materials such as wood siding, flooring and drywall shall be permitted to abut the masonry fireplace side walls and hearth extension in accordance Figure R1003.12, provided such combustible trim or sheathing is a minimum of 12 inches (305 mm) from the inside surface of the nearest firebox lining.

4. Exposed combustible mantels or trim may be placed directly on the masonry fireplace front surrounding the fireplace opening providing such combustible materials shall not be placed within 6 inches (152 mm) of a fireplace opening. Combustible material within 12 inches (306 mm) of the fireplace opening shall not project more than $1/8$ inch (3.2 mm) for each 1-inch (25 mm) distance from such an opening.

R1003.13 Mantel and trim. Woodwork or other combustible materials shall not be placed within 6 inches (152 mm) of a fireplace opening. Combustible material within 12 inches (305 mm) of the fireplace opening shall not project more than $1/8$ inch (3.2 mm) for each 1-inch (25.4 mm) distance from such opening.

R1003.14 Fireplace fireblocking. See Section R602.8.

R1003.15 Ash dump cleanout. Cleanout openings, when provided, shall be equipped with ferrous metal doors and frames constructed to remain tightly closed except when in use. Cleanouts shall be accessible and located so that ash removal will not create a hazard to combustible materials.

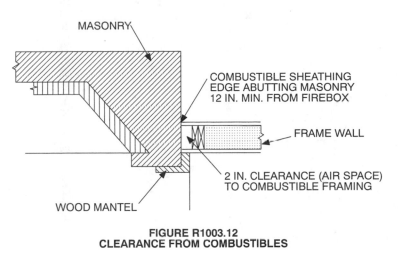

For SI: 1 inch = 25.4 mm.

FIGURE R1003.12
CLEARANCE FROM COMBUSTIBLES

SECTION R1004
FACTORY-BUILT FIREPLACES

R1004.1 General. Factory-built fireplaces shall be listed and labeled and shall be installed in accordance with the conditions of the listing. Factory-built fireplaces shall be tested in accordance with UL 127.

R1004.2 Hearth extensions. Hearth extensions of approved factory-built fireplaces shall be installed in accordance with the listing of the fireplace. The hearth extension shall be readily distinguishable from the surrounding floor area.

R1004.3 Decorative shrouds. Decorative shrouds shall not be installed at the termination of chimneys for factory-built fireplaces except where such shrouds are listed and labeled for use with the specific factory-built fireplace system and installed in accordance with the manufacturer's installation instructions.

R1004.4 Unvented gas log heaters. An unvented gas log heater shall not be installed in a factory-built fireplace unless the fireplace system has been specifically tested, listed and labeled for such use in accordance with UL 127.

SECTION R1005
EXTERIOR AIR SUPPLY

R1005.1 Exterior air. Factory-built or masonry fireplaces covered in this chapter shall be equipped with an exterior air supply to assure proper fuel combustion unless the room is mechanically ventilated and controlled so that the indoor pressure is neutral or positive.

R1005.1.1 Factory-built fireplaces. Exterior combustion air ducts for factory-built fireplaces shall be a listed component of the fireplace and shall be installed according to the fireplace manufacturer's instructions.

R1005.1.2 Masonry fireplaces. Listed combustion air ducts for masonry fireplaces shall be installed according to the terms of their listing and manufacturer's instructions.

R1005.2 Exterior air intake. The exterior air intake shall be capable of providing all combustion air from the exterior of the dwelling or from spaces within the dwelling ventilated with outside air such as crawl or attic spaces. The exterior air intake shall not be located within the garage or basement of the dwelling nor shall the air intake be located at an elevation higher than the firebox. The exterior air intake shall be covered with a corrosion-resistant screen of $^1/_4$-inch (6.4 mm) mesh.

R1005.3 Clearance. Unlisted combustion air ducts shall be installed with a minimum 1-inch (25.4 mm) clearance to combustibles for all parts of the duct within 5 feet (1524 mm) of the duct outlet.

R1005.4 Passageway. The combustion air passageway shall be a minimum of 6 square inches (3870 mm^2) and not more than 55 square inches (0.035 m^2), except that combustion air systems for listed fireplaces shall be constructed according to the fireplace manufacturer's instructions.

R1005.5 Outlet. The exterior air outlet is permitted to be located in the back or sides of the firebox chamber or within 24 inches (610 mm) of the firebox opening on or near the floor. The outlet shall be closable and designed to prevent burning material from dropping into concealed combustible spaces.

Part IV — Energy Conservation

CHAPTER 11

ENERGY

Provisions for energy, energy conservation, or references to the *International Energy Conservation Code* are deleted and replaced with Minnesota Statutes, section 16B.617.

CHAPTER 12

MECHANICAL

Provisions for mechanical or references to the *International Mechanical Code,* which include Chapters 12 through 24 of the IRC, are deleted and replaced with Minnesota Rules, Chapter 1346, the Minnesota Mechanical Code.

CHAPTER 25

PLUMBING ADMINISTRATION

Provisions for plumbing or references to the ICC *Plumbing Code,* which include Chapters 25 through 32 of the IRC, shall be deleted and replaced with Minnesota Rules, Chapter 4715, the Minnesota Plumbing Code.

CHAPTER 34

ELECTRICAL

Provisions for electrical or references to the ICC *Electrical Code,* which include Chapters 34 through 42 of the IRC, shall be deleted and replaced with Minnesota Rules, Chapter 1315, the Minnesota Electrical Code.

CHAPTER 43
REFERENCED STANDARDS

This chapter lists the standards that are referenced in various sections of this document. The standards are listed herein by the promulgating agency of the standard, the standard identification, the effective date and title, and the section or sections of this document that reference the standard. The application of the referenced standard shall be as specified in Section 102.4.

AAMA
American Architectural Manufacturers Association
1827 Walden Office Square, Suite 104
Schaumburg, IL 60173

Standard reference number	Title	Referenced in code section number
101—97	Voluntary Specifications for Aluminum Vinyl PVC and Wood Windows and Glass Doors	R613.3

ACI
American Concrete Institute
38800 Country Club Drive
Farmington Hills, MI 48331

Standard reference number	Title	Referenced in code section number
318-99	Building Code Requirements for Structural Concrete	R402.2, R404.1, R404.4.6.1, Table R404.4(1), Table R404.4(2), Table R404.4(3), Table R404.4(4), R611.1, R611.5, Table R611.3, Table R611.4(1), Table R611.5, Table R611.7(1), Table R611.7(2), Table R611.7(3), Table R611.7(4), Table R611.7(5), Table R611.7(6), Table R611.7(7), Table R611.7(8), R611.7.1.1, R612.1
ACI 530-99/ASCE 5-96/ TMS 0402-95	Building Code Requirements for Masonry Structures	R404.1, R606.1, R606.1.1, R606.11.1, R606.11.2.2.1, R606.11.2.2.2, R606.11.3.1

ACCA
Air Conditioning Contractors of America
1228 17th Street, NW
Washington DC 20046

Standard reference number	Title	Referenced in code section number
Manual J—86	Load Calculations for Residential Winter and Summer Air Conditioning	M1401.3

AFPA
American Forest and Paper Association
111 19th Street, NW, #800
Washington, DC 20036

Standard reference number	Title	Referenced in code section number
AFPA NDS-97	Wood Construction-Design Values for Wood Construction	R404.2.2, R502.2, Table R503.1, R602.3, R802.2
WFCM—96	Wood Frame Construction Manual for One- and Two-family Dwellings	R301.2.1.1
AFPA—93	Span Tables for Joists and Rafters	R502.3, R802.4, R802.5
TR7—87	Technical Report No. 7-The Permanent Wood Foundation System, Basic Requirements	R401.1

AGA
American Gas Association
1515 Wilson Boulevard
Arlington, VA 22209

Standard reference number	Title	Referenced in code section number
7—90	Requirements for Gas Convenience Outlets	Chapter 24

AHA

American Hardboard Association
1210 West Northwest Highway
Palatine, IL 60067

Standard reference number	Title	Referenced in code section number
A135.4—95	Basic Hardware	Table R602.3(1)
A135.5—95	Prefinished Hardboard Paneling	R702.5
A135.6—98	Hardboard Siding	Table R703.4
A194.1—85	Cellulosic Fiber Board	Table R602.3(1)

ANSI

American National Standards Institute
25 West 43rd Street
New York, NY 10036

Standard reference number	Title	Referenced in code section number
A108.1A&B—92	Glazed Wall Tile, Ceramic Mosaic Tile, Quarry Tile and Paver Tile Installed with Portland Cement Mortar	R702.4.1, M2103.9
A108.4—92	Ceramic Tile Installed with Organic Adhesives or Water-cleanable Tile Setting Epoxy Adhesive	R702.4.1, M2103.9.7
A108.5—92	Ceramic Tile Installed with Dry-Set Portland Cement Mortar or Latex Portland Cement Mortar	R702.4.1, M2103.9.1, M2103.9.2, M2103.9.3, M2103.9.5
A108.6—92	Ceramic Tile Installed with Chemical-Resistant, Water-cleanable Tile-Setting-and-Grout Epoxy	R702.4.1, M2103.9.4
A108.11—92	Standard Specification for Installation of Ceramic Tile	R702.4.1
A118.1—92	Standard Specification for Dry-Set Portland Cement Mortar	R702.4.1
A118.3—92	Standard Specification for Chemical Resistant, Water-cleanable Tile-Setting and Grouting Epoxy and Water-cleanable Tile Setting Epoxy Adhesive	R702.4.1
A136.1—92	Organic Adhesives for Installation of Ceramic Tile	R702.4.1
A137.1—88	Ceramic Tile	R702.4.1
A208.1—93	Particleboard	R503.3.1, R605.1
ANSI/AGA LC-1—91	Interior Fuel Gas Piping Systems Using Corrugated Stainless Steel Tubing	G2413.5.3, Chapter 24
Z21.1—96	Household Cooking Gas Appliances	G2436.1
Z21.5.1—95	Gas Clothes Dryers—Volume I—Type I Clothes Dryers	Chapter 24
Z21.8—94	Installation of Domestic Gas Conversion Burners	G2441.1
Z21.10.1—98	Gas Water Heaters—Volume I—Storage, Water Heaters with Input Ratings of 75,000 Btu per Hour or Less	G2446.1
Z21.10.3—98	Gas Water Heaters—Volume III—Storage, Water Heaters	G2446.1
Z21.11.1—91	Gas-Fired Room Heaters—Volume I—Vented Room Heaters	G2444.1
Z21.11.2—96	Gas-Fired Room Heaters—Volume II—Unvented Room Heaters	G2445.1
Z21.13—91	Gas-Fired low Pressure Steam and Hot Water Boilers	G2450.1
Z21.15—92	Manually Operated Gas Valves for Appliances, Appliance Connector Valves and Hose End Valves	G2419.1.1
Z21.22—86	Relief Valves and Automatic Gas Shutoff Devices for Hot Water Supply Systems	P2803.2
Z21.40.1—96	Gas-Fired Absorption Summer Air Conditioning Appliances	G2447.1
Z21.40.2—96	Gas-Fired Work Activated Air Conditioning and Heat Pump Appliances (Internal Combustion)	G2447.1
Z21.42—93	Gas-Fired Illuminating Appliances	G2448.1
Z21.47—93	Gas-Fired Central Furnaces (except Direct-Vent Central Furnaces)	G2440.1
Z21.48—92	Gas-Fired Gravity and Fan-Type Floor Furnace	G2435.1
Z21.49—92	Gas-Fired Gravity and Fan-Type Vented Wall Furnaces	G2434.1
Z21.50—98	Vented Gas Fireplaces	G2433.1
Z21.56—94	Gas-Fired Pool Heaters	G2439.1
Z21.58—91	Outdoor Cooking Gas Appliances	G2445.1
Z21.60—96	Decorative Gas Appliances for Installation in Vented Fireplaces	G2431.1
Z21.64—90	Direct Vent Central Furnaces	M1402.1
Z83.6—87	Gas-Fired Infrared Heaters—with 1989 Addenda	G2442.1, G2449.1
Z83.11—96	Gas Food Service Equipment (Ranges and Unit Broilers), Baking and Roasting Ovens, Fat Fryers, Counter Appliances and Kettles, Steam Cookers, and Steam Generators	G2445.1
Z97.1—94	Safety Performance Specifications and Methods of Test for Safety Glazing Materials Used in Buildings	R308.3
Z124.1—95	Plastic Bathtub Units	Table P2701.1
Z124.2—95	Plastic Shower Receptors and Shower Stalls	Table P2701.1
Z124.3—95	Plastic Lavatories	Table P2701.1
Z124.4—96	Plastic Water Closet Bowls and Tanks	Table P2701.1
Z124.6—97	Plastic Sinks	Table P2701.1

ASCE
American Society of Civil Engineers
1801 Alexander Bell Drive
Reston, VA 20191

Standard reference number	Title	Referenced in code section number
ASCE 7—98	Minimum Design Loads for Buildings and Other Structures	R301.2.1.1

ASHRAE
American Society of Heating, Refrigerating
and Air-Conditioning Engineers, Inc.
1791 Tullie Circle, NE
Atlanta, GA 30329

Standard reference number	Title	Referenced in code section number
ASNI/ASHRAE/34—92	Number Designation and Safety Classification of Refrigerants—with Addenda through 1997	M1411.1
ASHRAE—97	Handbook of Fundamentals	P3001.2, P3002.3, P3101.4, P3103.2, Appendix B

ASME
American Society of Mechanical Engineers
Three Park Avenue
New York, NY 10016-5990

Standard reference number	Title	Referenced in code section number
A112.1.2—91	Air Gaps in Plumbing Systems	P2902.2.1
A112.4.1—93	Water Heater Relief Valve Drain Tubes	P2803.6.2
A112.18.1M—96	Brass Plumbing Fixture Units	Table P2701.1, P2722.1
A112.19.1M—94	Enameled Cast Iron Plumbing Fixtures	Table P2701.1
A112.19.2M—98	Vitreous China Plumbing Fixtures	Table P2701.1, Table P2712.2
A112.19.3M—87	Stainless Steel Plumbing Fixtures (Designed for Residential Use)	Table P2701.1
A112.19.4M—94	Porcelain Enameled Formed Steel Plumbing Fixtures	Table P2701.1
A112.19.5—79	Trim for Water-Closet Bowls, Tanks, and Urinals	Table P2701.1
A112.19.6—95	Hydraulic Performance Requirements for Water Closets and Urinals	Table P2701.1, P2712.2
A112.19.7M—95	Whirlpool Bathtub Appliances	Table P2701.1
A112.19.8M—87	Suction Fittings for Use in Swimming Pools, Wading Pools, Spas, Hot Tubs, and Whirlpool Bathtub Appliances	Table P2701.1
A112.19.9—91	Nonvitreous Ceramic Plumbing Fixtures	Table P2701.1
A112.21.1—91	Floor Drains	Table P2701.1
B1.20.1—83	Pipe Threads, General Purpose (Inch)	G2413.9
B16.18-R94	Cast Copper Alloy Solder Joint Pressure Fittings	Table P2904.6
B16.33—90	Manually Operated Metallic Gas Valves for Use in Gas Piping Systems up to 125 psig (Sizes $^1/_2$ through 2)	G2419.1
B36.10—85	Welded and Seamless Wrought-Steel Pipe	G2413.4.2
CSD-1—98	Controls and Safety Devices for Automatically Fired Boilers	G2450.1, M2001.1.1
ASME—98	Boiler and Pressure Vessel Code, Section VIII, Divisions 1, 2 and 3	M2001.1.1

ASSE
American Society of Sanitary Engineering
28901 Clemens Road, #100
Westlake, OH 44145

Standard reference number	Title	Referenced in code section number
1001—90	Performance Requirements for Pipe Applied Atmospheric Type Vacuum Breakers	P2902.2.2, P2902.3.3
1002-79—99	Performance Requirements for Water Closet Flush Tank Ball Cocks	Table P2701.1, P2702.3.1
1003—95	Performance Requirements for Water Pressure	P2903.3.1
1006—89	Performance Requirements for Residential Use (Household) Dishwashers	Table P2701.1
1007—92	Performance Requirements for Home Laundry Equipment	Table P2701.1
1008—89	Performance Requirements for Household Food Waste Disposer Units	Table P2701.1

ASSE—continued

1010—98	Performance Requirements for Water Hammer Arresters—with 1982 Revision	P2903.5
1011—95	Performance Requirements for Hose Connection Vacuum Breakers	P2902.2.2, P2902.3.3
1012—95	Performance Requirements for Backflow Preventers with Intermediate Atmospheric Vent	P2902.2.3, P2902.3.3, P2902.4.1, P2902.4.5
1013—93	Performance Requirements for Reduced Pressure Principle Backflow Preventers	P2902.2.6, P2902.4.1, P2902.4.5
1014—90	Performance Requirements for Handheld Showers Reducing Valves for Domestic Water Supply Systems	Table P2701.1
1016—96	Performance Requirements for Individual Thermostatic, Pressure Balancing and Combination Control Valves for Bathing Facilities	Table P2701.1, P2708.3, P2709.4, P2722.2, P2723.2
1019—97	Performance Requirements for Wall Hydrants, Freezeless, Automatic Draining, Anti-Backflow Types	Table P2701.1, P2902.2.2, P2902.3.3
1020—98	Performance Requirements for Pressure Vacuum Breaker Assembly	P2902.2.5, P2902.3.3
1023—79	Hot Water Dispensers Household Storage Type Electrical	Table P2701.1
1025—78	Performance Requirements for Diverters for Plumbing Faucets with Hose Spray, Anti-Siphon Type, Residential Applications	Table P2701.1
1037—90	Performance Requirements for Pressurized Flushing Devices for Plumbing Fixtures	Table P2701.1
1050—91	Performance Requirements for Air Admittance Valves for Plumbing Drainage Systems	P3114.1
1051—98	Performance Requirements for Air Admittance Valves for Plumbing Drainage Systems, Fixture and Branch Devices	P3114.1
1052—94	Performance Requirements for Hose Connection Backflow Preventers	Table P2701.1, P2902.2.4, P2902.3.3
1056—95	Back Siphonage Vacuum Breaker	P2902.2.5, P2902.3.3

ASTM

American Society for Testing and Materials
100 Barr Harbor Drive
West Conshohocken, PA 19428

Standard reference number	Title	Referenced in code section number
A 36—97a	Standard Specification for Carbon Structural Steel	R606.14
A 53—98	Standard Specification for Pipe, Steel, Black and Hot-Dipped, Zinc-Coated Welded and Seamless	Table M2101.1, Table P2903.8(1); Table P3002.1, G2413.4.2
A 74—98	Standard Specification for Cast Iron Soil Pipe and Fittings	Table P3002.1, Table P3002.2
A 106—97a	Standard Specification for Seamless Carbon Steel Pipe for High-Temperature Service	M2101.1, G2413.4.2
A 126—95e01	Standard Specification for Gray Iron Castings for Valves, Flanges and Pipe Fittings	Table P3002.1
A 153M—95	Standard Specification for Zinc Coating (Hot Dip) on Iron and Steel Hardware	Table R606.14.1
A 167—96	Standard Specification for Stainless and Heat-Resisting Chromium-Nickel Steel Plate, Sheet, and Strip	R606.14, Table R606.14.1
A 197—92	Standard Specification for Cupola Malleable Iron	Table P3002.1
A 254—97	Standard Specification for Copper Brazed Steel Tubing	Table M2101.1, G2413.5.1
A 377—95e1	Standard Index of Standard Specification for Ductile Iron Pressure Pipe	Table P2904.4.1
A 510—96	Standard Specification for General Requirements for Wire Rods and Coarse Round Wire, Carbon Steel	R606.14
A 525	**(Discontinued 1994, replaced by A 653)**	Table R606.14.1, M1601.1.1
A 539—96	Standard Specification for Electronic-Resistance-Welded Coiled Steel Tubing for Gas and Fuel Oil Lines	M2202.1, G2413.5.1
A 615/A 615M—96a	Standard Specification for Deformed and Plain Billet Steel Bars for Concrete Reinforcement	R404.4.6.1, R611.6.2
A 616M—96a	Standard Specification for Rail Steel Deformed and Plain Bars for Concrete Reinforcement **(Discontinued 1999, replaced by A 996)**	R404.4.6.1, R611.6.2
A 617/A 617M—96	Standard Specification for Axle Steel Deformed and Plain Bars for Concrete Reinforcement **(Discontinued 1999, replaced by A 996)**	R404.4.6.1, R611.6.2
A 641M—98	Standard Specification for Zinc-Coated (Galvanized) Carbon Steel Wire	Table R606.14.1
A 653M—97	Standard Specification for Steel Sheet, Zinc-Coated Galvanized) or Zinc-Iron Alloy-Coated (Galvannealed) by the Hot-Dip Process	R505.2.1, R505.2.3, R603.2.1, R603.2.3, R804.2.1, R804.2.3, Table R905.10.3
A 706M—98	Standard Specification for Low-Alloy Steel Deformed Plain Bars for Concrete Reinforcement	R404.4.6.1, R611.6.2
A 755M—96	Standard Specification for Steel Sheet, Metallic Coated by the Hot Dip Process and Prepainted by the Coil Coating Process for Exterior Exposed Building Products	Table R905.10.3
A 792M—97a	Standard Specification for Steel Sheet, 55% Aluminum-Zinc Alloy-Coated by the Hot-Dip Process	R505.2.1, R603.2.1, R603.2.3, R804.2.1, R804.2.3
A 875M—97a	Standard Specification for Steel Sheet, Zinc-5%, Aluminum Alloy-Coated by the Hot-Dip Process	R505.2.1, R505.2.3, R603.2.1, R603.2.3, R804.2.1, R804.2.3
A 888—98e1	Standard Specification for Hubless Cast Iron Soil Pipe and Fittings for Sanitary and Storm Drain, Waste, and Vent Piping Application	Table P3002.1, Table P3002.2
A 951—98	Standard Specification for Masonry Joint Reinforcement	R606.14
B 32—96	Standard Specification for Solder Metal	P3003.3.4
B 42—98	Standard Specification for Seamless Copper Pipe, Standard Sizes	Table M2101.1, Table P3002.1
B 43—98	Standard Specification for Seamless Red Brass Pipe, Standard Sizes	Table M2101.1, G2413.5.2, Table P3002.1, Table P2904.4.1

ASTM—continued

Standard	Title	Reference
B 75—97	Standard Specification for Seamless Copper Tube [Metric]	Table M2101.1, Table P2904.4.1, Table P3002.1, Table P3002.2
B 88—96	Standard Specification for Seamless Copper Water Tube	Table M2101.1, G2413.5.2, Table P2904.4.1, Table P3002.1, Table P3002.2, Table P2903.8(1)
B 101—96	Standard Specification for Lead-Coated Copper Sheets and Strip for Building Construction	Table R905.10.3
B 135—96	Standard Specification for Seamless Brass Tube [Metric]	Table P2904.4.1, Table M2101.1
B 227—88(1993)e[1]	Standard Specification for Hard-Drawn Copper-Clad Steel Wire	R606.14
B 251—97	Standard Specification for General Requirements for Wrought Seamless Copper and Copper-Alloy Tube	Table M2101.1
B 280—98	Standard Specification for Seamless Copper Tube for Air Conditioning and Refrigeration Field Service	G2413.5.2
B 302—98	Standard Specification for Threadless Copper Pipe	Table M2101.1
B 306—96	Standard Specification for Copper Drainage Tube (DWV)	Table M2101.1, Table P3002.1, Table P3002.2
B 370—98	Standard Specification for Copper Sheet and Strip for Building Construction	Table R905.10.3, Table P2701.1
B 447—97	Standard Specification for Welded Copper Tube	Table P2904.4.1
B 633—98 (Re-approved 1994)e[1]	Standard Specification for Electrodeposited Coatings of Zinc on Iron and Steel	R505.2.4, R603.2.4, R804.2.4
B 813—93	Standard Standard Specification for Liquid and Paste Fluxes for Soldering Applications of Copper and Copper Alloy Tube	Table M2101.1, P3004.10, P3003.3.4
B 828—92e[1]	Standard Practice for Making Capillary Joints by Soldering of Copper and Copper Alloy Tube and Fittings	P3004.10
C 5—98	Standard Specification for Quicklime for Structural Purposes	R702.2
C 14—95	Standard Specification for Concrete Sewer, Storm Drain, and Culvert Pipe	Table P3002.2
C 27—98	Standard Classification of Fireclay and High-Alumina Refractory Brick	R1003.5, R1003.8
C 28—96	Standard Specification for Gypsum Plasters	R702.2
C 34—96	Standard Specification for Structural Clay Load-Bearing Wall Tile	Table R301.2(1)
C 35—95	Standard Specification for Inorganic Aggregates for Use in Gypsum Plaster	R702.2
C 36—97	Standard Specification for Gypsum Wallboard	R702.3.1
C 37—95	Standard Specification for Gypsum Lath	R702.2
C 55—97	Standard Specification for Concrete Brick	R202, Table R301.2(1)
C 59—95	Standard Specification for Gypsum Casting Plaster and Gypsum Molding Plaster	R702.2
C 61—95	Standard Specification for Gypsum Keene's Cement	R702.2
C 62—97a	Standard Specification for Building Brick (Solid Masonry Units Made from Clay or Shale)	R202, Table R301.2(1)
C 67—98	Standard Test Methods of Sampling and Testing Brick and Structural Clay Tile	R905.3.5
C 73—97a	Standard Specification for Calcium Silicate Face Brick (Sand Lime Brick)	R202, Table R301.2(1)
C 79M—97	Standard Specification for Treated Core and Nontreated Core Gypsum Sheathing Board	Table R602.3(1), R702.3.1
C 90—99(98)	Standard Specification for Load-Bearing Concrete Masonry Units	Table R301.2(1)
C 129—97	Standard Specification for Nonload-bearing Concrete Masonry Units	Table R301.2(1)
C 140—98	Standard Test Methods of Sampling and Testing Concrete Masonry Units	R905.3.5
C 143/C 143M—97	Standard Test Method for Slump or Hydraulic Cement Concrete	R404.4.5, R611.6.1
C 145—85	Standard Specification for Solid Load-bearing Concrete Masonry Units **(Discontinued, replaced by C 90)**	R202, Table R301.2(1)
C 199—84 (Reapproved 199A)e[1]	Standard Test Method for Pier Test for Refractory Mortar	R1001.9, R1003.5, R1003.8
C 208—95	Standard Specification for Cellulosic Fiber Insulating Board	Table R602.3(1)
C 216—98	Standard Specification for Facing Brick (Solid Masonry Units Made from Clay or Shale)	R202, Table R301.2(1)
C 236—89 (1993)e1	Standard Test Method for Steady-State Thermal Performance of Building Assemblies by Means of a Guarded Hot Box	N1102.1.1.1
C 270—99	Standard Specification for Mortar for Unit Masonry	AE602, R607.1
C 315—98b	Standard Specification for Clay Flue Linings	Table R1001.11(1), Table R1001.11(2), R1001.8.1
C 411—97	Standard Test Method for Hot-Surface Performance of High-Temperature Thermal Insulation	M1601.2.1
C 425—98	Standard Specification for Compression Joints for Vitrified Clay Pipe and Fittings	Table P3002.2
C 443—98	Standard Specification for Joints for Circular Concrete Sewer and Culvert Pipe, Using Rubber Gaskets	P3003.3.5
C 445	Discontinued 1980, Replaced by no Replacement	P3003.3.5
C 475—94	Standard Specification for Joint Compound and Joint Tape for Finishing Gypsum Board	R702.3.1
C 476—99	Standard Specification for Grout for Masonry	R609.1.1
C 514—96	Standard Specification for Nails for the Application of Gypsum Wallboard	R702.3.1
C 557—93a	Standard Specification for Adhesives for Fastening Gypsum Wallboard to Wood Framing	R702.3.1
C 578—95	Standard Specification for Rigid, Cellular Polystyrene Thermal Insulation	R403.3
C 587—97	Standard Specification for Gypsum Veneer Plaster	R702.2
C 588—95a	Standard Specification for Gypsum Base for Veneer Plasters	R702.2
C 630/630M—96a	Standard Specification for Water-Resistant Gypsum Backing Board	R702.3.1, R702.4.2
C 631—95a	Standard Specification for Bonding Compounds for Interior Gypsum Plastering	R702.2
C 645—99	Standard Specification for Nonstructural Steel Framing Members	R702.3.3
C 652—97	Standard Specification for Hollow Brick (Hollow Masonry Units Made from Clay or Shale)	R202, Table R301.2(1)

ASTM—continued

C 700—97	Standard Specification for Vitrified Clay Pipe, Extra Strength, Standard Strength, and Perforated	Table P3002.2
C 836—95	Standard Specification for High Solids Content, Cold Liquid-Applied Elastomeric Waterproofing Membrane for Use with Separate Wearing Course	R905.15.2
C 843—98	Standard Specification for Application of Gypsum Veneer Plaster	R702.2
C 844—98a	Standard Specification for Application of Gypsum Base to Receive Gypsum Veneer Plaster	R702.2
C 847—95	Standard Specification for Metal Lath	R702.2
C 887—79a(89)ae[01]	Standard Specification for Packaged, Dry, Combined Materials for Surface Bonding Mortar	R406.1
C 897—96	Standard Specification for Aggregate for Job-Mixed Portland Cement-Based Plasters	R702.2
C 933—96a	Standard Specification for Welded Wire Lath	R702.2
C 954—98	Standard Specification for Steel Drill Screws for the Application of Gypsum Panel Products or Metal Plaster Bases to Steel Studs From 0.033 in. (0.84 mm) to 0.112 in. (2.84 mm) in Thickness	R505.2.4, R603.2.4, R702.3.6, R804.2.4
C 955—98	Standard Specification for Load-Bearing (Transverse and Axial) Steel Studs, Runners (Tracks), and Bracing or Bridging for Screw Application of Gypsum Panel Products and Metal Plaster Bases	R702.3.3
C 957—93(1998)	Standard Specification for High-Solids Content, Cold-Liquid Applied Elastomeric Waterproofing Membrane for Use with Integral Wearing Surface	R905.15.2
C 960/C 960M—97	Standard Specification for Predecorated Gypsum Board	R702.3.1
C 976—90(1996)e	Standard Test Method for Thermal Performance of Building Assemblies by Means of a Guarded Hot Box	N1102.1.1.1
C 1002—98	Standard Specification for Steel Drill Screws for the Application of Gypsum Panel Products or Metal Plaster Bases	R702.3.1, R702.3.6, Table R702.3.4
C 1029—96	Standard Specification for Spray-Applied Rigid Cellular Polyurethane Thermal Insulation	R905.14.2
C 1032—96	Standard Specification for Woven Wire Plaster Base	R702.2
C 1047—98	Standard Specification for Accessories for Gypsum Wallboard and Gypsum Veneer Base	R702.2, R702.3.1
C 1063—98	Standard Specification for Installation of Lathing and Furring to Receive Interior and Exterior Portland Cement-Based Plaster	R702.2
C 1157—98a	Standard Performance Specification for Hydraulic Cements	R402.2
C 1167—96	Standard Specification for Clay Roof Tiles	R905.3, R905.3.4, R905.3.5
C 1173—97	Standard Specification for Flexible Transition Couplings for Underground Piping Systems	P3003.3.5
C 1177/C 1177M—96	Standard Specification for Glass Mat Gypsum Substrate for Use as Sheathing	R702.3.1
C 1178/C 1178M—96	Standard Specification for Glass Mat Water-Resistant Gypsum Backing Panel	R702.3.1, R702.4.2
C 1261—98	Standard Specification for Firebox Brick for Residential Fireplaces	R1003.5, R1003.8
C 1277—97	Standard Specification for Shielded Couplings Joining Hubless Cast Iron Soil Pipe and Fittings	Table P3002.1, Table P3002.2
C 1278/C 1278M—96	Standard Specification for Fiber-Reinforced Gypsum Panels	R702.3.1
C 1283—97	Standard Specification for Practice for Installing Clay Flue Lining	R1001.9
C 1395/C 1395M—98	Standard Specification for Gypsum Ceiling Board	R702.3.1
D 41—94	Standard Specification for Asphalt Primer Used in Roofing, Dampproofing, and Waterproofing	Table R905.9.2, Table R905.11.2
D 224—89(1996)	Standard Specification for Smooth-Surfaced Asphalt Roll Roofing(Organic Felt)	R905.2.8.2
D 225—95	Standard Specification for Asphalt Shingles (Organic Felt) Surfaced with Mineral Granules	R905.2.4
D 226—97a	Standard Specification for Asphalt-Saturated (Organic Felt) Used in Roofing and Waterproofing	R703.2, R703.9.1, Table R905.2.3, R905.4.3, R905.5.3, R905.5.4, R905.6.3, R905.7.3, R905.8.3, R905.8.4, Table 905.9.2
D 227—97a	Standard Specification for Coal Tar Saturated (Organic Felt) Used in Roofing and Waterproofing	Table R905.9.2
D 249—89(96)	Standard Specification for Asphalt Roll Roofing (Organic Felt) Surfaced with Mineral Granules	Table R905.9.2, R905.2.8.2, R905.3.3, R905.5.4
D 312—95a	Standard Specification for Asphalt Used in Roofing	R905.9.2
D 371—89(1996)	Standard Specification for Asphalt Roll Roofing (Organic Felt) Surfaced with Mineral Granules: Wide-Selvage	R905.5.4
D 422—63	Standard Test Method for Particle-Size Analysis of Soils	R403.1.7.5.1
D 406	Discontinued 1961, Replaced by No Replacement	R905.6.4
D 449—89	Standard Specification for Asphalt Used in Dampproofing and Waterproofing	R406.2
D 450—96	Standard Specification for Coal-Tar Pitch Used in Roofing, Dampproofing and Waterproofing	Table R905.9.2
D 1227—95	Standard Specification for Emulsified Asphalt Used as a Protective Coating for Roofing	Table R905.9.2, Table R905.11.2, R905.15.2
D 1248—84(89)e[01]	Standard Specification for Polyethylene Plastics Molding and Extrusion Materials	M1601.1.2
D 1527—96a	Standard Specification for Acrylonitrile-Butadiene-Styrene (ABS) Plastic Pipe, Schedules 40 and 80	Table P2904.4.1
D 1693—97a	Standard Test Method for Environmental Stress-Cracking of Ethylene Plastics	Table M2101.1
D 1784—97	Standard Specification for Rigid Poly (Vinyl Chloride) (PVC) Compounds and Chlorinated Poly (Vinyl Chloride) (CPVC) Compounds	M1601.1.2
D 1785—96b	Standard Specification for Poly (Vinyl Chloride) (PVC) Plastic Pipe, Schedules 40, 80 and 120	Table P2904.4.1
D 1861	**(Discontinued, 1992 Specification for Homogeneous Bituminized Fiber Drain and Sewer Pipe, Replaced by no replacement)**	Table P3002.2
D 1863—93(96)	Standard Specification for Mineral Aggregate Used in Built-Up Roofs	Table R905.9.2, Table R906.3.2
D 1869—95	Standard Specification for Rubber Rings for Asbestos-Cement Pipe	P2904.14
D 1970—97	Standard Specification for Self-Adhering Polymer Modified Bitumen Sheet Materials Used as Steep Roofing Underlayment for Ice Dam Protection	R905.2.3, R905.2.8.3

ASTM—continued

D 2104—96	Standard Specification for Polyethylene (PE) Plastic Pipe, Schedule 40	Table P2904.4.1
D 2178—97a	Standard Specification for Asphalt Glass Felt Used in Roofing and Waterproofing	Table R905.9.2
D 2235—96a	Standard Specification for Solvent Cement for Acrylonitrile-Butadiene-Styrene (ABS) Plastic Pipe and Fittings	P2904.8.1.1, Table P3002.1, Table P3002.2
D 2239—96a	Standard Specification for Polyethylene (PE) Plastic Pipe (SIDR-PR) Based on Controlled Inside Diameter	Table P2904.4.1
D 2241—96b	Standard Specification for Poly (Vinyl Chloride) (PVC) Pressure-Rated Pipe (SDR-Series)	Table P2904.4.1
D 2282—96a	Standard Specification for Acrylonitrile-Butadiene-Styrene (ABS) Plastic Pipe (SDR-PR)	Table P2904.4.1
D 2412—96a	Standard Test Method for Determination of External Loading Characteristics of Plastic Pipe by Parallel-Plate Loading	M1601.1.2
D 2447—99	Standard Specification for Polyethylene (PE) Plastic Pipe Schedules 40 and 80, Based on Outside Diameter	Table P2903.8(1), Table 2904.4.1, Table M2101.1
D 2466—97	Standard Specification for Poly(Vinyl Chloride) (PVC) Plastic Pipe Fittings, Schedule 40	P2904.6
D 2467—96a	Standard Specification for Poly (Vinyl Chloride) (PVC) Plastic Pipe Fittings, Schedule 80	Table P2904.6
D 2468—96a	Standard Specification for Acrylonitrile-Butadiene-Styrene (ABS) Plastic Pipe Fittings, Schedule 40	Table P2904.6
D 2513—98b	Standard Specification for Thermoplastic Gas Pressure Pipe, Tubing, and Fittings	G2413.6, G2413.6.1, G2413.11 G2414.14.2, Table M2101.1, M2104.2.1.3
D 2564—96a	Standard Specification for Solvent Cements for Poly (Vinyl Chloride) (PVC) Plastic Piping Systems	P2904.8.1.3, Table P3002.1, Table P3002.2
D 2609—97	Standard Specification for Plastic Insert Fittings for Polyethylene (PE) Plastic Pipe	Table P2904.6
D 2626—97b	Standard Specification for Asphalt-Saturated and Coated Organic Felt Base Sheet Used in Roofing	R905.3.3, Table R905.9.2
D 2661—97a	Standard Specification for Acrylonitrile-Butadiene-Styrene (ABS) Schedule 40 Plastic Drain, Waste, and Vent Pipe and Fittings	Table P3002.1, Table P3002.2
D 2662—96a	Standard Specification for Polybutylene (PB) Plastic Pipe (SIDR-PR) Based on Controlled Inside Diameter	Table P2904.4.1
D 2665—98	Standard Specification for Poly (Vinyl Chloride) (PVC) Plastic Drain, Waste, and Vent Pipe and Fittings	Table P3002.1, Table P3002.2
D 2666—96a	Standard Specification for Polybutylene (PB) Plastic Tubing	Table P2904.4.1
D 2672—96a	Standard Specification for Joints for IPS PVC Pipe Using Solvent Cement	Table P3002.1, Table, P3002.2, Table P2904.6
D 2683—98	Standard Specification for Socket-Type Polyethylene Fittings for Outside Diameter-Controlled Polyethylene Pipe and Tubing	Table M2101.1, M2104.2.1.1
D 2737—96a	Standard Specification for Polyethylene (PE) Plastic Tubing	Table P2904.4.1
D 2751—96a	Standard Specification for Acrylonitrile-Butadiene-Styrene (ABS) Sewer Pipe and Fittings	Table P3002.2
D 2822—91(1997)e[1]	Standard Standard Specification for Asphalt Roof Cement	Table R905.9.2, Table R905.11.2
D 2823—90(1997)e[1]	Standard Specification for Asphalt Roof Coatings	Table R905.9.2, Table R905.11.2
D 2824—94	Standard Specification for Aluminum Pigmented Asphalt Roof Coatings, Non-Fibered, Asbestos Fibered, and Fibered without Asbestos	Table R905.9.2, Table R905.11.2
D 2837—98	Standard Test Method for Obtaining Hydrostatic Design Basis for Thermoplastic Pipe Materials	Table M2101.1
D 2846/D 2846M—97	Standard Specification for Chlorinated Poly (Vinyl Chloride) (CPVC) Plastic Hot- and Cold-Water Distribution Systems	Table P2903.8(1), Table P2904.4.1, P2904.8.1.2, M2101.1
D 2898—94(1999)	Standard Test Methods for Accelerated Weathering of Fire-Retardant-Treated Wood for Fire Testing	R902.2
D 2949—98	Standard Specification for 3.25-in. Outside Diameter Poly (Vinyl Chloride) (PVC) Plastic Drain, Waste, and Vent Pipe and Fittings	Table P3002.1, Table P3002.2
D 3000—95ae[1]	Standard Specification for Polybutylene (PB) Plastic Pipe (SDR-PR) Based on Outside Diameter	Table P2904.4.1
D 3019—94	Standard Specification for Lap Cement Used with Asphalt Roll Roofing, Nonfibered, Asbestos Fibered, and Nonasbestos Fibered	Table R905.9.2, Table R905.11.2
D 3034—98	Standard Specification for Type PSM Poly (Vinyl Chloride) (PVC) Sewer Pipe and Fittings	Table P3002.2
D 3035—95	Standard Specification fro Polyethylene (PE) Plastic Pipe (DR-PR) Based On Controlled Outside Diameter	Table M2101.1
D 3212—96a	Standard Specification for Joints for Drain and Sewer Plastic Pipes Using Flexible Elastomeric Seals	Table P3002.2
D 3261—97	Standard Specification for Butt Heat Fusion Polyethylene (PE) Plastic Fittings for Polyethylene (PE) Plastic Pipe and Tubing	Table P2904.6
D 3309—97a	Standard Specification for Polybutylene (PB) Plastic Hot- and Cold-Water Distribution Systems	Table P2903.8(1), Table P2904.4.1, Table M2101.1
D 3350—93	Standard Specification for Polyethylene Plastic Pipe and Fitting Materials	Table M2101.1
D 3462—96	Standard Specification for Asphalt Shingles Made From Glass Felt and Surfaced with Mineral Granules	R905.2.4
D 3468—97	Standard Specification for Liquid-Applied Neoprene and Chlorosulfanated Polyethylene Used in Roofing and Waterproofings	Table R905.15.2
D 3679—96a	Standard Specification for Rigid Poly (Vinyl Chloride) (PVC) Siding	Table R703.4
D 3747—79(1995)	Standard Specification for Emulsified Asphalt Adhesive for Adhering Roof Insulation	Table R905.9.2, Table R905.11.2
D 3909—97b	Standard Specification for Asphalt Roll Roofing (Glass Felt) Surfaced with Mineral Granules	R905.5.4, Table R905.9.2, Table R906.3.2
D 4022—94	Standard Specification for Coal Tar Roof Cement, Asbestos Containing	Table R905.9.2
D 4068—96	Standard Specification for Chlorinated Polyethylene (CPE) Sheeting for Concealed Water-Containment Membrane	P2709.1, P2709.2
D 4318—98	Standard Test Method for Liquid Limit, Plastic Limit and Plasticity Index of Soils	R403.1.7.5.1
D 4434—96	Standard Specification for Poly (Vinyl Chloride) Sheet Roofing	R905.13.2

ASTM—continued

ASTM—continued

F 1055—95a	Standard Specification for Electrofusion Type Polyethylene Fittings for Outside Diameter Controlled Polyethylene Pipe and Fittings	Table M2101.1, M2104.2.1.2
F 1281—98	Crosslinked Polyethylene/Aluminum/Crosslinked Polyethylene (PEX-AL-PEX) Pipe	Table P2904.4.1
F 1282—98	Polyethylene/Aluminum/Polyethylene (PE-AL-PE) Pipe	Table P2904.4.1
F 1346—91	Standard Performance Standard Specification for Safety Covers and Labeling Requirements for All Covers for Swimming Pools, Spas and Hot Tubs	AG105.2, AG105.5, AG107
F 1380—95a	Standard Specification for Metal Insert Fittings for Polybutylene (PB) Tubing	Table P2904.6
F 1488—98	Standard Specification for Coextruded Composite Pipe	Table P3002.1, P3002.2
F 1667—97	Standard Specification for Driven Fasteners, Nails, Spikes, and Staples	R905.2.5
F 1807—98	Standard Specification for Metal Insert Fittings Utilizing a Copper Crimp Ring for SDR9 Cross-linked Polyethylene (PEX) Tubing	Table P2904.6, P2904.8.1.4.2, Table M2101.1

AWPA

American Wood-Preservers' Association
P.O. Box 5690
Granbury, Texas 76049

Standard reference number	Title	Referenced in code section number
C1—98	All Timber Products — Preservative Treatment by Pressure Processes	R323.1, R902.2.1
C2—98	Lumber, Timbers, Bridge Ties and Mine Ties — Preservative Treatment by Pressure Processes	R323.1, R327.1.7, Table R905.8.5
C3—97	Piles — Preservative Treatment by Pressure Processes	R323.1, R327.1.7
C4—90	Poles — Preservative Treatment by Pressure Processes	R323.1, R327.1.7
C9—97	Plywood — Preservative Treatment by Pressure Processes	R323.1, R327.1.7
C15—98	Wood for Commercial-Residential Construction Preservative Treatment by Pressure Process	R323.1, R327.1.7
C18—90	Standard for Pressure Treated Material in Marine Construction	R323.1, R327.1.7
C20—93	Structural Lumber-Fire-Retardant Treatment by Pressure Processes	R802.1.3.2
C22—96	Lumber and Plywood for Permanent Wood Foundations — Preservative Treatment by Pressure Processes	R323.1, R402.1.2, R504.3
C23—84	Round Poles and Posts Used in Building Construction-Preservative Treatment by Pressure Processes	R323.1, R327.1.7
C24—96	Sawn Timber Piles Used for Residential and Commercial Building	R323.1, R327.1.7
C27—88	Plywood-Fire-Retardant Treatment by Pressure Process	R802.1.3.2
C28—90	Standard for Preservative Treatment of Structural Glued Laminated Members and Laminations Before Gluing of Southern Pine, Pacific Coast Douglas Fir, Hem Fir and Western Hemlock by Pressure Process	R323.1, R327.1.7
P1—98	Standard for Coal Tar Creosote for Land and Fresh Water and Marine (Coastal Water) Use	R323.1, R327.1.7
P2—98	Standard for Creosote Solutions	R323.1, R327.1.7
P3—89	Standard for Creosote- Petroleum Oil Solution	R323.1, R327.1.7
M4—88	Standard for the Care of Preservative -Treated Wood Products	R324.3.1

CDA

The Copper Development Association, Inc.
260 Madison Avenue
New York, NY 10016

Standard reference number	Title	Referenced in code section number
4115—1929	Copper in Architecture—Design Handbook	Table R905.10.3

CGSB

Canadian General Standards Board
222 Queens Street
14th Floor, Suite 1402
Ottawa, Ontario, Canada KIA 1G6

Standard reference number	Title	Referenced in code section number
37-52M—84	Roofing and Waterproofing Membrane, Sheet Applied, Elastomeric	R905.12.2
37-54M—79	Roofing and Waterproofing Membrane, Sheet Applied, Flexible, Polyvinyl Chloride	R905.13.2
37-56M—80	Membrane, Modified Bituminous, Prefabricated and Reinforced for Roofing—with December 1985 Amendment	Table R905.11.2

CISPI

Cast Iron Soil Pipe Institute
Suite 419
5959 Shallowford Road
Chattanooga, TN 37421

Standard reference number	Title	Referenced in code section number
301—97	Standard Standard Specification for Hubless Cast Iron Soil Pipe and Fittings for Sanitary and Storm Drain, Waste and Vent Piping Applications	Table P3002.1, Table P3002.2
310—97	Standard Specification for Coupling for Use in Connection with Hubless Cast Iron Soil Pipe and Fittings for Sanitary and Storm Drain, Waste, and Vent Piping Applications	Table P3002.1, Table P3002.2

CPSC

Consumer Product Safety Commission
4330 East West Highway
Bethesda, MD 20814-4408

Standard reference number	Title	Referenced in code section number
16 CFR 1201—77	Safety Standard for Architectural Glazing	R308.1.1, R308.3
16 CFR 1209—79	Interim Safety Standard for Cellulose Insulation	R320.3
16 CFR 1404	Cellulose Insulation	R320.3

CSA

Canadian Standards Association
178 Rexdale Blvd.
Rexdale (Toronto), Ontario, Canada M9W IR3

Standard reference number	Title	Referenced in code section number
0325.0—92	Construction Sheathing	R503.2.1
0437-Series—93	Standards on OSB and Waferboard	R503.2.1, R803.2.1
A257.3—M92	Joints for Circular Concrete Sewer and Culvert Pipe, Manhole Sections, and Fittings Using Rubber Gaskets	P3003.3.5
B137.10M—98	Crosslinked Polyethylene/Aluminum/Polyethylene Composite Pressure Pipe Systems	Table M2101.1
B602M—90	Mechanical Couplings for Drain, Waste, and Vent Pipe and Sewer Pipe	Table P3002.1, Table P3002.2

CSSB

Cedar Shake & Shingle Bureau
515 116th Avenue, NE, #275
Bellevue, WA 98004-5294

Standard reference number	Title	Referenced in code section number
CSSB—97	Grading Rules for Wood Shakes and Shingles	Table R905.7.4, R702.6, R703.5
CSSB—97	Grading and Packing Rules for Certigrade Red Cedar Shingles	Table R905.7.4, R703.5

DOC

United States Department of Commerce
National Institute of Standards and Technology
Gaithersburg, MD 20899

Standard reference number	Title	Referenced in code section number
PS 1—95	Construction and Industrial Plywood	R404.2.1, Table R404.2.3, R503.2.1, R604.1, R803.2.1
PS 2—92	Performance Standard for Wood-Based Structural-Use Panels	R404.2.1, Table R404.2.3, R503.2.1, R604.1, R803.2.1
PS 20—94	American Softwood Lumber Standard	R404.2.1, R502.1, R602.1, R802.1

EWA
(formerly APA)

APA-The Engineered Wood Association
PO Box 11700
Tacoma, WA 98411-0700

Standard reference number	Title	Referenced in code section number
EWA E30—98	APA Design and Construction Guide: Residential and Commercial	R803.2.3

FEMA

Federal Emergency Management Agency
500 C Street, SW
Washington, DC 20472

Standard reference number	Title	Referenced in code section number
FEMA/FIA-TB-2—93	Flood-Resistant Materials Requirements For Buildings Located in Special Flood Hazard Areas in Accordance with the National Flood Insurance Progam	R327.1.7

FM

Factory Mutual
Standards Laboratories Department
1151 Boston Providence Turnpike
Norwood, MA 02062

Standard reference number	Title	Referenced in code section number
4450—90	Approval Standard for Class I Insulated Steel Deck Roofs—Supplements thru 7/92	R906.1
4880—94	Approval Standard for Class 1: A) Insulated Wall or Wall & Roof/Ceiling Panels, B) Plastic Interior Finish Materials, C) Plastic Exterior Building Panels, D) Wall/Ceiling Coating Systems and E) Interior or Exterior Finish Systems	R318.3

GA

Gypsum Association
810 First Street, Northeast, Suite 510
Washington, DC 20002-4268

Standard reference number	Title	Referenced in code section number
253—99	Recommended Standard Specification for the Application of Gypsum Sheathing	Table R602.3(1)

HPVA

Hardwood Plywood & Veneer Association
1825 Michael Faraday Drive
Reston, Virginia 20190-5350

Standard reference number	Title	Referenced in code section number
ANSI/HPVA HP-1—1994	The American National Standard for Hardwood and Decorative Plywood	R702.5

ICC

International Code Council
5203 Leesburg Pike, Suite 708
Falls Church, VA 22041

Standard reference number	Title	Referenced in code section number
IBC—2000	International Building Code®	R110.2, R1001.8.2
ICCEC—2000	ICC Electrical Code—Administrative Provisions	R107.3
IECC—2000	International Energy Conservation Code™	R104.11
IFC—2000	International Fire Code	R102.7
IFGC—2000	International Fuel Gas Code®	R104.11
[Note: See Chapter 7 of the International Fuel Gas Code® for all referenced standards listed in Chapter 24.]		
IMC—2000	International Mechanical Code®	R104.11, M2106.1
IPC—2000	International Plumbing Code®	R104.11
IPMC—2000	International Property Maintenance Code	R102.7
ICC Standard 18-1	Standard for Expansive Soil Tests	R403.1.7.5.1
SBCCI SSTD 10-99	Standard for Hurricane Resistant Construction	R301.2.1.1

NCMA

National Concrete Masonry Association
2302 Horse Pen Road
Herndon, VA 20171-3499

Standard reference number	Title	Referenced in code section number
TR 68-A	Discontinued by NCMA	R404.1

NFPA

National Fire Protection Association
Batterymarch Park
Quincy, MA 02269

Standard reference number	Title	Referenced in code section number
13—96	Installation of Sprinkler Systems	R321.1
31—97	Installation of Oil-Burning Equipment	M1801.3.1, M1805.3
58—98	Liquefied Petroleum Gas Code	G2411.2, G2413.6.2
70—99	National Electrical Code®	E3301.1, E3301.2
72—96	National Fire Alarm Code	R317.1
259—97	Standard Test Method for Potential Heat of Building Materials	R318.2.5
501A—92	Standard on Manufactured Housing	AE201, R202
8501—97	Single Burner Boiler Operation	G2450.1
8502—99	Prevention of Furmace Explosions/Implosions in Multiple Burner Boiler-Furnaces	G2450.1
8504—96	Atmospheric Fluidized-Bed Boiler Operation	G2450.1

NFRC

National Fenestration Rating Council, Inc.
Suite 120
1300 Spring Park
Silver Spring, MD 20910

Standard reference number	Title	Referenced in code section number
100—97	Prodedure for Determining Fenestration Product U-Factors	N1101.3.2, N1101.3.2.1
200—97	Prodedure for Determining Fenestration product Solar Heat Gain Coefficients at Normal Incidence	N1101.3.2, N1101.3.2.1

NSF

National Sanitation Foundation
3475 Plymouth Road
Ann Arbor, MI 48105

Standard reference number	Title	Referenced in code section number
ANSI/NSF 14—96	Plastic Piping System Components and Related Materials	P2608.1, P2907.3
ANSI/NSF 42—98	Drinking Water Treatment Units—Anesthetic Effects	P2907.1, P2907.3
ANSI/NSF 44—98	Cajon Exchange Water Softners	P2907.1, P2907.3
ANSI/NSF 53—98	Drinking Water Treatment Units—Health Effects	P2907.1, P2907.3
ANSI/NSF 58—97	Reverse Osmosis Drinking Water Treatment Systems	P2907.2, P2907.3
ANSI/NSF 61—99	Drinking Water System Components—Health Effects	P2608.2, P2722.1, P2904.5, P2907.3

NSPI

National Spa & Pool Institute
2111 Eisenhower Avenue
Alexandria, VA 22314

Standard reference number	Title	Referenced in code section number
ANSI/NSPI-3—1992	Standard for Permanently Installed Residential Spas	AG104.1

NSPI—continued

ANSI/NSPI-4—1992	Standard for Aboveground/Onground Residential Swimming Pools	AG103.2
ANSI/NSPI-5—1995	Standard for Residential Inground Swimming Pools	AG103.1
ANSI/NSPI-6—1992	Standard for Residential Portable Spas	AG104.2

RMA

Rubber Manufacturer's Association
1400 K Street N.W.
Washington, DC 20005

Standard reference number	Title	Referenced in code section number
RP1—90	Minimum Requirements for Non-Reinforced Black EPDM Rubber Sheets	R905.12.2
RP2—90	Minimum Requirements for Fabric-Reinforced Black EPDM Rubber Sheets	R905.12.2
RP3—85	Minimum Requirements for Fabric-Reinforced Black Polychloroprene Rubber Sheets	R905.12.2

SAE

Society of Automotive Engineers
4700 West Lake Avenue
Glenview, IL 60025

Standard reference number	Title	Referenced in code section number
J 78—79	Steel Self Drilling Tapping Screws	R505.2.4, R603.2.4, R804.2.4

SMACNA

Sheet Metal & Air Conditioning Contractors National Assoc., Inc.
4021 Lafayette Center Road
Chantilly, VA 22021

Standard reference number	Title	Referenced in code section number
SMACNA—92	Fibrous Glass Duct Construction Standards	M1601.1.1

TPI

Truss Plate Institute
583 D'Onofrio Drive, #200
Madison, WI 53719

Standard reference number	Title	Referenced in code section number
1—95	National Design Standard for Metal-Plate-Connected Wood Truss Construction	R502.11.1, R502.11.2 R802.10.2, R802.10.3, R802.11.1

UL

Underwriters Laboratories, Inc.
333 Pfingsten Road
Northbrook, IL 60062

Standard reference number	Title	Referenced in code section number
17—94	Vent or Chimney Connector Dampers for Oil-fired Appliances	M1802.2.2
58—96	Steel Underground Tanks for Flammable and Combustible Liquids	M2201.1
80—80	Steel Inside Tanks for Oil-Burner Fuel	M2201.1
103—98	Chimneys, Factory-Built, Residential Type and Building Heating Appliance—with Revision thru March 1999	G2429.1, R202, R1002.3
127—99	Factory-Built Fireplaces	G2443.7, R1002.4, R1003.12, R1004.1, R1004.4
174—98	Household Electric Storage Tank Water Heaters	M2005.1
181—98	Factory-made Air Ducts and Air Connectors—with Revisions thru December 1998	M1601.2, M1601.3.1
181A—98	Closure Systems for Use with Rigid Air Ducts and Air Connectors	M1601.2, M1601.3.1
181B—98	Closure Systems for Use with Flexible Air Ducts and Air Connectors—with Revisions thru December 1998	M1601.2, M1601.3.1

UL—continued

441—98	Gas Vents	G2425.1
559—85	Heat Pumps	M1403.1
641—98	Low-Temperature Venting Systems, Type L	G2425.1, M1804.2.4, R202, R1001.8.5
726—98	Oil-Fired Boiler Furnaces Assemblies—with Revisions thru January 1999	G2425.1, M2001.1.1, M2006.1
727—98	Oil-Fired Central Furnaces—with Revisions thru January 1999	M1402.1
729—98	Oil-Fired Floor Furnaces—with Revisions thru January 1999	M1408.1
730—98	Oil-Fired Wall Furnaces—with Revisions thru January 1999	M1409.1
732—95	Oil-Fired Storage Tank Water Heaters	M2005.1
737—96	Fireplaces Stoves—with Revisions thru May 1998	R1002.3, M1414.1
790—98	Tests for Fire Resistance of Roof Covering Materials	R902.1
795—98	Commercial-Industrial Gas Heating Equipment	G2440.1, G2450.1
834—98	Heating, Water Supply, and Power-Electric—with Revisions thru November 1995	M2001.1.1
896—98	Oil-Burning Stoves	M1410.1
959—95	Medium Heat Appliance Factory Built Chimneys—with Revisions thru April 1998	R1002.6
1040—98	Fire Test of Insulated Wall Construction	R318.3
1256—98	Fire Test of Roof Deck Construction	R906.1
1453—95	Electronic Booster and Commercial Storage Tank Water Heaters	M2005.1
1482—98	Room Heaters, Solid-Fuel Type—with Revisions thru September 1998	M1410.1
1715—97	Fire Test of Interior Finish Material	R318.3
1738—93	Venting Systems for Gas-Burning Appliances, Categories II, III and IV	G2425.1
1777—98	Chimney Liners—with Revisions thru July 1998	R1001.8.1, R1001.15, M1801.3.4, G2424.15.4
1995—98	Heating and Cooling Equipment—with Revisions thru July 1998	M1402.4, M1403.1, M1407.1
2158A—96	Clothes Dryer Transition Duct	M1501.1

ULC

Underwriters' Laboratories of Canada
7 Crouse Road
Scarborough, Ontario, Canada MIR 3A9

Standard reference number	Title	Referenced in code section number
CAN/ULC-S 102—88	Surface Burning Characteristics of Building Materials and Assemblies	R320.2

WDMA

Window & Door Manufacturers Association
1400 East Touhy Avenue, #470
Des Plaines, IL 60018

Standard reference number	Title	Referenced in code section number
ANSI/AAMA/NWWDA 101/I.S. 2—97	Units Voluntary Specifications for Aluminum Vinyl (PVC) and Wood Windows and Glass Doors	R613.3

Appendix Chapters A through J and L of the IRC have been deleted by the State of Minnesota.

MN

APPENDIX K
SOUND TRANSMISSION

SECTION AK101
GENERAL

AK101.1 General. Wall and floor-ceiling assemblies separating dwelling units shall provide airborne sound insulation for walls, and both airborne and impact sound insulation for floor-ceiling assemblies.

SECTION AK102
AIRBORNE SOUND

AK102.1 General. Airborne sound insulation for wall and floor-ceiling assemblies shall meet a Sound Transmission Class (STC) rating of 45 when tested in accordance with ASTM E 90.

SECTION AK103
STRUCTURAL-BORNE SOUND

AK103.1 General. Floor/ceiling assemblies between dwelling units or between a dwelling unit and a public or service area within a structure shall have an Impact Insulation Class (IIC) rating of not less than 45 when tested in accordance with ASTM E 492.

Final action on the contents of the Minnesota Plumbing Code had not taken place as of the printing of this document. Although the contents of this document were closely coordinated with the Minnesota Department of Health and it is believed that few, if any, changes will be made, the possibility does exist that changes could be made. The Association of Minnesota Building Officials will publish any such changes on its website at: *www.ambo.us* on the state amendments page.

MINNESOTA RULES, CHAPTER 4715

4715.0100
DEFINITIONS

Subpart 1. Scope. For the purpose of this code, the following terms shall have the meaning indicated in this part. No attempt is made to define ordinary words which are used in accordance with their established dictionary meaning except where it is necessary to define their meaning as used in this code to avoid misunderstanding.

Subp. 2. Administrative authority. "Administrative authority" means the commissioner of health. (When a governmental subdivision adopts and maintains a comprehensive plumbing enforcement program that is conducted by personnel who are knowledgeable about plumbing installation requirements, and includes enforcement of all code provisions including materials, methods, inspection, and testing, the administrative authority shall be the governing body of the adopting unit of government, its agents, and employees; however, the commissioner of health retains the ultimate authority to enforce Minnesota Statutes, sections 326.37 to 326.45, and provisions of this chapter that are necessary to ensure compliance.)

Subp. 3. Air break (drainage system). "Air break (drainage system)" means a piping arrangement in which a fixture, appliance, or device is protected from backflow by discharging at or below the flood level rim of another fixture or receptacle whose flood level rim is lower than the bottom of the protected fixture, appliance, or device.

Subp. 4. Air gap (drainage system). "Air gap (drainage system)" means the unobstructed vertical distance through the free atmosphere between the outlet of a waste pipe and the flood level rim of the fixture or receptacle into which it is discharging.

Subp. 5. Air gap (water distribution system). "Air gap (water distribution system)" means the unobstructed vertical distance through the free atmosphere between the lowest opening from any pipe or faucet supplying water to a tank, plumbing fixture, or other device, and the flood level rim of the receptacle.

Subp. 6. Anchors. See "supports."

Subp. 7. Approved. "Approved," as applied to a material, device, or mode of construction, means approved by the administrative authority in accordance with the provisions of this code, or by other authority designated by law to give approval in the matter in question.

Subp. 8. Area drain. "Area drain" means a receptacle designed to collect surface or storm water from an open area.

Subp. 9. Backflow. "Backflow" means the flow of water or other liquids, mixtures, or substances into the distributing pipes of the potable supply of water, from any source or sources other than its intended source. Back-siphonage is one type of backflow.

Subp. 10. Backflow connection. "Backflow connection" means any condition whereby backflow can occur.

Subp. 11. Backflow preventer. "Backflow preventer" means a device or means to prevent backflow into the potable water system.

Subp. 12. Backflow preventer (reduced pressure zone type). "Backflow preventer (reduced pressure zone type)" means an assembly of differential valves and check valves including an automatically opened spillage port to the atmosphere.

Subp. 13. Back-siphonage. "Back-siphonage" means the flowing back of used, contaminated, or polluted water from a plumbing fixture or vessel or other sources, into a potable water supply pipe due to negative pressure in such pipe.

Subp. 14. Barometric loop. "Barometric loop" means a loop of water piping rising approximately 35 feet at its topmost point above the highest fixture it supplies.

Subp. 15. Battery of fixtures. "Battery of fixtures" means any group of two or more similar adjacent fixtures which discharge into a common horizontal waste or soil branch.

Subp. 16. Boiler blowoff. "Boiler blowoff" means an outlet on a boiler to permit emptying or discharge of sediment.

Subp. 17. Boiler blowoff tank. "Boiler blowoff tank" means a vessel designed to receive the discharge from a boiler blowoff outlet and to cool the discharge to a temperature which permits its safe discharge to the drainage system.

Subp. 18. Branch. "Branch" means any part of the piping system other than a riser, main, or stack.

Subp. 19. Branch, fixture. See "fixture branch."

Subp. 20. Branch, horizontal. See "horizontal branch."

Subp. 21. Branch interval. "Branch interval" means a vertical length of stack corresponding in general to a story height, but in no case less than eight feet, within which the horizontal branches from one story or floor of the building are connected to the stack.

Subp. 22. Branch vent. "Branch vent" means a vent connecting one or more individual vents with a vent stack or a stack vent.

Subp. 23. Building classification. "Building classification" means the arrangement adopted by the administrative authority for the designation of buildings in classes according to occupancy.

Subp. 24. Building drain. "Building drain" means that part of the lowest piping of the drainage system which receives the discharge from soil, waste, and other drainage pipes inside the walls of the building and conveys it to the building sewer beginning at least one foot outside the building footings.

Subp. 25. Building drain, sanitary. "Building drain, sanitary" means a building drain which conveys sewage only.

Subp. 26. **Building drain, storm.** "Building drain, storm" means a building drain which conveys storm water but no sewage.

Subp. 27. **Building sewer.** "Building sewer" means that part of the drainage system which extends from the end of the building drain and conveys its discharge to the public sewer, private sewer, individual sewage-disposal system, or other point of disposal.

Subp. 28. **Building sewer, sanitary.** "Building sewer, sanitary" means a building sewer which conveys sewage only.

Subp. 29. **Building sewer, storm.** "Building sewer, storm" means a building sewer which conveys storm water but no sewage.

Subp. 30. **Building subdrain.** "Building subdrain" means that portion of a drainage system which cannot drain by gravity into the building sewer.

Subp. 31. **Circuit vent.** "Circuit vent" means a branch vent that serves two or more traps and extends from the downstream side of the highest fixture connection of a horizontal branch to the vent stack.

Subp. 32. **Combination fixture.** "Combination fixture" means a fixture combining one sink and laundry tray or a two or three compartment sink and laundry tray in one unit.

Subp. 33. **Common vent.** "Common vent" means a vent connecting at the junction of two fixture drains and serving as a vent for both fixture drains.

Subp. 34. **Conductor.** "Conductor" means a pipe inside the building which conveys storm water from the roof to a storm drain.

Subp. 35. **Continuous vent.** A "continuous vent" is a vertical vent that is a continuation of the drain to which it connects.

Subp. 36. **Continuous waste.** "Continuous waste" means a drain from two or three compartments of a fixture connected to a single trap.

Subp. 37. **Cross connection.** "Cross connection" means any connection or arrangement, physical or otherwise, between a potable water supply system and any plumbing fixture, or tank, receptacle, equipment, or device through which it may be possible for nonpotable, used, unclean, polluted, or contaminated water or other substance to enter any part of such potable water system under any condition.

Subp. 38. **Dead end.** "Dead end" means a branch leading from a soil, waste, or vent pipe, building drain, or building sewer and terminating at a developed length of two feet or more by means of a plug, cap, or other fitting.

Subp. 39. **Developed length.** "Developed length" means the length of pipe measured along the center line of the pipe and fittings.

Subp. 40. **Downspout.** See "leader."

Subp. 41. **Drain.** "Drain" means any pipe which carries waste water or waterborne wastes in a building drainage system.

Subp. 42. **Drainage system.** "Drainage system" includes all the piping which conveys sewage, rain water, or other liquid wastes to a legal point of disposal. It does not include the mains of a public sewer system, or a public sewage treatment or disposal plant.

Subp. 43. **Dwelling unit.** "Dwelling unit" means one or more rooms with provision for living, sanitary, and sleeping facilities arranged for the use of one family or individual.

Subp. 44. **Effective opening.** "Effective opening" means the minimum cross-sectional area at the point of water supply discharge measured or expressed in terms of diameter of a circle, or if the opening is not circular, the diameter of a circle of the equivalent cross sectional area.

Subp. 45. **Existing work.** "Existing work" is a plumbing system or any part thereof which has been installed prior to the effective date of this code.

Subp. 46. **Fixture.** See "plumbing fixture."

Subp. 47. **Fixture branch.** A "fixture branch" is a water supply pipe between the fixture supply pipe and a water distributing pipe.

Subp. 48. **Fixture drain.** "Fixture drain" means the drain from the trap of a fixture to the junction of that drain with any other drain pipe.

Subp. 49. **Fixture supply.** A "fixture supply" is a water supply pipe connecting the fixture with the fixture branch.

Subp. 50. **Fixture unit (drainage--d.f.u.).** A "drainage fixture unit" is a common measure of the probable discharge into the drainage system by various types of plumbing fixtures on the basis of one d.f.u. being equal to 7.5 gallons per minute discharge. The drainage fixture unit value for a particular fixture depends on its volume rate of drainage discharge, on the time duration of a single drainage operation, and on the average time between successive operations.

Subp. 51. **Fixture unit (supply - s.f.u.).** A "supply fixture unit" is a common measure of the probable hydraulic demand on the water supply by various types of plumbing fixtures. The supply fixture unit value for a particular fixture depends on its volume rate of supply operation, and on the average time between successive operations.

Subp. 52. **Flood level rim.** "Flood level rim" means the top edge of the receptacle from which water overflows.

Subp. 53. **Flow pressure.** "Flow pressure" the pressure in the water supply pipe near the faucet or water outlet while the faucet or water outlet is wide open and flowing.

Subp. 54. **Flushometer valve.** "Flushometer valve" means a device which discharges a predetermined quantity of water to fixtures for flushing purposes and is actuated by direct water pressure.

Subp. 55. **Flush valve.** "Flush valve" means a device located at the bottom of a flush tank for flushing water closets and similar fixtures.

Subp. 56. **Grade.** "Grade" means the fall (slope) of a line of pipe in reference to a horizontal plane. In drainage it is usually expressed as the fall in a fraction of an inch per foot length of pipe.

Subp. 57. Grease interceptor. See "interceptor."

Subp. 58. Hangers. See "supports."

Subp. 59. Horizontal branch drain. "Horizontal branch drain" means a drain pipe extending horizontally from a soil or waste stack or building drain with or without vertical sections or branches, which receives the discharge from one or more fixture drains on the same floor as the horizontal branch and conducts it to the soil or waste stack or to the building drain.

Subp. 60. Horizontal pipe. "Horizontal pipe" means any pipe or fitting which makes an angle of less than 45 degrees with the horizontal.

Subp. 61. Individual sewage disposal system. "Individual sewage disposal system" means a system for disposal of domestic sewage by means of a septic tank, cesspool, or mechanical treatment, designed for use apart from a public sewer to serve a single establishment or building.

Subp. 62. Indirect waste pipe. "Indirect waste pipe" means a waste pipe that does not connect directly with the drainage system but conveys liquid wastes by discharging into a plumbing fixture, interceptor, or receptacle which is directly connected to the drainage system.

Subp. 63. Individual vent. "Individual vent" means a pipe installed to vent a fixture trap and which connects with the vent system above the fixture served or terminates in the open air.

Subp. 64. Industrial wastes. "Industrial wastes" means liquid or waterborne waste from industrial or commercial processes except domestic sewage.

Subp. 65. Insanitary. "Insanitary" means a condition which is contrary to sanitary principles or injurious to health.

Subp. 66. Interceptor. "Interceptor" means a device designed and installed so as to separate and retain deleterious, hazardous, or undesirable matter from normal wastes while permitting normal sewage or liquid wastes to discharge into the drainage system by gravity.

Subp. 67. Leader. "Leader" means the water conductor from the roof to the building storm drain or other means of disposal.

Subp. 68. Liquid waste. "Liquid waste" means the discharge from any fixture, appliance, or appurtenance which does not receive fecal matter.

Subp. 69. Load factor. "Load factor" means the percentage of the total connected fixture unit flow which is likely to occur at any point in the plumbing system.

Subp. 70. Loop vent. "Loop vent" means a circuit vent which loops back to connect with a stack vent instead of a vent stack.

Subp. 71. Main. "Main" means the principle pipe artery to which branches may be connected.

Subp. 72. Main vent. "Main vent" means the principle artery of the venting system to which vent branches may be connected.

Subp. 73. May. The word "may" is a permissive or allowable term for alternative procedures.

Subp. 73a. Must. The word "must" is a mandatory term.

Subp. 74. Nonpotable water. Water not safe for drinking because it may contain impurities in amounts sufficient to cause disease or harmful physiological effects, or water that does not conform to the public water supply quality requirements of parts 4720.0100 to 4720.2500 or the regulations of the local public health authority having jurisdiction.

Subp. 75. Offset. "Offset" means a combination of elbows or bends which brings one section of the pipe out of line but into a line parallel with the other section.

Subp. 76. Plumbing. "Plumbing" means the business, trade, or work having to do with the installation, removal, alteration, or repair of plumbing and drainage systems or parts thereof.

Subp. 77. Plumbing appliance. "Plumbing appliance" means any one of a special class of plumbing fixture which is intended to perform a special function. Its operation and/or control may be dependent upon one or more energized components, such as motors, controls, heating elements, or pressure or temperature-sensing elements. Such fixtures may operate automatically through one or more of the following actions: a time cycle, a temperature range, a pressure range, a measured volume or weight, or the fixture may be manually adjusted or controlled by the user or operator.

Subp. 78. Plumbing appurtenance. "Plumbing appurtenance" means a manufactured device, or a prefabricated assembly, or an on-the-job assembly of component parts, and which is an adjunct to the basic piping system and plumbing fixtures. An appurtenance demands no additional water supply, nor does it add any discharge load to a fixture or the drainage system. It is presumed that it performs some useful function in the operation, maintenance, servicing, economy, or safety of the plumbing system.

Subp. 79. Plumbing inspector official. See "administrative authority."

Subp. 80. Plumbing fixture. "Plumbing fixture" means a receptacle or device which is either permanently or temporarily connected to the water distribution system, and demands a supply of water therefrom, or it discharges used water, liquid-borne waste materials, or sewage either directly or indirectly to the drainage system, or which requires both a water supply connection and a discharge to the drainage system. Plumbing appliances as a special class of fixture are further defined.

Subp. 81. Plumbing system. The "plumbing system" means and includes all potable water supplies and distribution pipes, all plumbing fixtures and traps, all drainage and vent pipes and all building drains, including their respective joints and connections, devices and appurtenances within the property lines of the premises and shall include potable water treatment or using equipment.

Subp. 82. Potable Water. Water free from impurities present in amounts sufficient to cause disease or harmful physiological effects and conforming in its bacteriological and chemical quality to parts 4720.0100 to 4720.2500 or the regulations of the local public health authority having jurisdiction.

Subp. 83. Private or private use. In the classification of plumbing fixtures, "private" applies to fixtures in residences and apartments, and to fixtures in private bathrooms of hotels, as well as similar installations in other buildings where fixtures are intended for use of one family or an individual.

Subp. 84. Public or public use. In the classification of plumbing fixtures, "public" applies to fixtures in general toilet rooms of schools, gymnasiums, hotels, railroad stations, bars, public comfort stations, and other installations (whether pay or free) where fixtures are installed so that their use is similarly unrestricted.

Subp. 84a. Readily accessible. "Readily accessible" means capable of being reached safely and quickly for operation, repair, or inspection without requiring those to whom ready access is requisite to remove obstacles, panels, or similar obstructions.

Subp. 85. Receptor. "Receptor" means an approved plumbing fixture or device of such material, shape, and capacity as to adequately receive the discharge from indirect waste pipes, so constructed and located as to be readily cleaned.

Subp. 86. Relief vent. "Relief vent" means a vent, the primary function of which is to provide additional circulation of air between drainage and vent systems or to act as an auxiliary vent on a specially designed system.

Subp. 87. Return offset. "Return offset" means a double offset installed so as to return the pipe to its original alignment.

Subp. 88. Revent pipe. See "individual vent."

Subp. 89. Rim. "Rim" means an unobstructed open edge of a fixture.

Subp. 90. Riser. "Riser" means a water supply pipe which extends vertically one full story or more to convey water to branches or to a group of fixtures.

Subp. 91. Roof drain. "Roof drain" means a drain installed to receive water collecting on the surface of a roof and to discharge it into a leader or conductor.

Subp. 92. Roughing in. "Roughing in" means the installation of all parts of the plumbing system which can be completed prior to the installation of fixtures. This includes drainage, water supply, and vent piping, and necessary fixture supports.

Subp. 93. Sand interceptor or trap. See "interceptor."

Subp. 94. Sanitary sewer. "Sanitary sewer" means a sewer which carries sewage and excludes storm, surface, and ground water.

Subp. 95. Sewage. "Sewage" means any liquid waste containing animal or vegetable matter in suspension or solution and may include liquids containing chemicals in solution.

Subp. 96. Sewage ejector. "Sewage ejector" means a device for moving sewage by entraining it in a high velocity jet of steam, air, or water.

Subp. 97. Sewer. "Sewer" means an artificial conduit, usually underground, for carrying off waste water and refuse.

Subp. 98. Slope. See "grade."

Subp. 99. Shall. The word "shall" is a mandatory term.

Subp. 100. Should. The word "should" is a nonmandatory term, but describes recommended procedures.

Subp. 101. Soil pipe. "Soil pipe" means a pipe which conveys the discharge of water closets or similar fixtures containing fecal matter with or without the discharge of other fixtures to the building drain or building sewer.

Subp. 102. Special wastes. "Special wastes" means wastes which require special treatment before entry into the normal plumbing system.

Subp. 103. Special waste pipe. "Special waste pipe" means pipe which conveys special wastes.

Subp. 104. Stack. "Stack" is a general term for any vertical line of soil, waste, or vent piping extending through one or more stories. Excepting vertical vent branches which do not extend through the roof and which pass through less than two stories, before being reconnected to a vent stack or stack vent.

Subp. 105. Stack group. "Stack group" means a group of fixtures located adjacent to the stack so that by means of proper fittings, vents may be reduced to a minimum.

Subp. 106. Stack vent. "Stack vent" means the extension of a soil or waste stack above the highest horizontal drain connected to the stack.

Subp. 107. Storm drain. See "building drain, storm."

Subp. 108. Storm sewer. "Storm sewer" means a sewer used for conveying ground water, rain water, surface water, or similar nonpollutional wastes.

Subp. 109. Sump. "Sump" means a watertight tank which receives sewage or liquid waste and which is located below the normal grade of the gravity system and must be emptied by mechanical means.

Subp. 110. Sump pump. "Sump pump" means a mechanical device other than an ejector for removing sewage or liquid waste from a sump.

Subp. 111. Supports. "Supports" means devices for supporting and securing pipe, fixtures, and equipment.

Subp. 112. Trap. "Trap" means a fitting or device which provides, when properly vented, a liquid seal to prevent the emission of sewer gases without materially affecting the flow of sewage or waste water through it.

Subp. 113. Trap seal. "Trap seal" means the vertical distance between the crown wire and the top dip of the trap.

Subp. 114. Vacuum. "Vacuum" means any pressure less than that exerted by the atmosphere.

Subp. 115. **Vacuum breaker, nonpressure type (atmospheric).** "Nonpressure type vacuum breaker" means a vacuum breaker which is not designed to be subjected to static line pressure.

Subp. 116. **Vacuum breaker, pressure type.** "Vacuum breaker pressure type" means a vacuum breaker designed to operate under conditions of static line pressure.

Subp. 117. **Vent pipe.** "Vent pipe" means any pipe provided to ventilate a building drainage system and to prevent trap syphonage and back pressure.

Subp. 118. **Vent stack.** "Vent stack" means a vertical vent pipe installed to provide circulation of air to and from the drainage system.

Subp. 119. **Vent system.** "Vent system" means a pipe or pipes installed to provide a flow of air to or from a drainage system or to provide a circulation of air within such system to protect trap seals from syphonage and back pressure.

Subp. 120. **Vertical pipe.** "Vertical pipe" means any pipe or fitting which makes an angle of 45 degrees or less with the vertical.

Subp. 121. **Waste.** See "liquid waste" and "industrial waste."

Subp. 122. **Waste pipe.** "Waste pipe" means a pipe which conveys only liquid waste free from fecal material.

Subp. 123. **Water distributing pipe.** "Water distributing pipe" means a pipe conveys water from the water service pipe to the point of usage.

Subp. 124. **Water outlet.** "Water outlet" means a discharge opening through which water is supplied to a fixture, into the atmosphere (except into an open tank which is part of the water supply system), to a boiler or heating system, or to any devices or equipment requiring water to operate.

Subp. 125. **Water service pipe.** "Water service pipe" means the pipe from the water main or other source of water supply to the water distributing system of the building served.

Subp. 126. **Water supply system.** "Water supply system" means the water service pipe, the water distributing pipes, and the necessary connecting pipes, fittings, control valves, and all appurtenances within the building or outside the building within the property lines.

Subp. 127. **Wet vent.** "Wet vent" means a vent which also serves as a drain.

Subp. 128. **Yoke vent.** A "yoke vent" is a pipe connecting upward from a soil or waste stack to a vent stack for the purpose of preventing pressure changes in the stacks.

4715.0200
BASIC PLUMBING PRINCIPLES

This code is founded upon certain basic principles of environmental sanitation and safety through properly designed, acceptably installed and adequately maintained plumbing systems. Some of the details of plumbing construction may vary but the basic sanitary and safety principles desirable and necessary to protect the health of the people are the same everywhere. As interpretations may be required, and as unforeseen situations arise which are not specifically covered in this code, the twenty three principles which follow shall be used to define the intent.

A. All premises intended for human habitation, occupancy, or use shall be provided with a potable water supply which meets the requirements of the commissioner of health. Such water supply shall not be connected with unsafe water sources nor shall it be subject to the hazards of backflow or back-siphonage.

B. Proper protection shall be provided to prevent contamination of food, water, sterile goods, and similar materials by backflow of sewage. When necessary, the fixtures, device, or appliance shall be connected indirectly with the building drainage system.

C. Each family dwelling unit shall have at least one water closet, one lavatory, one kitchen type sink, and one bathtub or shower to meet the basic requirements of sanitation and personal hygiene. All other structures for habitation shall be equipped with sufficient sanitary facilities.

D. Every building with installed plumbing fixtures and intended for human habitation, occupancy, or use when located on premises where a public sewer is available within a reasonable distance shall be connected to the sewer.

E. The building drainage system shall be designed to provide adequate circulation of air in all pipes with no danger of siphonage, aspiration, or forcing of trap seals under conditions of ordinary use.

F. The drainage system shall be designed, constructed, and maintained to conduct the waste water with velocities which will prevent fouling, deposition of solids, and clogging.

G. The drainage system shall be provided with an adequate number of cleanouts so arranged that in case of stoppage the pipes may be readily cleaned.

H. Where a building drainage system may be subjected to back flow of sewage, suitable provision shall be made to prevent its overflow in the building.

I. Each vent terminal shall extend to the outer air and be so installed as to minimize the possibilities of clogging and the return of foul air to the building.

J. No substance which will clog or accentuate clogging of pipes, produce explosive mixtures, destroy the pipes or their joints, or interfere unduly with the sewage disposal process shall be allowed to enter the drainage system.

K. The piping of the plumbing system shall be of durable material free from defective construction and so designed and constructed as to give satisfactory service for its reasonable expected life.

L. The plumbing system shall be subjected to adequate tests and to inspections in a manner that will disclose all leaks and defects in the work or the material.

M. Plumbing systems shall be maintained in a safe and serviceable condition from the standpoint of both mechanics and health.

N. Plumbing shall be installed with due regard to preservation of the strength of structural members and prevention of damage to the walls and other surfaces through fixture usage.

O. Plumbing fixtures shall be made of durable, smooth, nonabsorbent, and corrosion-resistant material and shall be free from concealed fouling surfaces.

P. Plumbing fixtures, devices, and appurtenances shall be supplied with water in sufficient volume and at pressures adequate to enable them to function properly and without undue noise under normal conditions of use.

Q. Plumbing fixtures shall be designed and adjusted to use the minimum quantity of water consistent with proper performance and cleaning. Hot water shall be supplied to all plumbing fixtures which normally need or require hot water for their proper use and function.

R. All plumbing fixtures shall be so installed with regard to spacing as to be accessible for their intended use and cleansing.

S. Each fixture shall be provided with a separate, accessible, self-scouring, reliable water-seal trap placed as near to the fixture as possible.

T. No water closet or similar fixture shall be located in a room or compartment which is not properly lighted and ventilated.

U. If water closets or other plumbing fixtures are installed in a building where there is no sewer within a reasonable distance, suitable provision must be made for treatment of the building sewage by methods which meet the design criteria of the Minnesota Pollution Control Agency as prescribed in chapter 7080. One-family and two-family dwellings must comply with applicable local ordinances.

V. Devices for heating water and storing it shall be designed and installed to prevent all dangers from explosion and overheating.

W. Sewage or other waste shall not be discharged into surface or subsurface water unless it first has been subjected to an acceptable form of treatment.

4715.0300
GENERAL REGULATIONS OF PLUMBING CONSTRUCTION

Subpart 1. **Grades of horizontal piping.** See parts 4715.2400 and 4715.2310, subpart 2.

Subp. 2. **Changes of direction.** See part 4715.2410.

Subp. 3. **Prohibited fittings.** See part 4715.2420.

Subp. 4. **Protection of material.** All pipes passing under or through walls shall be protected from breakage. All pipes passing through or in contact with cinder, concrete, or other corrosive material shall be protected against external corrosion by protective coating, wrapping, or other means that will resist such corrosion.

Subp. 5. **Construction.** Construction shall be of such character as to secure fully the results sought to be obtained in all sections of the code.

Subp. 6. **Exclusion of materials detrimental to drainage system.** See parts 4715.1600 and 4715.1610.

4715.0310
USE OF PUBLIC SEWER AND WATER SYSTEMS REQUIRED

If a public sewer is accessible in a street or alley to a building or premises and the connection is feasible, liquid wastes from any plumbing system in that building must be discharged into the public sewer unless otherwise prohibited by this code or a local ordinance.

If a public water supply system is accessible, the water distribution system must be connected to it unless otherwise permitted by the administrative authority. A water well taken out of service because a person is connecting to a public water supply must either be maintained for a use such as irrigation, or sealed and abandoned in accordance with the Minnesota Water Well Construction Code. (Minnesota Rules, chapter 4725)

If either a public sewer or water supply system or both are not available, an individual water supply or sewage disposal system, or both, conforming to the published standards of the administrative authority must be provided.

Every building must have its own independent connection with a public or private sewer, except that a group of buildings may be connected to one or more manholes which are constructed on the premises, and connected to a public or private sewer. These manholes must conform to the standards set by the local sewer authority.

4715.0320
CONFORMANCE WITH CODE

Subpart 1. **Scope.** As provided in Minnesota Statutes, section 326.37, the Minnesota Plumbing Code applies to all new plumbing installations, including additions, extensions, alterations, and replacements connected to a water or sewage disposal system owned or operated by or for a municipality, insti-

tution, factory, office building, hotel, apartment building, or other place of business regardless of location or the population of the city or town in which it is located.

Subp. 2. **New buildings.** All plumbing materials and plumbing systems or parts thereof must be installed to meet the minimum provisions of this code.

Subp. 3. **Existing buildings.** In existing buildings or premises in which plumbing installations are to be altered, renovated, or replaced, the new materials and work must meet the provisions of this code. If the administrative authority finds that the full performance of bringing the work into compliance with all requirements of this code would result in exceptional or undue hardship by reason of excessive structural or mechanical difficulty, or impracticability, a deviation may be granted by the administrative authority only to the extent the deviation can be granted without endangering the health and safety of the occupants and the public.

4715.0330
ALTERNATE FIXTURES, APPURTENANCES, MATERIALS, AND METHODS

Subpart 1. **Approval of alternate fixtures.** The administrative authority may approve the use of fixtures, appurtenances, materials, and methods of a type not expressly approved, nor expressly prohibited by, this code after determination that such fixtures, appurtenances, material, or method is of such design or quality, or both, as to appear to be suitable, safe, and sanitary for the use for which it is intended.

Subp. 2. **Proof of suitability of fixture.** Any person desiring to install or use a fixture, appurtenance, material, or method of a type not expressly authorized nor expressly prohibited by this code shall, prior to such installation or use, submit to the administrative authority such proof as may be required to determine whether such fixture, appurtenance, material, or method is of such design or quality, or both, as to appear to be suitable, safe, and sanitary for the use for which it is intended. If the administrative authority determines that it does appear to be suitable, safe, and sanitary for the use which it is intended, it may permit such use.

Subp. 3. **Tests.** When there is insufficient evidence to verify claims for alternate materials, the administrative authority may require as proof of suitability a test by a testing laboratory approved by the administrative authority, at the expense of the applicant, demonstrating that the performance characteristics of the alternate materials are substantially equal to or exceed those of authorized materials.

Tests shall be made in accordance with generally recognized standards; but in the absence of such standards, the administrative authority shall specify the test procedure.

The administrative authority may require tests to be repeated if at any time there is reason to believe that an alternate material no longer conforms to the requirements on which its approval was based.

Subp. 4. **Advisory council.** The administrative authority may appoint an advisory council to study and make recommendations concerning the uses of new fixtures, appurtenances, materials, and methods.

4715.0340
HEALTH AND SAFETY

Subpart 1. **Installation of additional plumbing.** Where a health or safety hazard exists by reason of an existing plumbing installation or lack thereof, the owner or the owner's agent shall be responsible for installing additional plumbing or making such corrections as may be necessary to abate such nuisance and bring the plumbing installation within the provisions of this code.

Subp. 2. **Condemned equipment.** Any plumbing equipment condemned by the administrative authority because of wear, damage, defects, or sanitary hazards shall not be reused for plumbing purposes.

Subp. 3. **Used material or equipment.** It shall be unlawful to install any used plumbing material or equipment unless it conforms to the standards and rules set forth in this code.

Subp. 4. **Freezing.** Water service piping shall be installed below normal frost penetration for below-grade piping unless special provisions are made to prevent freezing. Plumbing piping in exterior building walls shall be adequately protected against freezing by insulation or heat or both.

4715.0400
QUALITY OF MATERIALS

All materials used in any drainage or plumbing system or part thereof shall be free from defects, and no materials which are damaged or defective shall knowingly be installed.

4715.0410
IDENTIFICATION OF MATERIALS

All materials must be marked, unless otherwise easily identifiable, so as to provide a visual means of identification as to types, grades, weights, and strengths. The installer shall, as far as possible, position the identification marks so as to provide ease of inspection by the administrative authority.

4715.0420
STANDARDS FOR PLUMBING MATERIALS

Subpart 1. **Approved materials.** A material shall be considered approved if it meets one or more of the standards cited in subpart 3. Materials not listed in subpart 3 shall be used only as provided for in part 4715.0330, or as permitted elsewhere in this code.

Subp. 2. **Abbreviations.** Abbreviations in subpart 3 refer to the following:

A. ANSI, American National Standards Institute, 10 East 40th Street, New York, New York 10016;

B. ASTM, American Society for Testing and Materials, 100 Barr Harbor Drive, West Conshohocken, PA 19428-2959;

C. AWWA, American Water Works Association, 2 Park Avenue, New York City, New York 10016;

D. CSA, Canadian Standards Association, 178 Rexdale Boulevard, Rexdale (Toronto), Ontario, Canada M9W 1R3;

E. CS, Commercial Standards available from: Commodity Standards Division, Office of Industry and Commerce, U. S. Department of Commerce, Washington, D. C. 20234;

F. FS, Federal Specifications available from: Federal Supply Service, Standards Division, General Services Administration, Washington, D. C. 20406;

G. NSF, NSF International, Ann Arbor, Michigan 48106;

H. FHA, Federal Housing Authority, Architectural Standards Division, Washington, D. C.;

I. AASHTO, American Association of State and Highway Transportation Officials, 444 North Capital Street Northwest, Suite 249, Washington, D. C. 20001.

Subp. 3. **Standards for plumbing materials.**

DESCRIPTION		ANSI	ASTM	FS	OTHER
I.	CAST IRON PIPE AND FITTINGS				
		A21.2			
		A21.6	A-74	WW-P-401C	CS188
1A	Cast Iron Pipe and Fittings Extra Heavy	A21.8			
1B	Cast Iron Pipe Centrifugally Cast Only and Fittings Service Weight	A21.6 A21.8	A-74	WW-P-401C	CS188
1C	Cast Iron Mechanical (Gland Type) Pipe	A21.11 A21.2 A21.6		WW-P-421a	
1D	Cast Iron Mechanical (Gland Type) Pipe Cement Lined	A21.8 A21.4 A21.2 A21.6 A21.8			
1E	Cast Iron Short Body Water Service Fittings (2"-12")	A21.10			AWWA C100
1F	Cast Iron Threaded Pipe	A40.5			
1G	High Silicon Pipe, Fittings Cast Iron				
1H	Cast Iron Threaded Fittings Black and Galvanized 125#	B16.4		WW-P-501	
1J	Cast Iron Drainage Fittings Black and Galvanized	B16.12		WW-P-491	
1K	Hubless Cast Iron Pipe and Fittings				CISPI Standard 301-69T CSA/CAN 3-B70
1L	Ductile Iron Pipe Flanged	A21.15			AWWA C115
1M	Ductile Iron Pipe Rubber Gasket Joints	A21.51			AWWA C151
II.	STEEL AND WROUGHT IRON PIPE FITTINGS				
2A	Steel Pipe, Welded and Seamless Galvanized, Schedule 40 and Above	B36.1 B36.20	A53	WW-P-406 6(1)	

2B	Wrought Iron Pipe, Galvanized Schedule 40 and Above	B36.2		
2C(a)	Stainless Steel Pipe	B36.19		
2C(b)	Stainless Steel Pipe	A112.3.1		
2D	Galvanized Malleable Fittings 150 psi and Above	B16.3	A197	
2E	Steel Unions, Galvanized		WW-V-531 C	
2F	Corrugated Steel Pipe Aluminized and fittings 18- to 120-inch (Storm only)	A760 A796	AASHTO M36	

III. COPPER AND COPPER BASE PIPE AND FITTINGS

3A	Red Brass Pipe, Regular and Heavier	H27.1	B42B	
3B	Seamless Brass Tube	H36.1		
3C	Brass or Bronze Threaded Fittings 125 lbs. and Over	B16.15	B62	WW-P-460
3D	Brass or Bronze Flare Fittings 125 lbs. and Over, Heavy Duty Long Collar Type	B62		
3E	Seamless Copper Tube Type K, Soft Temper	H23.1	B88	
3F	Seamless Copper Tube Type K, Hard Temper	H23.1	B88	
3G	Seamless Copper Tube Type L, Soft Temper	H23.1	B88	
3H	Seamless Copper Tube Type L, Hard Temper	H23.1	B88	
3H(a)	Welded Copper Alloy 194 Water, Tube, Type "Heavy," Hard Temper	B543-72	OFT194-101A Navfac TS-15400	

3H(b)	Stainless Steel Water Tubing, Type SL, Copper Plated Coating (HWT-T439)	A-651		
3J	Seamless Copper Tube, Type M, Hard and Soft Temper	H23.1	B88	
3J(a)	Welded Copper Alloy 194 Water Tube, Type "Standard," Hard Temper	B543-72	OFT194-101A Navfac TS-15400	
3J(b)	Stainless Steel Water Tubing, Type SM, Copper Plated Coating (HWT-T439)	A-268 A-651		
3K	Seamless Copper Tube Type DW	H23.3	B306	
3L	Copper Pipe I.P.S.	H26.1	B42	
3M	Copper Pipe, Threadless Type T P and Fittings	H26.2	B302	
3N	Cast Bronze and Wrought Solder Joint Pressure Fitting	B16.22 H23.1 B16.18		
3O	Cast Bronze and Wrought Solder Joint D W V Fittings	B16.23		
3P	Copper Alloy Water Tube 1/2 Inch and 3/4 Inch	B447 B75		
3Q	Welded Brass Water Tube 1/2 Inch and 3/4 Inch	B587		

IV. LEAD PIPE AND FITTINGS

4A	Lead Pipe AA	WW-P-325-44	
4B	Lead Pipe AAA	WW-P-325-44	
4C	Lead Bends and Traps	WW-P-325-44	
4D	Sheet Lead	QQ-L201d	

V. SILICA AND EARTH PRODUCTS PIPE AND FITTINGS, NONMETALLIC

5A	Asbestos-Cement Pressure Pipe and Fitting	C500 C296	SS-P351

	Material				
5B	Asbestos Cement Water Pipe and Fittings	C500	SS-P-351	AWWA C400	
5C	Asbestos-Cement Nonpressure Pipe and Fittings	C428	XX-P-331		
5D	Asbestos-Cement Perforated Underdrain Pipe and Fittings	C508			
5E	Vitrified Clay Pipe, Standard Strength and Stronger Fittings	C13 C200			
5F	Unglazed Clay Pipe, Extra Strength and Fittings	C278			
5G	Perforated Clay Pipe and Fittings	C211			
5H	Borosilicate Glass Pipe and Fittings 60 psi				
5J	Nonreinforced Concrete Drain Tile	C412		AASHTO M178	
5K	Nonreinforced Concrete Pipe	C14	SS-P-371	AASHTO M86 CSA-A257.1	
5L	Perforated Concrete Pipe, Underdrainage	C444			
5M	Reinforced Concrete Pipe	C76	SS-P-375	CSA-A257.2	
5N	Reinforced and Prestressed Concrete Pipe, Pressure Type and Fittings				
5O	Bituminized Fiber Drain and Sewer Pipe	D1860	SS-P-1540A		
5P	Perforated Bituminized Fiber Pipe for General Drainage	D2311	SS-P-1540A		

VI. PLASTIC PIPE AND FITTINGS DRAIN, WASTE AND VENT

6A	Acrylonitrile-Butadiene-Styrene (ABS)	D2661	L-P-322a FHA-MPS	NSF14 CSA-B181.1 CS270	
	Type 1, Schedule 40 Cellular core	F628			
6B	(1) Polyvinyl Chloride (PVC) Schedule 40 Unthreaded Schedule 80 can be threaded	D2665	L-P-320a FHA-MPS	NSF14 CS272 CSA-B181.2	
	Cellular core	F891			
	Fabricated Fittings (8- to 24-inch)	D3311			
	Fabricated Fittings (8-inch and larger with mitered joints 4-inch and larger)	F1866			
6B	(2) Polyvinyl Chloride (PVC) Schedule 30 (3-inch only)	D2949	L-P-001221		
6B	(3) Polyvinyl Chloride (PVC) Schedule 40 (14- to 24-inch only) with ASTM D3311 fittings	D1785			
	Fabricated Fittings (8-inch and larger with mitered joints 4-inch and larger)	F1866			
6B	(4) Polyvinyl Chloride (PVC) Schedule 40 and 80 SDR 21 and SDR 26 (6-inch and larger)	D2241			
6B	(5) Corrugated Polyvinyl Chloride (PVC) Schedule 40 (4- to 36-inch) with ASTM D3212 fittings (Storm only)	F949			

BUILDING SEWER

	Material				
6C	(1) Styrene—Rubber	D2852		CS228	
6C	(2) Polyvinyl Chloride (PVC)	D3034	WW-P-00380a	CSA-B182.2	
	(18- to 27-inch only) (18-inch and larger)	F789 F679 F794			
6C	(3) Acrylonitrile-Butadiene-Styrene (ABS)	D2751		CSA-B182.1	
6C	(4) Corrugated High Density Polyethylene (Corrugated HDPE) (12- to 60-inch with ASTM D3212 fittings) (Storm only)			AASHTO M294 AASHTO MP7	

WATER SERVICE—Minimum working pressure rating shall be at least 150 psi for municipal water service and 100 psi for other service.

	Material				
6D	Polyethylene (PE)	B72.1	D2239 D2737	LP-315a FHA-UM-31C	NSF14 CS255 CSA-B137.1
6E	Acrylonitrile-Butadiene-Styrene (ABS)	B72.3	D2282		NSF14 CS254
6F	Polyvinyl Chloride (PVC)	B72.2	D2241 D1785	L-P-1036 FHA UM-41	NSF14 CS256 CSA-B137.3

6G	Polybutylene	D2662 D2666	NSF14 CSA- B137.7

WATER DISTRIBUTION - Polybutylene (PB) systems (PB tubing together with recommended fittings) and chlorinated polyvinyl chloride (CPVC) pipe together with fittings must be tested by the manufacturer at 150 psi and 210 degrees Fahrenheit for a period of not less than 48 hours by a qualified independent testing laboratory acceptable to the administrative authority. Cross-linked polyethylene (PEX) tubing systems together with approved fittings must be tested at 150 psi and 210 degrees Fahrenheit for a period of not less than 30 days by a qualified independent testing laboratory acceptable to the administrative authority.

6K	Polybutylene	D3309	CSA- B137.8 (tubing)
6L	Chlorinated polyvinyl chloride (CPVC)	119.1, 119.2 D2846	NSF14 FHA Bulletin #76 CSA- B137.6
6M	Cross-linked Polyethylene (PEX) Systems	F876 F877	NSF 14 NSF 61
6N	Metal Insert Fittings Utilizing a Copper Crimp Ring for PEX Tubing	F1807	NSF 14 NSF 61
6O	Cold Expansion Fittings with PEX Reinforcing Rings for Use with PEX Tubing	F1960	NSF 14 NSF 61

SPECIAL WASTES

6S	Polyethylene	D2239 LP 315a	PS10-69 PS11-69 PS12-69
6T	Polypropylene	F1412	
6U	Polyvinylidene Fluoride (PVDF)	F1673	

GENERAL DRAINAGE

6W	Polyethylene (corrugated)	F405	

VII. FIBERGLASS PIPE AND FITTINGS

7A	Fiberglass pipe (reinforced thermosetting resin pipe) (one- to 16-inch) (18- to 48-inch must be manufactured in accordance with ASTM D2996)	D2996	NSF14 NSF61 AWWA C-950

4715.0500
WATER SUPPLY SYSTEMS

When selecting the material and size for water service pipe, tubing, or fittings, due consideration shall be given to the action of the water on the interior of the pipe and of the soil, fill, or other material on the exterior of the pipe.

Pipe and fitting materials for water service and distribution must be of a type specifically permitted by parts 4715.0510 and 4715.0520, and must be verified to contain no more than eight percent lead.

4715.0510
WATER SERVICE PIPE

The following materials may be used for water service pipe:

A. Cast iron pipe 1C and 1D both with 1E fittings with the provisions that bends, tees, and plugs shall be anchored by rods. Poured in place concrete thrust blocks or anchor rods shall be used behind all changes of direction of 45 degrees or greater so as to maintain a water tight joint.

B. Steel pipe 2A, wrought iron pipe 2B, both with 2D and 2E fittings, with the provision that all exposed threads must be coal tar enamel coated and wrapped.

C. Red brass pipe 3A, and copper 3L, with 3C fittings, with the provision that every joint is supported by durable nonmetallic support and pipe to be laid on a continuous granular bed.

D. Copper tube 3E or 3G and 3D or 3N fittings.

E. Asbestos cement pipe 5A and fittings with the provision that this material be supported continuously and laid in granular soil and only in yard areas. Further that it not be used to convey extremely soft water, and shall pass through the floor within three feet of the outside wall.

F. Concrete pipe 5N.

G. Plastic pipe 6D, 6E, 6F, and 6G may be used for water service pipe only up to the water meter or pressure tank and provided there is no more than two feet of such piping exposed within the building. These materials shall be installed in accordance with ASTM D 2774-72. Particular care shall be taken to avoid sharp edges in contact with the pipe and to provide for expansion and contraction.

H. Ductile iron pipe 1L and 1M.

I. Fiberglass pipe 7A. Installation must be in accordance with the manufacturer's requirements, recommendations, and guidelines.

4715.0520
WATER DISTRIBUTION PIPE

The following materials may be used for water distribution pipe:

A. Cast iron with 1C and 1D fittings.

B. Steel pipe 2A and wrought iron 2B with 2D and 2E fittings with the provision that this material may not be laid underground nor embedded in masonry construction unless all threads are coal tar enamel coated and wrapped.

C. Steel pipe 2C(a), stainless.

D. Brass 3A pipe or tube 3B with 3C fittings.

E. Copper tube 3E or 3G with 3N wrought fittings or 3D fittings with provisions that it be installed to allow for expansion or contraction and that all stubs through concrete floors must be sleeved or protected by resilient material.

F. Copper tube 3H, 194 water tube 3H(a), or stainless water tubing 3H(b) with 3N fittings except that this material may not be buried under or embedded in a concrete slab.

G. Copper 3J, 194 water tube 3J(a), stainless steel water tubing 3J(b), copper alloy 3P, or welded brass 3Q with 3N fittings may be installed exposed or in frame partitions, or in tunnels and shafts, except that this material may not be laid underground or embedded in masonry or concrete.

H. Copper 3L and 3C fittings.

I. Copper 3M with fittings.

J. Plastic tubing 6K with fittings. Installation must be in accordance with International Association of Plumbing and Mechanical Officials (IAPMO) Installation Standard 22-84.

K. Plastic pipe 6L and corresponding fittings. Installation must be in accordance with International Association of Plumbing and Mechanical Officials (IAPMO) Installation Standards 20-98; however, this material may be air tested.

L. Cross-linked polyethylene (PEX) tubing 6M with fittings 6N or 6O shall be certified by an independent third-party certifier. The water distribution system shall be installed by a factory-trained installer in accordance with the manufacturer's installation instructions. Tubing and fittings must be marked with the appropriate ASTM designations by the manufacturer.

M. Fiberglass pipe 7A. Installation must be in accordance with the manufacturer's requirements, recommendations, and guidelines.

4715.0530
BUILDING SEWERS

The following materials may be used for building sewers:

A. Cast Iron 1A and 1B and fittings and Hubless Cast Iron 1K.

B. Cast Iron 1C and 1D with 1E fittings.

C. Asbestos cement 5A and 5C and fittings laid on a continuous granular bed.

D. Clay pipe and fittings 5E laid on a continuous granular bed.

E. Concrete pipe 5K in yard areas and not under permanent streets, laid on a continuous granular bed.

F. Concrete 5M and 5N and fittings.

G. Plastic 6A, 6B(1), 6B(3), 6C(1), 6C(2), and 6C(3) and corresponding fittings must be laid on a continuous granular bed. Installation must comply with ASTM D2321.

H. Bituminized-fiber drain and sewer pipe 5O, laid on a continuous granular bed.

I. Fiberglass pipe 7A for pressure sewers. Installation must be in accordance with the manufacturer's requirements, recommendations, and guidelines.

4715.0540
STORM WATER AND YARD DRAINAGE
(OUTSIDE FOUNDATION WALLS)

For storm water and yard drainage outside foundation walls the following materials may be used:

A. Those materials specified in part 4715.0530;

B. Corrugated, aluminized steel 2F. This material may not be used in any area requiring testing in accordance with part 4715.2820. Installation must comply with ASTM A798;

C. Corrugated high density polyethylene 6C(4) and approved joints. Installation must comply with ASTM D2321; and

D. Corrugated plastic 6B(5). Installation must comply with ASTM D2321.

4715.0550
STORM WATER OR CLEAR WATER DRAINAGE
(WITHIN BUILDINGS UNDERGROUND)

For storm water or clear water drainage within buildings underground:

A. Approved materials shall be as specified in part 4715.0570 with the following addition.

B. Concrete 5M and 5N and fittings.

4715.0560
STORM WATER OR CLEAR WATER DRAINAGE
(WITHIN BUILDINGS ABOVE GROUND)

For storm water or clear water drainage within buildings above ground, materials shall be as specified in part 4715.0580.

4715.0570
SOIL AND WASTE PIPING UNDERGROUND
OR EMBEDDED

For soil and waste piping, except special wastes, underground or embedded in masonry construction the following materials may be used:

A. Cast iron 1A or 1B and fittings, and hubless cast iron 1K;

B. Cast iron 1C or 1D with 1E fittings;

C. Steel pipe 2C(b), stainless;

D. Lead 4A pipe with wiped joints, fittings 4C; and

E. Plastic 6A, 6B(1), 6B(2), 6B(3), or 6B(4) and corresponding fittings must be laid on a continuous granular bed. Installation must comply with ASTM D2321.

4715.0580
SOIL AND WASTE PIPING ABOVE GROUND

For soil and waste piping, except special wastes, above ground, the following materials may be used:

A. Cast iron 1A and 1B and fittings, and hubless cast iron 1K. This pipe may be uncoated above ground.

B. Cast iron 1F with 1J fittings.

C. Steel pipe 2A, wrought iron 2B with 1J fittings, and stainless 2C(b).

D. Copper 3F, 3H, 3J (hard temper only), and 3K with 3O fittings except these materials shall not be used to receive the wastes from urinals nor wastes from water closets in battery. These materials are not recommended for use in buildings served by septic tank sewage disposal systems.

E. Lead 4A with wiped joints and fittings 4C.

F. Plastic 6A, 6B(1), 6B(2), 6B(3), or 6B(4) with corresponding fittings may be installed except that no horizontal drain may exceed 35 feet in total length. No stack may exceed 35 feet in total height unless an approved expansion and contraction joint is installed at intervals not to exceed 35 feet.

4715.0590
VENT PIPING BELOW GROUND

For vent piping below ground, the following materials may be used:

A. Cast iron 1A and 1B and fittings, and hubless cast iron 1K;

B. Cast iron 1F with fittings and with 1H fitting;

C. Steel pipe 2C(b), stainless;

D. Brass 3A or 3B with 3C fittings;

E. Copper 3F or 3B with 3C fittings;

F. Copper 3L with 3C fittings;

G. Copper 3M with fittings; and

H. Plastic 6A, 6B(1), 6B(2), 6B(3), or 6B(4) with corresponding fittings.

4715.0600
VENT PIPING ABOVE GROUND

For vent piping above ground, the following materials may be used:

A. Cast iron 1A and 1B and fittings, and hubless cast iron 1K (pipe may be uncoated);

B. Cast iron 1F with 1H fitting;

C. Steel 2A pipe, wrought iron 2B with 1H fitting, and stainless 2C(b);

D. Brass 3A or 3B with 3C fittings;

E. Copper 3F, 3H, 3J, and 3K, with 3N or 3O fittings, except see part 4715.0580, item D;

F. Copper pipe 3L with 3C fittings;

G. Copper pipe 3M with 3M fittings; and

H. Plastic 6A, 6B(1), 6B(2), 6B(3), or 6B(4) with corresponding fittings may be installed except that no horizontal vent may exceed 35 feet in total length.

No vent stack or stack vent may exceed 35 feet in total height unless an approved expansion and contraction joint is installed at intervals not to exceed 35 feet.

4715.0610
SPECIAL WASTES

For special wastes, the following materials may be used:

A. The following corrosion resistant materials are acceptable for chemical waste and vent systems: stainless steel 2C(b), chemically resistant glass pipe 5H, high silicon content cast iron 1G, and chemically resistant plastic pipe 6S, 6T, or 6U. Use of any other materials must be approved by the administrative authority, who shall grant approval if the applicant can show that the material in question is as resistant to corrosion as are those listed above. The installation shall be in accordance with manufacturer's installation recommendations. If 6S, 6T, or 6U is used, horizontal piping may not exceed 35 feet in total length; and stacks may not exceed 35 feet in total height unless an approved expansion and contraction joint is installed at intervals not to exceed 35 feet.

B. Pressure wastes or nonpressure wastes which are completely exposed or accessible, and which discharge indirectly to the drainage system may be of any materials in part 4715.0420, subpart 3, with due regard to the type of liquid being wasted.

4715.0620
SUBSOIL DRAINS

All materials listed in part 4715.0570 plus asbestos cement 5D, clay 5G, cement 5J, and cement 5L, perforated bituminized fiber pipe for general drainage 5P, and plastic 6A, 6B, 6C, and 6W, may be used for subsoil drains.

4715.0630
SPECIAL MATERIALS

Subpart 1. **Sheet lead.** Sheet lead for the following uses shall weigh not less than:

A. General use, four pounds per square foot;

B. Safe pans, four pounds per square foot; and

C. Flashings for vent pipes, three pounds per square foot.

Subp. 2. **Lead bends and traps.** The walls of lead bends and traps shall be at least one-eighth inch thick.

Subp. 3. **Sheet copper.** Sheet copper for the following uses shall weigh not less than:

A. General use, 12 ounces per square foot; and

B. Flashing for vent pipes, eight ounces per square foot.

Subp. 4. **Floor flanges.** Floor flanges for water closets or similar fixtures shall be not less than one-eighth inch thick for brass; one-fourth inch thick and not less than two inch caulking depth for cast iron or galvanized malleable iron.

If of hard lead, they shall weigh not less than one pound nine ounces, and be composed of lead alloy with not less than 7.75 percent antimony by weight. Flanges shall be soldered or threaded into other metal. Closet screws and bolts shall be of noncorrodible material.

Subp. 5. **Flush pipes and fittings.** Flush pipes and fittings shall be of nonferrous material. When of brass or copper tubing, the material shall be not less than No. 20 U.S. gauge.

Subp. 6. **Brass tubing traps and trap arms.** All brass tubing used for traps and trap arms shall be not less than 17 gauge (.045 inches) in thickness. Nuts used with brass tubing shall be of brass or other noncorrodible material.

Subp. 7. **Plastic tubular traps, plastic (ABS and PVC) tube and tubular fittings for waste connections.** All tubular fittings must comply with the requirements of ASTM Standard F 409.

4715.0640
FIXTURE MATERIALS

Plumbing fixtures shall have smooth, impervious surfaces, be free from defects and concealed surfaces. All receptacles used as water closets, urinals, or otherwise, for the disposal of human excreta, shall be vitreous china, or other material acceptable to the administrative authority, except trough urinals may be cast iron, enameled on the inside. Drinking fountains shall be constructed of impervious nonoxidizing material and shall be so designed that they may be easily cleaned. Plumbing fixtures shall conform to the applicable commercial standards, where such standards exist.

JOINTS AND CONNECTIONS

4715.0700
TIGHTNESS

Joints and connections in the plumbing system shall be gas-tight and watertight for the pressure required by test, with the exception of those portions of perforated or open joint piping which are installed for the purpose of collecting and conveying ground or seepage water. Portions of storm sewers that do not require testing as provided in part 4715.2820 must be constructed with a code-approved type of pipe and joint that has been certified by the manufacturer to be able to pass the air test specified in part 4715.2820, or an internal hydrostatic pressure of ten pounds per square inch for ten minutes with no leakage.

4715.0710
ASBESTOS CEMENT SEWER PIPE JOINTS

Joints in asbestos cement pipe shall be made with sleeve couplings of the same composition as the pipe, sealed with rubber rings. Joints between asbestos cement pipe and metal pipe shall be made by means of an adapter coupling caulked as required in part 4715.0740. No adapted coupling shall be used that does not have a center ridge. Pipe must not be able to pass through the coupling.

4715.0720
BITUMINIZED FIBER DRAIN PIPE JOINT

Pipe and bends shall be provided with accurately machined or molded tapered joints, and a taper sleeve coupling shall be provided for each length of pipe and for each bend. The slope of the taper in both pipe and coupling shall be two degrees.

4715.0730
BURNED LEAD JOINTS

Burned (welded) lead joints shall be fused together to form a uniform weld at least as thick as the lead being joined.

4715.0740
CAULKED JOINTS

Caulked joints for cast-iron bell and spigot soil pipe shall be firmly packed with oakum or hemp and filled with molten lead not less than one inch deep and shall extend not more than one-eighth inch below rim of hub. No paint, varnish, or any other coatings shall be permitted on the jointing material until after the joint has been tested and approved. Lead shall be caulked tight.

4715.0750
CEMENT MORTAR JOINTS

Except for repairs and connections of existing lines constructed with such joints, cement mortar joints are prohibited. Where permitted, cement mortar joints shall be made in the following manner: A layer of jute or hemp shall be inserted into the base of the annular joint space and packed tightly to prevent mortar from entering the interior of the pipe or fitting. Not more than 25 percent of the annular space shall be used for jute or hemp. The remaining space shall be filled in one continuous operation with a thoroughly mixed mortar composed of one part cement and two parts sand, with only sufficient water to make the mixture workable by hand. Additional mortar of the same composition shall then be applied to form a one to one slope with the barrel of the pipe. The bell or hub of the pipe shall be left exposed and when necessary the interior of the pipe shall be swabbed to remove any mortar or other material which may have found its way into such pipe.

4715.0760
COLD JOINT COMPOUND, TAR BASE

Cold joint compound (tar base) for clay and concrete pipe shall not be water absorbent, and shall bond itself to vitrified clay and concrete pipe. Half of the joint must be packed with oakum, and the remainder with cold tar compound.

4715.0770
FLARED JOINTS

Flared joints for soft copper water tubing shall be made with fittings meeting approved standards. (See part 4715.0420, subpart 3.) The tubing shall be reamed and expanded with proper flaring tools.

4715.0780
GASKET TYPE JOINTS

Resilient rubber joints for clay or concrete: Flexible joints between lengths of clay or concrete pipe may be made by using approved resilient or rubber materials, both on the spigot end and in the bell end of the pipe.

4715.0790
HOT-POURED JOINTS

Hot-poured compound for clay or concrete sewer pipe, or other materials, shall not be water-absorbent, and when poured against a dry surface shall have a bond of not less than 100 pounds per square inch. All surfaces of the joint shall be clean and dried before pouring. If wet surfaces are unavoidable, a suitable primer shall be applied.

The compound shall not soften sufficiently to destroy the effectiveness of the joint when subjected to a temperature of 160 degrees Fahrenheit nor soluble in any of the waste carried by the drainage system. Approximately 25 percent of the joint space at the base of the socket shall be filled with jute or hemp. A pouring collar, rope, or other device shall be used to hold the hot compound when pouring. Each joint shall be poured in one operation until the joint is filled. Joints shall not be tested until one hour after pouring.

4715.0800
MECHANICAL JOINTS

Subpart 1. **Mechanical joints for cast iron and steel water pipe.** Mechanical joints in cast iron and steel water pipe must be made by means of a flanged collar and rubber ring gasket, secured by the use of an adequate number of steel bolts. The rubber sealing ring must conform to ANSI-A21.11 (AWWA-C11).

Subp. 2. **Mechanical joints in cast iron soil pipe.** Mechanical joints in cast iron soil pipe shall be made by means of a pre-formed molded rubber ring, secured by pulling the pipe and fittings together in such a way as to compress the molded rubber ring in a manner that will assure a gas and water tight joint. The rubber sealing ring shall conform to ASTM 564-65 requirements.

Subp. 3. [Repealed by amendment, 9 SR 1557]

Subp. 4. **Mechanical joints in hubless cast iron soil pipe.** Mechanical joints for hubless cast iron soil pipe and fittings may be made by using a neoprene sleeve and stainless steel retaining band as specified in CISPI standard 301, by using a transition fitting made of elastomeric material (ASTM C 425 and ASTM C 564) and 300 series stainless steel bands and bolts, or by using a two-part coupling whose housing is fabricated of grey-cast iron (ASTM A 48), with a coupling gasket made of neoprene rubber (ASTM C 564 or CSA/CAN 3-B70), and coupling bolts and nuts made of 18-8 stainless steel.

Subp. 5. **Mechanical pipe couplings and fittings.** Couplings must be made with the housing fabricated in two or more parts of ductile or malleable iron castings in accordance with Federal Specification QQ-I-666c, Grade 11, or with ASTM A47 or ASTM A339. The coupling gasket must be molded synthetic rubber, per ASTM D-735-61, Grade No. R615BZ. Coupling bolts must be oval neck track head type with hexagonal heavy nuts, per ASTM-A-183-60, or ASTM A325.

Pipe fittings used with these pipe couplings must be fabricated or malleable iron castings in accordance with Federal Specifications QQ-I-666c, Grade 11, or with ASTM A47; ductile iron ASTM A339; segweld steel ASTM53 or A106; or IAPMO-approved copper fittings with rolled grooves intended to be used together with copper tubing with cold rolled grooved ends.

These couplings and fittings may be used above ground, for storm drains and leaders, and for water distribution pipe provided exposed parts in contact with water are galvanized, and may be used below ground for water distribution if couplings and fittings are galvanized and the exposed grooves are coal tar enamel coated and wrapped.

Saddle-type fittings secured by steel electroplated U-bolts may be used for aboveground water distribution, if the fittings are galvanized, include a collar fitting into the pipe opening with a gasket, and have IAPMO approval.

All grooving of galvanized pipe must be by the cut groove method.

Subp. 6. **Extracted mechanical joint.** An extracted mechanical joint in copper water distribution pipe must be made by drilling through copper pipe and on retraction must extract a cup shaped extruded collar. The height of the collar must be at least three times the thickness of the copper tube wall and the radius of the extruded collar must be the same thickness as the copper tube wall from which it is being extruded. The joining branch tube must be contour-notched and a retaining dimple must be made before insertion into the extracted collar or another acceptable method must be used to provide proper insertion depth. The joint must be brazed with a brazing material meeting the requirements of part 4715.0820. The joint may be used above ground only.

Subp. 6a. **Field formed coupling for copper tubing.** A field formed coupling in copper water distribution pipe must be made by first annealing the area of the tubing where expansion is desired, and then using a hand tube expander to expand the tube end to accept tubing of the same type and size. Joint clearances must be from .001 to .005 inches, and suitable for the brazing filler metal used. The depth of the expanded area must be as recommended by the tube expander manufacturer, but in all cases must be at least four times the wall thickness of the tubing. All joints must be brazed in accordance with the requirements of part 4715.0820. The couplings must be used above ground only.

Subp. 7. **Mechanical tee coupling for steel pipe.** Couplings utilizing an explosive charge and an internal cutting mechanism may be used to join galvanized steel pipe only. All portions of the coupling exposed to water must be of galvanized steel construction acceptable for contact with potable water. The coupling must only be used above ground and only in areas that are accessible. The coupling must be attached to the steel pipe by use of four allen screws which must be torqued in accordance with the coupling manufacturer's recommendation.

4715.0805
PUSH-ON JOINTS

Push-on joints may be used in cast iron and ductile iron water service pipe located underground outside the building, and must comply with ANSI-A21.11-85. Lead-tipped gaskets are prohibited.

4715.0810
PLASTIC JOINTS

Subpart 1. **Joint methods.** Every joint in plastic piping must be made with approved fittings using solvent welded connections, fusion welded connections, insert fittings with metal clamps and screws of corrosion-resistant material or approved crimp rings, threaded joints according to accepted standards, or special IAPMO listed fittings of other types. Large diameter water service pipe may have approved elastomeric-gasket push-on type joints which comply with ASTM D 3139. All solvent materials must meet approved recognized standards.

Expansion and contraction joint materials and dimensions must conform to ASTM D 2661 or ASTM D 2665 and shall be of an approved type. Gasketed sewer fittings must comply with ASTM F1336.

Subp. 2. Primer. Solvent weld joints in PVC and CPVC pipe must include use of a primer of contrasting color to the pipe and cement. Primers must comply with the National Sanitation Foundation (NSF) Standard Number 14. A mechanical method of preparing PVC or CPVC pipe for solvent cement is not acceptable in lieu of using a primer.

Exception: A one-step solvent cement complying with ASTM F493 and ASTM D2846 may be used for CPVC pipe.

4715.0815
JOINTS IN CHEMICAL WASTE PIPE

Joints for chemical waste and vent piping must be of corrosion resistant material, or coated or wrapped with a corrosion resistant material, and designed for use with the type of piping material selected. All joint materials and methods must be as approved by the administrative authority.

4715.0820
SOLDERED OR BRAZED JOINTS

Joints with copper tube with solder joint fittings must be soldered or brazed. Copper tubing must be reamed out to the full interior tubing dimension before soldered or brazed joints are made. Surfaces to be soldered or brazed must be thoroughly cleaned. Joints to be soldered must be properly fluxed with noncorrosive paste or liquid type flux complying with ASTM Standard B813-00. Solder and flux used in potable water systems must not contain more than 0.2 percent lead. Solder used for joints must have a nominal composition of 50 percent tin and 50 percent lead, 95 percent tin and five percent antimony, or 96 percent tin and four percent silver, conforming to ASTM Standard Specification for soft solder metal B32-94, except that 50 percent tin and 50 percent lead solder must not be used in potable water systems. Alternative solders may be used if specifically approved by the administrative authority after review of testing laboratory or listing agency documentation. Brazing must be done using a brazing filler metal which is manufactured for the particular application, and using methods specified by the filler metal manufacturer.

4715.0830
THREADED JOINTS—SCREWED JOINTS

Threaded joints shall conform to American National taper pipe thread, ASA B2.1-1945 or FS GGG-P-351a. All burrs shall be removed. Pipe ends shall be reamed out to size of bore and chips removed. Pipe joint compound shall be used on male threads only.

4715.0840
WIPED JOINTS

Joints in lead pipe or fittings, or between lead pipe or fittings and brass or copper pipe, ferrules, solder nipples, or traps, shall be full wiped joints. Wiped joints shall have an exposed surface on each side of the joint not less than three-fourths inch, and a minimum thickness at the thickest part of the joint of not less than three-eighths inch. Joints between lead pipe and cast iron, steel, or wrought iron shall be made by means of a caulking ferrule, soldering nipple, or bushing.

4715.0850
USE OF JOINTS

Subpart 1. Bituminized fiber pipe joints. Joints in bituminized fiber pipe shall be made as provided for in part 4715.0720.

Subp. 2. Cast-iron pipe. Joints in cast iron shall be either caulked or screwed, as provided in parts 4715.0740, 4715.0830, and 4715.0840.

Subp. 3. Cast-iron soil pipe. Joints in cast-iron soil pipe may be made by means as provided in part 4715.0740 or 4715.0800, subpart 2.

Subp. 4. Clay sewer pipe. Joints in clay sewer pipe, or between such pipe and metal pipe shall be made as provided in parts 4715.0750, 4715.0760, 4715.0780, and 4715.0790.

Subp. 5. Concrete sewer pipe. Joints in concrete sewer pipe, or between pipe and metal pipe, shall be made by means as provided in parts 4715.0750, 4715.0760, 4715.0780, and 4715.0790.

Subp. 6. Copper water tube. Joints in copper water tubing shall be made either by the appropriate use of approved brass or wrought copper water fittings properly soldered or brazed; by means of approved flared fittings as provided in part 4715.0770; or by means of press type copper and copper alloy fittings on aboveground water distribution copper tubing, sizes $1/2$-inch to 4-inch, installed in accordance with IAPMO Standard PS 117-2002.

Subp. 7. Lead to cast iron, wrought iron and steel. Joints between lead and cast iron, wrought iron, or steel shall be made by means of wiped joints to a caulking ferrule, soldering nipple, or bushing as provided in part 4715.0840.

Subp. 8. Plastic pipe joints. Joints in plastic pipe or between plastic and cast iron, steel, brass, or copper pipe shall be made as provided in part 4715.0810.

Subp. 9. Threaded pipe to cast iron. Every joint between wrought iron, steel, brass, copper, and cast-iron pipe shall be either caulked or threaded joints as provided in parts 4715.0740, 4715.0830, and 4715.0840 and shall be made with approved adapter fittings.

4715.0860
SPECIAL JOINTS

Subpart 1. Bituminized fiber to other types of pipe. When connecting bituminized fiber pipe to other types of materials, only approved types of fittings and adapters designed for the specific transition intended shall be used.

Subp. 2. **Cast-iron to copper tube.** Caulked joints between copper tubing and cast-iron soil pipe shall be made by means of brass or copper ferrules or other approved adapter fittings.

Subp. 3. **Copper tubing to threaded pipe joints.** Joints from copper tubing to threaded pipe shall be made by the use of brass or copper adapter fittings. The joint between the copper pipe and fitting shall be properly soldered, brazed, or flared.

Subp. 4. **Expansion joints.** Every expansion joint shall be of an approved type and the material used in its manufacture shall be compatible with the type of piping in which it is installed. Every expansion joint, other than an expansion loop, shall be accessible. (Also see part 4715.2770)

Subp. 5. **Slip joints.** In drainage piping, slip joints shall be used only on the inlet side of the trap or in the trap seal. Every slip joint shall be made using approved packings of gasket material or approved ground joint brass compression rings. Ground faced connections which allow adjustments of tubing but provide a durable rigid joint when made up shall not be considered as a slip joint.

Subp. 6. **Transition couplings.** A transition coupling is one which is to be used when pipes made of different materials are to be joined. A transition coupling may be made of elastomeric materials (ASTM C 425 and ASTM C 564) and 300 series stainless steel bands and bolts, except that an exterior corrosion-resistant shield to prevent outward expansion of the coupling must be included on above-ground installations. Any transition coupling joining plastic to plastic, copper to copper, or galvanized to galvanized, must be approved by the administrative authority.

Subp. 7. **Flexible joints for roof drain connections.** A flexible bellows-type joint may be used to join roof drains to approved storm drain piping. The flexible joint must be made of a bellowed neoprene or thermoplastic rubber sleeve and secured by 300 series stainless steel band and bolts. The joint must not be concealed nor installed at an angle of more than 45 degrees from the vertical.

4715.0870
FLANGED FIXTURE CONNECTIONS

Fixture connections between drainage pipes and water closets, pedestal urinals, and earthenware trap standards shall be made by means of brass, plastic, or iron flanges, caulked, soldered, solvent welded, or screwed to the drainage pipe in accordance with the manufacturer's recommendations and approved by the administrative authority. The connection shall be bolted, with an approved gasket, washer, or setting compound between the earthenware and the connection. Floor flanges of other equivalent materials may be used when approved by the administrative authority.

The bottom of the floor flange shall be set on the top of the finished floor or on a structurally firm base. Closet bends or stubs must be cut off so as to present a smooth surface, even

with the top of the closet flange. Use of commercial putty or plastic as fixture setting compound is prohibited.

4715.0880
PROHIBITED JOINTS AND CONNECTIONS

See part 4715.2420.

4715.0890
INCREASERS AND REDUCERS

Brass or cast-iron body cleanouts shall not be used as a reducer or adapter from cast-iron soil pipe to steel or wrought iron pipe. Where different sizes of pipe or pipes and fittings are to be connected, the proper size increasers, reducers, or reducing fittings shall be used between the two sizes. Hexagon screwed bushings shall not be used in drainage piping.

4715.0900
FIXTURE TRAP REQUIREMENTS

Each plumbing fixture, except those having an integral trap, shall be separately trapped by a water seal trap, installed as close to the fixture as possible, and in such a manner as to be readily accessible for cleaning and repairing.

A single trap may serve a two or three compartment sink or laundry tray. The trap shall be located not more than 30 inches from each compartment outlet. The vertical distance between the fixture outlet and the trap weir shall be as short as possible, but in no case more than 24 inches in length.

No food waste disposal unit shall be installed in a set of restaurant, commercial, or industrial sinks, served by a single trap. Each such disposal unit shall be individually trapped and connected to a separate waste opening. Each trap shall have the manufacturer's name or identification stamped legibly thereon and each tubing trap shall show the gauge of the tubing used in its manufacture.

4715.0910
TRAPS DESCRIBED

Every fixture trap shall be self-cleaning. Traps for bathtubs, lavatories, sinks, showers, laundry tubs, urinals, drinking fountains, and similar fixtures, shall be of standard design and weight and shall be of lead, brass, cast iron, or other approved materials, and have a smooth and uniform interior waterway.

4715.0920
TRAP PROTECTION

All fixture traps, except as otherwise provided in this code, shall be protected against siphonage and back pressure by means of a properly installed vent pipe. The vent shall be so located that the developed length from the fixture trap to the vent shall not exceed the distance given in part 4715.2620, subpart 4.

The vent pipe opening from a soil or waste pipe, except for water closets and similar fixtures, shall not be below the weir of the trap. The trap arm direction may be changed by the use of not more than two 45 degrees or one 90 degrees long turn elbows.

4715.0930
SIZES OF TRAPS

The minimum size (nominal interior diameter) of a trap for a given fixture shall be determined by part 4715.2300, subpart 3.

4715.0940
SLIP JOINTS AND UNIONS

Union joints on the sewer side of the trap shall be ground faced, shall be accessible, and shall provide a rigid connection when made up tight. Slip joints shall be used only on the inlet side of the trap or in the trap seal.

4715.0950
TRAP SEALS

Fixture traps shall have a water seal depth of not less than two inches and not more than four inches, except where, under special conditions, a trap with a deeper seal may be found necessary by the administrative authority.

The horizontal length of the seal of any fixture trap shall not exceed six inches where the waste pipe required is two inches or less in diameter.

Traps shall be set true and level with respect to their water seals and where necessary shall be protected from freezing.

4715.0960
TRAPS PROHIBITED

No form of trap which depends for its seal upon the action of movable parts or concealed interior partitions shall be used.

Full "S" traps, bell traps, and crown vented traps, are prohibited.

Traps shall not be made up with fittings, unless authorized by the administrative authority.

Water-cooled grease traps are prohibited.

No fixture shall be double-trapped.

Drum traps shall be installed only when permitted by the administrative authority for special conditions (laboratory tables, dental chairs, etc.).

4715.0970
TRAP CLEANOUTS

An accessible trap is considered a cleanout for the fixture branch serving the individual fixture.

4715.1000
LOCATION

There shall be at least two cleanouts in the building drain, one at or near the base of the stack and one near the connection between the building drain and the building sewer. The cleanout at the outside wall may be inside or outside the building, and shall be made with a full "Y" branch fitting and shall extend at least two inches above grade or finished floor, except that the administrative authority may grant permission to use a flush cover in traffic areas.

A cleanout which is easily accessible shall be provided at or near the foot of each vertical soil or waste stack and each vertical storm water leader.

Each horizontal branch drain pipe shall be provided with a cleanout at its upper terminal, except that a fixture trap or a fixture with an integral trap, readily removable without disturbing concealed piping, may be accepted as a cleanout equivalent for this purpose.

A trap opening from a lavatory, drinking fountain, urinal, sink, or similar fixture may serve as a cleanout for a horizontal branch drain up to two inches in size, if the drain opening is not more than one pipe size smaller than the horizontal branch drain.

4715.1010
SIZE OF CLEANOUTS

The cleanout shall be of the same nominal size as the pipes they serve up to four inches in diameter and not less than four inches for larger piping.

The distance between cleanouts in horizontal piping shall not exceed 50 feet for three inch or less in size and not over 100 feet for four inch and over in size.

4715.1020
CLEANOUT MATERIALS

The bodies of cleanout ferrules shall be made to standard pipe sizes, conform in thickness to that required for pipes and fittings of the same material and extend not less than one-fourth inch above the hub. The cleanout cover or plug shall be of brass, cast iron, or approved plastic and be provided with a raised nut or recessed socket for removal.

Neoprene or nordel rubber with a plastic disc and a single stainless steel (300 series) band may be used for a cleanout cover provided that it is exposed and readily accessible.

4715.1030
CLEANOUTS TO BE ACCESSIBLE

Each cleanout, unless installed under an approved cover plate or left flush with the finished floor, shall be at least two inches above grade, readily accessible, and shall not be covered with cement, plaster, or other permanent finish material. Where a soil stack cleanout is located within ten feet of where the building drain leaves the building, the cleanout at the outside wall may be eliminated.

4715.1100
INTERCEPTORS AND SEPARATORS REQUIRED

Interceptors for oil, grease, sand, and other substances harmful or hazardous to the building drainage system shall be provided as stated elsewhere in these rules.

The size, type, and location of each interceptor, and of each separator shall conform to the requirements of this chapter, except that units may be accepted which are engineered and manufactured specifically for the intended function and which are documented by the manufacturer and project design engineer to be properly designed and sized for the specific project, and no waste other than those requiring treatment or separation shall discharge into any interceptor.

4715.1110
GREASE INTERCEPTORS FOR COMMERCIAL BUILDINGS

A grease interceptor of sufficient size and efficiency shall be installed in the waste line leading from sinks, drains, or other fixtures when, in the opinion of the administrative authority, greasy wastes can be introduced into the drainage system in quantities that can cause line stoppage. Grease interceptors shall be placed as near as possible to the fixture and the grease interceptor shall be vented. No food waste disposer or dishwashing machine shall discharge into the building drainage system through a grease interceptor. Sinks or other fixtures served by grease interceptors shall be trapped and vented ahead of the grease interceptor.

Grease interceptors, when used, shall have a grease retention capacity in pounds of grease, of at least twice the flow-through rate, in gallons per minute.

Grease interceptors shall be equipped with devices to control the rate of water flow through the interceptors so that it does not exceed the rated flow of the interceptor. Air openings on flow control devices must connect to the plumbing vent system.

4715.1115
EXTERIOR GREASE INTERCEPTORS

Subpart 1. **Authorized uses.** An exterior grease interceptor may be installed if it is acceptable to the administrative authority. Only fixtures that discharge greasy waste may be piped to the interceptor. Dishwashing machines and food waste grinders may not be routed through the interceptor unless the routing is acceptable to the administrative authority.

Subp. 2. **Construction.** The grease interceptor tank must be readily accessible for inspection and maintenance. The tank must comply with parts 5 and 6 of ASTM Standard C1227-98. The name of the tank manufacturer, the liquid holding capacity, and compliance with ASTM C1227-98 for the tank construction must be permanently affixed to the tank.

The grease interceptor must allow a detention time of at least 30 minutes and must be protected from freezing. The landscape must be bermed to divert runoff. The tank must be

protected to prevent loadings that may lead to structural collapse.

The materials used in piping to the inlet of the tank must comply with building drain requirements. The tank outlet piping may comply with building sewer materials, unless the outlet piping reenters the building, in which case, the materials must be approved for building drain to point of connection to building sewer.

Baffles or tees must be provided at the inlet and outlet of the tank. The invert of the inlet must be at least two inches above the invert of the outlet. The inlet baffle/tee must extend at least six inches below the liquid level, and the outlet baffle/tee must extend at least 12 inches below the liquid level of the tank. Both inlet and outlet baffles/tees must extend at least six inches above the liquid level. Baffles, tees, and fasteners must be made of plastic or stainless steel.

The tank and baffle design must allow for continuous circulation of air throughout the tank. Vents, if provided, must be at least two inches in diameter, located within the building within ten feet of the interceptor, and must be labeled as the exterior grease interceptor vent. The vent must rise within 45 degrees of the vertical to a point at least six inches above the tank before offsetting horizontally.

Inspection pipes, at least four inches in diameter, must be provided above the baffles/tees. A manhole, at least 24 inches in diameter, must also be provided. The manhole cover must be locked in place, marked with a warning to not enter without proper equipment, and be provided with a label identifying the vessel as the exterior grease interceptor.

The inlet and outlet pipes must be connected to the tank with a sealed flexible joint to accommodate pipe movement. A cleanout, at least four inches in diameter, must be provided on the discharge line from the interceptor.

Subp. 3. **Inspection, testing, and records.** After installation, the tank must pass a manometer test with one inch of water column for five minutes, or a vacuum test with two inches of mercury for 60 minutes. The grease interceptor must be inspected at least once every three months, and must be pumped and cleaned regularly. Records of inspection and maintenance must be kept. The administrative authority shall set the frequency, duration, and availability of the inspections, cleaning, and recordkeeping information.

4715.1120
OIL AND FLAMMABLE LIQUIDS SEPARATOR

Enclosed garages of over 1,000 square feet or housing more than four motor vehicles, repair garages, gasoline stations with grease racks, work or wash racks, auto washes, and all buildings where oily and/or flammable liquid wastes are produced shall have a separator installed into which all oil, grease, and sand bearing and/or flammable wastes shall be discharged before emptying into the building drainage system or other point of disposal, when floor drains or trench drains are provided.

Exception: Private garages classified as Group U occupancies serving one- and two-family dwellings.

Each separator shall be of watertight construction and of not less than 35 cubic feet holding capacity, be provided with a water seal of not less than three inches on the inlet and not less than 18 inches on the outlet. The minimum depth below the invert of the discharge drain shall be three feet. The minimum size of the discharge drain shall be four inches. The separator may be constructed of monolithic poured reinforced concrete with a minimum floor and wall thickness of six inches, or of iron or steel of a minimum thickness of $^3/_{16}$ inch, protected with an approved corrosion resistant coating on both the inside and the outside.

The separator must be provided with a nonperforated iron or steel cover and ring of not less than 24 inches in diameter, and the air space in the top of the tank must have a three-inch vent pipe, constructed of approved metallic material, extending separately to a point at least 12 inches above the roof of the building. Drains and piping from motor vehicle areas must be a minimum of three inches in size. Drains discharging to an interceptor must not be trapped and must be constructed so as not to retain liquids. In motor vehicle wash facilities, a sand interceptor which meets the requirements of part 4715.1130, subpart 1, except that no water seal is permitted, may be installed to receive wastes before discharging into a flammable waste separator.

No cleanout, mechanical joint, or backwater valve shall be installed inside the separator which could provide a bypass of the trap seal. Only wastes that require separation shall discharge into the separator, except that a water supplied and trapped sink may be connected to the vent of the separator. Whenever the outlet branch drain serving a separator is more than 25 feet from a vented drain, such branch drain shall be provided with a two inch vent pipe. A backwater valve shall be installed in the outlet branch drain whenever in the judgment of the administrative authority backflow from the building drain could occur.

A separator must be installed to be readily accessible for service and maintenance, and must be maintained by periodic removal of accumulated liquids and solids from the separator.

4715.1130
INTERCEPTORS AND SEPARATORS FOR SPECIFIC INSTALLATIONS

Subpart 1. **Sand interceptors, commercial establishments.** Sand and similar interceptors for heavy solids shall be so designed and located as to be readily accessible for cleaning, and shall have a water seal of not less than six inches.

Subp. 2. **Laundries.** Commercial laundries shall be equipped with an interceptor having a wire basket or similar device, removable for cleaning, that will prevent passage into the drainage system of solids one-half inch or larger in size, string, rags, button, or other material detrimental to the public sewerage system.

Subp. 3. **Bottling establishments.** Bottling plants shall discharge their process wastes into an interceptor which will provide for separation of broken glass or other solids before discharging liquid wastes into the drainage system.

Subp. 4. **Slaughter houses.** Slaughtering and dressing room drains shall be equipped with separators or interceptors approved by the administrative authority, which shall prevent the discharge into the drainage system of feathers, entrails, or other material likely to clog the drainage system.

4715.1140
VENTING OF INTERCEPTORS AND SEPARATORS

Interceptors and separators shall be so designed that they will not become airbound if closed covers are used. Each interceptor or separator shall be properly vented.

4715.1150
MAINTENANCE OF INTERCEPTORS AND SEPARATORS

Interceptors and separators shall be maintained in efficient operating condition by periodic removal of accumulated grease, scum, oil, or other floating substances, and solids, deposited in the interceptor or separator.

Each interceptor and separator shall be so installed that it is readily accessible for removal of cover, servicing, and maintenance. If installed substantially below grade a manhole with flush manhole cover should be provided.

4715.1160
BACKWATER VALVES

Subpart 1. **Where used.** Drainage piping serving fixtures that are located below the elevation of the curb or property line at the point where the building sewer crosses under the curb or property line, and above the crown level of the main sewer, shall drain by gravity into the main sewer, and shall be protected from back flow of sewage by installing an approved backwater valve, and each such backwater valve shall be installed only in that branch or section of the drainage system which receives the discharge from fixtures located below the elevation of the curb or property line.

Further, in every building hereafter erected or remodeled so that the erection or remodeling creates a new dwelling use which is located below the elevation of the point where the building sewer crosses under the curb or property line, all fixtures installed below such point shall be connected to a separate branch drain. Each such branch drain shall be protected by an approved backwater valve and a gate valve. The gate valve shall be located on the sewer connection side of the backwater valve.

Further, the backwater valve and gate valve may be waived by the administrative authority whenever the sanitary sewer does not receive any storm water drainage and the building is located at a sufficient height above the public sanitary sewer so flooding by backflow will not occur, in the opinion of the administrative authority.

Subp. 2. **Construction of backwater valves.** Backwater valves shall be constructed so that a mechanical seal against backflow will be provided. Backwater valves shall have all balls or bearing parts of noncorrodible material and shall have bolted covers and be readily accessible for cleaning.

Subp. 3. **Venting of backwater valves.** Where the installation and operation of backwater valves interfere with the proper ventilation of the plumbing system, additional vents shall be provided so as to assure adequate ventilation of the plumbing system when the backwater valves are in a closed position.

Subp. 4. **Accessibility of backwater valves.** Backwater valves shall be installed so their working parts will be readily accessible for service and repairs. If installed substantially below grade a manhole with flush manhole cover shall be provided.

4715.1200
CONNECTIONS TO PLUMBING SYSTEM REQUIRED

All plumbing fixtures and drains used to receive or discharge liquid wastes or sewage shall be connected to the drainage system of the building in accordance with the requirements of the code.

4715.1210
REQUIRED MINIMUM NUMBER OF FIXTURES

Plumbing fixtures shall be provided for the type of building occupancy and in the minimum number shown as required in chapter 1305, Minnesota Building Code.

4715.1220
INSTALLATION OF FIXTURES

Subpart 1. **Fixtures.** Fixtures must be set level and in proper alignment with reference to adjacent walls. No water closet may be set closer than 15 inches from its center to any side wall or partition nor closer than 30 inches, center to center, between toilets. At least a 24-inch clearance must be provided in front of water closets. Note: The centerline of water closets used primarily by children 12 and younger must be a minimum of 12 inches to a maximum of 18 inches from the side wall or partition (see Minnesota Accessibility Code).

No urinal may be set closer than 15 inches from the center to any side wall or partition, nor closer than 24 inches, center to center, between urinals.

Wall-hung water closet bowls must be rigidly supported by a concealed metal hanger which is attached to the building structural members so that no strain is transmitted to the closet connector or any other part of the plumbing system.

Plumbing fixtures must be so installed as to afford easy access for cleaning both the fixture and the area about it. Where practical, all pipes from fixtures must be run to the nearest wall.

Subp. 2. **Joints.** Joints formed where fixtures come in contact with floors shall be sealed.

Fixtures having concealed slip joint connections shall be provided with an access panel or utility space or other convenient access so arranged as to make the slip joint connections accessible for inspection and repair.

Subp. 3. **Overflows.** In any fixture which is provided with an overflow, the waste shall be designed and installed so that the standing water in the fixture cannot rise in the overflow when the stopper is closed, nor shall any water remain in the overflow when the fixture is empty.

The overflow from any fixture shall discharge into the drainage system on the inlet or fixture side of the trap.

4715.1230
AUTOMATIC CLOTHES WASHERS

A water supply line to an automatic clothes washer shall be protected against backflow by the use of an air gap or vacuum breaker. The discharge shall be through an air break.

4715.1240
BATHTUBS

Subpart 1. **Outlets.** Bathtubs must have waste outlets and overflows at least one and one-half inches in diameter. The waste control device must be located at the tub outlet.

Subp. 2. **Whirlpool bathtubs.** Whirlpool bathtubs and their installation must comply with ANSI 112.19.7 and ANSI 112.19.8.

Subp. 3. **Drop-in bathtubs.** Bathtubs which do not have a factory applied flange for installation against a wall are considered drop-in-type and must not be installed against a wall.

4715.1250
DISHWASHING EQUIPMENT

Every dishwasher in a building for public use shall discharge to the drainage system through an air break. If a floor drain constructed without a backwater valve is installed on the individual dishwasher branch, the dishwasher may be connected directly to the drainage system. The water supply to any dishwasher in which the supply opening is located below the spill line of the machine shall be protected with a vacuum breaker.

4715.1260
DRINKING FOUNTAINS

Drinking fountains must be constructed of impervious nonoxidizing material and must be so designed that they may be easily cleaned. The water should be carried to the fixture in an independent pipe, and no part of the fixture must be used in conveying water to the jet. The design of the fixture must be such that no part of the supply pipe can be submerged in the fixture, or in the waste pipe from the fixture. The jet must be slanting and the orifice of the jet must be protected in such a manner that it cannot be contaminated by droppings from the mouth or by splashing from the basin. The orifice of the jet must be at least one inch above the rim of the basin. All fountains should be so designed that their proper use is self-evident.

Installation of a combined cold water faucet and drinking fountain bubbler is prohibited for public use. If a drinking fountain bubbler is provided at a public use sink, it must have at least an 18-inch separation from any other faucet spout.

4715.1300
FLOOR DRAINS

Subpart 1. **Floor drain trap and strainer.** A floor drain shall be considered a plumbing fixture and shall be provided with a trap seal and a removable strainer. The open area of the strainer shall be at least equal to the cross-section area of the drain line to which it connects.

Subp. 2. **Basement floor drains.** Basement floor drains or floor drains installed in floors which are laid directly on the ground shall be provided with either an integral trap constructed with a spigot outlet or a "P" trap of cast iron or other approved materials compatible with the drainage pipe with a spigot outlet and provisions for a caulked connection to the drain body. A vacuum breaker shall be installed on the water supply to flush rim floor drains.

Subp. 3. **Provision for evaporation.** Where floor drains are subject to evaporation, they shall be of the deep seal type, with a minimum water seal of three inches and may be provided with a water supply through an air gap, from a plumbing fixture, automatic priming device, or other approved means, to maintain the minimum water seal.

Subp. 4. **Venting of floor drains.** Floor drain fixture branches which are less than 25 feet in length and connect to a vented main or branch do not require an individual vent. Floor drains not meeting these requirements and floor drains used for shower drains, recessed slop, or similar receptors shall be vented in accordance with parts 4715.2520, subparts 5 and 6, 4715.2550, subpart 3, and 4715.2620, subpart 4.

Subp. 5. [Repealed, 19 SR 590]

Subp. 6. **Garage and parking area floor drains.** Floor area drains in open parking areas, including open areas of parking ramps, must discharge to the storm sewer if available. Floor drains in parking areas which are enclosed, and floor drains in areas open or enclosed which are used for maintenance or as a vehicle wash bay, must discharge to the sanitary sewer if a municipal sewer is available. Oil and flammable liquid separators must be provided if required by part 4715.1120.

> **Exception:** Floor drains in private garages classified as Group U, Division 1 occupancies serving one- and two-family dwellings may discharge to daylight if approved by the administrative authority.

4715.1305
ELEVATOR PIT DRAIN

An elevator pit drain must discharge to the sanitary sewer using an indirect connection that precludes the possibility of sewage backup into the pit. If a sump is used, it must be outside the pit with a dry pan drain flowing to it.

4715.1310
FOOD-WASTE GRINDER UNITS

Domestic food-waste grinders shall be connected to a drain of not less than $1^{1}/_{2}$ inches in diameter.

Commercial food-waste grinders shall be connected to a drain of sufficient size to serve the unit, but in no case connected to a drain of less than two inches in diameter, and shall

be connected, trapped, and vented separately from any other fixtures or compartments.

All food-waste grinders shall be provided with an adequate supply of water in sufficient flow rate to insure proper functioning of the unit. The water supply line to a commercial food waste grinder, which is equipped with a water rinsed funnel, shall be protected against back-siphonage by an air gap or vacuum breaker.

No food-waste grinders shall be connected so as to discharge through a grease interceptor.

4715.1320
FLUSHING DEVICES FOR WATER CLOSETS AND URINALS

Each water closet, urinal, clinical sink, or similar fixture shall be provided with a flushometer valve, flush tank, or similar device designed and installed so as to supply water in sufficient quantity and rate of flow to flush to the sewer the contents of the fixture to which it is connected to cleanse the fixture and refill the fixture trap.

A flushing device shall serve only one fixture with the exception that a single flush tank may be used to flush more than one urinal provided that the flushing cycle is controlled automatically and that each urinal or section thereof is thoroughly flushed. Automatically controlled flushometer valves may be substituted for flush tanks.

4715.1330
FLUSH TANKS

Subpart 1. **Water supply for flush tanks.** An adequate quantity of water shall be provided to flush and clean the fixture served. The fixture supply to a flush tank must have a shutoff valve. The water supply to flush tanks equipped for manual flushing shall be controlled by a float valve or other automatic device designed to refill the tank after each discharge and to completely shut off the water flow to the tank when the tank is filled to operational capacity. Provision shall be made to automatically supply water to the fixture so as to refill the trap seal after each flushing, the water supply to flush tanks equipped for automatic flushing shall be controlled by a suitable timing device. (See part 4715.1770, subpart 2.)

Subp. 2. **Overflows in flush tanks.** Flush tanks shall be provided with overflows discharging to the water closet or urinal connected thereto and of sufficient size to prevent flooding of the tank at the maximum rate of water supply. Where the float valve is below the rim of the flush tank, it shall be elevated above the overflow and provided with a vacuum breaker or air gap. (See part 4715.2150, subpart 2, protective devices.)

4715.1340
FLUSHOMETER VALVES

Flushometers shall be installed so that they will be readily accessible for repair. Flushometer valves shall not be used where the water pressure is insufficient to properly operate them. (See part 4715.1770, subpart 2.) When the valve is operated, it shall complete the cycle of operation automatically, opening fully and closing positively under the water line pressure. Each flushometer shall be provided with a means for regulating the flow through it. Flushometer valves installed on any plumbing fixture or equipment whose water supply inlet or portion thereof can be submerged shall be provided with a vacuum breaker.

4715.1350
GARBAGE CAN WASHERS

Garbage can washers shall be separately trapped and vented. The receptacle receiving the wash from the garbage cans shall be provided with a removable basket or strainer to prevent discharge of large particles into the building drainage system. Any water supply connection shall be protected against backflow by an air gap or a vacuum breaker.

4715.1360
LAUNDRY TRAYS

Each compartment of a laundry tray shall be provided with a waste outlet not less than $1^1/_2$ inches in diameter. A strainer or crossbar shall be provided to restrict the clear opening of the waste outlet. The water supply faucet shall have a plain end spout or, if threaded, shall be equipped with a vacuum breaker.

4715.1370
LAVATORIES

Lavatories shall have waste outlets not less than $1^1/_4$ inches in diameter. A strainer, pop-up stopper, crossbars, or similar device shall be provided.

Water supply to public lavatories shall not be spring closing unless they are of the delayed action type.

Each 18-inch unit of usable length of a straight-line or circumference of a circular multiple use lavatory shall be considered equivalent to one lavatory as it affects the fixture usage requirements; provided hot and cold or tempered water suitable for hand washing is available for each 18-inch interval.

4715.1380
SHOWERS

Subpart 1. **Water supply riser.** Every water supply riser from the shower valve to the shower head outlet, whether exposed or not, shall be securely attached to the structure.

Subp. 2. **Shower waste outlet.** Waste outlets, other than those in bathtubs, serving a single shower shall be at least $1^1/_2$ inches in diameter and have removable strainers not less than three inches in diameter having strainer openings not less than one-fourth inch in minimum dimension. Waste outlets shall be securely fastened to the waste pipe making a watertight connection thereto. Waste outlets serving showers, except single-head showers, must be at least two inches in diameter and must have removable strainers not less than three inches in diameter. Where each shower space is not provided with an

individual waste outlet, the waste outlet must be located and the floor pitched so that the water from one shower does not flow over the floor area serving another shower.

Subp. 3. **Shower floors or receptors.** Floors or receptors under shower compartments shall be laid on or be supported by a smooth and structurally sound base. Floors under shower compartments, other than those laid directly on the ground surface or where prefabricated receptors have been provided, shall be lined and made watertight by the provision of suitable shower pans of durable material. Such pans shall turn up on all sides at least two inches above the finished threshold level. Pans shall be securely fastened to the waste outlet at the seepage entrance making a watertight joint between the pan and the outlet. Finished floor surfaces shall be constructed of smooth, noncorrosive, nonabsorbent, and waterproofed materials.

Subp. 4. **Shower compartments.** No shower stall or receptor shall have a finished interior dimension which is less than 30 inches, and each shower compartment shall be of a finished size capable of completely encompassing a 30-inch circle measured at the height of the shower control handles, when the door or curtain is closed, and of a horizontal cross sectional area of not less than 900 square inches. The 30-inch requirement shall not apply to a bathtub used as a shower or to showers installed in remodeling.

Subp. 5. **Anti-scald devices.** A shower or combination shower-bath in a new or remodeled installation must be equipped with an anti-scald type shower control valve. The valve must be of the thermostatic or pressure-balancing type in accordance with ANSI/ASSE Standard 1016-96.

The temperature of mixed water to multiple showers must be controlled by a master anti-scald type thermostatic blender, or the showers must be individually equipped with approved anti-scald type shower control valves.

4715.1390
SINKS

Subpart 1. **Drain sizing.** Sinks shall be provided with waste outlets not less than $1^1/_2$ inches in diameter. A strainer, crossbar, or similar device shall be provided. Sinks on which a food grinder is installed shall have a waste opening of not less than $3^1/_2$ inches in diameter. Pot or scullery sinks must be provided with waste outlets not less than two inches in diameter.

Subp. 2. **Commercial kitchen sinks.** All pot, scullery, food preparation, and bar sinks must be connected directly to the drainage system. A floor drain constructed without a backwater valve must be installed on the individual branch serving the fixture to be protected.

4715.1400
SPECIAL PLUMBING FIXTURES

Baptisteries, ornamental and lily pools, aquariums, ornamental fountain basins, swimming pools, and similar constructions when provided with water supplies shall be protected from back-siphonage as required in parts 4715.2000 to 4715.2170.

4715.1410
URINALS

Floor-type trough urinals are prohibited.

4715.1420
WATER CLOSETS

Subpart 1. Prohibited water closets. Pan, valve, plunger, off-set, latrine, and frostproof water closets are prohibited. Water closets which have an invisible seal, an unventilated space, or walls that are not thoroughly washed at each discharge, are prohibited. Any water closet which might permit siphonage of the contents of the bowl back into the flush tank is prohibited.

Subp. 2. Water closet bowls. All water closet bowls must be of the elongated type, except that regular type round bowls may be used in residential or dwelling type occupancy.

Subp. 3. Water closet seats. Water closets must be equipped with seats of smooth nonabsorbent material. All seats of water closets of elongated type provided for public use must be of the open-front type. Integral water closet seats must be of the same material as the fixture. The top of the seat must not be over two inches above the rim of the fixture; seat lifts may not be used.

4715.1430
HANGERS AND SUPPORTS

Subpart 1. **Material.** Hangers, anchors, and supports shall be made of metal or other material of sufficient strength to support the piping and its contents. Piers may be concrete, brick, or other approved material.

Subp. 2. **Attachment to building.** Hangers and anchors shall be securely attached to the building construction at sufficiently close intervals to support the piping and its contents.

Subp. 3. **Vertical piping.** Vertical piping shall be secured at sufficiently close intervals to keep the pipe in alignment. Vertical piping of the following materials shall be supported at not more than the distance intervals shown:

A. Cast-iron soil pipe, at base and at each story height. Neoprene jointed pipe at five foot intervals, except where ten foot lengths are used.

B. Threaded pipe (SPS), every other story height.

C. Copper tubing, at each story.

D. Lead pipe, four foot intervals.

E. Plastic pipe, $1^1/_4$ inch and $1^1/_2$ inch sizes, exposed pipe at four foot intervals, concealed pipe same as item F (two inches and over).

F. Plastic pipe, two inch and over, at each story.

Subp. 4. **Horizontal piping.** Horizontal piping shall be supported at sufficiently close intervals to keep it in alignment and prevent sagging:

A. Cast-iron soil pipe, five foot intervals except where ten foot lengths of cast-iron soil pipe are used, ten foot intervals between supports are acceptable.

B. Threaded pipe, 12 foot intervals.

C. Copper tubing ($1^1/_4$ inch or less), six foot intervals.

D. Copper tubing ($1^1/_2$ inch or over), ten foot intervals.

E. Lead pipe, on continuous metal or wood strips for its entire length.

F. Plastic pipe, 32-inch intervals except where conveying waste from dishwashers or similar hot water wastes it shall be supported on continuous metal or wood strips for its entire length.

Subp. 5. **Closet bends.** Joined to a stack by means of neoprene gasketed or solvent welded joints shall be adequately supported both vertically and horizontally to prevent movement in any direction.

Subp. 6. **Base of stacks.** Stacks shall be adequately supported at their bases.

Subp. 7. **Piping in the ground.** Piping in the ground shall be laid on a firm bed for its entire length, except where support is otherwise provided which is adequate in the judgment of the administrative authority. Installation of plastic sewer pipe must comply with ASTM D2321.

4715.1440
PROTECTION OF PLASTIC PIPE

All plastic and copper pipe and tubing passing through studs or plates that are within one and one-fourth inches of the outside of the stud or plate must be protected by the provision of $1/_{16}$ inch or 0.060 mild steel plates attached to the outside of the stud or plate, or equivalent protection.

4715.1500
INDIRECT WASTE CONNECTIONS

No cold storage room, refrigerator, cooling counter, compartment, receptacle, appurtenance, or device, which is used, designed, or intended to be used for the storage or holding of food or drink, shall have any drain pipe in connection therewith directly connected to any soil, waste, or vent pipe. Such equipment shall be discharged to the drainage system through an airbreak as defined in part 4715.1580.

The foregoing does not apply to a dishwashing or culinary sink in a food preparation room.

4715.1510
INDIRECT WASTE PIPING

Indirect waste piping must be installed so as to permit ready access for flushing and cleaning, and must meet the material requirements of the code. Except as otherwise herein provided, the size and construction of indirect waste piping must be in accordance with parts 4715.2300 to 4715.2660, regulating the installation of waste and vent piping.

Indirect waste pipes from appliances, devices, or other equipment not regularly classed as plumbing fixtures, but which are equipped with drainage outlets, must be trapped, but the traps need not be vented and the waste pipe must be a minimum of three-fourths inch size, but not less than the size of the outlet or tail piece of the fixture, appliance, or equipment served. However, overflow pans and drip outlets need not be trapped and may be the same size as the outlet. Alternate materials may be accepted for drains from overflow pans and drip outlets if proper pitch, alignment, and support are maintained.

4715.1520
CONNECTIONS FROM WATER
DISTRIBUTION SYSTEM

Indirect waste connections shall be provided for drains, overflows, or relief vents from the water distribution system by means of an air gap.

4715.1530
STERILIZERS

Appliances, devices, equipment, or other apparatus such as stills, sterilizers, and similar equipment requiring water and waste shall be indirectly connected, or provided with an air gap between the trap and the appliance.

4715.1540
POTABLE CLEAR WATER WASTES

Expansion tanks, cooling jackets, sprinkler systems, or any similar devices which are directly connected to the potable water system and which waste clear water only shall be discharged to the drainage system through an air gap.

4715.1550
DRINKING FOUNTAINS

Drinking fountains may be installed with indirect wastes.

4715.1560
SWIMMING POOLS

Piping carrying waste water from swimming pools or wading pools, including pool drainage, backwash from filters, water from scum gutter drains, or floor drains which serve walks around pools, shall be installed as an indirect waste. Pumps may be utilized to lift waste water when the indirect waste line is below the sewer grade.

4715.1570
METHOD OF PROVIDING AN AIR GAP

The air gap between the indirect waste pipe and the building drainage system must be at least twice the effective diameter of the drain served and must be provided by one of the following methods:

A. To a receptor. Extend an indirect waste pipe to an open, accessible, individual waste sink, floor drain, or other suitable fixture which is properly trapped and vented.

The indirect waste pipe must terminate a sufficient distance above the flood level rim of the receiving fixture to provide the required air gap.

B. To the inlet side of a trap. Provide an air gap in the drain ahead of the connection to the inlet side of the trap, which receives the waste from the indirect waste.

4715.1580
METHOD OF PROVIDING AN AIR BREAK

The air break shall be so installed as to prevent back flow into the fixture, appliance, or device by one of the following methods:

A. Discharging to the inlet side of the trap of a floor drain, sink, or receptor whose flood level rim is below the bottom of the fixture to be protected.

B. Discharging at or below the spill rim of a floor drain, sink, or receptor whose flood level rim is below the bottom of the fixture to be protected.

4715.1590
RECEPTORS OR SUMPS

Subpart 1. **Installment.** Waste receptors or sumps receiving the indirect waste shall not be installed in any toilet room, nor in inaccessible or unventilated space, such as a closet or storeroom.

Subp. 2. **Cleanout location.** If the indirect waste receptor is set below floor level, it shall be equipped with a running trap adjacent thereto, with the trap cleanout brought up to floor level. All plumbing receptors receiving the discharge of the indirect waste pipes, shall be of such shape and capacity as to prevent splashing or flooding.

Subp. 3. **Domestic or culinary fixtures prohibited as receptors.** No plumbing fixture which is used for domestic or culinary purposes shall be used to receive the discharge of an indirect waste. Domestic dishwashers may discharge into a sink, sink tail-piece, or food-waste grinder.

Subp. 4. **Stand pipe receptors.** The stand pipe receptor for an automatic clothes washer shall be trapped and vented, except that multiple clothes washers in the same room may be discharged to multiple standpipes that are manifolded together and use a single trap. The stand pipe shall extend not more than 30 inches, nor less than 18 inches above its trap, and the trap shall be installed at least six inches above the floor.

Subp. 5. [Repealed, 19 SR 590]

4715.1600
CHEMICAL WASTES

Chemical or industrial liquid wastes which are likely to damage or increase maintenance costs on the drainage system, shall be pretreated to render them innocuous prior to discharge into the drainage system, when required by the administrative authority.

Piping conveying industrial, chemical, or process wastes from their point of origin to sewer connected pretreatment facilities shall be of such material and design as to adequately perform its intended function to the satisfaction of the administrative authority. Drainage discharge piping from pretreatment facilities or interceptors shall conform to standard drainage installation procedure.

No chemical vent shall intersect or tie into any vent for other services, except where permitted by the administrative authority.

The provision of this part relative to materials and construction for chemical piping need not apply to domestic photographic darkroom installations.

4715.1610
STEAM AND HOT WATER WASTES

The end of the blowoff piping from any boiler or the vent pipe from any blowoff tank shall not terminate in any location where the discharge can endanger the safety of any person or property.

The exhaust, blowoff, or drain from a boiler or heat exchanger shall not connect directly with any part of the drainage system, but may connect indirectly.

All such pipes from a high pressure steam source shall be indirectly connected by discharging into a blowoff tank or condenser as required by the state of Minnesota high pressure steam code.

All such pipes from low-pressure steam boilers and hot water boilers rated at 150 horsepower or more shall discharge into a tank or condenser such that the discharge shall be effectively lowered below 180 degrees Fahrenheit and the pressure reduced to atmospheric.

In a similar manner, all other such pipes which would cause a discharge of steam or water to enter the sewer above 180 degrees Fahrenheit for a period of more than ten minutes shall be equipped with a means of lowering the entering temperature below 180 degrees Fahrenheit. This provision is not meant to be applied to boilers or heat exchangers which are drained on rare occasions. Drains from pressing machines and similar equipment may waste into an open floor drain.

Any closed condenser or sump shall be provided with a relief vent not less than one pipe size larger than the largest inlet, which relief pipe or vent should be taken off the top, and extended separately full size through the roof.

4715.1700
WATER REQUIRED

Every building equipped with plumbing fixtures and used for human occupancy or habitation shall be provided with a supply of potable water, which meets the standards of the Department of Health, in the amounts and at the pressures specified in this chapter. For permanent residences or buildings in which people are employed, hot water shall be provided to all plumbing fixtures requiring hot water for proper use.

Only potable water shall be accessible to plumbing fixtures supplying water for drinking, bathing, culinary use, or the processing of food, medical, or pharmaceutical products.

4715.1710
WATER SERVICE

Subpart 1. **Size of water service.** The water service pipe shall be of sufficient size to furnish water to the building in quantities and at the pressures required elsewhere in the code. It shall in no case be less than three-fourths inch nominal diameter. Methods for sizing the water service pipe are described in parts 4715.3500 to 4715.3800.

Subp. 2. **Separation of water service and building sewer.** Except as permitted in this subpart, the underground water service pipe and the building drain or building sewer shall not be less than ten feet apart horizontally and shall be separated by undisturbed or compacted earth.

NOTE: See chapter 4725 relating to wells and borings regarding separation of buried sewers from wells.

The water service pipe may be placed in the same trench with the building drain and the building sewer provided approval is given by the administrative authority and the following conditions are met:

A. The bottom of the water service pipe, at all points, shall be at least 12 inches above the top of the sewer line at its highest point.

B. The water service pipe shall be placed on a solid shelf excavated at one side of the common trench. The water service pipe shall preferably be of one piece. Where this is not feasible the number of joints in the service pipe shall be kept to a minimum.

C. The sewer and water service pipes shall be tested prior to backfilling, as described in part 4715.2820, or by methods acceptable to the administrative authority.

D. Where the provisions of items A and B cannot be met, the sewer pipe shall be of cast iron or plastic 6A, 6B, 6C(2), or 6C(3) and the water pipe of copper, or cast iron, or plastic 6D, 6E, 6F, or 6G (part 4715.0420, subpart 3).

E. Where the water service pipe must cross the building sewer, the bottom of the water service pipe located within ten feet of the point of crossing shall be at least 12 inches above the top of the sewer, except where this is not feasible, the sewer shall be of cast iron or plastic 6A, 6B, 6C(2), or 6C(3) (part 4715.0420, subpart 3) for at least ten feet on either side of the crossing.

Subp. 3. **Water service near sources of pollution.** Potable water service pipes must not be located in, under, or above cesspools, septic tanks, septic tank drainage fields, seepage pits, soil treatment systems, buried tanks containing chemicals or petroleum products, or any other source of pollution that in the judgment of the administrative authority might contaminate the potable water supply. A horizontal separation of ten feet must be maintained.

4715.1720
DESIGN OF BUILDING WATER
DISTRIBUTION SYSTEM

The design of the building hot and cold water distribution system shall conform to good engineering practice. Methods used to determine pipe sizes shall be acceptable to the administrative authority. (A guide to the design of building water supply systems is given in parts 4715.3500 to 4715.3800.)

4715.1730
SIZE OF FIXTURE BRANCH

Subpart 1. **Requirement.** The minimum size of the fixture branch pipe shall be as shown in subpart 2. The branch pipe to any fixture shall terminate not more than 30 inches from the point of connection to the fixture and in every instance shall be brought to the floor or wall adjacent to the fixture. No concealed water branch pipe shall be less than one-half inch in size. In single-family dwelling units, not more than three fixtures located in the same room may be supplied by a one-half inch size pipe.

Subp. 2. **Table of minimum sizes of fixture water branch lines.**

Type of fixture or device	Nominal pipe size (inches)
Bath tubs	$1/2$
Combination sink and tray	$1/2$
Cuspidor	$1/2$
Drinking fountain	$1/2$
Dishwasher (domestic)	$1/2$
Kitchen sink (res.)	$1/2$
Kitchen sink (com.)	$3/4$
Lavatory	$1/2$
Laundry tray	$1/2$
Sinks (service, slop)	$1/2$
Sinks flushing rim	$3/4$
Urinal (flush tank)	$1/2$
Urinal (direct flush valve)	$3/4$
Water closet (tank type)	$1/2$
Water closet (flush valve type)	1
Hose bibs	$3/4$
Wall hydrant	$3/4$
Domestic clothes washer	$1/2$
Shower (single head)	$1/2$

4715.1740
WATER PRESSURE

When street main pressure exceeds 80 psi, an approved pressure reducing valve shall be installed in the water service pipe near its entrance to the building to reduce water pressure to 80 psi or lower. Where street water main pressures fluctuate significantly, the building water distribution system shall be so designed for the minimum pressure available.

Whenever water pressure from the street main or other source of supply is insufficient to provide flow pressure at fixture outlets as required under part 4715.1770, a booster pump and pressure tank or other approved means shall be installed on the building water supply system. See part 4715.1810, subpart 3 for installation.

4715.1750
WATER HAMMER

In all building supply systems in which devices or appurtenances are installed which cause noises due to water hammer, protective devices or approved mechanical shock absorbers shall be installed as close as possible to the quick-acting valve causing the water hammer. Where mechanical devices are used the manufacturer's specifications shall be followed as to location and method of installation.

4715.1760
SUPPLY DEMAND

The supply demand in gallons per minute in the building water distribution system shall be determined on the basis of the load in terms of supply fixture units and of the relationship between load and supply demand.

4715.1770
MINIMUM PRESSURES REQUIRED IN WATER DISTRIBUTION SYSTEM

Subpart 1. Requirement. Based on the minimum static water pressure available, pipe sizes shall be selected so that under conditions of peak demand a minimum flow pressure at the point of discharge shall not be less than shown in subpart 2.

In determining minimum pressures at the outlets, allowance shall be made for the pressure drop due to friction loss.

Subp. 2. Table of minimum flow pressure and flow rates.

Location	Flow Pressure (psi)	Flow Rate (gpm)
Ordinary basin faucet	8	2.0
Self-closing basin faucet	8	2.0
Sink faucet, $3/8$ inch	8	2.0
Sink faucet, $1/2$ inch	8	2.0
Bathtub faucet	8	6.0
Laundry tub cock, $1/2$ inch	8	5.0
Shower	8	2.0
Ball cock for closet	8	3.0
Flush valve for closet	15	15-35
Flushometer valve for urinal	15	15.0
Drinking fountains	15	0.75
Sill cock-wall hydrant	10	5.0

4715.1800
WATER SUPPLY CONTROL VALVES

Subpart 1. Stop and waste valves prohibited. Combination stop and waste valves or cocks should not be installed underground in water service piping. They may be installed only if approved by the administrative authority and when located at least two feet above the water table and at least ten feet from any sewer.

Subp. 2. Underground stop valve. On each water service from a street main to a building an approved gate valve or ground key stopcock shall be installed. This valve or stopcock shall be provided with an approved valve box and shall not be under the driveway. However, if there is an accessible stop valve in the street, no other stop is necessary underground.

Subp. 3. Building valve. Each building water service shall be provided with a gate valve or other full-way valve located inside the building near the point that the water service enters.

Subp. 4. Meter valve. A gate valve or other full-way valve shall be installed in the line on the discharge side of each water meter. The valve shall not be less in size than the building water supply.

Subp. 5. Valves in dwelling units. In each single or multiple unit dwelling, each family unit shall be controlled by an arrangement of shutoff valves which will permit each group of fixtures or the individual fixtures to be shut off without interference with the water supply to any other family unit or portion of the building.

Subp. 6. Valves in buildings other than dwellings. In all buildings other than dwellings, shutoff valves shall be installed, which permit the water supply to all equipment in each separate room or to each individual fixture to be shut off without interference with the water supply to any other room or portion of the building.

Subp. 7. Valves for sill cocks. All sill cocks and wall hydrants shall be separately controlled by a valve inside the building.

Subp. 8. Tank controls. Supply lines to and from pressure or gravity tanks shall be valved at or near the tanks.

Subp. 9. Water heating equipment valve. The cold water branch to each hot water storage tank or water heater shall be provided with a full way valve located near the equipment. Each tank or heater shall be equipped with an approved automatic relief valve as specified in parts 4715.2200 and 4715.2210.

Subp. 10. Valves to be accessible. All water supply control valves shall be placed so as to be accessible.

Subp. 11. Control valve design. Except to single fixtures, control valves on all water lines shall be full-way type and the same size as the line on which they are installed.

4715.1810
WATER PRESSURE BOOSTER SYSTEMS

Subpart 1. Water pressure booster systems required. When the water pressure in the public water main or individual water supply system is insufficient to supply the probable peak demand flow to all plumbing fixtures and other water needs freely and continuously with the minimum pressures and quantities specified in part 4715.1770, subpart 2 or elsewhere in this code and in accordance with good practice, the rate of supply shall be supplemented by an elevated water tank, a hydropneumatic pressure booster system, or a water pressure booster pump installed in accordance with subpart 5.

Subp. 2. **Support.** All water supply tanks shall be adequately supported.

Subp. 3. **Covers.** All water supply tanks shall be covered to keep out contaminants. The covers of gravity tanks shall be vented with a return bend vent pipe having an area not less than the area of the down feed riser pipe and the vent shall be screened with corrosion resistant screen of not less than 16 mesh.

Subp. 4. **Overflows for water supply tanks.** Each gravity or suction water supply tank shall be provided with an overflow having a diameter not less than shown in subpart 10. Sizes of overflow pipes for water supply tanks. The overflow outlet shall discharge above and within not less than six inches of a roof or roof drain, floor or floor drain, or over an open water supplied fixture. The overflow outlet shall be covered by a corrosion resistant screen of not less than 16 mesh.

Subp. 5. **Water supply to booster pumps.** When a booster pump is used on a water pressure booster system, it shall be supplied through a surge tank or if supplied through a direct connection, a low pressure cutoff switch (10 psi) and a vacuum relief valve or tank shall be installed on the suction side of the booster pump to prevent the creation of a vacuum or a negative pressure on the suction side of the pump. If installed below grade it shall be installed in a normally occupied area and on a pedestal at least 24 inches above the floor.

Subp. 6. **Potable water inlet to tanks.** Potable water inlets to gravity, surge, or break tanks shall be controlled by a ball cock or other automatic supply valve so installed as to prevent the tank from overflowing. The inlet shall be terminated so as to provide an accepted air gap but in no case less than four inches above the overflow.

Subp. 7. **Tank drain pipes.** Each tank shall be provided at its lowest point with a valved pipe to permit emptying the tank, which shall discharge as required for overflow pipes, and not smaller in size than shown in subpart 11.

Subp. 8. **Prohibited location of potable supply tanks.** Potable water tanks shall not be located directly under any soil or waste piping.

Subp. 9. **Pumps and other appliances.** Water pumps, filters, softeners, tanks, and all other devices and appliances used to handle or treat potable water shall be protected against contamination.

Subp. 10. **Sizes for overflow pipes for water supply tanks.**

Maximum Capacity of Water Supply Line to Tank	Diameter of Overflow Pipe (Inches ID)
0 - 50 gpm	2
50 - 150 gpm	2$\frac{1}{2}$
100 - 200 gpm	3
200 - 400 gpm	4
400 - 700 gpm	5
700 - 1000 gpm	6
Over 1000 gpm	8

Subp. 11. **Size of drain pipes for water tanks.**

Tank Capacity (gallons)	Drain Pipe (Inches)
Up to 750	1
751 to 1500	1$\frac{1}{2}$
1501 to 3000	2
3001 to 5000	2$\frac{1}{2}$
5001 to 7500	3
Over 7500	4

4715.1900
DESIGN, MAINTENANCE, AND INSTALLATION

A potable water supply system shall be designed, installed, and maintained in such manner as to prevent contamination from nonpotable liquids, solids, or gases, from being introduced into the potable water supply through cross-connection or any other piping connections to the system.

4715.1910
IDENTIFICATION OF POTABLE AND
NONPOTABLE WATER

Subpart 1. **Identification methods.** In all buildings where dual water distribution systems, one potable water and other nonpotable water, are installed, each system shall be identified, either by color marking or metal tags.

Subp. 2. **Color marking.** When color marking is used, potable water lines should be painted green and nonpotable water lines should be painted yellow. This requirement may be met by painting three-inch-wide bands green or yellow at intervals of not more than 25 feet and at points where piping passes through walls, floors, or roofs in which case the bands shall be applied to the piping on both sides of the walls and both above and below the floor or roof. Points of outlets for nonpotable water shall be marked with a tag or color coded.

Subp. 3. **Metal tags.** When tags are used, potable water lines shall be identified by three-inch diameter metal tags bearing the legend "SAFE WATER" in letters not less than one-half inch in height.

Nonpotable water lines shall be identified by firmly attached metal tags having the shape of a four-inch equilateral triangle bearing the legend "NONPOTABLE WATER" in letters not less than $7/16$ inch in height.

As in the use of color bands, tags shall be attached to pipes at intervals of not more than 25 feet, and, at either side of points where pipes pass through walls and above and below points where pipes pass through floors or roofs.

4715.1911
TOXIC MATERIALS AND USED PIPE

Piping conveying potable water shall be constructed of non-toxic material.

No material or substances that could produce either toxic conditions, taste, odor, or discoloration in a potable water system shall be introduced into or used in such systems.

The interior surface of a potable water tank shall not be lined, painted, or repaired with any material which will affect either the taste, odor, color, or potability of the water supply when the tank is placed in or returned to service.

Piping which has been used for any other purpose then conveying potable water shall not be used for conveying potable water.

4715.1912
USED WATER RETURN PROHIBITED

Water used for cooling of equipment or other processes shall not be returned to the potable water system. Such water shall be discharged into the drainage system through an air gapped indirect waste or other approved method of disposal.

4715.1920
CROSS-CONNECTION CONTROL

Cross-connections between potable water systems and other systems or equipment containing water or other substances of unknown or questionable safety are prohibited, except when and where, as approved by the authority having jurisdiction, suitable protective devices such as break tanks, reduced pressure zone backflow preventer, or equal, are installed, tested, and maintained to ensure proper operation on a continuing basis.

Cross-connections between an individual water supply and a potable public supply shall not be made unless specifically approved by the authority having jurisdiction.

4715.1940
POTABLE WATER CONNECTIONS TO
HEATING OR COOLING SYSTEMS

Potable water connections to boiler feed water systems, cooling systems, or other liquid systems, in which water conditioning chemicals may be introduced shall be made through an air gap or provided with an approved backflow preventer located in the potable water line before the point where such chemicals may be introduced. Where a system is filled with an antifreeze or toxic solution a permanent tag will be placed in plain view stating "Caution, this system contains antifreeze/toxic solution."

4715.1941
HEAT EXCHANGERS

Subpart 1. **Construction requirement.** Devices utilizing any heat transfer medium to exchange thermal energy with potable water must be constructed so that a single failure of any wall in the system will not cause a cross-connection with or permit back siphonage of heat transfer medium into the potable water system.

Subp. 2. **Double-wall heat exchanger.** A double-wall heat exchanger must be designed in a way that any failure of a wall must allow the discharge to the atmosphere of the heat transfer medium or the potable water contained by the wall. The discharge location must be visible to the operator or owner of the system and be located so that no hazards are created by the discharge.

Subp. 3. **Single-wall heat exchanger.** A single-wall heat exchanger may be used if it satisfies all of the following conditions:

A. The heat transfer medium contains only substances which are recognized as safe or approved by the United States

Food and Drug Administration for food contact as listed in Code of Federal Regulations, title 21, part 182 of the Food Additive Regulations.

B. Except where steam is used as the heat transfer medium, the pressure of the heat transfer medium must be less than the normal minimum operating pressure of the potable water system, and the system must be fitted with devices arranged to function automatically to maintain the pressure of the heat transfer medium entering the exchanger at a level below that of the potable water leaving the exchanger.

C. The equipment is permanently labeled to specify all constituents of the heat transfer medium, to indicate that only additives recognized as safe by the United States Food and Drug Administration may be used, and to show the hazards and reasons for not using another type of medium.

4715.1950
PROHIBITED CONNECTIONS TO
FIXTURES AND EQUIPMENT

Connections to the potable water supply system for the following shall be protected against backflow:

A. Bidets;

B. Operating, dissection, embalming, and mortuary tables or similar equipment; in such installation the hose used for water supply shall be equipped with a vacuum breaker installed at least six feet, six inches above the floor;

C. Pumps for nonpotable water, chemicals, or other substances; priming connections may be made only through an air gap;

D. Building drainage, sewer, or vent systems; and

E. Any other fixture of similar hazard.

4715.1960
REFRIGERATING UNIT CONDENSERS AND
COOLING JACKETS

Except where potable water provided for a refrigerator condenser or cooling jacket is entirely outside the piping or tank containing a toxic refrigerant, with two separate thicknesses of metal separating the refrigerant from the potable water supply, inlet connection shall be provided with an approved backflow preventer. Also, adjacent to and at the outlet side of the backflow preventer, an approved pressure relief valve set to relieve at 5 psi above the maximum water pressure at the point of installation shall be provided if the refrigeration units contain more than 20 pounds of refrigerants.

4715.2000
WATER OUTLETS

A potable water system shall be protected against backflow and back-siphonage by providing and maintaining at each outlet:

A. An air gap as specified herein between the potable water outlet and the flood level rim of the fixture it supplies or between the outlet and any other source of contamination; or

B. A backflow preventer device or assembly to prevent the drawing of contamination into the potable water system.

4715.2010
MINIMUM REQUIRED AIR GAP

Subpart 1. **Measurement.** The minimum required air gap shall be measured vertically from the lowest end of a potable water outlet to the flood rim or line of the fixture or receptacle into which it discharges.

Subp. 2. **Requirement.** The minimum required air gap shall be twice the effective opening of a potable water outlet unless the outlet is a distance less than three times the effective opening away from a wall or similar vertical surface in which cases the minimum required air gap shall be three times the effective opening of the outlet. In no case shall the minimum required air gap be less than shown in subpart 4.

Subp. 3. **Effect of walls, ribs, and similar obstructions.** Side walls, ribs, or similar obstructions do not affect air gaps when spaced from inside edge of spout opening a distance greater than three times the diameter of the effective opening for a single wall, or a distance greater than four times the diameter of the effective opening for two intersecting walls.

Vertical walls, ribs, or similar obstructions extending from the water surface to or above the horizontal plane of the spout opening require a greater air gap when spaced closer to the nearest inside edge of spout opening than specified in this subpart. The effect of three or more such vertical walls or ribs has not been determined. In such cases, the air gap shall be measured from the top of the wall.

Subp. 4. **Minimum air gaps for plumbing fixtures.**

Fixture	Minimum Air Gap	
	When Not Affected By Near Wall (1) (Inches)	When Affected By Near Wall (2) (Inches)
Lavatories and other fixtures with effective opening not greater than $1/2$ inch diameter	1.0	1.50
Sink, Laundry trays, gooseneck bath faucets and other fixtures with effective openings not greater than $3/4$ inch diameter	1.5	2.25
Over rim bath fillers and other fixtures with effective openings not greater than 1 inch diameter	2.0	3.0
Drinking water fountains	1.0	1.50
Effective openings greater than one inch	2x diameter of effective opening	3x diameter of effective opening

4715.2020
DEVICES OR ASSEMBLIES FOR THE PROTECTION OF THE POTABLE WATER SUPPLY

Approved devices or assemblies to protect against backflow and back-siphonage must be installed at any plumbing fixture or equipment where backflow or back-siphonage may occur and where a minimum air gap cannot be provided between the water outlet to the fixture or equipment and its flood level rim.

4715.2030
APPROVAL OF DEVICES OR ASSEMBLIES

Before any device or assembly for the prevention of backflow or back-siphonage is installed, it shall have first been certified by a recognized testing laboratory acceptable to the administrative authority. Devices or assemblies installed in a building potable water supply distribution system for protection against backflow shall be maintained in good working condition by the person or persons responsible for the maintenance of the system.

4715.2100
BACKFLOW PREVENTERS

A. Atmospheric vacuum breaker (AVB):
   (1) must be installed at least six inches above spill line (see special requirements in part 4715.2150);
   (2) no possibility of back pressure permitted;
   (3) only permitted on discharge side of last control valve; and
   (4) no more than eight hours of continuous line pressure permitted.

B. Pressure vacuum breaker assembly (PVB):
   (1) must be installed at least 12 inches above spill line;
   (2) no possibility of back pressure permitted; and
   (3) continuous line pressure permitted.

C. Spill-proof vacuum breaker (SVB):
   (1) must be installed at least six inches above spill line;
   (2) no possibility of back pressure permitted;
   (3) continuous line pressure permitted; and
   (4) field testable.

D. Hose connection vacuum breaker (Hose VB):
   (1) required for threaded hose connections;
   (2) back pressure not permitted;
   (3) continuous line pressure not permitted; and
   (4) any new device must be field testable. Exception: a vacuum breaker installed as an integral part of a product, approved to a standard, and installed at the factory will not be required to be field testable.

E. Double-check valve with intermediate atmospheric vent (DCVIAV):
   (1) permitted for low hazard with small pipe sizes;
   (2) back pressure permitted; and
   (3) continuous line pressure permitted.

F. Reduced pressure zone backflow preventer assembly (RPZ):
   (1) any degree of hazard permitted;
   (2) back pressure permitted; and
   (3) continuous line pressure permitted.

G. Double-check valve assembly (DCVA):
   (1) permitted only for nontoxic, low hazard installations with nuisance or aesthetic concern;
   (2) back pressure permitted; and
   (3) continuous line pressure permitted.

4715.2110
TYPES OF DEVICES REQUIRED WHERE AN AIR GAP CANNOT BE PROVIDED[1]

	RPZ	DCV IAV	DCVA	Only allowed where no back pressure is possible		
				SVB or PVB	AVB	HOSE VB
A. Boiler, other than one- or two-family residential	X					
B. Boiler, one- or two-family residential	X	X				
C. Car wash	X			X	X	
D. Carbonated beverage machine (postmix) (see part 4715.2163)		X				
E. Chemical line	X					
F. Chemical tank	X			X	X	
G. Chiller	X					
H. Cooling tower	X	X		X	X	
I. Dental units (separate assembly required for each unit)	X					
J. Dishwasher, commercial				X	X	
K. Fire sprinkler system[2]	X	X	X			
L. Flush tank (water closet, urinal, similar) (see part 4715.2150)	X			X	X	
M. Flush valve (water closet, urinal, similar) (see part 4715.2150)	X			X	X	
N. Food and beverage equipment or system	X	X	X	X	X	
O. Garbage can washer	X			X	X	
P. Glycol or other antifreeze system	X					
Q. Lab equipment	X			X	X	
R. Lab faucet					X	
S. Laundry machine, commercial	X	X		X	X	
T. Lawn, garden or greenhouse sprinkler system	X			X	X	

(Continued)

	RPZ	DCV IAV	DCVA	Only allowed where no back pressure is possible		
				SVB or PVB	AVB	HOSE VB
U. Operating, dissection, embalming or mortuary table (see part 4715.1950)	X			X	X	
V. Private potable water supply (where permitted by administrative authority)	X	X	X			
W. Private nonpotable water supply (where permitted by administrative authority)	X					
X. Process line	X	X				
Y. Process tank	X			X	X	
Z. RV dump station	X	X		X	X	
AA. Sewage treatment	X			X	X	
BB. Soap dispenser	X	X		X	X	
CC. Swimming pool, fountain, pond, baptistry, aquarium or similar	X	X		X	X	
DD. Threaded hose connections, including: hose bibbs, hydrants, service sinks, laundry trays					X[3]	X
EE. Truck fill	X			X	X	
FF. Vacuum systems or aspirators	X			X	X	

[1] For installations not listed in this part, review with the Administrative Authority.

[2] Installations must comply with AWWA-M14, chapter 6 (1990) except that the following statement is deleted from section 6.3: At any time where the fire sprinkler piping is not an acceptable potable water system material, there shall be a backflow-prevention assembly isolating the fire sprinkler system from the potable water system.

[3] A vacuum breaker installed as an integral part of a product approved to a standard does not require additional backflow prevention on the hose threads; the product must be constructed so that if the integral backflow preventer is removed, the remaining threads will not be hose thread type. An unprotected threaded hose connection must be protected against backflow by addition of a backflow preventer complying with ASSE 1052.

4715.2120
LOCATION OF BACKFLOW PREVENTERS

Backflow and back-siphonage preventing devices or assemblies must be located so as to be readily accessible, preferably in the same room with the fixture they serve. Installation in utility or service spaces, provided they are readily accessible, is also permitted.

The access area must provide enough space for testing and maintenance of the device. A backflow preventer must not be installed in a pit or other confined area subject to recurrent flooding. When a conductor pipe is provided from a backflow preventer drain, a visible air gap must be provided at the device. New installations of reduced pressure zone backflow preventers must be at least 12 inches, but not more than six feet, above the finished floor or ground level.

4715.2150
CONNECTIONS NOT SUBJECT TO BACK PRESSURE

Subpart 1. **Requirements.** Where a water connection is not subject to back pressure an atmospheric type vacuum breaker shall be installed on the discharge side of the last valve on the line serving the fixture or equipment. Where a valve is installed on the discharge side of a vacuum breaker, that vacuum breaker must be a pressure-type vacuum breaker assembly which complies with part 4715.2030. A list of some conditions requiring protective devices of this kind is given in subpart 2.

Subp. 2. **Cross-connections where protective devices are required and critical level (C-L) settings for backflow preventers.** Critical level (C-L) is defined as the level to which the backflow preventer (vacuum breaker) may be submerged before backflow will occur. Where the C-L is not shown on the preventer, the bottom of the device shall be taken as the C-L.

Fixture or Equipment	Method of Installation
Aspirators and Ejectors	C-L at least 6 inches above flood level of receptacle.
Dental units	On models without built-in vacuum breakers C-L at least 6 inches above flood level rim of bowl.
Dishwashing machines	C-L at least 6 inches above flood level of machine. Install on both hot and cold water supply lines.
Flushometer (Closet & Urinal)	C-L at least 6 inches above top of fixture supplied.
Garbage can cleaning machine	C-L at least 6 inches above flood level of machine. Install on both hot and cold water supply lines.
Hose outlets	C-L at least 6 inches above highest point on hose line.
Laundry machines	C-L at least 6 inches above flood level of machine. Install on both hot and cold water supply lines.
Lawn sprinklers	C-L at least 12 inches above highest sprinkler or discharge outlet.
Steam tables	C-L at least 6 inches above flood level.
Tank and vats	C-L at least 6 inches above flood level rim or line.
Trough urinals	C-L at least 30 inches above perforated flush pipe.
Flush tanks	Equip with approved ball cock. Where ball cocks touch tank water equip with vacuum breaker with C-L at least 1 inch above overflow outlets. Where ball cock does not touch tank water, install ball cock outlet at least 1 inch above overflow outlet or provide vacuum breaker as specified above.
Hose bibbs (Where aspirators or ejectors could be connected)	C-L at least 6 inches above flood level of receptacle served.

4715.2160
CONNECTIONS SUBJECT TO BACK PRESSURE

Where a potable water connection is made to a line, fixture, tank, vat, pump, or other equipment with a hazard of backflow or back-siphonage, where the water connection is subject to back pressure, and an air gap cannot be installed, the administrative authority may require the use of break tank and booster pump or, where conditions permit, an approved reduced pressure zone backflow preventer. A partial list of such connections is as follows: chemical lines, dock water outlets, individual water supplies, industrial process water lines, pressure tanks, pumps, steam lines, and tanks and vats-bottom inlets.

4715.2161
INSTALLATION OF REDUCED PRESSURE BACKFLOW PREVENTERS

Subpart 1. **Notification of installation.** The administrative authority must be notified before installation of a reduced pressure backflow preventer assembly.

Subp. 2. **Testing and maintenance.** The installation of reduced pressure backflow preventers shall be permitted only when a periodic testing and inspection program conducted by qualified personnel will be provided by an agency acceptable to the administrative authority. Inspection intervals shall not exceed one year, and overhaul intervals shall not exceed five years. The administrative authority may require more frequent testing if deemed necessary to assure protection of the potable water. Backflow preventers shall be inspected frequently after initial installation to assure that they have been properly installed and that debris resulting from the piping installation has not interfered with the functioning of the assembly.

Subp. 3. **Inspection and records.** A test and inspection tag must be affixed to the device. The tester shall date and sign the tag and include the tester's backflow preventer tester identification number. Written records of testing and maintenance must be maintained and submitted to the administrative authority.

4715.2162
DOUBLE CHECK—DOUBLE GATE VALVE ASSEMBLIES

The administrative authority may authorize the installation of approved, double check—double gate valve assemblies with test cocks as protective devices against back flow in connections between a potable water system and other nontoxic fluid systems which present no significant health hazards.

4715.2163
CARBONATED BEVERAGE MACHINES

Postmix type carbonated beverage machines must have an approved double-check valve with an intermediate atmospheric vent type backflow preventer in the water line preceding the carbonator. The backflow preventer must be installed in accordance with ASSE Standard 1022. There must be no copper tubing in the system down line of the backflow preventer.

4715.2165
CHEMICAL/SOAP DISPENSING SYSTEMS

The installation of backflow preventers for chemical/soap dispensing systems must comply with ASSE Standard 1055.

Exception: An atmospheric vacuum breaker integrally mounted on a faucet that is connected to a chemical/soap dispenser must be protected against back pressure by the installation of a pressure bleeding device and a backflow preventer complying with ASSE Standard 1052. The backflow preventer must be installed on the side outlet of the pressure bleeding device. No wye connector that has an integral shutoff may be connected to a faucet that has an integral atmospheric vacuum breaker.

4715.2170
BAROMETRIC LOOP

Water connections where an actual or potential backflow or back-siphonage hazard exists may in lieu of devices specified in parts 4715.2140 to 4715.2160 be provided with a barometric loop. Barometric loops shall precede the point of connection.

4715.2180
HOT WATER SUPPLY SYSTEM

Hot water shall be supplied to all plumbing fixtures and equipment used for bathing, washing, culinary purpose, cleansing, laundry, or building maintenance, where necessary for proper functioning. Hot water supply systems in four-story buildings or buildings where the developed length of hot water piping from the source of hot water supply to the farthest fixture supplied exceeds 100 feet should be of the return circulation type, to conserve water.

4715.2190
COMBINATION WATER AND SPACE HEATING EQUIPMENT

Equipment used for heating domestic or service hot water and for space heating must be installed with a mixing valve to permit the user to control the temperature of the domestic or service hot water regardless of the space heating demand.

The installation must include a drainage port and isolation valve to permit the user to purge the heating coils to waste after the nonheating season, or the system must be designed to automatically prevent stagnation.

The water heater must be specifically designated by the manufacturer for use as a combination hot water and space heater.

All pipes, joints, and appurtenances in the system must be of a type approved for potable water distribution. This provision is not intended to address the wall thickness of heating coils, which must be the responsibility of the manufacturer.

4715.2200
PRESSURE RELIEF VALVES AND TEMPERATURE RELIEF VALVES DEVICES REQUIRED

Equipment used for heating water or storing hot water shall be protected by approved safety devices in accordance with one of the following methods: a separate pressure relief valve and a separate temperature relief valve; or a combination pressure and temperature relief valve. All safety devices shall meet the current requirements of the A.N. Standards Institute, American Society of Mechanical Engineers, or the Underwriters Laboratories. Listing by Underwriters Laboratories, American Gas Association, or National Board of Boiler and Pressure Vessel Inspectors shall constitute evidence of conformance with these standards. Where a device is not listed by any of these, it must have certification by an approved laboratory as having met these requirements.

4715.2210
PRESSURE RELIEF VALVES

Subpart 1. **Installation.** Pressure relief valves shall have a relief rating adequate to meet the pressure conditions in the equipment served. They shall be installed in the cold water supply line to the heating equipment served except where scale formation from hard water may be encountered in which case they may be installed in the hot water supply line from the heating equipment served. There shall be no shutoff valve between the pressure relief valve and the tank. The setting shall not exceed the tank working pressure.

Subp. 2. **Temperature relief valves.** Temperature relief valves shall be of adequate relief rating, expressed in Btu/hr, for the equipment served. They shall be installed so that the temperature sensing element is immersed in the hottest water in the head or within the top six inches of the vertical portion of the tank. The valve shall be set to open when the stored water temperature is 210 degrees Fahrenheit (or less).

Subp. 3. **Combination pressure-temperature relief valves.** Combination pressure temperature relief valves may be used for storage equipment provided the other applicable requirements for individual pressure and individual temperature relief valves are met.

Subp. 4. **Installation of relief valves.** No check valve or shutoff valve shall be installed between any safety device and the hot water equipment used, nor shall there be any shutoff valve in the discharge pipe from the relief valve. The discharge pipe shall be full size and run to within 18 inches of the floor or a safe place of disposal.

4715.2215
THERMAL EXPANSION CONTROL

A device for controlling thermal expansion shall be installed on the water distribution system when thermal expansion within the system, in combination with a check valve or backflow preventer, causes the water pressure to exceed the pressure setting of the pressure relief valve on the water heater.

4715.2220
HOT WATER STORAGE TANKS

Subpart 1. **Pressure marking of hot water storage tank.** Hot water storage tanks shall be permanently marked in an accessible place with the maximum allowable working pressure.

Subp. 2. **Drain cocks or valves for hot water storage tanks.** Drain cocks or valves for emptying shall be installed at the lowest point of each hot water storage tank.

4715.2230
TANKLESS AND INSTANTANEOUS
TYPE HEATERS

Tankless and instantaneous type water heaters require pressure relief valves only. Instantaneous electric water heaters that have Underwriters Laboratory approval for use without a relief valve, and that have space containing the heating element of less than three inches in diameter, may be installed without a pressure relief valve.

4715.2240
ACCESS TO WATER HEATERS

Every water heater installation shall be readily accessible for inspection, repair, or replacement. The appliance space shall be provided with an opening or doorway of sufficient size to provide such access.

Exception: A water heater with a tank capacity not greater than six gallons may be concealed in a ceiling space provided the water heater has been set in an overflow pan that has been constructed of a corrosion-resistant material, has side walls extending at least four inches upward, and has an outlet that shall not be sized less than the supply line to the water heater. This outlet shall be piped undiminished in size to a point of safe disposal below the ceiling area. No tools shall be required to gain access to a water heater.

4715.2250
DISINFECTION OF POTABLE WATER SYSTEM

New or repaired potable water systems shall be disinfected prior to use whenever required by the authority having jurisdiction. The method to be followed shall be that prescribed by the health authority or, in case no method is prescribed, the following:

A. The pipe system shall be flushed with clean, potable water until no dirty water appears at the points of outlet;

B. The system or part thereof shall be filled with a water chlorine solution containing at least 50 parts per million of chlorine and the system or part thereof shall be valved off and allowed to stand for 24 hours; or

C. The system or part thereof shall be filled with a water-chlorine solution containing at least 200 parts per million of chlorine and allowed to stand for three hours; and

D. Following the allowed standing time the system shall be flushed with clean potable water until no chlorine remains in the water coming from the system.

4715.2280
WATER METER INSTALLATION

Water meters shall be placed at least 12 inches above the finished floor and shall be rigidly supported with a permanent support in order to prevent the meter from vibrating when the water is passing through it.

4715.2300
LOAD ON DRAINAGE PIPING

Subpart 1. Computation of drain load. The load on drainage system piping shall be computed in terms of drainage fixture units in accordance with subparts 2, 2a, and 3, except the administrative authority may allow variations where it is shown by a hydraulic analysis of the piping system, submitted to the administrative authority, that such variation would result in a more desirable flow rate in the piping system.

Subp. 2. Values for continuous flow. Fixture unit values for continuous or semicontinuous flow into the drainage system, such as from a pump, sump ejector, air conditioning equipment, or similar device shall be computed on the basis of one fixture unit for each gallon per minute flow.

Subp. 2a. Values for intermittent flows. Fixture unit values for intermittent flows from appliances and equipment which are specially designed for low water use, and used for retrofit in existing plumbing systems only, may be determined as follows:

Discharge Capacity (in gallons per minute)	Fixture Unit Value
up to 7^1/$_2$	1 unit
8 to 15	2 units
16 to 30	4 units
31 to 50	6 units

A standpipe used for discharge from such appliances and equipment which is sized using these values must be labeled as intended for special low-water-use equipment only. Drainage piping in new construction must comply with subpart 3.

Subp. 3. Table of fixture unit values for various plumbing fixtures.

Type of Fixture	Fixture Unit Value	Minimum Fixture Trap and Drain Size
Clothes washer (domestic use)	2	1^1/$_2$
Clothes washer (single unit, discharge to standpipe)	2	2
Clothes washer (public use in groups of 3 or more)	6 each	
Bath tub with or without shower	2	1^1/$_2$
Bidet	2	1^1/$_2$
Dental unit or cuspidor	1	1^1/$_4$
Drinking fountain	1	1^1/$_4$
Dishwasher, domestic (gravity drain)	2	1^1/$_2$
Dishwasher, commercial	4	2
Floor drain with 2 inch waste	2	2
Floor drain with 3 inch waste	3	3
Floor drain with 4 inch waste	4	4
Lavatory	1	1^1/$_4$
Laundry tray (1 or 2 compartment)	2	1^1/$_2$
Shower stall, domestic	2	1^1/$_2$
Shower (gang) per head	1	
SINKS:		
Classroom, with or without drinking fountain	2	1^1/$_2$

Combination, sink and tray (with disposal unit)	3	1^1/$_2$
Combination, sink and tray (with one trap)	2	1^1/$_2$
Domestic	2	1^1/$_2$
Domestic, with disposal unit	2	1^1/$_2$
Surgeons	3	1^1/$_2$
Laboratory, cup sink	1	1^1/$_2$
Flushrim or bedpan washer	6	3
Service	3	2
Pot or scullery	4	2
Soda fountain	2	1^1/$_2$
Commercial, flat rim, bar, or counter	3	1^1/$_2$
Wash, circular, or multiple (per set of faucets)	2	1^1/$_2$
URINAL pedestal, wall hung, with 3 inch trap (blowout and syphon jet)	6	3
Wall hung with 2 inch trap	3	2
Wall hung with 1^1/$_2$ inch trap	2	1^1/$_2$
Trough (per 6 foot section)	2	1^1/$_2$
Stall	3	2
WATER CLOSET	6	3
Unlisted Fixture or Trap Size		
1^1/$_4$ inch	1	
1^1/$_2$ inch	2	
2 inch	3	
2^1/$_2$ inch	4	
3 inch	5	
4 inch	6	

4715.2310
SELECTING SIZE OF DRAINAGE PIPING

Subpart 1. Determination of size. Pipe sizes shall be determined from subparts 2 and 3 on the basis of drainage load computed from part 4715.2300, subparts 2 and 3.

Subp. 2. Maximum loads for horizontal drains in fixture units.

Diameter of Drain	Horizontal Fixture Branch*	Building Sewer, Building Drain and Building Drain Branches - from Stacks****			
		Slope			
(inches)	(f.u.)	^{1}/$_{16}$ in/ft. (f.u.)	^{1}/$_8$ in/ft. (f.u.)	^{1}/$_4$ in/ft. (f.u.)	^{1}/$_2$ in/ft. (f.u.)
1^1/$_4$	1				
1^1/$_2$	3				
2	6			21	26
2^1/$_2$	12			24	31
3**	32***		36***	42***	50***
4	160		180	216	250
5	360		390	480	575
6	620		700	840	1,000
8	—	1,400	1,600	1,920	2,300
10	—	2,500	2,900	3,500	4,200

(Continued)

Diameter of Drain	Horizontal Fixture Branch*	Building Sewer, Building Drain and Building Drain Branches - from Stacks****			
		Slope			
(inches)	(f.u.)	$1/16$ in/ft. (f.u.)	$1/8$ in/ft. (f.u.)	$1/4$ in/ft. (f.u.)	$1/2$ in/ft. (f.u.)
12	—	3,900	4,600	5,600	6,700
15	—	7,000	8,300	10,000	12,000

*Includes Horizontal Branches of the Building Drain.
**No water closet shall discharge into a drain less than 3 inch.
***Not over 2 Water Closets.
****Every building drain that receives the discharge of (3) or more water closets, shall not be less than 4 inch in diameter.
*****No building sewer shall be less than 4 inches in diameter.

Subp. 3. Maximum loads for soil and waste stacks in fixture units.

Diameter of Stack	Stacks of not more than 3 stories or Branch Intervals	Stacks of more than 3 stories or Branch Intervals	Total at One Story or Branch Interval
$1^1/_4$*	2	2	1
$1^1/_2$*	4	4	2
2*	9	18	6
$2^1/_2$*	20	42	9
3	36***	72***	24**
4	240	500	90
5	540	1,100	200
6	960	1,900	350
8	—	3,600	600
10	—	5,600	1,000
12	—	8,400	1,500

*No water closets permitted.
**Not over 2 water closets permitted.
***Not over 6 water closets permitted, and not over 6 branch intervals on a 3 inch soil stack.

4715.2320
MINIMUM SIZE OF SOIL AND WASTE STACKS

No soil or waste stack shall be smaller than the largest horizontal branch connected thereto except that a four by three water closet connection shall not be considered as a reduction in pipe size.

4715.2330
MINIMUM SIZE OF STACK VENT OR VENT STACK

Any structure in which a building drain is installed shall have at least one stack vent or vent stack carried full size through the roof not less than three inches in diameter. Where one or more soil stacks are required to extend through the roof undiminished in size they should be the stack or stacks most remote from the location where the building drain leaves the building. When a soil or waste stack receives the discharge of fixtures located on two or more floors, and the uppermost fixture is located three or more floors above the building drain, such stack and stack vent shall continue undiminished in size through the roof. For purposes of this part, "floor" means any building floor level which is above the floor level of the building drain.

4715.2340
PROVISION FOR FUTURE FIXTURES

When provision is made for future installation of fixtures, those provided for shall be considered in determining the required sizes of drain and vent pipes. Construction to provide for such future installations shall be terminated with a plugged fitting or fittings.

4715.2350
MINIMUM SIZE OF UNDERGROUND DRAINAGE PIPING

No portion of the drainage system installed underground shall be less than two inches in diameter.

4715.2360
SIZING OF OFFSETS ON DRAINAGE PIPING

Subpart 1. **Offsets of 45 degrees or less.** An offset in a vertical stack with a change of direction of 45 degrees or less from the vertical may be sized as a straight vertical stack.

Subp. 2. **Offsets of more than 45 degrees.** A stack with an offset of more than 45 degrees from the vertical shall be sized as follows:

A. The portion of the stack above the offset shall be sized as for a regular stack based on the total number of fixture units above the offset.

B. The offset shall be sized as for a building drain branch, part 4715.2310, subpart 2.

C. The portion of the stack below the offset shall be sized at least as large as the offset.

Subp. 3. **Above highest branch.** An offset above the highest branch connection is an offset in the stack vent and shall be considered only as it affects the developed length of the vent.

Subp. 4. **Below lowest branch.** In the case of an offset in a soil or waste stack below the lowest branch connection, there shall be no change in diameter required if the offset is made at an angle of not greater than 45 degrees from the vertical.

If such offset is made at an angle of greater than 45 degrees from the vertical, the required diameter of the offset and the stack below it shall be sized as for a building drain. (Part 4715.2310, subpart 2.)

4715.2370
FIXTURE CONNECTIONS TO AN OFFSET OF MORE THAN 45 DEGREES OR AT BASE OF STACK

When stacks in buildings of five or more stories in height receive the discharge of fixtures four or more stories above the offset, no fixtures on the floor at which the offset occurs shall be connected to the stack within eight feet of the base of the offset measured vertically or horizontally. Said fixtures may also be connected into vertical section of the stack more than two feet below the offset. Fixture connections to horizontal piping at the bases of such stacks shall be made in the same manner, or at a point acceptable to the administrative authority.

4715.2400
PITCH ON HORIZONTAL DRAINAGE PIPING

Horizontal drainage piping shall be installed in uniform alignment at uniform slopes in accordance with the following requirements and in no case at a slope which will produce a computed velocity of less than two feet per second, unless otherwise permitted by the administrative authority, based on hydraulic analysis of the piping system.

Size of Piping	Minimum Slope
Less than 3 inches	$^1/_4$ inch per foot
3 inches to 6 inches	$^1/_8$ inch per foot
8 inches and over	$^1/_{16}$ inch per foot

4715.2410
CHANGE IN DIRECTION

Changes in direction in drainage piping shall be made by the appropriate use of 45 degree wyes, long or short sweep quarter bends, sixth, eighth, or sixteenth bends, or by combination of these or equivalent fittings. Single and double sanitary tees, quarter bends, and long turn ells may be used in drainage lines only where the direction of the flow is from the horizontal to the vertical. Short sweep bends or long turn ells three inch or larger in diameter may be used in soil or waste lines where the change in direction of flow is from either the horizontal to the vertical or from the vertical to the horizontal.

4715.2420
PROHIBITED FITTINGS AND CONNECTIONS

Subpart 1. **General prohibitions.** No fittings having a hub in the direction opposite to flow, or straight tee branch shall be used as a drainage fitting. No fitting or connection which has an enlargement chamber or recess with a ledge or shoulder, or reduction in pipe area shall be used. No drainage or vent piping shall be drilled, tapped, or welded unless otherwise permitted by the administrative authority. Fittings used for back-to-back, wall outlet, blowout type water closet bowls shall have a baffle plate or other device to prevent the waste water from one water closet from entering the opposite water closet. No fixture connection shall be made to a closet bend. No running threads, bands, or saddles shall be used. The short pattern fitting in a horizontal position is prohibited in underground work.

Subp. 2. **Heel or side-inlet bends.** A heel or side-inlet quarter bend shall not be used as a vent when the inlet is placed in a horizontal position or any similar arrangement of pipe or fittings producing a similar effect.

Subp. 3. **Obstruction to flow.** No fitting, connection, device, or method of installation which obstructs or retards the flow of water, wastes, sewage, or air in the drainage or venting system in an amount greater than the normal frictional resistance to flow shall be used unless it is indicated as acceptable to this code by having a desirable and acceptable function and as of ultimate benefit to the proper and continuing functioning of the plumbing system. The enlargement of a three-inch closet

bend or stub to four inches shall not be considered an obstruction, provided the horizontal flow line or insert is continuous without forming a ledge.

Subp. 4. **Dead ends.** In the installation of a drainage system, dead ends shall be avoided except where necessary to extend piping for a cleanout so as to be accessible.

4715.2430
BUILDING DRAINS BELOW BUILDING SEWER

Building drains which cannot be discharged to the sewer by gravity flow shall discharge into an approved watertight, gastight vented sump or receiving tank, so located as to receive the sewage or wastes by gravity. From such sump or receiving tank the sewage or other liquid wastes shall be lifted and discharged into the building gravity drain by approved automatic pumping equipment. The system or drainage piping entering such sump shall be installed and vented as required in this section for a gravity system.

4715.2440
DESIGN OF SUMPS

Subpart 1. **Construction.** Sumps and receiving tanks shall be constructed of poured concrete, metal, or other approved materials. If constructed of poured concrete, the walls and bottom shall be adequately reinforced and designed to acceptable standards. Metal sumps or tanks shall be of such thickness as to serve their intended purpose and shall be treated internally and externally to resist corrosion.

Subp. 2. **Discharge line.** The discharge line from such pumping equipment shall be provided with an accessible backwater valve and gate valve, and if the gravity drainage line to which such discharge line connects is horizontal, the method of connection shall be from the top through a wye branch fitting. The minimum size of any pump or discharge pipe from a sump having a water closet connected thereto shall not be less than two inches.

Subp. 3. **Sumps for buildings.** Building drains or building sewers receiving discharge from any pumping equipment shall be adequately sized to prevent overloading. In all buildings, other than single- and two-family dwellings, should three or more water closets discharge into the sump, duplicate pumping equipment shall be installed.

Subp. 4. **Covers.** Sumps and receiving tanks must be provided with gastight covers, except that float control or switch rods must operate without binding. The cover must be of a bolt and gasket type or equivalent manhole opening to permit access for inspection, repairs, and cleaning. Covers must be metal or other structurally sound material that is water-resistant and impervious to moisture, and must be adequate to support anticipated loads in the area of use.

Subp. 5. **Single-family dwellings.** In single-family dwellings the minimum capacity of a sump shall be 18 gallons.

Subp. 6. **Sump vent.** The top of the sump tank shall be provided with a vent pipe which shall extend separately through the roof, or may be combined with other vent pipes. Such vent shall be large enough to maintain atmospheric pressure within the sump under all normal operating conditions and in no case less than in accordance with the number of fixture units discharging into the sump. When the foregoing requirements are met and the vent, after leaving the sump, is combined with vents from fixtures discharging into the sump, the size of the combined vent need not exceed that required for the total number of fixtures discharging into the sump. No vent from an air operated sewage ejector shall combine with other vents.

Subp. 7. **Clear water sumps.** Sumps and receiving tanks which receive only clear water drainage, and from which sewage is excluded, need not be airtight or vented. Sumps and receiving tanks must be provided with covers fastened or secured so as to prevent entry by children. The covers must be adequate to support anticipated loads in area of use. In nonresidential buildings guard rails constructed in accordance with chapter 1305, Minnesota Building Code, may be used in lieu of covers.

4715.2500
SELECTING SIZE OF VENT PIPING

Subpart 1. Size determined. Vent pipe sizes shall be determined from part 4715.2520, subparts 5 and 6, on the basis of length and drainage load computed from part 4715.2300, subparts 2 and 3.

Subp. 2. Minimum diameter of vent piping. No vent pipe shall be less than $1^1/_4$ inches in diameter.

Subp. 3. Individual vents. The diameter of the individual vents shall be determined from part 4715.2520, subpart 6, but shall in no case be less than one-half the diameter of the fixture drain served.

Subp. 4. Relief and yoke vents. The diameter of relief and yoke vents shall be at least one-half the diameter of the soil and waste branch or stack served, nor less than the size of the vent to which they are connected.

Subp. 5. Circuit or loop vents. The diameter of circuit or loop vents shall be at least one-half the diameter of the horizontal soil or waste branch to which they connect. Maximum developed length as shown for fixture units in part 4715.2520, subpart 6. See part 4715.2600.

Subp. 6. Branch vents. The diameter of branch vents connecting more than one individual vent to a vent stack or stack vent shall be in accordance with part 4715.2520, subpart 6. The branch vent size shall be based upon the number of fixture units connected thereto, and the developed length of the branch vent measured from its vent stack (or stack vent) connection to the farthest fixture drain connection served by the branch vent.

Subp. 7. Vent headers. The diameter of vent headers shall be in accordance with part 4715.2520, subpart 6. The vent header size shall be based upon the sum of the fixture unit loads at the stacks vented through such section of the header, and the developed length shall be that of the vent stack having the longest developed length to the open air.

Subp. 8. Vent stacks. The diameter of the vent stacks shall be determined from part 4715.2520, subpart 5, based upon the size of the soil or waste stacks served thereby, the number of fixture units connected to the soil or waste stack, and the developed length of the vent stack. Such developed length shall be measured from the lowest connection of the vent stack with the soil or waste stack to the open air.

4715.2510
PROTECTION OF TRAP SEALS

The protection of trap seals from siphonage or back pressure shall be accomplished by the appropriate use of soil or waste stacks or vents, installed in accordance with requirements of this chapter, so that at no time the trap shall be subjected to a pressure differential of more than one inch of water.

4715.2520
VENT STACKS AND STACK VENTS

Subpart 1. Vent stack required. Every building in which plumbing is installed shall have at least one three-inch vent stack (or stack vent) carried full size through the roof as provided in part 4715.2330. A vent stack or main vent shall be installed with a soil or waste stack whenever individual vents, relief vents, or branch vents are required for stacks of three or more branch intervals.

Subp. 2. Connections at base and top. For stacks of three or four branch intervals in height, all main vents or vent stacks shall connect full size at their base to the main soil or waste stack below, through, or not more than 18 inches above the lowest fixture branch.

For stacks of five or more branch intervals in height, a main vent or vent stack shall connect full size with the soil or waste stack it serves, with a wye and one-eighth bend below the lowest fixture branch connected to such soil or waste stack, or at a point approved by the administrative authority.

Each such soil or waste stack, and vent stack shall be similarly cross-connected with a yoke vent at intervals of not more than five branch intervals as described in part 4715.2640.

Subp. 3. Offsets for stacks of five or more branch intervals or stories. As provided in part 4715.2360, soil and waste stacks offset at an angle of more than 45 degrees from the vertical, that receive the discharge of fixtures four or more branch intervals or stories above the offset, shall have a yoke vent installed (as per part 4715.2640) at the base of the upper stack section.

Subp. 4. Vent headers. Where stack vents and vent stacks are connected into a vent header, such connections shall be made at the tops of the stacks. The vent header shall connect to a vent extension through the roof.

Subp. 5. Size and lengths of vent stacks.

SIZE OF SOIL OR WASTE STACK IN INCHES	FIXTURE UNITS CONNECTED in d.f.u.	DIAMETER OF VENT IN INCHES										
		$1^1/_4$	$1^1/_2$	2	$2^1/_2$	3	4	5	6	8	10	12
		Maximum Developed Length of Vent, in Feet										
$1^1/_4$	2	50										
$1^1/_2$	4	40	200									
2	9		100	200								
2	18		50	150								
$2^1/_2$	42		30	100	300							
3	72			50	80	400						
4	240			40	70	250						
4	500				50	180	700					

(continued)

SIZE OF SOIL OR WASTE STACK IN INCHES	FIXTURE UNITS CONNECTED in d.f.u.	DIAMETER OF VENT IN INCHES										
		1¼	1½	2	2½	3	4	5	6	8	10	12
		Maximum Developed Length of Vent, in Feet										
5	540					150	600					
5	1100					50	200	700				
6	1900						50	200	700			
8	2200							150	500			
8	3600							60	250	800		
10	3800								200	600		
10	5600								60	250	800	
12	6000									200	600	
12	8400									100	300	900
15	10500									50	200	600
15	50000										75	180

Subp. 6. Size and length of vents; individual, branch, circuit, and header.

Fixture Units connected in d.f.u.	Diameter of Vent, in Inches						
	1¼	1½*	2	2½	3	4	5
	Maximum Developed Length of Vent, in Feet						
2	50	ul					
4	40	200	ul				
8	np	150	250				
10		100	200	ul			
24		50	150	400	ul		
42		30	100	300	500		
72		np	50	80	400		
240			np	50	200	ul	
500				np	180	700	ul
1100					50	200	700

*Except 6 fixture unit fixtures.

ul — Unlimited length.

np — Not permitted.

4715.2530
VENT TERMINALS

Subpart 1. Extension above roofs. Extension of vent pipes through a roof shall be terminated not less than 12 inches above it. Where a roof is to be used for any purpose other than weather protection, the vent extensions shall be run at least seven feet above the roof.

Subp. 2. Waterproof flashings. Each vent terminal shall be made watertight with the roof by proper flashing of copper, lead, galvanized iron, or other approved flashings or flashing materials. Vent pipe terminals shall pass through the roof and shall be at least two inches in diameter. When approved by the administrative authority, other materials or methods may be used which provide adequate protection.

Subp. 3. Location of vent terminal. No vent terminal shall be located directly beneath any door, window, or other ventilating opening of the building or of an adjacent building nor shall any such vent terminal be within ten feet horizontally of such an opening unless it is at least two feet above the top of such opening.

Subp. 4. Terminals adjoining high buildings. In the event that a new building is built higher than an existing building, the owner of the new building shall not locate openable windows, doors, or other ventilating openings within ten feet of any existing vent stack on the lower building unless the owner of such new building shall defray the expenses or shall make such alterations to conform to part 4715.2530, subpart 3.

4715.2540
VENT GRADES AND CONNECTIONS

Subpart 1. Vent grade. All vent and branch vent pipes shall be so graded and connected as to drain back to a soil or waste pipe by gravity.

Subp. 2. Vertical rise. Where vent pipes connect to a horizontal soil or waste pipe, the vent shall be taken off above the center line of the pipe. The vent pipe shall rise vertically, or at an angle not more than 45 degrees from the vertical, to a point at least six inches above flood-level rim of the fixture it is venting, before offsetting horizontally or before connecting to the branch vent.

Subp. 3. Height above fixtures. A connection between a vent pipe and a vent stack or stack-vent shall be made at least six inches above the flood-level rim of the highest fixture served by the vent. Horizontal vent pipes forming branch vents, relief vents, or loop vents shall be at least six inches above the flood-level rim of the highest fixture served.

4715.2550
WET VENTING

Subpart 1. Single bathroom groups. A single bathroom group of fixtures may be installed with the drain from a back-vented lavatory, kitchen sink, or combination fixture serving as a wet vent for a bathtub or shower stall provided that:

A. Not more than one fixture unit is drained into a 1½ inch diameter wet vent or not more than four fixture units drain into a two inch diameter wet vent; and

B. The horizontal branch drain connects to the stack at or below the same level as the water closet drain when installed on the top floor.

Subp. 2. **Double bathroom groups back-to-back.** Bathroom groups back-to-back consisting of two lavatories and two bathtubs or shower stalls may be installed on the same horizontal branch with a common vent for the lavatories and with no back vent for the bathtubs or shower stalls, provided the wet vent is not less than two inches in diameter.

Subp. 3. **Basement shower.** A basement shower may be wet vented through the waste from a laundry tub, lavatory, or sink, provided the wet vent is not less than two inches in diameter, and the drain conforms to part 4715.2620, subpart 4.

Subp. 4. **Basement and cellar closet.** A basement or cellar lavatory may be connected to a properly installed vent from a floor set, basement or cellar, water closet, provided the vent is not less than two inches in diameter.

4715.2560
STACK VENTING

A group of fixtures consisting of one bathroom group and a kitchen sink or combination fixture may be installed without individual fixture vents at the uppermost branch interval of a stack, if each fixture drain connects independently to a stack at least three inches in diameter extended full size through the roof, and bathtub or shower stall drain enters the stack at or above the same level as the water closet drain, and in accordance with requirements in part 4715.2620, subpart 4. Where the trap arm distances are exceeded the fixtures must be revented. When a water closet discharges to a sanitary tee in the vertical position, and a bathtub or shower on the same floor level also discharges to the sanitary tee through a side inlet, the water closet vent must be at least three inches in size unless the bathtub or shower is revented.

4715.2570
INDIVIDUAL FIXTURE REVENTING REQUIRED

When fixtures other than water closets discharge downstream from a water closet, each fixture connecting downstream shall be individually vented, under provisions set down in this code.

4715.2580
COMMON VENTS

Subpart 1. **Individual vent as common vent.** An individual vent, installed vertically, may be used as a common vent for similar fixtures when both fixture drains connect with a vertical drain at the same level.

Subp. 2. **Fixtures connected to vertical drain at different levels.** Except for water closets or similar fixtures, a common vent may be used for two fixtures set on same floor level but connecting at different levels in the vertical drain, provided the vertical drain is one pipe diameter larger than the upper fixture drain but in no case smaller than the lower fixture drain, whichever is the larger and that both drains conform to part 4715.2620, subpart 4.

4715.2600
CIRCUIT AND LOOP VENTING

Subpart 1. **Battery venting.** A branch or waste pipe to which two, but not more than eight water closets (except blowout type) are connected in battery, may be vented by circuit or loop vent which shall be taken off in front of the last fixture connection of the battery. When the battery consists of not more than four closets, the vent shall be two inches; when the battery consists of five or six closets, the vent shall be $2^{1}/_{2}$ inches; and when the battery consists of seven or eight closets, the vent shall be three inches. In addition, lower floor branches shall be provided with a relief vent which shall be the same size as the branch vent, taken off in front of the first fixture connection of the battery. When lavatories, or similar fixtures discharge into such branches, each vertical branch from such fixtures shall be provided with a continuous vent. When closets are installed back to back, such installation shall be as per subpart 2 or 4.

Subp. 2. **Dual branches.** When parallel horizontal branches serve a total of eight water closets (four on each branch), each branch shall be provided with a relief vent at a point between the two most distant water closets. When fixtures such as lavatories discharge into the horizontal branch drain, each such fixture shall be vented.

Subp. 3. **Vent connections.** When the circuit, loop, or relief vent connections are taken off the horizontal branch, the vent branch connection shall be taken off at a vertical angle or from the top of the horizontal branch.

Subp. 4. **Fixtures back-to-back in battery.** When fixtures are connected to one horizontal branch through a double wye or a sanitary cross in a vertical position, a common vent for each two fixtures back-to-back or double connection shall be provided. The common vent shall be installed in a vertical position as a continuation of the double connection.

4715.2610
FIXTURES BACK-TO-BACK

Two fixtures set back-to-back, within the distance allowed between a trap and its vent, may be served with one continuous soil or waste-vent pipe, provided that each fixture wastes separately into an approved double fitting, having inlet openings at the same level. (See part 4715.2580, subpart 2.)

4715.2620
FIXTURE VENTS

Subpart 1. **Distance of trap from vent.** Each fixture trap shall have a protecting vent so located that the slope and the developed length in the fixture drain from the trap weir to the vent fitting are within the requirements set forth in subpart 4.

Subp. 2. **Trap dip.** The vent pipe opening from a soil or waste pipe, except for water closets and similar fixtures, shall not be below the weir of the trap.

Subp. 3. **Crown venting limitation.** No vent shall be installed within two pipe diameters of the trap weir.

Subp. 4. **Distance of fixture trap from vent.**

Size of Fixture Drain, Inches	Distance Trap to Vent
1¼	2 ft 6 in
1¼	3 ft 6 in
2	5 feet
3	6 feet
4	10 feet

Note: The developed length between the trap of the water closet or similar fixture and its vent shall not exceed four feet.

4715.2630
VENTS FOR FIXTURE TRAP BELOW TRAP DIP

Fixture drains shall be vented within the hydraulic gradient between the trap outlet and vent connection, but in no case shall the unvented drain exceed the distance provided for in part 4715.2620, subpart 4.

4715.2640
YOKE VENTS FOR STACKS OF MORE THAN FIVE BRANCH INTERVALS

Soil and waste stacks in buildings having more than five branch intervals shall be provided with a relief vent at each fifth interval installed, beginning with the top floor. The size of the relief vent shall be equal to the size of the vent stack to which it connects. The lower end of the yoke vent shall connect to the soil or waste stack through a wye and one-eighth bend located below the horizontal branch drain serving fixtures on that floor and the upper end shall connect to the vent stack through a tee or inverted wye not less than three feet above the floor level.

4715.2650
COMBINATION WASTE AND VENT SYSTEM

Subpart 1. **Where permitted.** A combination waste-and-vent system shall be permitted only where structural conditions preclude the installation of a conventional system as otherwise provided in this code.

Subp. 2. **Limits of use.** A combination waste-and-vent system is limited to floor drains and sinks which will not be used for greasy wastes. It consists of an installation of waste piping in which the trap of the fixture is not individually vented. Every drainage pipe and trap in the waste and vent system shall be at least two pipe sizes larger than the size required in part 4715.2310. Vents shall be provided at both ends of the system.

Subp. 3. **Island fixture venting.** Traps for island sinks and similar equipment may be vented, when structural conditions preclude the use of conventional vents, by extending the vent as high as possible under the sink enclosure and then returning it downward and connecting it to the horizontal drain through a wye branch fitting downstream from the vertical fixture drain. In addition, a horizontal vent shall be taken off the vertical section of the fixture vent by means of a wye branch fitting

and extended to the partition where it can be extended vertically to the open air or connected to another vent at least six inches above the flood level of the fixture served. Drainage fittings should be used on all sections of the vent below floor level and a minimum slope of one-fourth inch per foot to the drainage point shall be provided. Cleanouts shall be provided on the vent piping.

4715.2655
ISLAND FIXTURE VENTING

Traps for island sinks and similar equipment may be vented, when structural conditions preclude the use of conventional vents, by extending the vent as high as possible under the sink enclosure and then returning it downward and connecting it to the horizontal drain through a wye branch fitting downstream from the vertical fixture drain. In addition, a horizontal vent must be taken off the vertical section of the fixture vent by means of a wye branch fitting and extended to the partition where it can be extended vertically to the open air or connected to another vent at least six inches above the flood level of the fixture served. Drainage fittings must be used on all sections of the vent below floor level and a minimum slope of one-fourth inch per foot to the drainage point shall be provided. Cleanouts must be provided on the vent piping.

4715.2660
VENTING OF SUMPS AND SEWERS

Drainage piping below sewer level shall be vented in similar manner to that for a gravity system. Building sump vents shall be sized in accordance with parts 4715.2520, subpart 6, and 4715.2440, subpart 6, but in any case not less than 1½ inches. Vents from pneumatic ejectors, flammable waste traps, or similar equipment shall be terminated separately at the open air.

4715.2700
STORM SEWER SYSTEMS

All roofs shall be drained into a separate storm sewer system, or a combined sewer system where such systems are available, or to a place of disposal satisfactory to the administrative authority. In no case shall water from roofs be allowed to flow upon the public sidewalk. Storm water shall not be drained into sewers intended for sanitary sewage only.

4715.2710
SIZE OF BUILDING STORM DRAINS AND LEADERS

Subpart 1. Size of building storm drain. The size of the building storm drain or any of its horizontal branches having a slope of one-half inch or less per foot, shall be based upon the maximum projected roof or paved area to be handled according to subpart 4.

Subp. 2. Size of vertical leaders. Vertical leaders shall be sized on the maximum projected roof area, according to subpart 5.

Subp. 3. Reduction in size prohibited. Storm drain piping shall not reduce in size in the direction of flow, including changes in direction from horizontal to vertical.

Subp. 4. Size of horizontal storm drains.

Diameter of Drain	Maximum projected Roof Area for Drains of Various Slopes		
	1/8 in. Slope	1/4 in. Slope	1/2 in. Slope
Inches	Square Feet	Square Feet	Square Feet
3	822	1,160	1,644
4	1,880	2,650	3,760
5	3,340	4,720	6,680
6	5,350	7,550	10,700
8	11,500	16,300	23,000
10	20,700	29,200	41,400
12	33,300	47,000	66,600
15	59,500	84,000	119,000

Use a rate of rainfall of four inches per hour for sizes not listed in this table.

Subp. 5. Size of vertical leaders.

Size of Leader or Conductor Inches	Maximum Projected Roof Area Square Feet
2	720
2 1/2	1,300
3	2,200
4	4,600
5	8,650
6	13,500
8	29,000

Use a rate of rainfall of four inches per hour for sizes not listed in this table.

The equivalent diameter of square or rectangular leader may be taken as the diameter of that circle which may be inscribed within the cross-sectional area of the leader.

Subp. 6. Values for continuous flow. If there is a continuous or semicontinuous discharge into the building storm drain or building storm sewer, as from a pump, ejector, air-conditioning plant, or similar device, each gallon per minute of the discharge must be computed as being equivalent to 24 square feet of roof area, based upon a four-inch rainfall.

4715.2720
SUBSOIL DRAINS

When the subsoil drain for a building is subject to backwater, it shall be protected by an accessibly located backwater valve. Subsoil drains may discharge into a properly trapped area drain or sump. Such sumps do not require vents. (See parts 4715.2430 and 4715.2440.)

4715.2730
BUILDING SUBDRAINS

Building subdrains, receiving subsoil drainage, located below the public sewer level shall discharge into a sump or receiving tank the contents of which shall be automatically lifted and discharged into the drainage system as required for building sumps. (See parts 4715.2430 and 4715.2440.)

4715.2740
TRAPS ON STORM DRAINS AND LEADERS

No traps shall be required for stormwater drains which are connected to a sewer carrying storm water exclusively.

Leaders and storm drains that are connected to a combined sewer shall be trapped if:

A. The drain is located within ten feet of any door, window, or other opening into an occupied area; and

B. An outside leader of sheet metal is connected to the storm drain and the joint of connection is within ten feet of any door, window, or other opening into an occupied area. Such connection shall be at least six inches above grade. The trap shall be located inside the building and be provided with an accessible cleanout.

4715.2750
CONDUCTORS AND CONNECTIONS

Subpart 1. Not to be used improperly. Conductor pipes shall not be used as soil, waste, or vent pipes nor shall drainage or vent pipes be used as conductors.

Subp. 2. Separate storm and sanitary drainage. The sanitary and storm building drains shall be separate and shall be run to a point at least five feet outside the building. The sanitary and storm building sewers shall be separate except where a combined sewer is available and where permitted by local authorities they may be joined together preferably in a manhole prior to discharging to a combined sewer. The sizing of the combined building sewer shall conform to good engineering practices and be acceptable to the administrative authority.

4715.2760
ROOF AND DECK DRAINS

Subpart 1. Roof drain strainers. All roof areas, except those draining to hanging gutters, shall be equipped with roof drains having strainers extending not less than four inches above the surface of the roof immediately adjacent to the roof drain. Strainers shall have an available inlet area, above roof level, equal to that of the conductor or leader to which the drain is connected.

Subp. 2. Overflow drains. For overflow drains refer to Chapter 1305, Minnesota Building Code.

Subp. 3. Flat deck and area drains. Drain strainers for use on sun decks, and similar area, normally serviced and maintained, may be of the flat surface type, level with the deck and shall have an available inlet area of not less than two times the area of the conductor or leader to which the drain is connected.

Subp. 4. Roof drain flashings required. The connection between roofs and roof drains which pass through the roof and into the interior of the building shall be made watertight by use of proper flashing material.

4715.2770
PROVISIONS FOR EXPANSION

Expansion joints, sleeves, or suitable offsets shall be provided where warranted by temperature variations or physical conditions.

4715.2780
CONTROL FLOW STORM WATER DRAINAGE
FOR DEAD LEVEL ROOFS

Subpart 1. General requirements. In lieu of sizing the storm drainage system from conventional methods as previously described in this chapter, the roof drainage may be sized on the controlled flow and storage of the storm water on the roof provided the following conditions are met:

A. The roof drainage system shall be sized on the basis of a rate of rainfall of four inches per hour;

B. The roof is dead level and 45 degree cants, properly flashed, are installed at any well or parapet;

C. The roof design is based on a minimum of 40 pounds per square foot live load, with overflow line of roof edge, coping, or relieving scupper in parapet wall at least four inches in height above the roof and at no greater height than will provide a safety factor of two for the structural design live load;

D. Roof drainage pipe sizing may be designed on the basis of controlled flow sizing tables provided by manufacturers of

roof drains approved by the administrative authority or by the tables in subparts 2 and 3;

E. The plans or specifications for the storm drainage system shall indicate the method used as the basis for the design.

Subp. 2. Size of vertical leaders.

Size of Leader Inches	Maximum Projected Roof Area in Square Feet
3	7,500
4	15,000
5	21,000

Roof areas of more than 15,000 square feet shall contain two or more roof drains.

Subp. 3. Size of horizontal storm drains.

Diameter of Drain Inches	Maximum Projected Roof Area in Square Feet 1/4 in. Slope
3	3,500
4	8,200
5	11,750
6	18,500
8	40,000
10	75,850
12	118,000
15	214,000

4715.2800
INSPECTIONS

New plumbing systems and parts of existing systems which have been altered, extended, or repaired shall be inspected and tested by the proper administrative authority to ensure compliance with all the requirements of this code and the installation and construction of the system in accordance with the approved plan and the permit, except that testing may be waived for work which does not include addition to, replacement, alteration, or relocation of any water supply, drainage, or vent piping.

All the piping shall be tested and after the plumbing fixtures have been set, and before the system is put into use, the system shall be given a final inspection and test by the proper administrative authority.

The equipment, material, power, and labor necessary for the inspection must be furnished by the plumbing contractor.

4715.2810
NOTIFICATIONS

It shall be the duty of the plumbing contractor to notify the proper administrative authority and the owner or the owner's authorized agent orally, by telephone, or in writing, not less than eight working hours between the hours of 8:00 a.m. and 4:00 p.m. before the work is to be inspected or tested. It shall be the duty of the plumbing contractor to make sure that the work will stand the test prescribed before giving the above notification. If the proper administrative authority finds that the work will not stand the test, the plumbing contractor shall be required to renotify as above. If the proper administrative authority does not appear for an inspection within 24 hours of the time set, excluding Saturdays, Sundays, and holidays, the inspection or test shall be deemed to have been made, and the plumbing contractor is required to file an affidavit with the proper administrative authority that the work was installed in accordance with the code, the approved plans and permit, and that it was free from defects and that the required tests had been made and the system found free from leaks; also whether the owner or the owner's authorized agent was present when such inspection or test was made.

4715.2820
METHOD OF TESTING

Subpart 1. **Testing.** The air tests shall be applied to the plumbing drainage system in its entirety or in sections. Sections which are found satisfactory need not be retested after completion of the entire system unless considered necessary by the proper administrative authority.

Subp. 2. **Rough plumbing.** The piping of plumbing drainage and venting systems shall be tested upon completion of the rough piping. The method of testing shall be specified by the designer and shall either be an air test or hydrostatic test as described in this subpart, or an alternative test as approved by the administrative authority. The air test shall be made by attaching the air compressor or testing apparatus to any suitable

opening and closing all other inlets and outlets to the system by means of proper testing plugs. Plaster of paris shall not be used in roof terminals. Air shall be forced into the system until there is a uniform pressure of five pounds per square inch on the portion of the system being tested. The pressure shall remain constant for 15 minutes without the addition of air. The hydrostatic test, for thermoplastic piping materials, shall be conducted by tightly closing all openings in the entire system to be tested except the highest opening. The system shall be filled with water to the point of overflow. If the system is tested in sections, each opening shall be tightly plugged except the highest opening of the section under test. Each section shall be filled with water, but a section shall not be tested with less than 10 foot head of water. In testing successive sections, at least the upper 10 feet of the next preceding section shall be tested, so that no joint or pipe in the building, except the uppermost 10 feet of the system, is subjected to a test of less than 10 foot head of water. The water shall be kept in the system or in the portion under test for at least 15 minutes before inspection begins. The system shall be tight at all points.

In lieu of five pound air test, concrete manholes and sewer lines may be tested by negative pressure in accordance with ASTM Standards C1214-92 and C1244-93.

Subp. 2a. **Exceptions.**

A. Testing is not required for:
    (1) outside leaders;
    (2) perforated or open drain tile; or
    (3) portions of storm sewers located more than ten feet from buildings, more than ten feet from buried water lines, and more than 50 feet from water wells, and not passing through soil or water identified as being contaminated.

B. Building storm sewers may be tested in accordance with the Hydrostatic Test Method from the City Engineers Association of Minnesota, except that an air test may be required for any section of the building storm sewer that passes through contaminated soils or contaminated water. The Hydrostatic Test Method, provisions H2 and H3, as specified in Standard Utilities Specifications for Watermain and Service Line Installation and Sanitary Sewer and Storm Sewer Installation, written and published by the City Engineers Association of Minnesota, 1988 edition, is incorporated by reference, is not subject to frequent change, and is available in the office of the commissioner of administration.

Subp. 3. **Finished plumbing.** After the plumbing fixtures have been set and their traps filled with water, their connections shall be tested and proven gas and water tight by plugging the stack openings on the roof and the building drain where it leaves the building, and air introduced into the system equal to the pressure of a one inch water column. Such pressure shall remain constant for the period of inspection without the introduction of additional air.

Subp. 4. **Conductor pipes.** Conductor pipes and their roof connections inside the building shall be tested with air. (See subpart 2)

Subp. 5. **Test of water distribution system.** Upon the completion of a section or of the entire water distribution system, it shall be tested and proved tight with the use of air or water not less than the maximum working pressure under which it is to be used. If tested with water, the water used for the test shall be obtained from a potable source.

Subp. 6. **Material and labor for tests.** The equipment, material, power, and labor necessary for the inspection and test shall be furnished by the plumbing contractor.

Subp. 7. **Test plugs or caps.** Test plugs or caps for roof terminals must extend above or outside the end of the vent pipe to provide a visible indication for removal after the test has been completed.

4715.2830
COVERING OF WORK

No building drainage or plumbing system or part thereof shall be covered until it has been inspected, tested, and approved as herein prescribed.

If any building drainage or plumbing system or part thereof is covered before being regularly inspected, tested, and approved, as herein prescribed, it shall be uncovered upon the direction of the proper administrative authority.

4715.2840
DEFECTIVE WORK

If the inspection or test shows defects, such defective work or material shall be replaced and the inspection and test repeated.

All installed fixtures found defective or in an insanitary condition shall be repaired, replaced, or removed upon written notice from the proper administrative authorities.

4715.2850
AIR TEST OF DEFECTIVE PLUMBING

The air test shall be used in testing the sanitary condition of the drainage or plumbing system of all buildings where there is reason to believe that it has become defective. In buildings condemned by the proper administrative authority because of insanitary conditions of the plumbing system, the alterations in such system shall not be considered as repairs, but as new plumbing.

Where buildings are moved from one location to another, or raised for foundations, or where part of the plumbing system has been damaged by fire, storm, or other means, a final air test shall be applied and shall hold tight, if in the opinion of the administrative authority it is warranted in order to assure a sanitary plumbing system.

4715.2860
MAINTENANCE

The plumbing system of every building shall be maintained in a sanitary and safe operating condition.

4715.2870
DISINFECTION OF WATER PIPING

See part 4715.2250.

4715.2880
BUILDING SEWER

The building sewer shall be inspected by the proper administrative authority to ensure compliance with the provisions of the code.

4715.2890
CERTIFICATE OF APPROVAL

Upon the satisfactory completion and final inspection of the plumbing system, a certificate of approval shall be issued by the proper administrative authority.

4715.3130
PLANS AND SPECIFICATIONS

Prior to the installation by any person, corporation, or public agency, of a system of plumbing that serves the public or that serves any considerable number of persons, or any plumbing system that shall affect the public health in any manner, complete plans and specifications, together with any additional information that the commissioner of health may require, shall be submitted in duplicate and approved by the commissioner. The appraisal of the commissioner shall reflect the degree to which these plans and specifications affect the public health and conform to the provisions of the Minnesota Plumbing Code. No constructions shall proceed except in accordance with approved plans. Any material alteration or extension of the existing system shall be subject to these same requirements. This rule shall not apply to cities of the first class, except those plumbing installations in hospitals or in buildings in these cities owned by the federal or the state government.

There shall be no physical connection between water supply systems that are safe for domestic use and those that are unsafe for domestic use. There shall be no apparatus through which unsafe water may be discharged or drawn into a safe water supply system.

4715.3140
EXAMINATION AND LICENSING OF PLUMBERS

Subpart 1. **Examinations.** An applicant for a plumber's license must satisfactorily pass an examination given by the commissioner of health. Examinations for journeyman and master plumber licenses shall be held in March and September of each year. Applications for the March examination must be filed not later than February 15 and for the September examination not later than August 15.

A. An applicant for the master plumber examination must, in addition to the practical plumbing experience requirement for a master plumber specified in subpart 2, have at least one of the following:

    (1) a current Minnesota journeyman plumber license;

    (2) a master plumber license from another state where the requirements of the licensing jurisdiction are equivalent to those of Minnesota, as determined by the commissioner; or

    (3) five years of verifiable experience in business as a plumbing contractor in Minnesota.

B. An applicant for the journeyman examination must be a registered apprentice in Minnesota and have satisfied the practical plumbing experience requirement specified in subpart 2 for a journeyman plumber or must hold a current state journeyman plumber's license from another state where the licensing jurisdiction requires at least four years of practical plumbing experience and an examination to qualify for licensure.

Subp. 2. **Experience.** An applicant for the journeyman plumber's license examination must have not less than four years of practical plumbing experience and the applicant for a master plumber's license examination must have not less than five years of practical plumbing experience.

A. One year of practical plumbing experience consists of at least 1,750 hours.

B. Not more than two years of the practical plumbing experience from a state other than Minnesota shall be credited unless the applicant first obtains a plumber's license in the other state.

C. The apprentice or applicant is responsible for verifying practical plumbing experience. The commissioner of health may require work records, time cards, pay records, or other documentation necessary to evaluate practical plumbing experience. The commissioner shall make the final determination about the adequacy and acceptability of an apprentice's or applicant's practical plumbing experience.

4715.3150
FEES

Subpart 1. **Examination application fee.** Applications to take the journeyman or master plumber's examination must be submitted to the commissioner of health on forms prepared by the commissioner together with a fee of $50. The fee must be submitted with the application and is not refundable.

Subp. 2. **Fees for license.** Any applicant who receives a passing grade on the examination may submit an application for license on forms prepared by the commissioner of health. The application must be accompanied by a fee of $55 for a journeyman plumber's license or $120 for a master plumber's license, except that an application for initial licensure that is submitted during the last three months of a licensing year must be accompanied by a fee of $27.50 for a journeyman plumber's license or $60 for a master plumber's license.

4715.3160
EXPIRATION OF LICENSES

Subpart 1. **Issuance and expiration.** Initial and renewal journeyman and master plumber's licenses shall be issued for the calendar year for which application is made and shall expire on December 31 of such year. Any journeyman or master plumber who submits a renewal application after December 31 shall not work as a journeyman or master plumber until the person has submitted an application, fee, and penalty fee. Any licensee who does not renew a license within two years is no longer eligible for renewal. Such person must retake and pass the examination before a new license will be issued.

Subp. 2. **License renewals.** Applications for license renewal must be submitted to the commissioner of health on forms prepared by the commissioner no later than December 31 of the year preceding the year for which application is made. The application must be accompanied by a fee of $55 for a journeyman plumber and $120 for a master plumber. Journeyman and master plumbers who submit their license renewal applications after the time specified in subpart 1 but within two years after expiration of the previously issued license must pay all past due renewal fees plus an additional $25.

Subp. 3. **Fee for filing bond and insurance.** Master plumbers who file a bond and evidence of liability insurance with the secretary of state, pursuant to Minnesota Statutes, section 326.40, shall pay an additional fee of $40.

4715.3170
REGISTRATION OF PLUMBER'S APPRENTICE

Effective July 1, 1987, no person shall work as a plumber's apprentice until that person has submitted an application and fee for registration to the commissioner of health. Registration must be renewed annually and shall be for the period from July 1 of each year to June 30 of the following year. Applications for initial and renewal registration must be submitted to the commissioner of health before July 1 of each registration period on forms provided by the commissioner, and must be accompanied by a fee of $25. A plumber's apprentice who submits a registration application after July 1 in any year must pay the past due renewal fee plus an additional $25 late fee.

A. A plumber's apprentice must be at least 18 years of age or be a high school graduate, except that an apprentice employed and supervised by the apprentice's parent must be at least 16 years of age.

B. At the time of registration, an apprentice must provide a name, address, date of birth, social security number, and information about education and practical plumbing experience on forms prepared by the commissioner of health.

C. The practical plumbing experience for an apprentice must include at least the following number of hours in the plumbing aspects specified in subitems (1) to (3). The remaining required hours of practical plumbing experience may be in any aspect of plumbing work included in the definition of plumbing in part 4715.0100, however, the type of work and corresponding number of hours must be specified:

(1) water distribution system installation, 2,000 hours;

(2) drain, waste, and vent system installation, 2,000 hours; and

(3) fixture installation, 1,000 hours.

D. All practical plumbing experience for an apprentice must be certified by the licensed plumber or plumbing contractor responsible for the work performed. A licensed plumber or plumbing contractor may only certify that part of the practical plumbing experience work done under the licensed plumber's or plumbing contractor's supervision.

E. Only practical plumbing experience gained in the 12-month period immediately prior to registration or submission of the renewal application for registration shall be considered, except that late registration renewals may be accepted for a period not exceeding three months, with payment of a late fee.

F. The 1,750 hours necessary to gain one year of practical plumbing experience may be worked in more than one 12-month registration period as a plumber's apprentice, however, not more than 1,750 hours shall be credited for one registration period.

4715.3500
GENERAL

Parts 4715.3500 to 4715.3700 outline a procedure for the sizing of the water supply piping. The design procedure is based on the minimum pressure available from the street main or individual source of supply, the head changes in the system due to friction and elevation, the volume rates of flow required for satisfactory operation of the fixtures, and the probability of simultaneous use.

4715.3600
TOTAL DAILY WATER REQUIREMENTS

Subpart 1. Basic needs. The calculation of total daily requirements for water may be based on the unit quantities shown in subparts 2 and 3. The total daily water requirement does not constitute the peak or simultaneous water requirement of the supply and shall not be used in sizing water distribution systems. The total of the daily water requirement shall be used only to determine whether the source of the water supply is sufficient to provide the water requirements of people, animals, irrigation, and other water using facilities served. The rate of flow and pressures at which the total daily water requirements shall be delivered shall be determined as prescribed hereinafter.

Subp. 2. Design criteria for daily water requirements based on building occupancy.

Type of occupancy	Minimum quantity of water per person per day in gallons (or as indicated)
Small dwellings and cottages with seasonal occupancy	50
Single family dwellings	75
Multiple family dwellings (apartments)	60
Rooming houses	40
Boarding houses	50
Additional kitchen usage for nonresident boarders	10
Hotels without private baths	50
Hotels with private baths (2 persons per room)	60
Restaurants (toilet and kitchen usage per patron)	7 to 10
Restaurants (kitchen usage per meal served)	$2^1/_2$ to 3
Additional for bars and cocktail lounges	2
Tourist camps or trailer parks with central bathhouse	35
Tourist camps or mobile home parks with individual bath units	50
Resort camps (night and day) with limited plumbing	50
Luxury camps	100 to 150
Work or construction camps (semipermanent)	50
Camp (with complete plumbing)	45 (Ind.w.s.)
Camp (with flush toilets--no showers)	25 (Ind.w.s.)
Day camps (no meals served)	15
Day schools, without cafeterias, gymnasiums, or showers	15
Day schools with cafeterias, but no gymnasiums or showers	20
Day schools with cafeterias, gymnasiums and showers	25
Boarding schools	75 to 100
Day workers at schools and offices (per shift)	15
Hospitals (per bed)	150 to 250
Institutions other than hospitals (per bed)	75 to 125

(continued)

Type of occupancy	Minimum quantity of water per person per day in gallons (or as indicated)
Factories (gallons per person per shift, exclusive of industrial wastes)	15 to 35
Picnic parks (toilet usage only) (gallons per picnicker)	5
Picnic parks with bathhouses, showers, and flush toilets	10
Swimming pools and bathhouses	10
Luxury residences and estates	100 to 150
Country clubs (per resident member)	100
Country clubs (per nonresident member)	25
Motels (per bed space)	40
Motels with bath, toilet, and kitchen range	50
Drive-in theaters (per car space)	5
Movie theaters (per auditorium seat)	5
Airports (per passenger)	3 to 5
Self-service laundries (gallons per wash, i.e., per customer)	50
Stores (per toilet room)	400
Service stations (per vehicle serviced)	10

Subp. 3. Daily water requirements for common farm animals.

Animal	Minimum daily water requirements in gallons
Horse, mule, or steer	12
Dairy cow (drinking only)	15
Dairy cow (drinking and dairy servicing)	35
Sheep	2
Hog	4
Chickens (100)	4
Turkeys (100)	7

Subp. 4. Calculating total daily requirement. Total daily water requirements should be calculated by multiplying the unit daily requirement by the total number of persons in the occupancy involved. See subpart 6. To this figure must be added any special use quantity, such as lawn watering, industrial requirement, etc.

Subp. 5. Special requirements. The total daily amount of any special requirement shall be added to the figure as obtained under subpart 4. Part 4715.1770, subpart 2 gives special use quantities for some conditions. While the quantity of special use water shall be computed on the rates given in part 4715.1770, subpart 2, the total amount shall be figured for appropriate periods and conditions of use. See subpart 7.

Subp. 6. Example 1. Example: assume there is a hospital outside the limits of a community. The hospital has 300 beds. In addition, the hospital supplies its own dairy products and has a farm with 40 head of cattle. In subpart 2, the daily water requirement per hospital bed is taken as 250 gallons per bed. From subpart 3, the water requirement per head of cattle is taken as 35 gallons per animal. Therefore the total daily water requirement is 300 x 250 plus 40 x 35 or 76,400 gallons.

Subp. 7. **Example 2.** Example: it is assumed that at the hospital cited in subpart 6 there is a lawn sprinkling system operating from 12 sill cocks three hours each day. From part 4715.1770, subpart 2 it is seen that each sill cock requires 300 gallons per hour. Therefore, the total special use water will equal 12 x 300 x 3 or 10,800 gallons. This amount is added to that obtained in subpart 6. The total quantity required is, therefore, 76,400 plus 10,800 or 87,200 gallons per day.

4715.3700
DETERMINATION OF PEAK DEMAND

Subpart 1. Estimating water supply demand. In determining the size of water supply distribution piping, the maximum momentary volume rate of flow of water shall first be determined. This is the supply demand which is based on the numbers and kinds of fixtures installed, on the rates of flow required by the different kinds of fixtures, and on the probable simultaneous operation of the various fixtures. The total daily requirements do not enter into this determination. In computing supply demand, use shall be made of subpart 2.

Subp. 2. Supply fixture unit values for various plumbing fixtures.

Fixture of group[1]	Type of supply control	Supply fixture unit values		
		Hot	Cold	Total[2]
Bathroom group	Flush valve	3	6	8
Bathroom group	Flush tank	3	4.5	6
Bathtub	Faucet	1.5	1.5	2
Combination fixture	Faucet	2	2	3
Kitchen sink	Faucet	1.5	1.5	2
Laundry tray	Faucet	2	2	3
Lavatory	Faucet	1.5	1.5	2
Pedestal urinal	Flush valve		10	10
Restaurant sink	Faucet	3	3	4
Service sink	Faucet	1.5	1.5	2
Shower head	Mixing valve	3	3	4
Stall or wall urinal	Flush valve		5	5
Stall or wall urinal	Flush tank		3	3
Water closet	Flush valve		10	10
Water closet	Flush tank		5	5

[1]For fixtures not listed, factors may be assumed by comparing the fixture to a listed one using water in similar quantities and at similar rates.

[2]For fixtures with both hot and cold water supplies, the weights for maximum separate demands may be taken as three-fourths of the total supply fixture unit value.

Subp. 3. Calculation of demand. When the water supply fixture units are used to estimate the supply demand, the supply fixture unit values as given in subpart 2 shall be used in conjunction with subpart 4.

Subp. 4. Supply demand for various loads in supply fixture units.

Load	Supply demand	
	Flush valve water closets predominate (subpart 5, curve 1)	Tank water closets predominate (subpart 5, curve 2)
Supply fixture units:	gpm	gpm
5	22	4
10	27	8
20	35	14
30	42	20
40	46	24
50	51	28
60	54	32
88	64	40
124	74	48
160	81	56
226	98	72
300	108	85
400	127	106
470	135	118
500	143	124
600	157	143
660	162	152
700	170	161
800	183	178
850	189	185
900	197	195
1,000	208	208
1,060	216	216
1,280	243	243
1,510	270	270
1,990	324	324
2,480	378	378
2,990	432	432

Subp. 5. Graph of supply demand for various loads in supply fixture units.

The estimated demand load in gallons per minute for fixtures used intermittently on any water supply pipe shall be obtained by multiplying the total number of each kind of fixture, supplied through that pipe by its supply fixture unit value from subpart 2, adding the products, and then, referring to the appropriate columns of subpart 4, or using subpart 5, select the demand in GPM. Examples are given below. The additional load of any continuously flowing outlets such as hose outlets shall be computed separately and added to the total demand of intermittently used fixtures. See subpart 6.

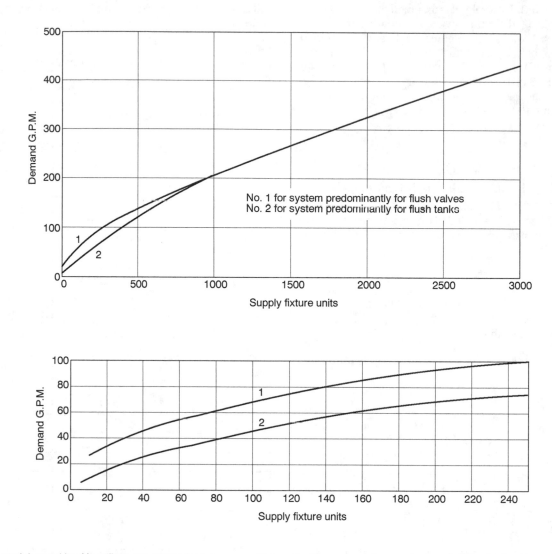

The estimated demand load in gallons per minute for fixtures used intermittently on any water supply pipe shall be obtained by multiplying the total number of each kind of fixture, supplied through that pipe by its supply fixture unit value from subpart 2, adding the products, and then, referring to the appropriate columns of subpart 4, or using subpart 5, select the demand in GPM. Examples are given below. The addition al load of any continuously flowing outlets such as hose outlets shall be computed separately and added to the total demand of intermittently used fixtures. See subpart 6.

Subp. 6. Example. Assume a water line serving a public washroom in which are three flushometer pedestal urinals, six flushometer closets and six lavatories with hot and cold water. First prepare a tabulation as shown.

Name of plumbing fixture	Number on system (or section)[1]	Supply fixture unit value per fixture (Subpart 2)			Total supply fixture units		
		Hot	Cold	Total	Hot	Cold	Total
Pedestal Urinal, Flush Valve	3		10	10		30	30
Flushometer Closet	6		10	10		60	60
Lavatory	6	1.5	1.5	2	9	9	12
Total					9	99	102
Supply demand in GPM					7	67	68

[1] See subpart 8.

Referring to subpart 2 for these fixtures, it is found that the total demand in supply fixture units for hot was 9 s.f.u., for cold was 99 s.f.u., and for a total demand of 102 s.f.u. By using subpart 5 curve number 2 it is determined that the supply demand in GPM for hot water is 7 and by using the same figure but curve 1 it is determined that the demand for cold water in GPM is 67 and the total demand in GPM is 68. This breakdown is used in order to size the hot water supply branch, the cold water supply branch and the building service line.

Subp. 7. Example. Assume an apartment building (private type occupancy) having 200 bathroom groups with flushometer closets and 200 kitchen sinks. The apartment lawn has installed in it a sprinkler system operating from (7) sill cocks. What is the demand flow for which the water service to the apartment must be designed? The intermittent use fixtures are figured as in subpart 6 to have a demand of 326 GPM.

Name of fixture	Number on system	Supply fixture unit value per fixture (Subpart 2)			Total supply fixture units		
		Hot	Cold	Total	Hot	Cold	Total
Bathroom group	300	3	6	8	600	1,200	1,600
Kitchen sink	200	1.5	1.5	2	300	300	400
Total					900	1,500	2,000
Demand in GPM (Subpart 4)					208	270	326

The lawn sprinkler system outlets have a demand of 5 GPM each, part 4715.1770. The total sprinkler system demand is, therefore, 35 GPM. This is added to the total demand (326) of the intermittently used fixtures making a total water demand of 361 GPM. This total figure would then be used to determine the size of the building service pipe. The 35 GPM demand figure would also be added to the cold water demand figure of 270 giving total cold water demand of 305 GPM and this figure would be used in sizing the cold water distribution piping.

Subp. 8. **Selection of pipe size.** Pipe sizes may be selected according to the following water pipe sizing procedure except that in no case shall a pipe size be less than shown in part 4715.1730, subpart 2, nor in the case of water service lines, less than specified in part 4715.1710.

The water pipe sizing procedure is based on a system of pressure requirements and losses, the sum of which must not exceed the minimum pressure available at the street main or other source of supply. These pressures are expressed as follows:

A. Pressure required at fixture to produce adequate flow—See part 4715.1770.

B. Static pressure loss—This is computed at 0.43 psi per ft of pipe rise or drop and is added or subtracted respectively.

C. Loss through water meter—Pressure or friction losses for various size meters are shown in subpart 9 or 10.

D. Loss through taps in water main—Losses for various size taps are shown in subpart 12.

E. Losses through special devices such as filters, water softeners, backflow preventers, etc.—These must be obtained from the manufacturer, or estimated and added to the total.

F. Loss through fittings and valves—Losses for these devices are computed by converting the fittings or valves to equivalent straight sections of pipe and adding this length to the total for the pipe section being considered. Subpart 11 shows equivalent lengths of pipe for fittings and valves.

G. Loss due to pipe friction—This loss may be readily computed when the pipe size, its length and the flow through the pipe are known. When these three factors are known the friction loss can be determined from either the tables in subparts 13 and 19 or the figures in subparts 14, 16, 18, and 20. The table and the figure used depends on the type of pipe used. An example of this sizing procedure is given in subpart 21.

Subp. 9. **Loss of pressure through disk-type meters in pounds per square inch.**

Gallons per minute	Size of meter							
	5/8"	3/4"	1"	1 1/2"	2"	3"	4"	6"
4	1.0							
5	1.6							
6	2.2							
7	3.0	1.1						
8	4.0	1.4						
9	5.0	1.7						
10	6.1	2.1						
15	14	5.0	2.0					
20		8.8	3.5	1.0				
30		19	8.0	2.3				
40			14	4.0	1.6			
50			22	6.2	2.4			
60				9.0	3.6			
70				12	4.9	1.3		
80				16	6.2	1.7		
90				20	8.0	2.0		
100					10	2.5	1.0	
120					14	3.7	1.3	
140					20	5.1	2.0	
160						6.2	2.4	
180						8.1	3.3	
200						10	4.0	1.0
250						16	6.1	1.7
300						23	9.0	2.3
350							13.0	3.0
400							16.0	4.0
500							25.0	6.1
600								9.0
700								13
800								16
900								20

Subp. 10. **Graph of loss of pressure through disk-type meters in pounds per square inch.**

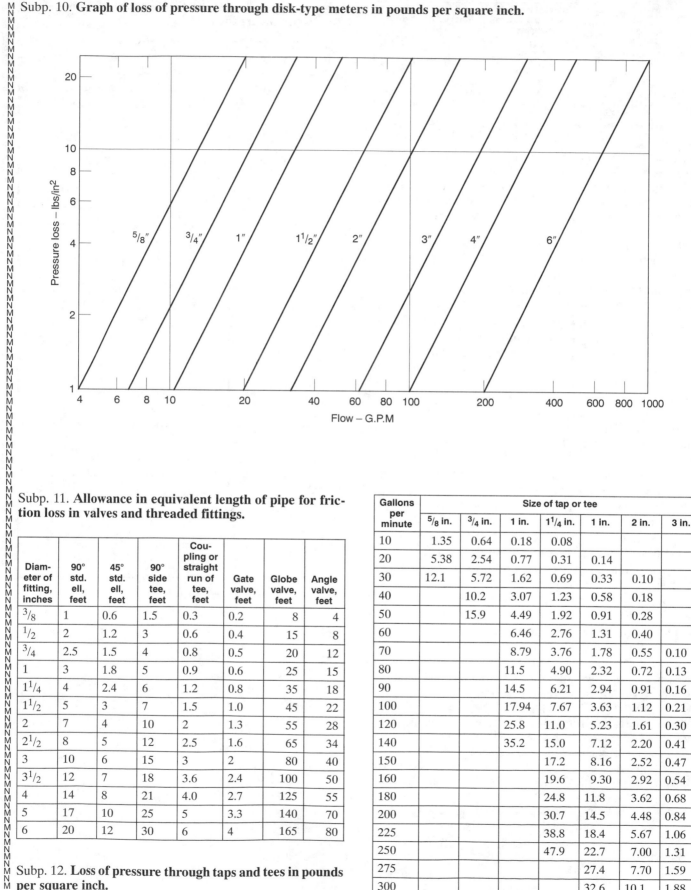

Subp. 11. **Allowance in equivalent length of pipe for friction loss in valves and threaded fittings.**

Diameter of fitting, inches	90° std. ell, feet	45° std. ell, feet	90° side tee, feet	Coupling or straight run of tee, feet	Gate valve, feet	Globe valve, feet	Angle valve, feet
3/8	1	0.6	1.5	0.3	0.2	8	4
1/2	2	1.2	3	0.6	0.4	15	8
3/4	2.5	1.5	4	0.8	0.5	20	12
1	3	1.8	5	0.9	0.6	25	15
1 1/4	4	2.4	6	1.2	0.8	35	18
1 1/2	5	3	7	1.5	1.0	45	22
2	7	4	10	2	1.3	55	28
2 1/2	8	5	12	2.5	1.6	65	34
3	10	6	15	3	2	80	40
3 1/2	12	7	18	3.6	2.4	100	50
4	14	8	21	4.0	2.7	125	55
5	17	10	25	5	3.3	140	70
6	20	12	30	6	4	165	80

Gallons per minute	5/8 in.	3/4 in.	1 in.	1 1/4 in.	1 in.	2 in.	3 in.
10	1.35	0.64	0.18	0.08			
20	5.38	2.54	0.77	0.31	0.14		
30	12.1	5.72	1.62	0.69	0.33	0.10	
40		10.2	3.07	1.23	0.58	0.18	
50		15.9	4.49	1.92	0.91	0.28	
60			6.46	2.76	1.31	0.40	
70			8.79	3.76	1.78	0.55	0.10
80			11.5	4.90	2.32	0.72	0.13
90			14.5	6.21	2.94	0.91	0.16
100			17.94	7.67	3.63	1.12	0.21
120			25.8	11.0	5.23	1.61	0.30
140			35.2	15.0	7.12	2.20	0.41
150				17.2	8.16	2.52	0.47
160				19.6	9.30	2.92	0.54
180				24.8	11.8	3.62	0.68
200				30.7	14.5	4.48	0.84
225				38.8	18.4	5.67	1.06
250				47.9	22.7	7.00	1.31
275					27.4	7.70	1.59
300					32.6	10.1	1.88

Subp. 12. **Loss of pressure through taps and tees in pounds per square inch.**

Subp. 13. Pressure loss of water in pounds per square inch per 100 feet of fairly smooth pipe.

GALLONS PER MINUTE	3/4"	1"	1 1/4"	1 1/2"	2"	2 1/2"	3"	4"	5"	6"	8"	10"	12"
1	0.16												
2	0.57	0.17											
3	1.2	0.37	0.1										
4	2.0	0.61	0.17										
5	3.0	0.95	0.25	0.12									
10	11	3.5	0.9	0.43	0.13								
15	22	7.1	1.8	0.9	0.26	0.11							
20	39[1]	13	3.0	1.5	0.45	0.18							
25	58[2]	18	4.7	2.3	0.68	0.28	0.10						
30		25[1]	6.6	3.2	0.93	0.4	0.13						
35		35[1]	8.5	4.3	1.2	0.53	0.18						
40		43[2]	11	5.5	1.6	0.63	0.22						
45			14	6.7	2.0	0.8	0.3						
50			17[1]	8.1	2.4	1.0	0.35	0.1					
60			23[1]	12	3.3	1.3	0.5	0.13					
70			32[2]	15[1]	4.4	1.8	0.63	0.17					
80				19[1]	5.7	2.3	0.83	0.23					
90				24[1]	7.0	2.9	1.1	0.27					
100				30[1]	8.5	3.7	1.3	0.35	0.12				
150					17[1]	7.8	2.6	0.7	0.23				
200					30[2]	13[1]	4.5[1]	1.2	0.4	0.16			
250						18[2]	6.3	1.8	0.59	0.23			
300							9.0[1]	2.4	0.8	0.34			
350							13[2]	3.3	1.1	0.45	0.12		
400								4.2[1]	1.3	0.59	0.15		
450								5.1[1]	1.7	0.7	0.19		
500								6.2[1]	2.1	0.85	0.23		
600								9.0[1]	2.9	1.2	0.32	0.11	
700									3.9[1]	1.6	0.43	0.14	
800									4.9[1]	2.0	0.56	0.18	
900										2.5[1]	0.69	0.23	
1,000										3.0[1]	0.81	0.28	0.12
1,500										6.5[2]	1.8[1]	0.59	0.24
2,000											3.0[1]	0.98	0.4
2,500											4.5[3]	1.5[1]	0.61
3,000												3.0[1]	0.89

[1] Velocity at or exceeding 10 fps.
[2] Velocity exceeds 15 fps.

M Subp. 14. **Graph of pressure loss of water in pounds per square inch per 100 feet of fairly smooth pipe.**

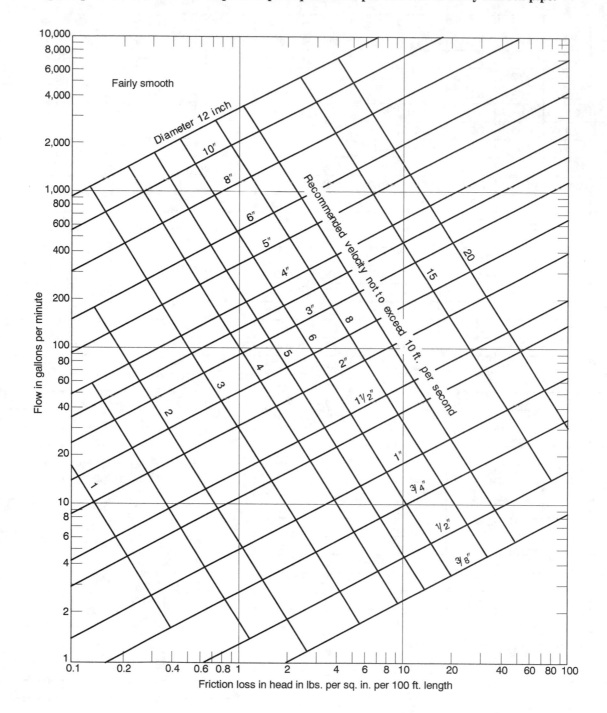

Subp. 15. Pressure loss of water in pounds per square inch per 100 feet of fairly rough pipe.

GALLONS PER MINUTE	3/4"	1"	1 1/4"	1 1/2"	2"	2 1/2"	3"	4"	5"	6"	8"	10"	12"
1	0.26												
2	0.91	0.22											
3	2.0	0.47	0.17										
4	3.3	0.82	0.30	0.12									
5	5.2	1.3	0.45	0.18									
10	20	4.9	1.7	0.67	0.17								
15	43[1]	12	3.7	1.4	0.36	0.12							
20	80[2]	18	6.2	2.5	0.62	0.20							
25		29[1]	9.9	3.9	0.97	0.31	0.13						
30		42[1]	14	5.6	1.3	0.45	0.18						
35		55[1]	18	7.3	1.8	0.60	0.25						
40		70[2]	24[1]	9.3	2.3	0.75	0.32						
45			30[1]	12	3.0	0.96	0.42						
50			37[1]	15	3.7	1.2	0.51	0.12					
60			52[2]	21[1]	5.2	1.7	0.70	0.17					
70				28[1]	7.0	2.2	0.92	0.22					
80				37[1]	9.0	2.9	1.3	0.29	0.10				
90				45[1]	12	3.7	1.5	0.36	0.12				
100					14[1]	4.6	1.8	0.44	0.16				
150					30[2]	10	4.2	1.0	0.34	0.13			
200						17[1]	7.0	1.7	0.59	0.23			
250						26[2]	11[1]	2.6	0.90	0.35			
300							15[1]	3.6	1.3	0.50	0.12		
350							21[2]	4.9	1.7	0.69	0.17		
400								6.1[1]	2.2	0.88	0.22		
450								7.6[1]	2.7	1.1	0.27		
500								9.4[1]	3.3	1.3	0.33	0.11	
600								13[2]	4.9[1]	1.8	0.46	0.15	
700									6.2[1]	2.5	0.61	0.20	
800									8.1[1]	3.3	0.80	0.26	0.11
900									11[1]	4.1[1]	1.0	0.33	0.13
1,000									13[2]	5.0[1]	1.25	0.40	0.17
1,500										12[2]	2.8	0.90	0.37
2,000											4.7[1]	1.6	0.63
2,500											7.2[3]	2.4[1]	1.0
3,000												3.4[1]	1.3

[1]Velocity at or exceeding 10 fps.

[2]Velocity exceeds 15 fps.

Subp. 16. **Graph of pressure loss of water in pounds per square inch per 100 feet of fairly rough pipe.**

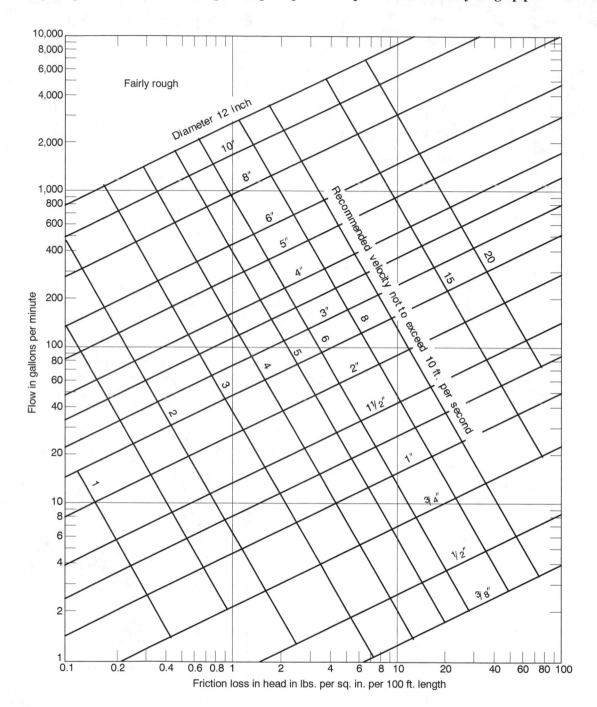

Subp. 17. Pressure loss of water in pounds per square inch per 100 feet of rough pipe.

GALLONS PER MINUTE	3/4"	1"	1 1/4"	1 1/2"	2"	2 1/2"	3"	4"	5"	6"	8"	10"	12"
1	0.31												
2	1.20	0.27											
3	2.7	0.62	0.20										
4	4.7	1.2	0.36	0.15									
5	6.0	1.4	0.46	0.18									
10	30	7.0	2.3	0.94	0.22								
15	67[1]	16.0	6.2	2.1	0.49	0.17							
20		27	9.1	3.7	0.89	0.29	0.12						
25		43[1]	14	5.8	1.3	0.45	0.18						
30		62[1]	21	8.5	2.0	0.63	0.27						
35		85[1]	28	12	2.7	0.90	0.36						
40			37[1]	14	3.5	1.20	0.47	0.12					
45			47[1]	19	4.5	1.45	0.60	0.14					
50			58[1]	23	5.5	1.8	0.74	0.18					
60			83[2]	33[1]	7.9	2.6	1.10	0.25					
70				46[1]	12	3.5	1.40	0.35	0.12				
80				60[1]	14	4.7	1.85	0.43	0.15				
90				76[1]	18	5.9	2.3	0.58	0.19				
100					23[1]	7.2	3.0	0.71	0.23				
150					50[2]	17	6.6	1.7	0.53	0.21			
200						29[1]	12	2.9	0.95	0.37			
250						45[2]	18[1]	4.5	1.49	0.58	0.13		
300							26[1]	6.4	2.20	0.80	0.19		
350							36[2]	8.9	2.9	1.20	0.27		
400								12[1]	3.8	1.45	0.35	0.12	
450								15[1]	4.7	1.8	0.44	0.14	
500								18[1]	6.0	2.3	0.55	0.18	
600								25[2]	8.3	3.2	0.78	0.26	0.11
700									12[1]	4.5	1.20	0.36	0.14
800									16[1]	6.0	1.4	0.47	0.19
900									20[1]	7.7[1]	1.8	0.60	0.24
1,000										8.4[1]	2.3	0.75	0.31
1,500										22[2]	5.1	1.7	0.70
2,000											9.0[1]	3.0	1.25
2,500											14[3]	4.7[1]	2.0
3,000												6.8[1]	2.7

[1] Velocity at or exceeding 10 fps.

[2] Velocity exceeds 15 fps.

Subp. 18. **Pressure loss of water in pounds per square inch per 100 feet of rough pipe.**

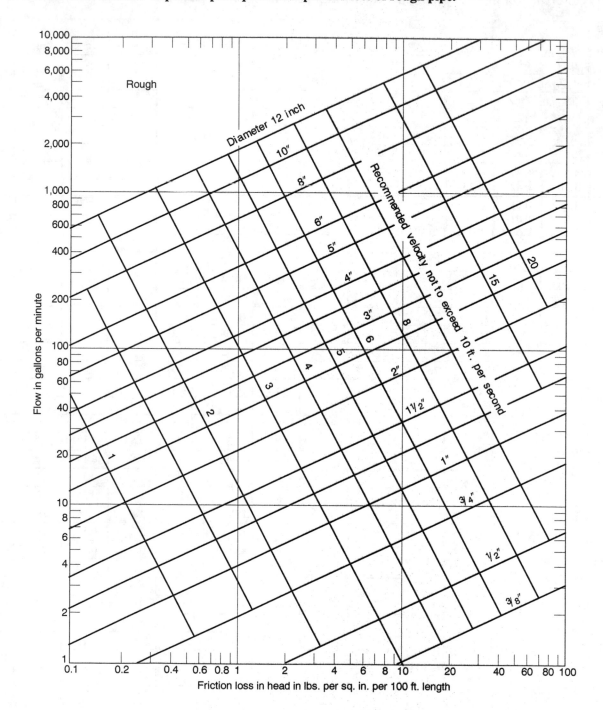

Subp. 19. Pressure loss of water in pounds per square inch per 100 feet of copper pipe.

GALLONS PER MINUTE	3/4"[1]	1"[1]	1¹/₄"	1¹/₂"	2"	2¹/₂"	3"	4"	5"	6"	8"	10"	12"
1	0.17 0.21 0.27												
2	0.56 0.66 0.84	0.16 0.18 0.21											
3	1.15 1.30 1.70	0.31 0.37 0.42	0.13										
4	1.8 2.2 2.8	0.51 0.61 0.69	0.22	0.10									
5	2.7 3.3 4.2	0.76 0.90 1.05	0.34	0.15									
6	3.8 4.5 5.7	1.1 1.25 1.4	0.47	0.21									
7	5.0 6.0 7.5	1.4 1.7 1.8	0.61	0.27									
8	6.1 7.2 9.6	1.7 2.1 2.4	0.68	0.33									
9	7.6 8.9 12	2.2 2.5 2.8	0.93	0.42	0.12								
10	9.1 11.5 14.5	2.6 3.0 3.5	1.2	0.50	0.14								
15	18.5 23[3] 28[3]	5.2 6.1 7.1	2.4	1.10	0.27								
20	32[2] 37[2] 45[3]	8.9 9.9 12	3.8	1.70	0.44	0.16							
25	46[3] 53[2] 67[2]	13 15 17[3]	5.8	2.5	0.68	0.23							
30		18[2] 21[2] 24[2]	8.0	3.5	0.91	0.32	0.13						
35		24[2] 27[2] 32[2]	11	4.6	1.25	0.42	0.17						
40		30[3] 33[3] 38[3]	13[3]	5.8	1.50	0.52	0.22						
45		37[3] 43[3] 48[3]	17[3]	7.1	1.85	0.66	0.28						
50			19[2]	8.7	2.3	0.79	0.33						
60			27[3]	12	3.1	1.2	0.46	0.12					

(continued)

Subp. 19. **Pressure loss of water in pounds per square inch per 100 feet of copper pipe.—continued**

GALLONS PER MINUTE	3/4"[1]	1"[1]	1 1/4"	1 1/2"	2"	2 1/2"	3"	4"	5"	6"	8"	10"	12"
70				16^3	4.2	1.4	0.62	0.16					
80				19^2	5.2	1.8	0.79	0.20					
90				24^3	6.2	2.25	0.96	0.24					
100					7.6^3	2.75	1.2	0.30	0.11				
150					17^3	5.8^3	2.5	0.62	0.22				
200						9.3^3	4.1	1.10	0.36	0.15			
250						14^3	6.1^2	1.60	0.52	0.22			
300							8.4^3	2.1	0.72	0.31			
350							12^3	2.8	0.98	0.41			
400								3.5	1.25	0.52			
450								4.3^3	1.6	0.63			
500								5.2^3	1.8	0.76			
600								7.2^3	2.7^3	1.15			
700									3.4^3	1.4			
800									4.4^3	1.8			
900									5.2^3	2.2^3			
1,000										2.7^3			

[1]For the 3/4" and 1" pipe sizes the three values shown opposite each flow figures are, reading from the top, for Types M, L and K copper tubing respectively.
[2]Velocity at or exceeding 10 fps.
[3]Velocity exceeds 15 fps.

Subp. 20. **Graph of pressure loss of water in pounds per square inch per 100 feet of copper pipe.**

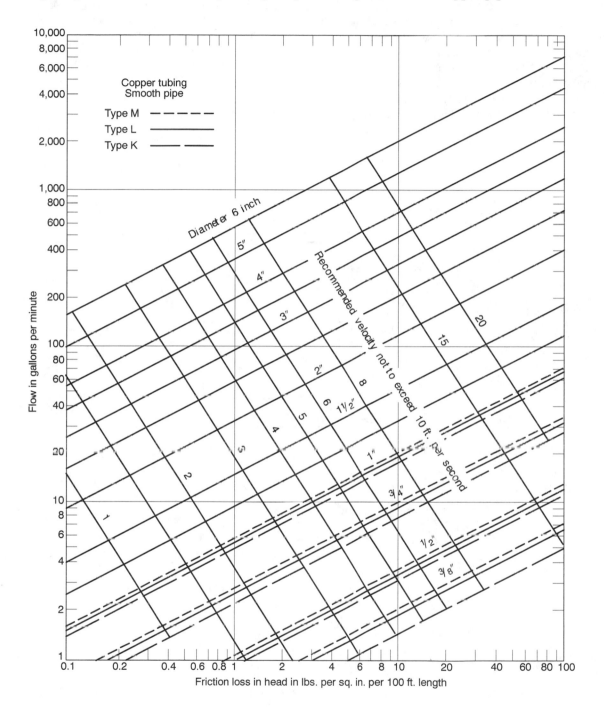

Subp. 21. Example. What size copper water pipe, service and distribution will be required to serve a two story factory building having on each floor, back-to-back, two toilet rooms each equipped with four flushometer closets, two flushometer pedestal urinals and four lavatories with hot and cold water? The highest fixture is 21 feet above the street main which is tapped with $2^1/_2$ inch corporation at which point the minimum pressure is 55 psi. In the building basement a two-inch meter and three-inch reduced pressure zone backflow preventer with a maximum pressure drop of 9 psi are to be installed. The system is shown by the following diagram. To be determined are the pipe sizes for the service main, and the cold and hot water distribution pipes. A tabular arrangement such as shown in subpart 10 should first be constructed. The steps to be followed in solving the problem are indicated by the table itself as they are in sequence, columns 1 through 8 and lines a through 1.

Subp. 22. Illustration.

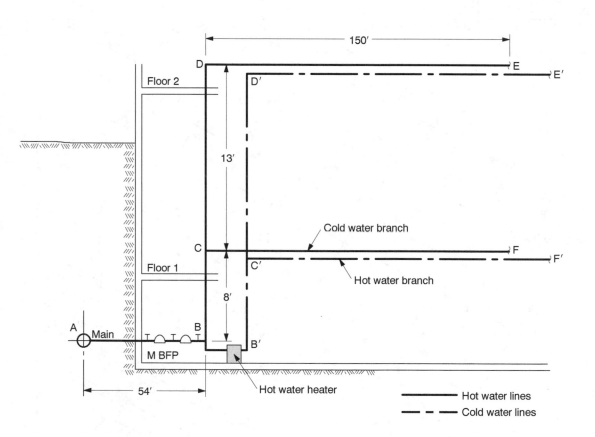

Subp. 23. **Recommended tabular arrangement for use in solving pipe sizing problems.**

	LINE	DESCRIPTION	LBS. PER SQUARE INCH psi
SERVICE AND COLD WATER DISTRIBUTION PIPING	a	Minimum pressure available at main	55.00
	b	Highest pressure required at a fixture (part 4715.1770, subpart 2)	15.00
	c	Meter loss 2″ meter (subpart 9)	11.00
	d	Tap in main-loss 2$^1/_2$″ tap (subpart 12)	1.29
	e	Static head loss 21 × 0.43 psi	9.03
	f	Special fixture loss—backflow preventer	9.00
	g	Special fixture loss—filter	0.00
	h	Special fixture loss—other	0.00
	i	**Total overall losses and requirements, sum of lines b through h**	45.32
	j	**Pressure available to overcome pipe friction, line a minus sum of lines b to h**	9.68

1	2	3	4	5	6	7	8	
PIPE SECTION	GAL. PER MIN. THROUGH SECTION (DETERMINED AS IN SUBPART 3)	LENGTH OF SECTION (ft.)	TRIAL PIPE SIZE (in.)	EQUIVALENT LENGTH OF FITTINGS AND VALVES (SUBPART 11)	TOTAL EQUIVALENT LENGTH COL. 3 AND COL. 5 (100 ft.)	FRICTION LOSS PER 100′ OF TRIAL SIZE PIPE (SUBPART 19)	FRICTION LOSS IN EQUIVALENT LENGTH COL. 6 × COL. 7 (psi)	
AB	107	54	2$^1/_2$	12.8	0.67	3.0	2.00	
BC	101	8	2$^1/_2$	8	0.16	2.8	0.45	
CF	76	150	2$^1/_2$	1.6	1.52	1.7	2.58	
CD	76	13	2$^1/_2$	8	0.21	1.7	0.36	
DE	76	150	2$^1/_2$	1.6	1.52	1.7	2.58	
	k	**Total pipe friction losses (cold) 7.97 psi**						7.97
	l	**Difference line j minus line k**						1.71
HOT WATER DISTRIBUTION PIPING								
AB′	107	54	2$^1/_2$	12.8	0.67	3.0	2.00	
B′C′	37	8	2	15.3	0.23	1.2	0.22	
C′F′	28	150	2	1.3	1.51	0.8	1.21	
C′D′	28	13	1$^1/_2$	5	0.18	3.2	0.58	
D′E′	28	150	1$^1/_2$	1.0	1.51	3.2	4.84	
	k	**Total pipe friction losses (hot) 8.85 psi**						8.85
	l	**Difference line j minus line k**						0.83

Subp. 24. **Directions for constructing tabular arrangement.** Step 1, column 1: divide the system into sections breaking at major changes in elevation or where branches lead to fixture groups. After point (B) (see sketch in subpart 22) separate consideration will be given to the hot and cold water piping. Enter the sections to be considered in the service and cold water piping in column 1 of the tabular arrangement.

Column 3: according to the method given in subpart 3 determine the GPM of flow to be expected in each section of the system. These flows range from 28 to 107 GPM.

Step 2, line a: enter the minimum pressure available at the main source of supply. This is 55 psi.

Line b: determine from part 4715.1770, subpart 2 the highest pressure required for the fixtures on the system, which is 15 psi to operate a flushometer valve.

Line c: select from subpart 9 the pressure loss for the meter size given or assumed. The total water flow from the main through the service as determined in step 1 will serve to aid in the meter selected.

Line d: select from subpart 12 and enter the pressure loss for the tap size given or assumed.

Line e: determine the difference in elevation between the main or source of supply and the highest fixture on the system and multiply this figure, expressed in feet, by 0.43 psi. Enter the resulting psi product on line e.

Line f, g, h: the pressure losses through filters, backflow preventers, or other special fixtures must be obtained from the manufacturer or estimated and entered on these lines.

Step 4, line i: the sum of (lines b through h) the pressure requirements and losses which affect the overall system is entered on this line.

Step 5, line j: subtract line i from line a. This gives the pressure which remains available for overcoming friction losses in the system. This figure is a guide to the pipe size which is chosen for each section as the total friction losses through all the sections should not exceed this value.

Step 5, line j: subtract line i from line a. This gives the pressure which remains available for overcoming friction losses in the system. This figure is a guide to the pipe size which is chosen for each section as the total friction losses through all the sections should not exceed this value.

Step 6, column 3: enter the length of each section.

Step 7, column 4: select a trial pipe size. A rule of thumb is that size will become progressively smaller as the system extends farther from the main or source of supply.

Step 8, column 5: select from subpart 11 the equivalent lengths for the trial pipe size of fittings and valves on the section. Enter the sum for each section in column 5. (The number of fittings to be used in the installation of this piping must be an engineering estimate.)

Step 9, column 6: add the figures from column 3 and column 5, and enter in column 6. Express the sum in hundreds of feet.

Step 10, column 7: select from subpart 19 the friction loss per 100 feet of pipe for the GPM flow in a section (column 2) and the trial pipe size (column 4).

Step 11, column 8: multiply the figures in columns 6 and 7 for each section and enter in column 8.

Step 12, line k: enter the sum of the values in column 8.

Step 13, line l: subtract line k from line j. The result should always be a positive or plus figure. If it is not, it is necessary to repeat the operation utilizing columns 4, 5, 7 and 8 until a balance or near balance is obtained. If the difference between lines j and k is positive and large, it is an indication that the pipe sizes are too large and may, therefore, be reduced thus saving materials. In such a case the operations utilizing columns 4, 5, 7, and 8 should again be repeated.

Answer: the final figures entered in column 4 become the design pipe size for the respective sections. Repeating this operation a second time using the same sketch but considering the demand for hot water, it is possible to size the hot water distribution piping. This has been worked up as a part of the overall problem in the tabular arrangement used for sizing the service and cold water distribution piping. It should be noted that consideration must be given the pressure losses from the street main to the water heater (section AB) in determining the hot water pipe sizes.

4715.3800
RECOMMENDED GUIDE FOR SIZING WATER SUPPLY SYSTEM

Subpart 1. Conditions to be determined. On any proposed water piping installation sized pursuant to subpart 9, the following conditions shall be determined:

A. Total number of fixture units as determined from the table of equivalent fixture units (subpart 8) for the fixtures to be installed.

B. Developed length of supply pipe from meter to most remote outlet, or if the pressure at the meter is unknown, use the developed length from the street main to most remote outlet.

C. Difference in elevation between the meter or other source of supply and the highest fixture or outlet.

D. Pressure in the street main or other source of supply at the locality where the installation is to be made. Calculations shall be based on not to exceed 100 psi pressure in the system.

E. In localities where there is a wide fluctuation of pressure in the main throughout the day, the water piping systems shall be designed on the basis of the minimum pressure available.

Subp. 2. Size of street service, meter and building supply pipe using subpart 9. Knowing the available pressure at the water meter, water main, or other source of supply, and after subtracting one-half pound per square inch pressure for each foot of difference in elevation between such source of supply and the highest water supply outlet in the building or on the premises, use the "pressure range" group within which this pressure will fall. Select the "length" column which is equal to or longer than the required length. Follow down the column to a fixture unit value equal to or greater than the total number of fixture units required by the installation. Having located the proper fixture unit value for the required length, sizes of meter and building supply pipe will be found in the two left-hand columns.

Subp. 3. Size of branches. The size of each branch shall be determined by the number of fixture units to be served by that branch, following the methods in subpart 2.

Subp. 4. Sizing for flushometer valves. Branches and mains serving water closet or similar flushometer valves may be sized from subpart 9 when the following values are assigned to each flushometer valve beginning with the most remote valve on each branch:

A. For the first flushometer valve, 40 fixture units;

B. For the second flushometer valve, 30 fixture units;

C. For the third flushometer valve, 20 fixture units;

D. For the fourth flushometer valve, 15 fixture units; and

E. For the fifth flushometer valve, ten fixture units.

After the fifth valve on any branch, subsequent loadings may be computed using the values given in subpart 8 of this chapter. Piping supplying a flushometer valve shall not be less in size than the valve inlet.

Subp. 5. Hot water sizing. In sizing the hot water piping or water supply systems from subpart 9, the greatest developed length of the cold water supply piping may be used and the length of the hot water piping ignored when the hot water piping friction loss is compensated for by the following method:

A. Compute the total hot water fixture unit demand, using those values given in subpart 8 for the combined hot and cold water use.

B. Assign the total demand computed as required in item A, as the fixture unit demand at the hot water heater supply branch and inlet.

Subp. 6. Cold water piping. Starting at the most remote outlet on the cold water piping and working back toward the water meter, compute the pipe sizing for the system from the column originally selected in subpart 9, using the fixture unit values given in subpart 8, and adding in the fixture unit demand of the hot water heater supply inlet as computed in subpart 5, at the point where it occurs. The final size of the cold water main need not be larger than the originally established size required by subpart 9 for the total building supply.

Subp. 7. Hot water piping. Starting at the most remote outlets on the hot water piping and working back toward the water heater, compute the pipe sizing for the system from the column originally selected in subpart 9, using the fixture unit values given in subpart 8.

Subp. 8. Equivalent fixture units, including combined hot and cold water demand.

Fixture	Number of Private Use	Fixture Unit Public Use
Bar sink	1	2
Bathtub (with or without shower over)	2	4
Dental unit or cuspidor	—	1
Drinking fountain (each head)	—	1
Hose Bibb of sill cock (standard type)	3	5
House trailer (each)	6	6
Laundry tub or clothes washer (each pair of faucets)	2	4
Service sink	—	4
Lavatory	1	2
Lavatory (dental)	1	1
Lawn sprinklers (standard type, each head)	1	1

(continued)

Fixture	Number of Private Use	Fixture Unit Public Use
Shower (each head)	2	4
Sink (bar)	1	2
Sink or dishwasher	2	4
Sink (flushing rim, clinic)	—	10
Sink (washup, each set of faucets)	—	2
Sink (washup, circular spray)	—	4
Urinal (pedestal or similar type)	—	10
Urinal (stall)	—	5
Urinal (wall)	—	5
Urinal (flush tank)	—	3
Water closet (flush tank)	3	5
Water closet (flushometer valve)	—	10

Water supply outlets for items not listed above shall be computed at their maximum demand, but in no case less than:

$3/8$ inch	1	2
$1/2$ inch	2	4
$3/4$ inch	3	6
1 inch	6	10

* See subpart 4 for method of sizing flushometer valve installations using this subpart.

Subp. 9. Fixture unit table for determining water pipe and meter sizes for water supply systems.

Pressure Range — 30 TO 45 psi											
Meter and Street Service	Building Supply and Branches	Maximum allowable length in feet									
		40	60	80	100	150	200	250	300	400	500
$3/4''$	$1/2''$	6	5	4	4	3	2	—	—	—	—
$3/4''$	$3/4''$	18	16	14	12	9	6	—	—	—	—
$3/4''$	$1''$	29	25	23	21	17	15	13	12	10	9
$1''$	$1''$	36	31	27	25	20	17	15	13	12	10
$1''$	$1^1/4''$	54	47	42	38	32	28	25	23	19	17
$1^1/2''$	$1^1/4''$	90	68	57	48	38	32	28	25	21	19
$1^1/2''$	$1^1/2''$	151	124	105	91	70	57	49	45	36	31
$2''$	$1^1/2''$	210	162	132	110	80	64	53	46	38	32
$1^1/2''$	$2''$	220	205	190	176	155	138	127	120	105	96
$2''$	$2''$	372	329	292	265	217	185	164	147	124	107
$2''$	$2^1/2''$	445	418	390	370	330	300	280	265	240	220
Pressure Range — 46 TO 60 psi											
$3/4''$	$1/2''$	9	8	7	6	5	4	3	2	—	—
$3/4''$	$3/4''$	27	23	19	17	14	11	9	8	6	5
$3/4''$	$1''$	44	40	36	33	28	23	21	19	17	14
$1''$	$1''$	60	47	41	36	30	25	23	20	18	15
$1''$	$1^1/4''$	102	87	76	67	52	44	39	36	30	27
$1^1/2''$	$1^1/4''$	168	130	106	89	66	52	44	39	33	29
$1^1/2''$	$1^1/2''$	270	225	193	167	128	105	90	68	62	52
$2''$	$1^1/2''$	360	290	242	204	150	117	98	84	67	55
$1^1/2''$	$2''$	380	360	340	318	272	240	220	198	170	146
$2''$	$2''$	570	510	470	430	368	318	280	250	205	173
$2''$	$2^1/2''$	680	640	610	580	535	500	470	440	400	365

(continued)

Subp. 9. Fixture unit table for determining water pipe and meter sizes for water supply systems.—continued

Meter and Street Service	Building Supply and Branches	Maximum allowable length in feet									
Pressure Range — 30 TO 45 psi		40	60	80	100	150	200	250	300	400	500
Pressure Range — Over 60 psi											
$3/4''$	$1/2''$	11	9	8	7	6	5	4	3	2	—
$3/4''$	$3/4''$	34	28	24	22	17	13	11	10	8	—
$3/4''$	$1''$	63	53	47	42	35	30	27	24	21	18
$1''$	$1''$	87	66	55	48	38	32	29	26	22	19
$1''$	$1 1/4''$	140	126	108	96	74	62	53	47	39	34
$1 1/2''$	$1 1/4''$	237	183	150	127	93	74	62	54	43	37
$1 1/2''$	$1 1/2''$	366	311	273	240	186	154	130	113	88	73
$2''$	$1 1/2''$	490	395	333	275	220	170	142	122	98	82
$1 1/2''$	$2''$	380*	380*	380*	380*	370	335	305	282	244	212
$2''$	$2''$	690*	670	610	560	478	420	375	340	288	245
$2''$	$2 1/2''$	690*	690*	690*	690*	690*	650	610	570	510	460

*Maximum Allowable Load on Meter

Subp. 10. See repealer.

Subp. 10a. Example of cold water sizing using subpart 9.

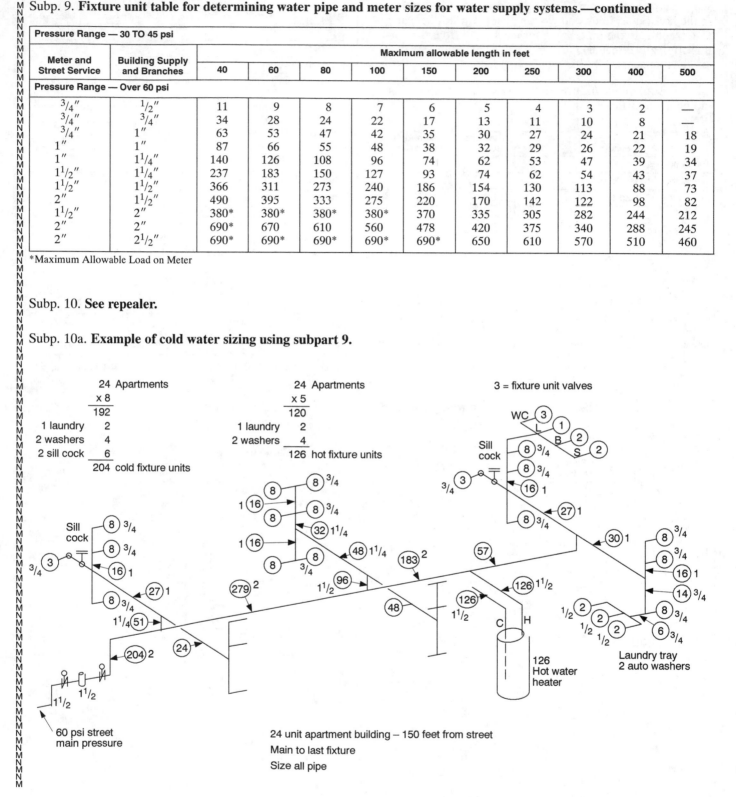

24 Apartments
x 8
192

1 laundry 2
2 washers 4
2 sill cock 6
204 cold fixture units

24 Apartments
x 5
120

1 laundry 2
2 washers 4
126 hot fixture units

3 = fixture unit valves

60 psi street main pressure

24 unit apartment building – 150 feet from street
Main to last fixture
Size all pipe

126 Hot water heater

Laundry tray 2 auto washers

Subp. 11. **See repealer.**

Subp. 11a. **Example of hot water sizing using subpart 9.**

```
   24  Apartments
   x 5
   ____
   120
1 laundry    2
2 washers    4
   ____
   126  hot water fixture units
```

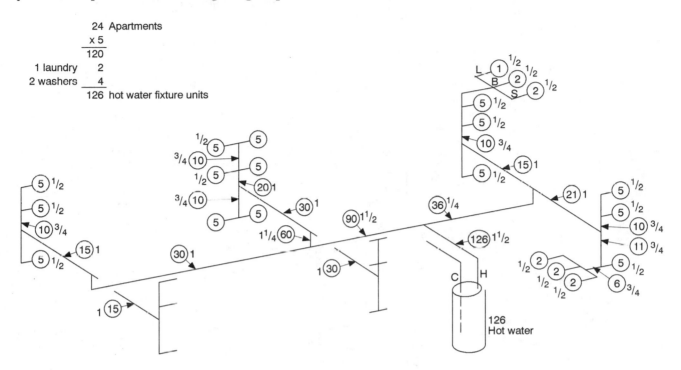

24 unit apartment building – 150 feet from street
Main to last cold water outlet
Size all hot water pipe

REPEALER. Minnesota Rules, parts 4715.2650, subpart 3; and 4715.3800, subparts 10 and 11, are repealed.

EFFECTIVE DATE. These rules are effective 60 days after the notice of adoption is published in the State Register.

4715.4100
USEFUL INFORMATION

Subpart 1. **Weights and measures.**

Commercial Weights

16 drams or 437.5 grains	=	1 ounce
16 ounces or 7000 grains	=	1 pound
16 ounces	=	1 pound
2000 pounds	=	1 ton

Square Measure

144 square inches	=	1 sq. foot
9 square feet	=	1 sq. yard
$30^1/_4$ square yards	=	1 sq. rod
$272^1/_4$ square feet	=	1 sq. rod
43,560 square feet	=	1 acre

Cubic Measure

231 cubic inches	=	1 gallon
1728 cubic inches	=	1 cu. ft.
27 cubic feet	=	1 cu. yd.

Long Measure

12 inches	=	1 foot
3 feet	=	1 yard
$16^1/_2$ feet	=	1 rod
320 rods	=	1 mile
5280 feet	=	1 mile

Liquid Measure

4 gills	=	1 pint
2 pints	=	1 quart
4 quarts	=	1 gallon
$31^1/_2$ gallons	=	1 U.S. barrel

Water Pressure

To find the pressure in pounds per square inch corresponding to any head in feet, multiply the head by 0.434.

To find the head in feet when the pressure in pounds per square inch is known, multiply the pressure by 2.3.

One pound pressure per square inch is caused by 2.3 feet head of water.

Subp. 2. Pressure and head equivalents. Table based on water at 62.5 pounds per cubic foot.

Head (feet)	Pressure (pounds per square inch)	Head (feet)	Pressure (pounds per square inch)
2.304	1	1	0.434
4.608	2	2	0.868
6.912	3	3	1.302
9.216	4	4	1.736
11.520	5	5	2.170
13.824	6	6	2.604
16.128	7	7	3.038
18.432	8	8	3.472
20.736	9	9	3.906
23.040	10	10	4.340

Subp. 3. Water pressure. Example: What pressure in pounds per square inch corresponds to a head of 123′-6″?

$$123'-6'' = 123.5' \text{ (See table III)}$$

From table I (right half)

120′	=	12x10	=	12x4.34	=	52.08
3′	=	1x3	=	1x1.302	=	1.302
.5′	=	.5x1	=	.5x.434	=	.217

53.599 lbs/sq. in. (Ans.)

Example: How many feet of head is equivalent to a pressure of 28 pounds per square inch?

From table I (left half)

20	=	10x2	=	10x4.608 =	46.08
8	=	1x8	=	1x18.432 =	18.432

64.512′ or 64′-6″ (Ans.)

Subp. 4. Effect of variations of temperatures on water. Water freezes at 32 degrees Fahrenheit. Water boils at 212 degrees Fahrenheit. Water expands when freezing to about one and one-twelfth of its bulk. Fifteen hundred and ninety-five cubic inches of water will expand in freezing to one cubic foot of ice, which weighs approximately 57.5 pounds.

Water freezing in a pipe or closed vessel exerts a pressure of approximately 2,000 pounds per square inch which is the force that causes pipes to burst.

Subp. 5. Changing common fractions into decimals. In several computations used in plumbing work it is desirable to convert fractions into decimals and decimals into fractions in order to facilitate computations and measurements.

A. Example: Change 1/8 to decimals of an inch.

$$^{1}/_{8} = 8)\overline{1.000} = .125 \text{ (Ans.)}$$

B. Example: Change .3125 to closest 1/16 of an inch.

$$^{1}/_{16} = .0625$$

.0625).3125 = 5 hence 5/16 (Ans.)

C. Example: Change 2″ into decimals of a foot.

$$2'' = 2/12 = 2x1/12 = 2x.08333 = .16667 \text{ (Ans.)}$$

Subp. 6. Decimal equivalents of common fractions in inches.

Fraction	Decimal	Fraction	Decimal
$^{1}/_{32}$	0.03125	$^{17}/_{32}$	0.53125
$^{1}/_{16}$	.0625	$^{9}/_{16}$	.5625
$^{3}/_{32}$	.09375	$^{19}/_{32}$	.59375
$^{1}/_{8}$	.125	$^{5}/_{8}$	.625
$^{5}/_{32}$	.15625	$^{21}/_{32}$	.65625
$^{3}/_{16}$	.1875	$^{11}/_{16}$	.6875
$^{7}/_{32}$	.21875	$^{23}/_{32}$	.71875
$^{1}/_{4}$	.25	$^{3}/_{4}$	.75
$^{9}/_{32}$	.28125	$^{25}/_{32}$	.78125
$^{5}/_{16}$	.3125	$^{13}/_{16}$	.8125
$^{11}/_{32}$	.34375	$^{27}/_{32}$	.84375
$^{3}/_{8}$	.375	$^{7}/_{8}$	.875
$^{13}/_{32}$	.40625	$^{29}/_{32}$	.90625
$^{7}/_{16}$	.4375	$^{15}/_{16}$	.9375
$^{15}/_{32}$	.46875	$^{31}/_{32}$	.96875
$^{1}/_{2}$	.5	1	1.0

Subp. 7. Decimal equivalents of inches in feet.

Inches	Decimal
1	0.08333
2	0.16667
3	0.25000
4	0.33333
5	0.41667
6	0.5000
7	0.58331
8	0.66667
9	0.75
10	0.83333
11	0.91666
12	1.00

Subp. 8. **Geometric calculations.**

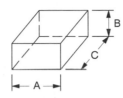

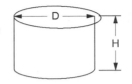

Circle
D = diameter
r   = radius
C = circumference
Area = 3.1416 × r²
Area = 0.7854 × D²
C = 3.1416 × D
D = 0.31831 × C

Sphere
Area = 3.1416 × D²
Volume = 0.5236 × D²

Square or oblong tank
Volume = A × B × C

Cylindrical tank
Volume = 0.7854 × D² × H

Subp. 9. **Diameter, area, circumference, and volume.**

Diameter (inches)	Area (sq. inch)	Circumference (inches)	Volume (gal. per ft.)
¹/₂	0.19635	1.5708	0.010
⁵/₈	0.30680	1.9635	.016
³/₄	0.44179	2.3562	.023
1	0.7854	3.1416	.041
1¹/₄	1.22719	3.9270	.064
1¹/₂	1.76715	4.71240	.092
2	3.1416	6.2832	.163
2¹/₂	4.90875	7.8540	.255
3	7.0686	9.4248	.367
4	12.5664	12.5664	.652
5	19.6350	15.7080	1.020
6	28.2744	18.8496	1.470
8	50.2656	25.1328	2.610
10	78.5400	31.4160	4.080
12	113.0976	37.6992	5.870

A. Example: What is the area of a pipe in square inches having a diameter of six inches?

$$(A = Pi/4 \times D^2) \quad A = 0.7854 \times D^2$$

$$A = 0.7854 \times 6 \times 6 = 28.27 \text{ sq. in. (Ans.)}$$

B. Example: What is the diameter in inches of a pipe having a circumference of approximately 15³/₄ inches?

$$(D = C \times 1/Pi) \quad D = C \times 0.31831$$

$$D = 15.75 \times 0.31831 = 5 \text{ inches (Ans.)}$$

C. Example: What is the volume of a tank in cubic feet and gallons having a length of eight feet, a width of four feet, and a depth of six feet?

$$V = 8' \times 4' \times 6' = 192 \text{ cubic feet (Ans.)}$$

$$1 \text{ cu. ft.} = 7^1/_2 \text{ gallons}$$

$$V = 192 \times 7.5 = 1440 \text{ gallons (Ans.)}$$

D. Example: What is the volume of a tank in cubic feet and gallons having a diameter of 18 inches and a height of 4 feet?

$$V = 0.7854 \times D^2 \times H$$

$$= 0.7854 \times 1.5' \times 1.5' \times 4' = 7.0686 \text{ cubic feet (Ans.)}$$

$$V = 7.0686 = 53.01 \text{ gallons (Ans.)}$$

Doubling the diameter of a pipe increases its area four times.

Doubling the diameter of a pipe increases its volume four times per unit of length.

The side of a square equal in area to a given circle equals diameter × 0.8862.

A gallon of water (U.S. standard) weighs 8¹/₃ lbs.

A cubic foot of water contains 7¹/₂ gallons, 1728 cubic inches and weighs 62¹/₂ pounds.

Subp. 10. **Illustration of measurements.**

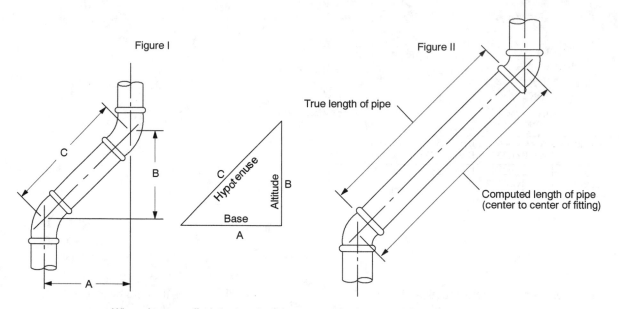

Figure I

Figure II

True length of pipe

Computed length of pipe
(center to center of fitting)

C

B

A

C

Hypotenuse

Altitude

B

Base

A

When pipes are offset, the length of the connecting pipe may be figured, when the angle of the fitting is known and one of the dimensions A, B, or C is known.

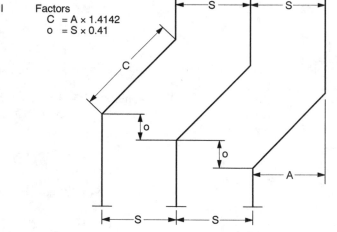

Figure III

Factors
C = A × 1.4142
o = S × 0.41

C

o

o

S

S

A

S

S

Subp. 11. **Pipe fitting angle calculations.**

Fittings		A	B	C
$^1/_{64}$ bend	$5^5/_8$ degrees	A = Cx.098 A = Bx.0985	B = Cx.9952 B = Ax10.1532	C = Bx1.005 C = Ax10.204
$^1/_{32}$ bend	$11^1/_4$ degrees	A = Cx.195 A = Bx.1989	B = Cx.981 B = Ax5.0273	C = Bx1.019 C = Ax5.1258
$^1/_{16}$ bend	$22^1/_2$ degrees	A = Cx.3827 A = Bx.4142	B = Cx.9239 B = Ax2.4142	C = Bx1.0823 C = Ax2.6131
$^1/_{12}$ bend	30 degrees	A = Cx.5 A = Bx.5774	B = Cx.866 B = Ax1.7321	C = Bx1.1547 C = Ax2.00
$^1/_8$ bend	45 degrees	A = Cx.7071 A = B	B = Cx.7071 B = A	C = Bx1.4142 C = Ax1.4142
$^1/_6$ bend	60 degrees	A = Cx.866 A = Bx1.732	B = Cx.5 B = Ax.5774	C = Bx2.0 C = Ax1.1547
$^3/_{16}$ bend	$67^1/_2$ degrees	A = Cx.9239 A = Bx2.4142	B = Cx.3827 B = Ax.4142	C = Bx2.6131 C = Ax1.0923
$^1/_5$ bend	72 degrees	A = Cx.951 A = Bx3.0777	B = Cx.309 B = Ax.325	C = Bx.324 C = Ax1.0514

When the figures from this table are used, it will be necessary to allow for the distance taken up by the fittings. (See Fig. II, in subpart 10.)

Examples:

A. What is the length of pipe center to center of 45 degree elbows, with an offset of 22 inches?

From table V under 45 degree fittings

C = A x 1.4142

C = 22 x 1.4142 = 31.1124 inches

$31.1124' = 2' \ 7^1/_8''$ (Ans.)

B. What is the length of pipe center to center of 60 degree fittings, with an offset of 2' 8"?

From table V under 60 degree fittings

C = A x 1.1547

C = 32 x 1.1547 = 36.9504 inches

$36.9504'' = 3' \ ^{15}/_{16}''$ (Ans.)

4715.5000
SCOPE AND APPLICABILITY

Parts 4715.5000 to 4715.6000 prescribe minimum standards and procedures for all water conditioning installations and servicing in single-family dwellings. Any person who installs or services water conditioning equipment, whether or not such person is licensed pursuant to Minnesota Statutes 1978, sections 328.57 to 328.66, must comply with the standards and procedures prescribed in parts 4715.5000 to 4715.6000, and with the applicable provisions of the current version of the Minnesota Plumbing Code, parts 4715.0100 to 4715.2860.

4715.5100
DEFINITIONS

Subpart 1. **Commissioner.** "Commissioner" means the commissioner of health.

Subp. 2. **Disinfect.** "Disinfect" means to destroy pathogenic bacteria and other harmful organisms.

Subp. 3. **Installation.** "Installation" as defined in Minnesota Statutes 1978, section 326.61, subdivision 1 includes:

A. The connection of any water conditioning equipment to an existing water distribution system;

B. The connection of the line carrying conditioned water to a water distribution system, or raw water to points not needing conditioned water;

C. The connecting of drain and overflow lines which drain the equipment; and

D. The providing of an air gap between the drain and overflow lines and the receiving building receptor.

Subp. 4. **Raw water.** "Raw water" means water which has not passed through any water conditioning equipment.

Subp. 5. **Receptor.** "Receptor" means an open, accessible, individual waste sink, floor drain, or other fixture which is trapped and vented in accordance with the Minnesota Plumbing Code (parts 4715.0100 to 4715.2860).

Subp. 6. **Servicing.** "Servicing" means repairs or adjustments to any water conditioning installations.

Subp. 7. **Water conditioning contractor.** "Water conditioning contractor" means the person in a firm or corporation who has demonstrated skill in planning, superintending, installing, and servicing water conditioning installations.

Subp. 8. **Water conditioning equipment.** "Water conditioning equipment" (equipment) means any appliance, appurtenance, or fixture designed to treat water, so as to alter, modify, add, or remove any minerals, chemicals, or bacteria contained in water.

Subp. 9. **Water conditioning installer.** "Water conditioning installer" means a person, other than a water conditioning contractor, who has demonstrated practical knowledge of water conditioning installation and servicing.

Subp. 10. **Water distribution system.** "Water distribution system" means a water supply system as defined in the Minnesota Plumbing Code (part 4715.0100).

4715.5200
CONNECTION WITH WATER DISTRIBUTION SYSTEM

Any water conditioning equipment may be installed only in connection with a water distribution system which has already been constructed. Such connection may be made either by cutting into a cold water line or by connecting to a joint specifically installed for the purpose. In connecting the equipment the contractor or installer may use only the type of pipe material which is permitted in the Minnesota Plumbing Code (parts 4715.0100 to 4715.2860).

Every installation shall include the installation of a bypass valve which would allow the equipment to be serviced or removed without the need for shutting off the water service completely.

If the homeowner so requests, the installer or contractor is permitted to install a line which bypasses the water conditioning equipment and to connect this raw water line to any existing service outlet.

4715.5300
EQUIPMENT DRAIN

The equipment drain line shall drain into the existing receptor such as a floor drain or laundry tub. No drain or overflow line leading from the equipment shall be directly connected to any receptor. Between the delivery end of the drain or overflow line and the receptor, there must be an air gap which is at least two times the diameter of the drain or overflow line, but in no case shall the air gap be less than 1.5 inches. This air gap distance shall apply above the flood level rim of the receiving fixture to provide the required air gap. If flexible drain line is used, it must be secured in some manner to prevent its being accidentally moved.

4715.5400
LOCATION

Any water conditioning equipment and the piping necessary to install such equipment shall not be placed in such a location or manner so as to interfere with the normal operation of existing windows, doors, or other exits or openings, nor shall it be located in such a place so as to make other existing equipment inaccessible.

4715.5500
REGENERATION SANITATION PROCEDURES

All new or used water conditioning equipment shall be disinfected before being installed. All portable exchange water conditioning equipment shall be disinfected during every regeneration. Disinfection shall be achieved by the application of chlorine or a chlorine compound such as sodium or calcium hypochlorite, during the fresh water rinse, to provide an effluent minimum chlorine residual and time combination as given in the following table:

Minimum Time Minutes	Minimum Chlorine Residual—parts per million
4	20
5	15
10	7.5
15	5.0
20	4.0

4715.5600
VARIANCE

If an installation cannot be made in conformance with the Minnesota Plumbing Code (parts 4715.0100 to 4715.2860) or with the provisions contained in parts 4715.5000 to 4715.6000, the water conditioning contractor or installer shall consult with the appropriate plumbing inspector, and obtain a variance from the state rules before the installation may proceed. Such a variance can be granted only if the nonconforming alternative will not create a risk to health. The commissioner shall grant variances to parts 4715.5000 to 4715.6000 only according to the procedures and criteria specified in parts 4717.7000 to 4717.7050.

4715.5700
EQUIPMENT AND MATERIALS USED IN INSTALLATIONS

Where applicable, the following shall conform to the Minnesota Plumbing Code (parts 4715.0100 to 4715.2860): all materials and connections used in the installation of water conditioning and treatment equipment; all attachments to the building.

In accordance with the Minnesota Plumbing Code (parts 4715.0100 to 4715.2860):

A. The bypass valve assembly shall be the same size as the line in which it is installed and shall be a full-way valve unless a bypass valve which complies with part 4715.5200 is supplied as an integral part of the water conditioning equipment;

B. Joints and connections which are made in the course of installing water conditioning and treatment equipment shall be tested for water tightness;

C. Copper tube joints shall be soldered or brazed;

D. Soft copper tubing joints may be flared or soldered;

E. Vertical piping shall be secured at sufficiently close intervals to keep the pipe in alignment and carry the weight of the pipe; and

F. Horizontal piping shall be supported at sufficiently close intervals to keep it in alignment and prevent sagging.

4715.5800
LICENSING

Subpart 1. **Examination.** A written examination for the licensing of water conditioning equipment contractors and installers shall be given at least once per year. The licensing examination for contractors and installers shall include questions covering one or more of the following subject areas: relevant plumbing and installation provisions, materials and tools of the trade, general principles of water conditioning processes, and operation of water conditioning equipment. In addition to the above, the contractor's licensing examination shall include questions covering one or more of the following subjects: calculations to determine appropriate equipment size, and specific functions and processes involved in different types of water conditioning.

Subp. 2. **Examination requirements for installers.** The examination for the installer's license shall be given only to persons who have had at least six months experience in the field of water conditioning installation and servicing.

Subp. 3. **Contractor's license requirement.** The examination for the contractor's license shall be given only to persons who have had at least 12 months experience in planning and supervising the installation and servicing of water conditioning equipment.

Subp. 4. **Application.** A person applying to take an examination shall complete an application supplied by the Minnesota Department of Health and return the completed application along with the appropriate examination fee.

Subp. 5. **Results of the examination and license.** A grade of 70 percent shall be considered a passing grade. The applicant shall be notified of the results of the examination. A license shall be issued to an applicant who has passed the examination upon receipt of the appropriate license fee.

4715.5900
FEES

Subpart 1. **Examination application fee.** The fee for application for examination or re-examination is $50 for a water conditioning installer, and $50 for a water conditioning contractor. The examination application fee is not refundable.

Subp. 2. **License fee.** The fee for a new license or for renewal of an existing license is as follows: water conditioning installer, $35; water conditioning contractor, $70, except that an application for initial licensure that is submitted during the last three months of the calendar year must be accompanied by a fee of $17.50 for a water conditioning installer or $35 for a water conditioning contractor.

Subp. 3. **Fee for filing bond and insurance.** Water conditioning contractors who file a bond and evidence of liability insurance with the secretary of state, pursuant to Minnesota Statutes, section 326.601, shall pay an additional fee of $40.

4715.6000
RENEWAL

A license expires on December 31 of the year for which it was issued. An application for renewal of a license must be received by the Minnesota Department of Health no later than December 31. Any person who submits an application for license renewal after December 31 must pay a penalty of $25 in addition to the annual license fee. A person who does not renew a license issued pursuant to parts 4715.5000 to 4715.6000, within two years of the date on which the former license expired, is no longer entitled to a renewal license. The person must apply for re-examination and a new license.